HAESE & HARRIS PUBLICATIONS

Specialists in mathematics publishing

Mathematics

for the international student

Pre-Diploma Studies SL (MYP 5)

Presumed Knowledge for Mathematical Studies SL

Keith Black

Pamela Vollmar

Michael Haese

Robert Haese

Sandra Haese

Mark Humphries

for use with
IB Middle Years
Programme

MATHEMATICS FOR THE INTERNATIONAL STUDENT
Pre-Diploma Studies SL (MYP 5)
Presumed Knowledge for Mathematical Studies SL

Keith Black	B.Sc.(Hons.), Dip.Ed.
Pamela Vollmar	B.Sc.(Hons.), PGCE.
Michael Haese	B.Sc.(Hons.), Ph.D.
Robert Haese	B.Sc.
Sandra Haese	B.Sc.
Mark Humphries	B.Sc.(Hons.)

Haese & Harris Publications
3 Frank Collopy Court, Adelaide Airport, SA 5950, AUSTRALIA
Telephone: +61 8 8355 9444, Fax: + 61 8 8355 9471
Email: info@haeseandharris.com.au
Web: www.haeseandharris.com.au

National Library of Australia Card Number & ISBN 978-1-876543-10-5

© Haese & Harris Publications 2008

Published by Raksar Nominees Pty Ltd
3 Frank Collopy Court, Adelaide Airport, SA 5950, AUSTRALIA

First Edition   2008

Cartoon artwork by John Martin. Artwork by Piotr Poturaj and David Purton.
Cover design by Piotr Poturaj.
Computer software by David Purton and Thomas Jansson.

Typeset in Australia by Susan Haese (Raksar Nominees). Typeset in Times Roman $10\frac{1}{2}/11\frac{1}{2}$

The textbook and its accompanying CD have been developed independently of the International Baccalaureate Organization (IBO). The textbook and CD are in no way connected with, or endorsed by, the IBO.

Acknowledgements: The publishers acknowledge the cooperation of Oxford University Press, Australia, for the reproduction of material originally published in textbooks produced in association with Haese & Harris Publications.

While every attempt has been made to trace and acknowledge copyright, the authors and publishers apologise for any accidental infringement where copyright has proved untraceable. They would be pleased to come to a suitable agreement with the rightful owner.

Disclaimer: All the internet addresses (URL's) given in this book were valid at the time of printing. While the authors and publisher regret any inconvenience that changes of address may cause readers, no responsibility for any such changes can be accepted by either the authors or the publisher.

FOREWORD

Pre-Diploma Studies SL (MYP 5) is an attempt to cover, in one volume, the Presumed Knowledge required for the IB Diploma course "Mathematical Studies SL" as well as including some extension topics. It may also be used as a general textbook at about Grade 10 level in classes where students might be expected to embark on an "Applications" type of Mathematics course in their final two years of high school.

In terms of the IB Middle Years Programme (MYP), this book does not pretend to be a definitive course. In response to requests from teachers who use "Mathematics for the International Student" at Diploma level, we have endeavoured to interpret their requirements, as expressed to us, for a book that would prepare students for Mathematical Studies SL at Diploma level. We have developed the book independently of the International Baccalaureate Organization (IBO) in consultation with experienced teachers of IB Mathematics. The text is not endorsed by the IBO.

It is not our intention that each chapter be worked through in full. Time constraints may not allow for this. Teachers must select exercises carefully, according to the abilities and prior knowledge of their students, to make the most efficient use of time and give as thorough coverage of content as possible.

To avoid producing a book that would be too bulky for students, we have presented these chapters on the CD as printable pages:

> Chapter 25: Transformation geometry
>
> Chapter 26: Sine and cosine rules

The above were selected because the content could be regarded as extension beyond what might be regarded as an essential prerequisite for Diploma.

This package is language rich and technology rich. We hope the combination of textbook and interactive Student CD will foster the mathematical development of students in a stimulating way. Frequent use of the interactive features on the CD should nurture a much deeper understanding and appreciation of mathematical concepts. The inclusion of our new 🔊Self Tutor software (see p. 4) is intended to help students who have been absent from classes or who experience difficulty understanding the material.

The book contains many problems from the basic to the advanced, to cater for a range of student abilities and interests. While some of the exercises are simply designed to build skills, every effort has been made to contextualise problems, so that students can see everyday uses and practical applications of the mathematics they are studying, and appreciate the universality of mathematics. We understand the emphasis that the IB MYP places on the five Areas of Interaction and in response there are links on the CD to printable pages which offer ideas for projects and investigations to help busy teachers (see p. 8).

The interactive CD also allows immediate access to our own specially designed geometry packages, graphing packages and more.

In this changing world of mathematics education, we believe that the contextual approach shown in this book, with the associated use of technology, will enhance the students' understanding, knowledge and appreciation of mathematics, and its universal application.

We welcome your feedback.   Email: info@haeseandharris.com.au

Web: www.haeseandharris.com.au

KB, PV, PMH, RCH, SHH, MH

Acknowledgements

The authors and publishers would like to thank all those teachers who have read proofs and offered advice and encouragement.

Among those who submitted courses of study for Middle Years Mathematics and who offered to read and comment on the proofs of the textbook are: Margie Karbassioun, Kerstin Mockrish, Todd Sharpe, Tamara Jannink, Yang Zhaohui, Cameron Hall, Brendan Watson, Daniel Fosbenner, Rob DeAbreu, Philip E. Hedemann, Alessandra Pecoraro, Jeanne-Mari Neefs, Ray Wiens, John Bush, Jane Forrest, Dr Andrzej Cichy, William Larson, Wendy Farden, Chris Wieland, Kenneth Capp, Sara Locke, Rae Deeley, Val Frost, Mal Coad, Pia Jeppesen, Wissam Malaeb, Eduardo Betti, Robb Kitcher, Catherine Krylova, Julie Tan, Rosheen Gray, Jan-Mark Seewald, Nicola Cardwell, Tony Halsey, Ros McCabe, Alison Ryan, Vivienne Verschuren, Mark Willis, Curtis Wood, Ufuk Genc, Fran O'Connor. Special thanks to Heather Farish. To anyone we may have missed, we offer our apologies.

The publishers wish to make it clear that acknowledging these individuals does not imply any endorsement of this book by any of them, and all responsibility for the content rests with the authors and publishers.

USING THE INTERACTIVE CD

The interactive CD is ideal for independent study.

Students can revisit concepts taught in class and undertake their own revision and practice. The CD also has the text of the book, allowing students to leave the textbook at school and keep the CD at home.

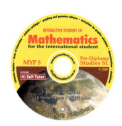

By clicking on the relevant icon, a range of new interactive features can be accessed:

- ♦ Self Tutor
- ♦ Areas of Interaction links to printable pages
- ♦ Printable Chapters
- ♦ Interactive Links – to spreadsheets, video clips, graphing and geometry software, computer demonstrations and simulations

INTERACTIVE LINK

SELF TUTOR is a new exciting feature of this book.

The ◄⁾ **Self Tutor** icon on each worked example denotes an active link on the CD.

NEW!

Simply 'click' on the ◄⁾ **Self Tutor** (or anywhere in the example box) to access the worked example, with a teacher's voice explaining each step necessary to reach the answer.

Play any line as often as you like. See how the basic processes come alive using movement and colour on the screen.

Ideal for students who have missed lessons or need extra help.

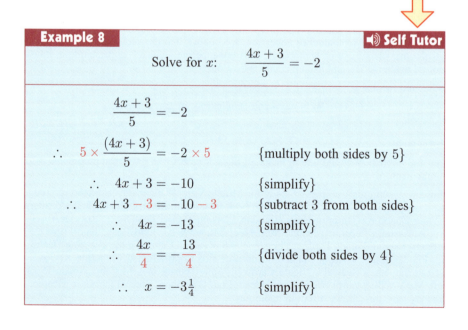

Example 8   ◄⁾ **Self Tutor**

Solve for x: $\dfrac{4x + 3}{5} = -2$

$$\dfrac{4x + 3}{5} = -2$$

$\therefore \quad 5 \times \dfrac{(4x + 3)}{5} = -2 \times 5$ {multiply both sides by 5}

$\therefore \quad 4x + 3 = -10$ {simplify}

$\therefore \quad 4x + 3 - 3 = -10 - 3$ {subtract 3 from both sides}

$\therefore \quad 4x = -13$ {simplify}

$\therefore \quad \dfrac{4x}{4} = -\dfrac{13}{4}$ {divide both sides by 4}

$\therefore \quad x = -3\frac{1}{4}$ {simplify}

AREAS OF INTERACTION

The International Baccalaureate Middle Years Programme focuses teaching and learning through five Areas of Interaction:

- ◆ Approaches to learning
- ◆ Community and service
- ◆ Human ingenuity
- ◆ Environments
- ◆ Health and social education

The Areas of Interaction are intended as a focus for developing connections between different subject areas in the curriculum and to promote an understanding of the interrelatedness of different branches of knowledge and the coherence of knowledge as a whole.

In an effort to assist busy teachers, we offer the following printable pages of ideas for projects and investigations:

Click on the heading to access a printable 'pop-up' version of the link.

LINKS
click here

ERRORS IN MEASUREMENT

Areas of interaction:
Approaches to learning

Links to printable pages of ideas for projects and investigations

Chapter 1: Measurement and units p. 39	**ERRORS IN MEASUREMENT** Approaches to learning
Chapter 4: Rounding and estimating p. 88	**AREA AND VOLUME ERRORS** Approaches to learning
Chapter 5: The Rule of Pythagoras p. 99	**PYTHAGORAS** Human ingenuity
Chapter 7: Length and area p. 137	**ESTIMATING AREAS** Approaches to learning/Human ingenuity
Chapter 10: Statistics p. 217	**HOW MANY TROUT ARE IN THE LAKE?** Environments/Human ingenuity
Chapter 12: Ratios and rates p. 252	**ALL THAT GLITTERS IS NOT GOLD** Human ingenuity
Chapter 14: Congruence and similarity p. 294	**HOW WIDE IS THE CANAL?** Human ingenuity
Chapter 16: Trigonometry p. 326	**HOW FAR AWAY IS THE MOON AND HOW LARGE IS IT?** Human ingenuity
Chapter 19: Probability p. 392	**WHAT ARE YOUR SURVIVAL PROSPECTS?** Environments/Health and social education
Chapter 21: Geometry p. 434	**WHAT REGION CAN BE EATEN BY A GOAT?** Approaches to learning/Environments
Chapter 23: Finance p. 472	**HOW MUCH CAN I SAVE BY NOT SMOKING?** Environments/Health and social education
Chapter 24: Quadratic functions p. 485	**WHAT IS THE STRONGEST ARCH?** Approaches to learning/Environments/Human ingenuity

TABLE OF CONTENTS

GRAPHICS CALCULATOR INSTRUCTIONS   **9**

A	Basic calculations	10
B	Basic functions	12
C	Secondary function and alpha keys	15
D	Memory	15
E	Lists	18
F	Statistical graphs	20
G	Working with functions	21

1   MEASUREMENT AND UNITS   **25**

A	Standard units	26
B	Converting units	29
C	Area units	32
D	Volume units	33
E	Capacity	34
F	Mass	35
G	Time	36
H	24-hour time	39
	Review set 1A	40
	Review set 1B	41

2   NUMBER OPERATIONS   **43**

A	Operations with integers	44
B	Operations with fractions	49
C	Index notation	53
D	Laws of indices	57
	Review set 2A	59
	Review set 2B	60

3   SETS, SEQUENCES AND LOGIC   **61**

A	Set notation	62
B	Important number sets	63
C	Constructing sets (Interval notation)	66
D	Venn diagrams	67
E	Union and intersection	69
F	Simple set problems	72
G	Number sequences	73
H	Introduction to logic	75
	Review set 3A	79
	Review set 3B	80

4   ROUNDING AND ESTIMATION   **81**

A	Rounding numbers	82
B	Rounding money	83
C	One figure approximations	86
D	Rounding decimal numbers	88
E	Using a calculator to round off	90
F	Significant figure rounding	92
G	Rounding time	94
	Review set 4A	95
	Review set 4B	96

5   THE RULE OF PYTHAGORAS   **97**

A	The Rule of Pythagoras (Review)	99
B	Further problem solving	103
C	Testing for right angles	106
D	Navigation	107
	Review set 5A	109
	Review set 5B	110

6   ALGEBRA   **111**

A	Changing words into symbols	112
B	Generalising arithmetic	113
C	Converting into algebraic form	115
D	Formula construction	116
E	Number patterns and rules	118
F	The value of an expression	120
	Review set 6A	124
	Review set 6B	125

7   LENGTH AND AREA   **127**

A	Perimeter and length	128
B	Area	133
C	Surface area	139
D	Problem solving	145
	Review set 7A	147
	Review set 7B	148

8   DECIMALS AND PERCENTAGE   **149**

A	Decimal numbers	150
B	Percentage	152
C	Working with percentages	154
D	Unitary method in percentage	156
E	Percentage increase and decrease	157
F	Scientific notation (Standard form)	159
	Review set 8A	163
	Review set 8B	164

9   ALGEBRAIC SIMPLIFICATION AND EXPANSION   **167**

A	Collecting like terms	168
B	Product notation	170
C	The distributive law	172
D	The expansion of $(a+b)(c+d)$	177
E	The expansion rules	179
F	Perimeters and areas	183
	Review set 9A	185
	Review set 9B	185

10   STATISTICS   **187**

A	Terminology for the study of statistics	189
B	Quantitative (numerical) data	194
C	Grouped discrete data	197

D	Frequency histograms	199
E	Measuring the centre	202
F	Cumulative data	208
G	Measuring the spread	211
H	Box-and-whisker plots	213
I	Statistics from technology	217
	Review set 10A	218
	Review set 10B	219

11 EQUATIONS   221

A	Solution by inspection or trial and error	223
B	Maintaining balance	224
C	Formal solution of linear equations	226
D	Equations with a repeated unknown	228
E	Fractional equations	230
F	Unknown in the denominator	231
G	Forming equations	233
H	Problem solving using equations	235
I	Finding an unknown from a formula	237
J	Formula rearrangement	240
	Review set 11A	243
	Review set 11B	244

12 RATIOS AND RATES   245

A	Ratio	246
B	Simplifying ratios	247
C	Equal ratios	249
D	The unitary method for ratios	251
E	Using ratios to divide quantities	252
F	Scale diagrams	254
G	Rates	255
H	Rate graphs	259
I	Travel graphs	261
	Review set 12A	262
	Review set 12B	264

13 ALGEBRAIC FACTORISATION   265

A	Common factors	266
B	Factorising with common factors	268
C	Factorising expressions with four terms	272
D	Factorising quadratic trinomials	273
E	Factorisation of $ax^2 + bx + c$ $(a \neq 1)$	275
F	Difference of two squares factorising	278
	Review set 13A	278
	Review set 13B	279

14 CONGRUENCE AND SIMILARITY   281

A	Congruence of figures	282
B	Congruent triangles	283
C	Similarity	287
D	Similar triangles	289
E	Problem solving with similar triangles	292
	Review set 14A	295
	Review set 14B	296

15 VOLUME AND CAPACITY   297

A	Volume	298
B	Capacity	304
C	Problem solving	307
	Review set 15A	309
	Review set 15B	310

16 TRIGONOMETRY   311

A	Labelling sides of a right angled triangle	312
B	Trigonometric ratios	315
C	Using the sine ratio	316
D	Using the cosine ratio	318
E	Using the tangent ratio	319
F	Problem solving with trigonometry	321
G	Bearings	325
	Review set 16A	326
	Review set 16B	328

17 COORDINATES AND LINES   329

A	Plotting points on the Cartesian plane	330
B	Distance between two points	332
C	Midpoints	334
D	Gradient (or slope)	335
E	Linear relationships	338
F	Linear functions	340
G	Finding equations of straight lines	342
H	Graphing lines	347
I	Points on lines	348
J	Other line forms	349
K	Parallel and perpendicular lines	350
L	Using gradients	353
	Review set 17A	354
	Review set 17B	355

18 SIMULTANEOUS LINEAR EQUATIONS   357

A	The point of intersection of linear graphs	358
B	Simultaneous equations	360
C	Algebraic methods for solving simultaneous equations	362
D	Problem solving	366
E	Using a graphics calculator to solve simultaneous equations	368
	Review set 18A	370
	Review set 18B	370

19 PROBABILITY   371

A	Probability by experiment	373
B	Theoretical probability	374
C	Expectation	376
D	Probabilities from tabled data	378
E	Representing combined events	379
F	Probabilities from lists and diagrams	381

G	Multiplying probabilities	384
H	Using tree diagrams	385
I	Sampling with and without replacement	388
J	Mutually exclusive and non-mutually exclusive events	390
K	Independent events	392
	Review set 19A	393
	Review set 19B	394

20 FUNCTIONS, GRAPHS AND NOTATION   395

A	Graphical interpretation	396
B	Interpreting line graphs	398
C	Conversion graphs	400
D	Time series data	402
E	Step graphs	403
F	Mappings	405
G	Functions	406
H	Function notation	409
	Review set 20A	410
	Review set 20B	412

21 GEOMETRY   413

A	Angle properties	417
B	Triangles	422
C	Isosceles triangles	424
D	Angles of a quadrilateral	427
E	Polygons	430
F	The exterior angles of a polygon	433
G	Nets of solids	434
	Review set 21A	435
	Review set 21B	437

22 QUADRATIC AND OTHER EQUATIONS   439

A	Quadratic equations	440
B	Problem solving with quadratics	443
C	Exponential equations	446
D	Solving harder equations with technology	447
	Review set 22A	449
	Review set 22B	450

23 FINANCE   451

A	Profit and loss	452
B	Percentage profit and loss	454
C	Discount	456
D	Using a multiplier	459
E	Chain percentage problems	461
F	Simple interest	463
G	Compound interest	467
H	Foreign exchange	470
	Review set 23A	472
	Review set 23B	474

24 QUADRATIC FUNCTIONS   475

A	Graphs of quadratic functions	476
B	Axes intercepts	478
C	The axis of symmetry	480
D	Quadratic modelling	483
	Review set 24A	485
	Review set 24B	486

25 TRANSFORMATION GEOMETRY   487

Chapter on CD only

A	Reflection	3
B	Rotation	6
C	Translation	9
D	Enlargement	11
	Review set 25A	14
	Review set 25B	15

26 SINE AND COSINE RULES   488

Chapter on CD only

A	Obtuse angles	2
B	Area of a triangle using sine	4
C	The sine rule	5
D	The cosine rule	10
E	Problem solving with the sine and cosine rules	13
	Review set 26A	14
	Review set 26B	15

ANSWERS   489

INDEX   526

Graphics calculator instructions

Contents:

A Basic calculations
B Basic functions
C Secondary function and alpha keys
D Memory
E Lists
F Statistical graphs
G Working with functions

In this course it is assumed that you have a **graphics calculator**. If you learn how to operate your calculator successfully, you should experience little difficulty with future arithmetic calculations.

There are many different brands (and types) of calculators. Different calculators do not have exactly the same keys. It is therefore important that you have an instruction booklet for your calculator, and use it whenever you need to.

However, to help get you started, we have included here some basic instructions for the **Texas Instruments TI-83** and the **Casio fx-9860G** calculators. Note that instructions given may need to be modified slightly for other models.

GETTING STARTED

Texas Instruments TI-83

The screen which appears when the calculator is turned on is the **home screen**. This is where most basic calculations are performed.

You can return to this screen from any menu by pressing 2nd MODE .

When you are on this screen you can type in an expression and evaluate it using the ENTER key.

Casio fx-9860g

Press MENU to access the Main Menu, and select **RUN·MAT**.

This is where most of the basic calculations are performed.

When you are on this screen you can type in an expression and evaluate it using the EXE key.

A BASIC CALCULATIONS

Most modern calculators have the rules for **Order of Operations** built into them. This order is sometimes referred to as BEDMAS. You will learn more about it in **Chapter 2**.

This section explains how to enter different types of numbers such as negative numbers and fractions, and how to perform calculations using grouping symbols (brackets), powers, and square roots. It also explains how to round off using your calculator.

NEGATIVE NUMBERS

To enter negative numbers we use the **sign change** key. On both the **TI-83** and **Casio** this looks like .

Simply press the sign change key and then type in the number.

For example, to enter -7, press (−) 7.

FRACTIONS

On most scientific calculators and also the **Casio** graphics calculator there is a special key for entering fractions. No such key exists for the **TI-83**, so we use a different method.

Texas Instruments TI-83

To enter common fractions, we enter the fraction as a division.

For example, we enter $\frac{3}{4}$ by typing 3 ÷ 4. If the fraction is part of a larger calculation, it is generally wise to place this division in brackets, i.e., (3 ÷ 4) .

To enter mixed numbers, either convert the mixed number to an improper fraction and enter as a common fraction *or* enter the fraction as a sum.

For example, we can enter $2\frac{3}{4}$ as   (11 ÷ 4)   *or*   (2 + 3 ÷ 4) .

Casio fx-9860g

To enter fractions we use the **fraction** key a b/c .

For example, we enter $\frac{3}{4}$ by typing 3 a b/c 4 and $2\frac{3}{4}$ by typing 2 a b/c 3 a b/c 4. Press SHIFT a b/c ($a\frac{b}{c} \leftrightarrow \frac{d}{c}$) to convert between mixed numbers and improper fractions.

SIMPLIFYING FRACTIONS & RATIOS

Graphics calculators can *sometimes* be used to express fractions and ratios in simplest form.

Texas Instruments TI-83

To express the fraction $\frac{35}{56}$ in simplest form, press 35 ÷ 56 MATH 1 ENTER . The result is $\frac{5}{8}$.

To express the ratio $\frac{2}{3} : 1\frac{1}{4}$ in simplest form, press (2 ÷ 3) ÷ (1 + 1 ÷ 4) MATH 1 ENTER .

The ratio is 8 : 15.

```
35/56►Frac
              5/8
(2/3)/(1+1/4)►Fr
ac
             8/15
```

Casio fx-9860g

To express the fraction $\frac{35}{56}$ in simplest form, press 35 a b/c 56 EXE . The result is $\frac{5}{8}$.

To express the ratio $\frac{2}{3} : 1\frac{1}{4}$ in simplest form, press 2 a b/c 3 ÷ 1 a b/c 1 a b/c 4 EXE . The ratio is 8 : 15.

```
35⌐56            5⌐8
2⌐3÷1⌐1⌐4        8⌐15

►MAT
```

ENTERING TIMES

In questions involving time, it is often necessary to be able to express time in terms of hours, minutes and seconds.

Texas Instruments TI-83

To enter 2 hours 27 minutes, press 2 [2nd] [MATRX] (ANGLE)
1: ^{o} 27 [2nd] [MATRX] **2:'**. This is equivalent to 2.45 hours.

To express 8.17 hours in terms of hours, minutes and seconds,
press 8.17 [2nd] [MATRX] **4:▶DMS** [ENTER]. This is equivalent to 8 hours, 10 minutes and 12 seconds.

Casio fx-9860g

To enter 2 hours 27 minutes, press 2 [OPTN] [F6] [F5] (ANGL)
[F4] $(^{o\prime\prime\prime})$ 27 [F4] $(^{o\prime\prime\prime})$ [EXE]. This is equivalent to 2.45 hours.

To express 8.17 hours in terms of hours, minutes and seconds,
press 8.17 [OPTN] [F6] [F5] (ANGL) [F6] [F3] (▶DMS) [EXE].
This is equivalent to 8 hours, 10 minutes and 12 seconds.

B BASIC FUNCTIONS

GROUPING SYMBOLS (BRACKETS)

Both the **TI-83** and **Casio** have bracket keys that look like [(] and [)].

Brackets are regularly used in mathematics to indicate an expression which needs to be
evaluated before other operations are carried out.

For example, to enter $2 \times (4 + 1)$ we type 2 [×] [(] 4 [+] 1 [)].

We also use brackets to make sure the calculator understands the expression we are typing in.

For example, to enter $\frac{2}{4+1}$ we type 2 [÷] [(] 4 [+] 1 [)]. If we typed 2 [÷] 4 [+] 1
the calculator would think we meant $\frac{2}{4} + 1$.

In general, it is a good idea to place brackets around any complicated expressions which need
to be evaluated separately.

POWER KEYS

Both the **TI-83** and **Casio** also have power keys that look like [∧]. We type the base first,
press the power key, then enter the index or exponent.

For example, to enter 25^3 we type 25 [∧] 3.

Note that there are special keys which allow us to quickly evaluate squares.

Numbers can be squared on both **TI-83** and **Casio** using the special key [x^2].

For example, to enter 25^2 we type 25 [x^2].

SQUARE ROOTS

To enter square roots on either calculator we need to use a secondary function (see the **Secondary Function and Alpha Keys** section).

Texas Instruments TI-83

The **TI-83** uses a secondary function key ⌈2nd⌉ .

To enter $\sqrt{36}$ we press ⌈2nd⌉ ⌈x^2⌉ 36 ⌈)⌉ .

The end bracket is used to tell the calculator we have finished entering terms under the square root sign.

Casio fx-9860g

The Casio uses a shift key ⌈SHIFT⌉ to get to its second functions.

To enter $\sqrt{36}$ we press ⌈SHIFT⌉ ⌈x^2⌉ 36.

If there is a more complicated expression under the square root sign you should enter it in brackets.

For example, to enter $\sqrt{18 \div 2}$ we press ⌈SHIFT⌉ ⌈x^2⌉ ⌈(⌉ 18 ⌈÷⌉ 2 ⌈)⌉ .

ROUNDING OFF

You can use your calculator to round off answers to a fixed number of decimal places.

Texas Instruments TI-83

To round to 2 decimal places, press ⌈MODE⌉ then ⌈▼⌉ to scroll down to Float.

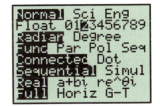

Use the ⌈▶⌉ button to move the cursor over the 2 and press ⌈ENTER⌉ . Press ⌈2nd⌉ ⌈MODE⌉ to return to the home screen.

If you want to unfix the number of decimal places, press ⌈MODE⌉ ⌈▼⌉ ⌈ENTER⌉ to highlight Float.

Casio fx-9860g

To round to 2 decimal places, select **RUN·MAT** from the Main Menu, and press ⌈SHIFT⌉ ⌈MENU⌉ to enter the setup screen. Scroll down to Display, and press ⌈F1⌉ (**Fix**). Press 2 ⌈EXE⌉ to select the number of decimal places. Press ⌈EXIT⌉ to return to the home screen.

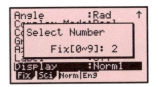

To unfix the number of decimal places, press ⌈SHIFT⌉ ⌈MENU⌉ to return to the setup screen, scroll down to Display, and press ⌈F3⌉ (**Norm**).

INVERSE TRIGONOMETRIC FUNCTIONS

To enter inverse trigonometric functions, you will need to use a secondary function (see the **Secondary Function and Alpha Keys** section).

Texas Instruments TI-83

The inverse trigonometric functions $\sin^{-1}$, $\cos^{-1}$ and $\tan^{-1}$ are the secondary functions of SIN , COS and TAN respectively. They are accessed by using the secondary function key 2nd .

For example if $\cos x = \frac{3}{5}$, then $x = \cos^{-1}\left(\frac{3}{5}\right)$.

To calculate this, press 2nd COS 3 ÷ 5) ENTER .

Casio fx-9860g

The inverse trigonometric functions $\sin^{-1}$, $\cos^{-1}$ and $\tan^{-1}$ are the secondary functions of sin , cos and tan respectively. They are accessed by using the secondary function key SHIFT .

For example, if $\cos x = \frac{3}{5}$, then $x = \cos^{-1}\left(\frac{3}{5}\right)$.

To calculate this, press SHIFT cos (3 ÷ 5) EXE .

SCIENTIFIC NOTATION

If a number is too large or too small to be displayed neatly on the screen, it will be expressed in scientific notation, that is, in the form $a \times 10^k$, where $1 \leqslant a < 10$ and k is an integer.

Texas Instruments TI-83

To evaluate 2300^3, press 2300 ∧ 3 ENTER . The answer displayed is 1.2167E10, which means 1.2167×10^{10}.

To evaluate $\frac{3}{20\,000}$, press 3 ÷ 20 000 ENTER . The answer displayed is 1.5E−4, which means 1.5×10^{-4}.

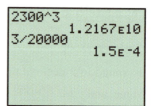

You can enter values in scientific notation using the EE function, which is accessed by pressing 2nd , . For example, to evaluate $\frac{2.6 \times 10^{14}}{13}$, press 2.6 2nd , 14 ÷ 13 ENTER . The answer is 2×10^{13}.

Casio fx-9860g

To evaluate 2300^3, press   2300 3 EXE .   The answer displayed is   1.2167E+10,   which means 1.2167×10^{10}.

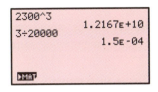

To evaluate $\frac{3}{20\,000}$, press   3 ÷ 20 000 EXE .   The answer displayed is   1.5E−04,   which means 1.5×10^{-4}.

You can enter values in scientific notation using the EXP key. For example, to evaluate $\frac{2.6 \times 10^{14}}{13}$, press   2.6 EXP 14 ÷ 13 EXE .   The answer is 2×10^{13}.

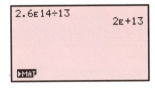

C   SECONDARY FUNCTION AND ALPHA KEYS

Texas Instruments TI-83

The **secondary function** of each key is displayed in yellow above the key. It is accessed by pressing the 2nd key, followed by the key corresponding to the desired secondary function. For example, to calculate $\sqrt{36}$, press   2nd x^2 36) ENTER .

The **alpha function** of each key is displayed in green above the key. It is accessed by pressing the ALPHA key followed by the key corresponding to the desired letter. The main purpose of the alpha keys is to store values into memory which can be recalled later. Refer to the **Memory** section.

Casio fx-9860g

The **shift function** of each key is displayed in yellow above the key. It is accessed by pressing the SHIFT key followed by the key corresponding to the desired shift function.

For example, to calculate $\sqrt{36}$, press SHIFT x^2 36 EXE .

The **alpha function** of each key is displayed in red above the key. It is accessed by pressing the ALPHA key followed by the key corresponding to the desired letter. The main purpose of the alpha keys is to store values which can be recalled later.

D   MEMORY

Utilising the memory features of your calculator allows you to recall calculations you have performed previously. *This not only saves time, but also enables you to maintain accuracy in your calculations.*

SPECIFIC STORAGE TO MEMORY

Values can be stored into the variable letters A, B, ..., Z using either calculator. Storing a value in memory is useful if you need that value multiple times.

Texas Instruments TI-83

Suppose we wish to store the number 15.4829 for use in a number of calculations. Type in the number then press $\boxed{\text{STO}\blacktriangleright}$ $\boxed{\text{ALPHA}}$ $\boxed{\text{MATH}}$ (A) $\boxed{\text{ENTER}}$.

We can now add 10 to this value by pressing $\boxed{\text{ALPHA}}$ $\boxed{\text{MATH}}$ $\boxed{+}$ 10 $\boxed{\text{ENTER}}$, or cube this value by pressing $\boxed{\text{ALPHA}}$ $\boxed{\text{MATH}}$ $\boxed{\wedge}$ 3 $\boxed{\text{ENTER}}$.

```
15.4829→A
             15.4829
A+10
             25.4829
A^3
         3711.563767
```

Casio fx-9860g

Suppose we wish to store the number 15.4829 for use in a number of calculations. Type in the number then press $\boxed{\rightarrow}$ $\boxed{\text{ALPHA}}$ $\boxed{\text{X},\theta,\text{T}}$ (A) $\boxed{\text{EXE}}$.

We can now add 10 to this value by pressing $\boxed{\text{ALPHA}}$ $\boxed{\text{X},\theta,\text{T}}$ $\boxed{+}$ 10 $\boxed{\text{EXE}}$, or cube this value by pressing $\boxed{\text{ALPHA}}$ $\boxed{\text{X},\theta,\text{T}}$ $\boxed{\wedge}$ 3 $\boxed{\text{EXE}}$.

```
15.4829→A
             15.4829
A+10
             25.4829
A^3
         3711.563767
►MAT
```

ANS VARIABLE

Texas Instruments TI-83

The variable **Ans** holds the most recent evaluated expression, and can be used in calculations by pressing $\boxed{\text{2nd}}$ $\boxed{(-)}$.

For example, suppose you evaluate 3×4, and then wish to subtract this from 17. This can be done by pressing 17 $\boxed{-}$ $\boxed{\text{2nd}}$ $\boxed{(-)}$ $\boxed{\text{ENTER}}$.

```
3*4
              12
17-Ans
               5
```

If you start an expression with an operator such as $\boxed{+}$, $\boxed{-}$, etc, the previous answer **Ans** is automatically inserted ahead of the operator. For example, the previous answer can be halved simply by pressing $\boxed{\div}$ 2 $\boxed{\text{ENTER}}$.

If you wish to view the answer in fractional form, press $\boxed{\text{MATH}}$ 1 $\boxed{\text{ENTER}}$.

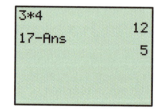

```
              12
17-Ans
               5
Ans/2
             2.5
Ans►Frac
             5/2
```

Casio fx-9860g

The variable **Ans** holds the most recent evaluated expression, and can be used in calculations by pressing SHIFT (−) . For example, suppose you evaluate 3×4, and then wish to subtract this from 17. This can be done by pressing 17 − SHIFT (−) EXE .

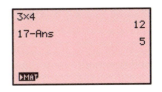

If you start an expression with an operator such as + , − , etc, the previous answer Ans is automatically inserted ahead of the operator. For example, the previous answer can be halved simply by pressing ÷ 2 EXE .

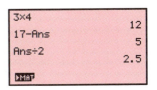

If you wish to view the answer in fractional form, press F↔D .

RECALLING PREVIOUS EXPRESSIONS

Texas Instruments TI-83

The **ENTRY** function recalls previously evaluated expressions, and is used by pressing 2nd ENTER .

This function is useful if you wish to repeat a calculation with a minor change, or if you have made an error in typing.

Suppose you have evaluated $100 + \sqrt{132}$. If you now want to evaluate $100 + \sqrt{142}$, instead of retyping the command, it can be recalled by pressing 2nd ENTER .

The change can then be made by moving the cursor over the 3 and changing it to a 4, then pressing ENTER .

If you have made an error in your original calculation, and intended to calculate $1500 + \sqrt{132}$, again you can recall the previous command by pressing 2nd ENTER .

Move the cursor to the first 0.

You can insert the digit 5, rather than overwriting the 0, by pressing 2nd DEL 5 ENTER .

Casio fx-9860g

Pressing the left cursor key allows you to edit the most recently evaluated expression, and is useful if you wish to repeat a calculation with a minor change, or if you have made an error in typing.

Suppose you have evaluated $100 + \sqrt{132}$.

If you now want to evaluate $100 + \sqrt{142}$, instead of retyping the command, it can be recalled by pressing the left cursor key.

Move the cursor between the 3 and the 2, then press DEL 4 to remove the 3 and change it to a 4. Press EXE to re-evaluate the expression.

LISTS

Lists are used for a number of purposes on the calculator. They enable us to enter sets of numbers, and we use them to generate number sequences using algebraic rules.

CREATING A LIST

Texas Instruments TI-83

Press [STAT] 1 to take you to the **list editor** screen.

To enter the data $\{2, 5, 1, 6, 0, 8\}$ into **List1**, start by moving the cursor to the first entry of L_1. Press 2 [ENTER] 5 [ENTER] ...... and so on until all the data is entered.

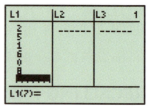

Casio fx-9860g

Selecting **STAT** from the Main Menu takes you to the **list editor** screen.

To enter the data $\{2, 5, 1, 6, 0, 8\}$ into **List 1**, start by moving the cursor to the first entry of **List 1**. Press 2 [EXE] 5 [EXE] ...... and so on until all the data is entered.

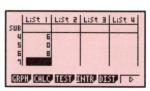

DELETING LIST DATA

Texas Instruments TI-83

Pressing [STAT] 1 takes you to the **list editor** screen.

Move the cursor to the heading of the list you want to delete then press [CLEAR] [ENTER] .

Casio fx-9860g

Selecting **STAT** from the Main Menu takes you to the **list editor** screen.

Move the cursor to anywhere on the list you wish to delete, then press [F6] (▷) [F4] (**DEL-A**) [F1] (**Yes**).

REFERENCING LISTS

Texas Instruments TI-83

Lists can be referenced by using the secondary functions of the keypad numbers 1–6.

For example, suppose you want to add 2 to each element of **List1** and display the results in **List2**. To do this, move the cursor to the heading of L_2 and press [2nd] 1 [+] 2 [ENTER] .

Casio fx-9860g

Lists can be referenced using the List function, which is accessed by pressing SHIFT 1.

For example, if you want to add 2 to each element of **List 1** and display the results in **List 2**, move the cursor to the heading of **List 2** and press SHIFT 1 (**List**) 1 + 2 EXE.

Casio models without the List function can do this by pressing OPTN F1 (**LIST**) F1 (**List**) 1 + 2 EXE.

NUMBER SEQUENCES

Texas Instruments TI-83

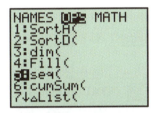

You can create a sequence of numbers defined by a certain rule using the *seq* command.

This command is accessed by pressing 2nd STAT ▶ to enter the **OPS** section of the List menu, then selecting **5:seq**.

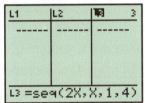

For example, to store the sequence of even numbers from 2 to 8 in **List3**, move the cursor to the heading of **L3**, then press 2nd STAT ▶ 5 to enter the *seq* command, followed by 2 X,T,θ,n , X,T,θ,n , 1 , 4) ENTER.

This evaluates $2x$ for every value of x from 1 to 4.

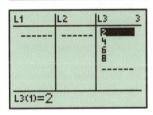

Casio fx-9860g

You can create a sequence of numbers defined by a certain rule using the *seq* command.

This command is accessed by pressing OPTN F1 (**LIST**) F5 (**Seq**).

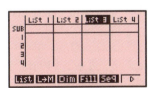

For example, to store the sequence of even numbers from 2 to 8 in **List 3**, move the cursor to the heading of **List 3**, then press OPTN F1 F5 to enter a sequence, followed by 2 X,θ,T , X,θ,T , 1 , 4 , 1) EXE.

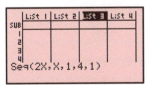

This evaluates $2x$ for every value of x from 1 to 4 with an increment of 1.

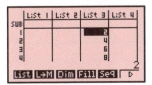

STATISTICAL GRAPHS

STATISTICS

Your graphics calculator is a useful tool for analysing data and creating statistical graphs.

In this section we will produce descriptive statistics and graphs for the data set 5 2 3 3 6 4 5 3 7 5 7 1 8 9 5.

Texas Instruments TI-83

Enter the data set into **List1** using the instructions on page **18**. To obtain descriptive statistics of the data set, press [STAT] [▶] **1:1-Var Stats** [2nd] **1 (L1)** [ENTER] .

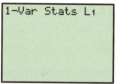 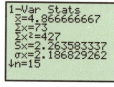

To obtain a boxplot of the data, press [2nd] [Y=] (STAT PLOT) **1** and set up **Statplot1** as shown. Press [ZOOM] **9:ZoomStat** to graph the boxplot with an appropriate window.

 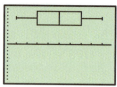

To obtain a vertical bar chart of the data, press [2nd] [Y=] **1**, and change the type of graph to a vertical bar chart as shown. Press [ZOOM] **9:ZoomStat** to draw the bar chart. Press [WINDOW] and set the **Xscl** to 1, then [GRAPH] to redraw the bar chart.

 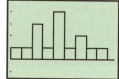

We will now enter a second set of data, and compare it to the first.

Enter the data set 9 6 2 3 5 5 7 5 6 7 6 3 4 4 5 8 4   into **List2**, press [2nd] [Y=] **1**, and change the type of graph back to a boxplot as shown. Move the cursor to the top of the screen and select **Plot2**. Set up **Statplot2** in the same manner, except set the **XList** to **L2**. Press [ZOOM] **9:ZoomStat** to draw the side-by-side boxplots.

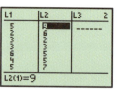 

 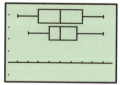

Casio fx-9860g

Enter the data into **List 1** using the instructions on page **18**. To obtain the descriptive statistics, press [F6] (▷) until the **GRPH** icon is in the bottom left corner of the screen, then press [F2] (CALC) [F1] (1VAR).

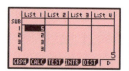 

To obtain a boxplot of the data, press [EXIT]
[EXIT] [F1] **(GRPH)** [F6] **(SET)**, and set up
StatGraph 1 as shown. Press [EXIT] [F1]
(GPH1) to draw the boxplot.

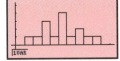

To obtain a vertical bar chart of the data, press
[EXIT] [F6] **(SET)** [F2] **(GPH 2)**, and set up
StatGraph 2 as shown. Press [EXIT] [F2]
(GPH 2) to draw the bar chart (set Start to 0,
and Width to 1).

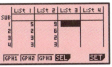
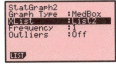

We will now enter a second set of data, and
compare it to the first.

Enter the data set   9 6 2 3 5 5 7 5 6 7 6
3 4 4 5 8 4   into **List 2**, then press [F6]
(SET) [F2] **(GPH2)** and set up **StatGraph 2** to
draw a boxplot of this data set as shown. Press
[EXIT] [F4] **(SEL)**, and turn on both **StatGraph**

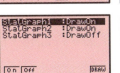
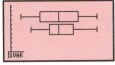
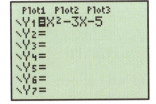
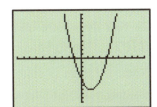

1 and **StatGraph 2**. Press [F6] **(DRAW)** to draw the side-by-side boxplots.

G — WORKING WITH FUNCTIONS

GRAPHING FUNCTIONS

Texas Instruments TI-83

Pressing [Y=] selects the **Y=** editor, where you can store functions
to graph. Delete any unwanted functions by scrolling down to
the function and pressing [CLEAR] .

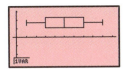

To graph the function $y = x^2 - 3x - 5$,   move the cursor to
Y₁, and press [X,T,θ,n] [x²] [−] 3 [X,T,θ,n] [−] 5 [ENTER] .   This
stores the function into **Y₁**. Press [GRAPH] to draw a graph of
the function.

Casio fx-9860g

Selecting **GRAPH** from the Main Menu takes you to the Graph
Function screen, where you can store functions to graph. Delete
any unwanted functions by scrolling down to the function and
pressing [DEL] [F1] **(Yes)**.

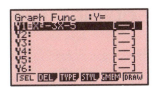

To graph the function $y = x^2 - 3x - 5$, move the cursor to **Y1** and press X,θ,T x^2 $-$ 3 X,θ,T $-$ 5 EXE . This stores the function into **Y1**. Press F6 **(DRAW)** to draw a graph of the function.

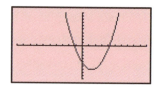

FINDING POINTS OF INTERSECTION

It is often useful to find the points of intersection of two graphs, for instance, when you are trying to solve simultaneous equations.

Texas Instruments TI-83

We can solve $y = 11 - 3x$ and $y = \dfrac{12 - x}{2}$ simultaneously by finding the point of intersection of these two lines. Press Y= , then store $11 - 3x$ into **Y1** and $\dfrac{12 - x}{2}$ into **Y2**. Press GRAPH to draw a graph of the functions.

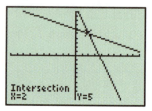

To find their point of intersection, press 2nd TRACE **(CALC)** **5**, which selects **5:intersect**. Press ENTER twice to specify the functions **Y1** and **Y2** as the functions you want to find the intersection of, then use the arrow keys to move the cursor close to the point of intersection and press ENTER once more.

The solution $x = 2$, $y = 5$ is given.

Casio fx-9860g

We can solve $y = 11 - 3x$ and $y = \dfrac{12 - x}{2}$ simultaneously by finding the point of intersection of these two lines. Select **GRAPH** from the Main Menu, then store $11 - 3x$ into **Y1** and $\dfrac{12 - x}{2}$ into **Y2**. Press F6 **(DRAW)** to draw a graph of the functions.

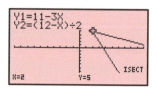

To find their point of intersection, press F5 **(G-Solv)** F5 **(ISCT)**. The solution $x = 2$, $y = 5$ is given.

Note: If there is more than one point of intersection, the remaining points of intersection can be found by pressing ▶ .

SOLVING $f(x) = 0$

In the special case when you wish to solve an equation of the form $f(x) = 0$, this can be done by graphing $y = f(x)$ and then finding where this graph cuts the x-axis.

Texas Instruments TI-83

To solve $x^3 - 3x^2 + x + 1 = 0$, press $\boxed{\text{Y=}}$ and store $x^3 - 3x^2 + x + 1$ into **Y1**. Press $\boxed{\text{GRAPH}}$ to draw the graph.

To find where this function first cuts the x-axis, press $\boxed{\text{2nd}}$ $\boxed{\text{TRACE}}$ (CALC) 2, which selects **2:zero**. Move the cursor to the left of the first zero and press $\boxed{\text{ENTER}}$, then move the cursor to the right of the first zero and press $\boxed{\text{ENTER}}$. Finally, move the cursor close to the first zero and press $\boxed{\text{ENTER}}$ once more. The solution $x \approx -0.414$ is given.

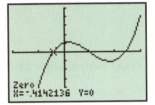

Repeat this process to find the remaining solutions $x = 1$ and $x \approx 2.41$.

Casio fx-9860g

To solve $x^3 - 3x^2 + x + 1 = 0$, select **GRAPH** from the Main Menu and store $x^3 - 3x^2 + x + 1$ into **Y1**. Press $\boxed{\text{F6}}$ (**DRAW**) to draw the graph.

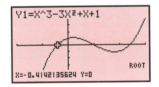

To find where this function cuts the x-axis, press $\boxed{\text{F5}}$ (**G-Solv**) $\boxed{\text{F1}}$ (**ROOT**). The first solution $x \approx -0.414$ is given.

Press $\boxed{\blacktriangleright}$ to find the remaining solutions $x = 1$ and $x \approx 2.41$.

TURNING POINTS

Texas Instruments TI-83

To find the turning point (vertex) of $y = -x^2 + 2x + 3$, press $\boxed{\text{Y=}}$ and store $-x^2 + 2x + 3$ into **Y1**. Press $\boxed{\text{GRAPH}}$ to draw the graph.

From the graph, it is clear that the vertex is a maximum, so press $\boxed{\text{2nd}}$ $\boxed{\text{TRACE}}$ (CALC) 4 to select **4:maximum**. Move the cursor to the left of the vertex and press $\boxed{\text{ENTER}}$, then move the cursor to the right of the vertex and press $\boxed{\text{ENTER}}$. Finally, move the cursor close to the vertex and press $\boxed{\text{ENTER}}$ once more. The vertex is $(1, 4)$.

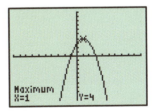

Casio fx-9860g

To find the turning point (vertex) of $y = -x^2 + 2x + 3$, select **GRAPH** from the Main Menu and store $-x^2 + 2x + 3$ into **Y1**. Press $\boxed{\text{F6}}$ (**DRAW**) to draw the graph.

From the graph, it is clear that the vertex is a maximum, so to find the vertex press F5 (G-Solv) F2 (MAX).

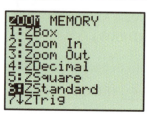

The vertex is $(1, 4)$.

ADJUSTING THE VIEWING WINDOW

When graphing functions it is important that you are able to view all the important features of the graph. As a general rule it is best to start with a large viewing window to make sure all the features of the graph are visible. You can then make the window smaller if necessary.

Texas Instruments TI-83

Some useful commands for adjusting the viewing window include:

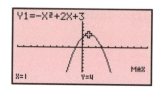

ZOOM **0:ZoomFit** :   This command scales the y-axis to fit the minimum and maximum values of the displayed graph within the current x-axis range.

ZOOM **6:ZStandard** :   This command returns the viewing window to the default setting of $-10 \leqslant x \leqslant 10$, $-10 \leqslant y \leqslant 10$.

If neither of these commands are helpful, the viewing window can be adjusted manually by pressing WINDOW and setting the minimum and maximum values for the x and y axes.

Casio fx-9860g

The viewing window can be adjusted by pressing   SHIFT F3 (**V-Window**).   You can manually set the minimum and maximum values of the x and y axes, or press F3 (**STD**) to obtain the standard viewing window $-10 \leqslant x \leqslant 10$, $-10 \leqslant y \leqslant 10$.

Chapter 1

Measurement and units

Contents:

A   Standard units
B   Converting units
C   Area units
D   Volume units
E   Capacity
F   Mass
G   Time
H   24-hour time

A STANDARD UNITS

The IB course requires a knowledge of the SI (Systeme International) and other basic units. The important ones are as follows:

Measurement of	Standard unit	What it means
Length	metre	How long or how far.
Mass	gram	How heavy an object is.
Capacity	litre	How much liquid or gas is contained.
Time	hours, minutes, seconds	How long it takes.
Temperature	degrees Celsius and Fahrenheit	How hot or cold.
Speed	metres/second ($m\,s^{-1}$)	How fast it is travelling.

The conversion between various units is dealt with in **Section B**, but it is important that you connect quantities with appropriate units.

OTHER UNITS

There are other units you may see, in everyday life and in other subjects. These are:

Measurement of	Base units	What it means
Area	square metres (m^2)	How much surface it has.
Volume	cubic metres (m^3)	How much space is occupied.
Acceleration	metres per second^2 ($m\,s^{-2}$)	How much speed is changing over time.
Force	newtons	What force is being applied.
Power	watts	How much electricity we are using.
Energy	joules	How much energy is being used.

The measurement of **length, time** and **speed** is of great importance.

Builders, architects, engineers and manufacturers need to measure the sizes of objects to great accuracy.

Constructing a skyscraper, building a long bridge across a river, and coordinating the repair of a satellite in space all require the use of measurement with skill and precision.

POTTS

©Jim Russell, General Features Pty Ltd

OPENING PROBLEM   FENCING THE SCHOOL

The fence at Jahmadahl High School needs to be replaced. Metal posts will be used with mesh fencing between them.

Things to discuss:

- How would you find the length of fencing needed?
- How would you find the number of posts needed?
- How would you find the total cost of materials and labour?

THE METRIC SYSTEM

The Metric System was developed in France in 1789 and uses the decimal system to convert from one unit to another.

Common prefixes show size. They are used with the basic units such as metres, grams, litres, watts, and joules.

For example:

kilo means 1000	**mega** means $1\,000\,000$
centi means $\frac{1}{100}$	**milli** means $\frac{1}{1000}$
deci means $\frac{1}{10}$	

These prefixes will be used in **Section B**.

READING INSTRUMENTS AND METERS

In this exercise we read various instruments and meters.

Example 1   ◀) Self Tutor

Read this electricity meter to find the electrical energy used since the meter was originally installed. If the pointer is between two numbers we use the smaller number.

The total number of kilowatt-hours is $14\,666$.

EXERCISE 1A

1 Read the following electricity meters:

a

b

2 Read the following off peak electricity meters:

a

OFF PEAK KWH

b

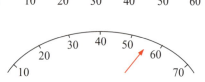

OFF PEAK KWH

3 Estimate the readings on the following meters:

a

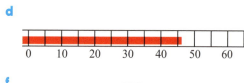

b

c

d

e

f

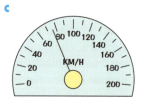

4 Estimate the fraction of fuel remaining in the following:

a

b

c

5 Estimate the speeds from the following speedometers:

a

b

c

Example 2   🔊 **Self Tutor**

The given tachometer shows the speed of
an engine in revolutions per minute (rpm).

Find the speed of the engine for the tachometer
shown.

The meter reading is approximately $3\frac{1}{4}$.

$\therefore$ speed of motor $= 3\frac{1}{4} \times 1000 = 3250$ rpm.

6 Find the speeds of the following engines:

7 Read the following thermometers:

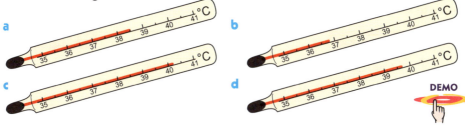

DEMO

B	**CONVERTING UNITS**

The base unit of length in the International System of units is the **metre** (m).
Other units of length based on the metre are:

- **millimetres** (mm) used to measure the length of a bee
- **centimetres** (cm) used to measure the width of your desk
- **kilometres** (km) used to measure the distance between two cities.

The table below summarises the connection between these units of length:

> 1 **kilometre** (km) = 1000 **metres** (m)
> 1 **metre** (m) = 100 **centimetres** (cm)
> 1 **centimetre** (cm) = 10 **millimetres** (mm)

LENGTH UNITS CONVERSIONS

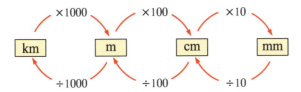

So, to convert cm
into km we ÷ 100
and then ÷ 1000.

Notice that, when converting from:
- smaller units to larger units we **divide** by the conversion factor
- larger units to smaller units we **multiply** by the conversion factor.

EXERCISE 1B

1 Suggest an appropriate unit of length for measuring the following:

a	the length of a baby	**b**	the width of an eraser
c	the distance from Perth to Darwin	**d**	the height of an old gum tree
e	the length of an ant	**f**	the length of a pen

2 Estimate the following and then check by measuring:

    a the length of your desk   **b** the width of your pencil case

    c the height of a friend   **d** the dimensions of your classroom

    e the length of a tennis court   **f** the width of a hockey pitch

CONVERTING LENGTH UNITS

Larger to smaller

Example 3	◀) **Self Tutor**
Convert: **a** 4.5 km to m **b** 1.25 m to mm	**a** km to m: $\times 1000$ $\therefore$ 4.5 km $= (4.5 \times 1000)$ m $= 4500$ m **b** m to mm: $\times 100$ then $\times 10$ $\therefore$ 1.25 m $= (1.25 \times 100 \times 10)$ mm $= 1250$ mm

3 Convert:

    a 52 km to m   **b** 115 cm to mm   **c** 1.65 m to cm

    d 6.3 m to mm   **e** 0.625 km to cm   **f** 8.1 km to mm

Smaller to larger

Example 4	◀) **Self Tutor**
Convert: **a** 350 cm to m **b** 23 000 mm to m	**a** cm to m: $\div 100$ $\therefore$ 350 cm $= (350 \div 100)$ m $= 3.5$ m **b** mm to m: $\div 10$ then $\div 100$ $\therefore$ 23 000 mm $= (23\,000 \div 10 \div 100)$ m $= 23$ m

4 Convert:

    a 480 cm to m   **b** 54 mm to cm   **c** 5280 m to km

    d 2000 mm to m   **e** 580 000 cm to km   **f** 7 000 000 mm to km

5 Convert the following lengths:

    a 42.1 km to m   **b** 210 cm to m   **c** 75 mm to cm

    d 1500 m to km   **e** 1.85 m to cm   **f** 42.5 cm to mm

    g 2.8 km to cm   **h** 16 500 mm to m   **i** 0.25 km to mm

A **reminder** about prefixes for metric units:

Prefix	Example
kilo means 1000	1 kilogram (kg) = 1000 grams (g)
mega means 1 000 000	1 megajoule (MJ) = 1 000 000 joules (J)
deci means $\frac{1}{10}$	1 decilitre (dL) = $\frac{1}{10}$ litre (L)
centi means $\frac{1}{100}$	1 centimetre (cm) = $\frac{1}{100}$ metre (m)
milli means $\frac{1}{1000}$	1 millimetre (mm) = $\frac{1}{1000}$ metre (m)

These prefixes go with: metres   grams   litres
                            newtons   watts   joules

6 Convert:

  a 7 g into mg   **b** 7 g into kg   **c** 580 g into kg   **d** 580 kg into g

  e 2.3 g into cg   **f** 56 g into mg   **g** 0.45 g into mg   **h** 450 cg into g

  i 20 mg into g   **j** 240 mg into cg   **k** 3 kg into mg   **l** 6500 mg into kg

7 Convert:

  a 2 litres into mL   **b** 45 cL into litres   **c** 1.2 kilowatts into watts

  d 2 cL into mL   **e** 2 mL into cL   **f** 3500 dL into litres

  g 0.045 L into dL   **h** 40 msec into sec   **i** 2000 watts into kilowatts

8 Mike ran 8.5 km while Mal walked 3200 m. How much farther did Mike run than Mal walk?

9 I have 45 coils of fencing wire and each coil is 275 m long. How many kilometres of wire do I have?

10 Liesel swims eighty 25 m laps in 1 hour. If she continues to swim at that speed, how many kilometres will she swim in 3 hours?

11 John has 3.85 km of copper wire and needs to cut it into 1.5 cm lengths to be used in electric toasters. How many lengths can he make?

12 How many 5 dL glasses can be filled from a jug containing 2 litres of water?

13 An electric light bulb has a power rating of 75 watts. A kettle has a rating of 3 kilowatts. How many light bulbs must be switched on to use the same power as 2 kettles?

14 A postage stamp has a mass of 2 cg. How many of these stamps would have a total mass of 1 kg?

15 A pack of 500 sheets of paper has a mass of 2.5 kg. Find the mass of one sheet, giving your answer in the most appropriate unit.

16 A bottle of medicine has a capacity of 50 cL. How many 5 mL spoonfuls can be obtained from the bottle?

17 A small car has a mass of 0.96 tonnes and a larger car is 600 kg heavier. Given that 1 tonne = 1000 kg, find the mass, in tonnes, of the larger car.

18 Maria's stride length is 0.9 m. How many strides does she take when she walks 2.7 km?

 # AREA UNITS

The **area** enclosed by a shape is a measure of how large the surface is. It is measured in *square* units.

UNITS OF AREA

Area can be measured in square millimetres, square centimetres, square metres and square kilometres; there is also another unit called a hectare (ha).

$$\begin{aligned}
\mathbf{1\ mm^2} &= 1\ mm \times 1\ mm \\
\mathbf{1\ cm^2} &= 10\ mm \times 10\ mm = 100\ mm^2 \\
\mathbf{1\ m^2} &= 100\ cm \times 100\ cm = 10\,000\ cm^2 \\
\mathbf{1\ ha} &= 100\ m \times 100\ m = 10\,000\ m^2 \\
\mathbf{1\ km^2} &= 1000\ m \times 1000\ m = 1\,000\,000\ m^2 \text{ or } 100\ ha
\end{aligned}$$

AREA UNITS CONVERSIONS

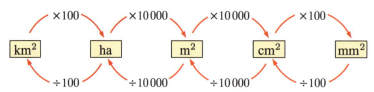

EXERCISE 1C

1 Suggest an appropriate area unit for measuring the following:

   a the area of a postage stamp   **b** the area of your desktop

   c the area of a vineyard   **d** the area of your bedroom floor

   e the area of Tasmania   **f** the area of a toe-nail

Example 5   ◀) **Self Tutor**

Convert: **a** 6 m^2 to cm^2 **b** 18 500 m^2 to ha

a m^2 to cm^2:   ×10 000

   ∴ 6 m^2 = (6 × 10 000) cm^2
        = 60 000 cm^2

b m^2 to ha: ÷10 000

   ∴ 18 500 m^2 = (18 500 ÷ 10 000) ha
        = 18 500.÷10 000 ha
        = 1.85 ha

---

2 Convert:

   a 23 mm^2 to cm^2 **b** 3.6 ha to m^2 **c** 726 cm^2 to m^2

   d 7.6 m^2 to mm^2 **e** 8530 m^2 to ha   **f** 0.354 ha to cm^2

   g 13.54 cm^2 to mm^2 **h** 432 m^2 to cm^2 **i** 0.004 82 m^2 to mm^2

j 3 km^2 into m^2 **k** 0.7 km^2 into ha   **l**   660 ha into m^2

m   660 ha into km^2 **n** 0.05 m^2 into cm^2 **o** 25 cm^2 into m^2

p 5.2 mm^2 into cm^2 **q** 0.72 km^2 into mm^2

3 Calculate the area of the following rectangles:

a   50 cm by 0.2 m in cm^2 **b**   0.6 m by 0.04 m in cm^2

c   30 mm by 4 mm in cm^2 **d**   0.2 km by 0.4 km in m^2

4 **a** I have purchased a 4.2 ha property. Council regulations allow me to have 5 free range chickens for every 100 m^2. How many free range chickens am I allowed to have?

    b Sam purchased 2 m^2 of material, and needed to cut it into rectangles of area 200 cm^2 for a patchwork quilt. This can be done with no waste. How many rectangles can Sam cut out?

> Make sure you change both length units into the units required in the answer.

D   VOLUME UNITS

The **volume** of a solid is the amount of space it occupies. It is measured in *cubic* units.

UNITS OF VOLUME

Volume can be measured in cubic millimetres, cubic centimetres or cubic metres.

1 cm^3
$= 10 \text{ mm} \times 10 \text{ mm} \times 10 \text{ mm}$
$= 1000 \text{ mm}^3$

1 m^3
$= 100 \text{ cm} \times 100 \text{ cm} \times 100 \text{ cm}$
$= 1\,000\,000 \text{ cm}^3$

VOLUME UNITS CONVERSIONS

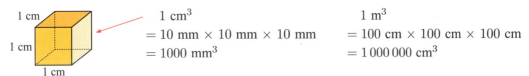

$\times 1\,000\,000\,000$ $\times 1\,000\,000$ $\times 1000$

| km^3 | | m^3 | | cm^3 | | mm^3 |

$\div 1\,000\,000\,000$ $\div 1\,000\,000$ $\div 1000$

Example 6   ◀) **Self Tutor**

Convert the following: **a** 5 m^3 to cm^3 **b** $25\,000 \text{ mm}^3$ to cm^3

a m^3 to cm^3: $\times 100^3$

    5 m^3
    $= (5 \times 100^3) \text{ cm}^3$
    $= (5 \times 1\,000\,000) \text{ cm}^3$
    $= 5\,000\,000 \text{ cm}^3$

b mm^3 to cm^3: $\div 10^3$

    $25\,000 \text{ mm}^3$
    $= (25\,000 \div 10^3) \text{ cm}^3$
    $= (25\,000 \div 1000) \text{ cm}^3$
    $= 25 \text{ cm}^3$

EXERCISE 1D

1 Convert the following:

    a 8.65 cm^3 to mm^3 **b** $86\,000$ mm^3 to cm^3 **c** $300\,000$ cm^3 to m^3

    d 124 cm^3 to mm^3 **e** 300 mm^3 to cm^3 **f** 3.7 m^3 to cm^3

2 **a** $30\,000$ ingots of lead, each with volume 250 cm^3, are required by a battery manufacturer. How many cubic metres of lead does the manufacturer need to purchase?

    b A manufacturer of lead sinkers for fishing has 0.237 m^3 of lead. If each sinker is 5 cm^3 in volume, how many sinkers can be made?

E   CAPACITY

> The **capacity** of a container is the quantity of fluid used to fill it.

UNITS OF CAPACITY

The basic unit of capacity is the **litre (L)**.

> **1 litre (L)** = 1000 millilitres (mL)
> **1 kilolitre (kL)** = 1000 litres (L)
> **1 megalitre (ML)** = 1000 kilolitres (kL)

CONNECTING VOLUME AND CAPACITY

Reminder: **1 millilitre (mL)** of fluid fills a container of size 1 cm^3.

We say: 1 mL $\equiv 1$ cm^3, $\ 1$ L $\equiv 1000$ cm^3 and 1 kL $= 1000$ L $\equiv 1$ m^3.

CAPACITY UNITS CONVERSION

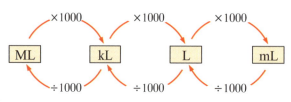

$\equiv$ reads 'is equivalent to'.

Example 7	🔊 **Self Tutor**

Convert: **a** 4.2 L to mL   **b** $36\,800$ L to kL

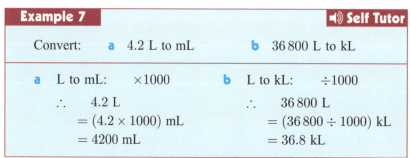

a L to mL: $\times 1000$

    $\therefore \quad 4.2$ L
    $= (4.2 \times 1000)$ mL
    $= 4200$ mL

b L to kL: $\div 1000$

    $\therefore \quad 36\,800$ L
    $= (36\,800 \div 1000)$ kL
    $= 36.8$ kL

EXERCISE 1E

1 Give the most appropriate units of capacity for measuring the amount of water in a:

    a reservoir   **b** small drink bottle

    c swimming pool   **d** laundry tub

2 Convert:

    a 3.76 L into mL   **b** 47 320 L into kL   **c** 3.5 kL into L

    d 0.423 L into mL   **e** 0.054 kL into mL   **f** 58 340 mL into kL

3   **a** A chemist makes up 20 mL bottles of eye drops from a drum of eye drop solution. If the full drum has a capacity of 0.275 kL, how many bottles of eye drop solution can the chemist fill?

    b 1000 dozen bottles of wine, each of capacity 750 mL, need to be emptied into tanks of capacity 1000 L for export.

    How many tanks are needed?

4 A jug has capacity 0.005 kL. How many 6 dL glasses can be filled from a full jug of water?

5 The capacity of a car engine is quoted as 1800 cc, meaning 1800 cubic centimetres. What is this in litres?

6 One litre of water has a mass of 1 kg. Find the mass of 20 cL of water, giving your answer in grams.

7 The capacity of a cuboid can be calculated by multiplying its length, width and depth. The following cuboids are filled with gas. Find the capacity of each in the units stated:

    a 85 cm by 65 cm by 20 cm (litres)   **b** 4 mm by 3 mm by 3 mm (mL)

    c 1.2 m by 1.2 m by 0.9 m (litres)   **d** 4 m by 3 m by 2 m (kL)

    e 3 cm by 2.5 cm by 2 cm (litres)   **f** 1.3 m by 80 cm by 90 cm (kL)

8   **a** What is the capacity (in mL) of a bottle of volume 25 cm^3?

    b Find the volume of a tank (in m^3) if its capacity is 3200 kL.

    c How many litres are there in a tank of volume 7.32 m^3?

F   MASS

The **mass** of an object is the amount of matter in it.

1 gram (g) is the mass of 1 mL of pure water.	1 g = 1000 mg
1 kilogram (kg) is the mass of 1 L of pure water.	1 kg = 1000 g
1 tonne (t) is the mass of 1 kL of pure water.	1 t = 1000 kg

MASS UNITS CONVERSIONS

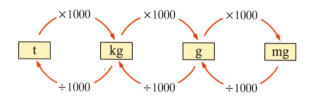

EXERCISE 1F

1 Convert:

a   3200 g to kg

b   1.87 t to kg

c   47 835 mg to kg

d   4653 mg to g

e   2.83 t to g

f   0.0632 t to g

g   74 682 g to t

h   1.7 t to mg

i   91 275 g to kg

2 a   In peppermint flavoured sweets, 1 gram of peppermint extract is used per sweet. How many sweets can be made from a drum containing 0.15 t of peppermint extract?

b   A publisher produces a book weighing 856 grams. 6000 of the books are printed and are to be transported interstate.

   i   How many tonnes of books are to be sent?

   ii If the transport costs $450 per tonne, what will be the total cost of sending the books?

3 A glass fish tank has dimensions as shown. Sand is placed in the tank to a depth of 3 cm. Water is then added until it is 3 cm from the top of the tank. The sand is 3.7 times heavier than water.

Find:

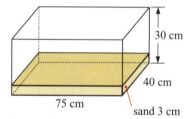

a   the volume of sand

b   the volume of water

c   the mass of water

d   the mass of sand

e   the total mass of the tank and contents if the mass of the glass is 15.6 kg.

G   TIME

In early civilisations, time was measured by regular changes in the sky. The recurring period of daylight and darkness came to be called a **day**. The Babylonians divided the day into hours, minutes and seconds. Ancient astronomers found the time taken for the Earth to complete one orbit around the Sun. This became known as a **year**.

The base unit of time in the International System of Units is the **second**, abbreviated **s**.

UNITS OF TIME

1 minute = 60 seconds	**1 hour** = 60 minutes = 3600 seconds
1 day = 24 hours	**1 week** = 7 days
1 year = 12 months = $365\frac{1}{4}$ days	**1 decade** = 10 years
	1 century = 100 years
	1 millennium = 1000 years

Example 8 ◀)) **Self Tutor**

Convert 8 days 7 hours and 6 minutes to minutes.

$$8 \text{ days} \times 24 \times 60 = 11\,520 \quad \text{minutes}$$
$$7 \text{ hours} \times 60 = \quad\;\; 420 \quad \text{minutes}$$
$$6 \text{ minutes} = \quad\quad\; 6 \quad \text{minutes}$$
$$\therefore \quad \text{total} = \overline{11\,946} \quad \text{minutes}$$

EXERCISE 1G

1 Convert the following times to minutes:

  a 5 hours   **b** 3 days   **c** 2 days 15 hours   **d** 2220 seconds

Example 9 ◀)) **Self Tutor**

Convert 30 240 minutes to days.

$$30\,240 = (30\,240 \div 60) \text{ hours} \quad \{60 \text{ min in 1 hour}\}$$
$$= 504 \text{ hours}$$
$$= (504 \div 24) \text{ days} \quad\quad \{24 \text{ hours in 1 day}\}$$
$$= 21 \text{ days}$$

2 Convert the following times to days:

  a 1248 hours   **b** 23 040 min   **c** 3 years   **d** 6 hours

Example 10 ◀)) **Self Tutor**

Convert 3 hours, 14 minutes to seconds.

$$3 \text{ hours, 14 minutes} = (3 \times 60) \text{ min} + 14 \text{ min} \quad \{60 \text{ min in 1 hour}\}$$
$$= 194 \text{ min}$$
$$= (194 \times 60) \text{ s} \quad\quad\quad\quad \{60 \text{ sec in 1 min}\}$$
$$= 11\,640 \text{ s}$$

3 Convert the following times to seconds:

  a 35 minutes   **b** 3 hours 19 min   **c** 5 days   **d** 1 week 2 days

4 Calculate the following, expressing your answers in hours, minutes and seconds:

  a 1 h 19 min + 2 h 42 min + 1 h 7 min

  b 4 h 51 min 16 s + 2 h 19 min 54 s

  c 12 h − 7 h 55 min

  d 5 h 23 min − 2 h 48 min

The abbreviation for hours is **h** and for minutes is **min**.

5 Xani has 6 science lessons a week, each of 45 minutes duration. Find the total time spent in science lessons in a twelve week term.

Example 11   ◀))) **Self Tutor**

What is the time difference between 9.55 am and 1.25 pm?

$$9.55 \text{ am to } 10.00 \text{ am} = 5 \text{ min}$$
$$10.00 \text{ am to } 1.00 \text{ pm} = 3 \text{ h}$$
$$1.00 \text{ pm to } 1.25 \text{ pm} = 25 \text{ min}$$
$$\text{i.e.,} \quad \overline{3 \text{ h } 30 \text{ min}}$$

---

6 Find the time difference between:

    a 4.30 am and 6.55 am   **b** 10.08 am and 5.52 pm

    c 3.15 pm and 9.03 pm   **d** 7.54 am and 2.29 pm

7 Henry left home at 7.48 am and arrived at work at 9.02 am. How long did it take him to get to work?

8 Your time schedule shows you worked the following hours last week:

Monday	8.45 am - 5.05 pm
Tuesday	8.50 am - 5.10 pm
Wednesday	8.45 am - 4.55 pm
Thursday	8.30 am - 5.00 pm
Friday	8.35 am - 5.15 pm

  a How many hours did you work last week?

  b If you are paid €9.00 per hour, what was your income for the week?

Example 12   ◀))) **Self Tutor**

What is the time $3\frac{1}{2}$ hours after 10.40 am?

$$10.40 \text{ am} + 3\tfrac{1}{2} \text{ hours} = 10.40 \text{ am} + 3 \text{ h} + 30 \text{ min}$$
$$= 1.40 \text{ pm} + 30 \text{ min}$$
$$= 2.10 \text{ pm}$$

---

9 Calculate the time:

    a 3 hours after 8.16 am   **b** 3 hours before 11.45 am

    c $5\frac{1}{2}$ hours after 10.15 am   **d** $3\frac{1}{2}$ hours before 1.18 pm

10 Boris caught a plane flight at 8.45 am. The flight was $6\frac{1}{2}$ hours. At what time did he arrive at his destination, assuming it was in the same time zone?

11 If a train is travelling at 36 m s^{-1}, how far will it travel in 1 hour? Give your answer in kilometres.

24-HOUR TIME

24-hour time is used by the armed forces and in train and airline timetables. It avoids the need for using **am** and **pm** to indicate morning and afternoon.

In 24-hour time, four digits are always used. For example:

- 0800 is 8.00 am

  "Oh eight hundred hours"

- 0000 is midnight
- 2359 is one minute before midnight

- 2000 is 8.00 pm

  "twenty hundred hours"

- 1200 is noon or midday

Morning times (am) are from midnight (0000) to midday (1200).

Afternoon times (pm) are from midday (1200) to midnight (0000).

Note:
- Midnight is 0000 not 2400.
- To convert afternoon 24-hour time to pm times we subtract 1200.

EXERCISE 1H

1 Change to 24-hour time:

a 9.57 am	**b** 11.06 am	**c** 4 o'clock pm
d 2.25 pm	**e** 8 o'clock am	**f** 1.06 am
g 8.58 pm	**h** noon	**i** 2 minutes past midnight

2 Change to am/pm time:

a 1140	**b** 0346	**c** 1634	**d** 1900
e 0800	**f** 2330	**g** 1223	**h** 2040

3 Copy and complete the following railway schedule:

	Departure	Travelling time	Arrival
a	0520	6 h 20 min	
b	0710		1405
c		56 min	1027
d		4 h 23 min	1652
e	2012		0447 (next day)

LINKS
click here

ERRORS IN MEASUREMENT

Areas of interaction:
Approaches to learning

REVIEW SET 1A

1 Read the following meters and instruments:

a

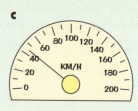

OFF PEAK KWH

b

c

2 a Convert: **i** 3.28 km to m   **ii** 755 mm to cm   **iii** 32 cm to m

  b A staple is made from a piece of wire 3 cm long. How many staples can be made from a roll of wire 1200 m long?

3 Convert:

  a 5 g to mg   **b** 23 g to kg   **c** 512 600 mg to kg

  d 2.5 L to mL   **e** 4 ML to L   **f** 25 L to dL

4 Convert:

  a 5600 watts into kilowatts   **b** 4.5 kilojoules into joules

5 Mika ran 5 laps of a 1500 metre circuit. How far in kilometres did he run?

6 Convert:

  a 1950 mm^2 to cm^2 **b** 6.4 m^2 to cm^2 **c** 2 500 000 m^2 to km^2

7 Calculate:

  a the perimeter of a rectangle with width 15 cm and length 0.2 m (in m)

  b the area of a rectangle with length 25 cm and width 0.09 m (in cm^2).

8 Convert:

  a 2600 mm^3 to cm^3 **b** 8 000 000 cm^3 to m^3 **c** 1.2 m^3 to cm^3

  d 5.6 L to mL   **e** 250 L to kL   **f** 56 cm^3 to mL

9 How many 375 mL cans of drink would you need to buy to have at least as much drink as in a 1.25 L bottle?

10 Convert:

  a 56 mg to g   **b** 450 g to kg   **c** 0.25 t to kg

11 A truck with a load limit of 4 tonnes is required to deliver 9000 bricks to a building site. If one brick has a mass of 1.25 kilograms, how many trips will be required?

12 A five set tennis match starts at 2.10 pm. The sets take the following times to complete: 16 minutes, 35 minutes, 28 minutes, 20 minutes, 24 minutes. There is an extra 20 minutes during the match for rests and other reasons.

At what time did the match finish?

13 What is the time difference between 3.49 am and 2.13 pm?

14 a Write 5.31 pm in 24-hour time.   **b** Write 0014 in 12-hour time.

REVIEW SET 1B

1 Read the following measuring instruments:

a

b
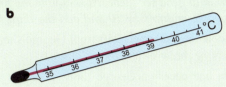

2 **a** Convert:

    i 1560 m to km   **ii** 26.5 cm to mm   **iii** 1.8 m to cm

  b Large paper clips are made from pieces of wire 16 cm long. How many metres of wire would be needed to make 500 large paper clips?

3 Convert:

  a 350 mg to g   **b** 250 kg to t   **c** 16.8 kg to g

  d 150 mL to L   **e** 260 L to ML   **f** 0.8 L to mL

4 Convert:

  a 2.5 kilowatts to watts   **b** 550 joules to kilojoules

5 Because he has a cough, Dien has to take 15 mL of cough medicine 3 times a day for 10 days. How much medicine will be left if he buys a 0.5 L bottle?

6 Carl ran 1.2 km in 2 minutes, and Hilda ran 1650 m in 3 minutes. Which of them ran faster?

7 Convert:

  a 5.4 cm^2 to mm^2 **b** $56\,000 \text{ cm}^2$ to m^2 **c** 0.8 km^2 to m^2

  d 0.6 cm^3 to mm^3 **e** 0.018 m^3 to cm^3 **f** $25\,000\,000 \text{ mm}^3$ to m^3

8 Calculate the area in hectares of a rectangular field with sides 300 m and 0.2 km.

9 How many 600 mL cartons of milk could be filled from a tank containing 5.4 kL of milk?

10 How many cubic metres of molten metal would be required to fill 8000 moulds each with 150 cm^3 of metal?

11 A truck was loaded with 300 lawnmowers, each weighing 25 kg. Find the total weight of this load, in tonnes.

12 Convert: **a** 256 hours to days and hours   **b** 2 hours 19 minutes to seconds

13 Calculate the time: **a** $3\frac{1}{2}$ hours after 11.15 am **b** $2\frac{1}{4}$ hours before 10.14 am

14 Change: **a** 4.30 pm to 24-hour time   **b** 0745 hours to 12-hour time.

THE THREE DICE TRICK

Adele says to George: *"Throw three dice and write down the numbers which result without letting me see them. Now double the first number, add 5, multiply by 5, add the second number, multiply by 10 and add the third number. Now tell me your answer."*

Adele then subtracts 250 from George's answer and immediately informs him of the numbers he threw on the dice.

On one occasion George threw a 4, a 2 and a 3. He then did his calculation and told Adele his answer was 673. When Adele subtracted 250 she got an answer of 423 and so predicted that the dice were 4, 2 and 3. George was amazed.

Try this trick with a friend. Can you explain why it always shows the correct dice results?

PUZZLE   ARE YOU A GOOD CONVERTER?

Answer the questions below, then place the letter for each question in the box corresponding to the correct solution, to reveal the message.

A   5.6 m = ... cm

C   430 g = ... kg

D   5.6 L = ... dL

E $50\,000$ m^2 = ... km^2

F   17 280 minutes = ... days

G   5600 cm^3 = ... m^3

H $43\,000$ m^2 = ... ha

I $50\,000$ L = ... kL

M   0.043 Mg = ... g

N   4 days, 2 h, 27 min = ... min

O   How many metres farther is 1.9 km than 1590 m?

R   How many minutes does it take to run 3 km at 5 m s^{-1}?

T   How many litres of soft drink are in a drink machine containing 240 cans holding 375 mL each?

U   A truck holds ninety 11 litre water containers. How many tonnes does the truck's load weigh?

V   How many hours are there between 9 pm and 2 pm the next day?

Y   How many seconds are there in 1 week?

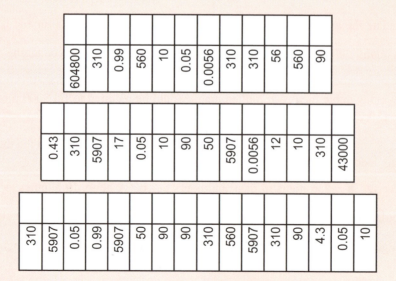

| 604800 | 310 | 0.99 | 560 | 10 | 0.05 | 0.0056 | 310 | 310 | 56 | 560 | 90 |

| 0.43 | 310 | 5907 | 17 | 0.05 | 10 | 90 | 50 | 5907 | 0.0056 | 12 | 10 | 310 | 43000 |

| 310 | 5907 | 0.05 | 0.99 | 5907 | 50 | 90 | 90 | 310 | 560 | 5907 | 310 | 90 | 4.3 | 0.05 | 10 |

Chapter **2**

Number operations

Contents:

A   Operations with integers
B   Operations with fractions
C   Index notation
D   Laws of indices

A **OPERATIONS WITH INTEGERS**

> The negative whole numbers, zero, and the positive whole numbers form the set of all **integers**,
>
> i.e., ... − 5, −4, −3, −2, −1, 0, 1, 2, 3, 4, 5 ......

We can show these numbers on a number line. Zero is neither positive nor negative.

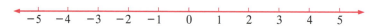

We can classify integers as follows:

We have previously developed the following **rules** for handling **addition** and **subtraction** of **integers**:

> + **(positive)** gives a **(positive)**
> − **(positive)** gives a **(negative)**
> + **(negative)** gives a **(negative)**
> − **(negative)** gives a **(positive)**

Example 1 ◀⟩ **Self Tutor**

Simplify:
a $4 + -9$ **b** $4 - -9$ **c** $-3 + -5$ **d** $-3 - -5$

a	**b**	**c**	**d**
$4 + -9$	$4 - -9$	$-3 + -5$	$-3 - -5$
$= 4 - 9$	$= 4 + 9$	$= -3 - 5$	$= -3 + 5$
$= -5$	$= 13$	$= -8$	$= 2$

EXERCISE 2A

1 Find the value of:

a $17 - 9$	**b** $17 + -9$	**c** $17 - -9$	**d** $-17 + 9$
e $-17 - 9$	**f** $-17 - -9$	**g** $9 - 17$	**h** $17 + 9$
i $13 + 27$	**j** $13 - 27$	**k** $13 + -27$	**l** $13 - -27$
m $-13 + 27$	**n** $-13 + -27$	**o** $-13 - -27$	**p** $27 - 13$

We have also developed the following **rules for multiplication** of integers:

> **(positive)** × **(positive)** gives a **(positive)**
> **(positive)** × **(negative)** gives a **(negative)**
> **(negative)** × **(positive)** gives a **(negative)**
> **(negative)** × **(negative)** gives a **(positive)**

Example 2   ◀) **Self Tutor**

Find the value of:
a 3×4 b 3×-4 c -3×4 d -3×-4

a $3 \times 4 = 12$ b $3 \times -4 = -12$ c $-3 \times 4 = -12$ d $-3 \times -4 = 12$

2 Find the value of:
a 6×8 b 6×-8 c -6×8 d -6×-8
e 9×7 f 9×-7 g -9×7 h -7×-9

Example 3   ◀) **Self Tutor**

Simplify:
a -4^2 b $(-4)^2$ c -2^3 d $(-2)^3$

a $\quad -4^2$ b $\quad (-4)^2$ c $\quad -2^3$ d $\quad (-2)^3$
$\quad = -4 \times 4$ $\quad = -4 \times -4$ $\quad = -2 \times 2 \times 2$ $\quad = -2 \times -2 \times -2$
$\quad = -16$ $\quad = 16$ $\quad = -8$ $\quad = -8$

3 Find the value of:
a -6^2 b $(-6)^2$ c $(-3)^3$ d -3^3
e $4 \times -3 \times 6$ f $-4 \times 2 \times -6$ g $-4 \times -3 \times -6$ h $2 \times (-4)^2$
i $-3 \times (-4)^2$ j -3^4 k $(-3)^4$ l $(-5)^2 \times (-3)^2$

The following **rules** have also been developed **for division** with integers:

$\text{(positive)} \div \text{(positive)} = \text{(positive)}$
$\text{(positive)} \div \text{(negative)} = \text{(negative)}$
$\text{(negative)} \div \text{(positive)} = \text{(negative)}$
$\text{(negative)} \div \text{(negative)} = \text{(positive)}$

Example 4   ◀) **Self Tutor**

Find the value of:
a $14 \div 2$ b $14 \div -2$ c $-14 \div 2$ d $-14 \div -2$

a $\quad 14 \div 2$ b $\quad 14 \div -2$ c $\quad -14 \div 2$ d $\quad -14 \div -2$
$\quad = 7$ $\quad = -7$ $\quad = -7$ $\quad = 7$

4 Find the value of:
a $18 \div 3$ b $18 \div -3$ c $-18 \div 3$ d $-18 \div -3$
e $35 \div 7$ f $35 \div -7$ g $-35 \div 7$ h $-35 \div -7$
i $\dfrac{6}{18}$ j $\dfrac{-6}{18}$ k $\dfrac{6}{-18}$ l $\dfrac{-6}{-18}$

ORDER OF OPERATIONS RULES:

- Perform the operations within **brackets** first.
- Calculate any part involving **exponents**.
- Starting from the left, perform all **divisions** and **multiplications** as you come to them.
- Finally, restart from the left and perform all **additions** and **subtractions** as you come to them.

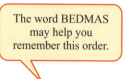

The word BEDMAS may help you remember this order.

Brackets are **grouping symbols** that tell us what to evaluate first.

RULES FOR BRACKETS:

- If an expression contains *one set* of grouping symbols, i.e., brackets, work that part first.

- If an expression contains *two or more sets* of grouping symbols one inside the other, work the innermost first.

- The division line of fractions also behaves as a grouping symbol. This means that the numerator and the denominator must be found separately before doing the division.

Example 5   ◀) **Self Tutor**

Simplify: **a** $3 + 7 - 5$ **b** $6 \times 3 \div 2$

a $3 + 7 - 5$ {Work left to right as only $+$ and $-$ are involved.}
$= 10 - 5$
$= 5$

b $6 \times 3 \div 2$ {Work left to right as only $\times$ and $\div$ are involved.}
$= 18 \div 2$
$= 9$

---

5 Simplify:

a $6 + 9 - 5$	**b** $6 - 9 + 5$	**c** $6 - 9 - 5$
d $3 \times 12 \div 6$	**e** $12 \div 6 \times 3$	**f** $6 \times 12 \div 3$

Example 6   ◀) **Self Tutor**

Simplify: **a** $23 - 10 \div 2$ **b** $3 \times 8 - 6 \times 5$

a $23 - 10 \div 2$
$= 23 - 5$ {$\div$ before $-$}
$= 18$

b $3 \times 8 - 6 \times 5$
$= 24 - 30$ {$\times$ before $-$}
$= -6$

6 Simplify:

a	$5 + 8 \times 4$	**b**	$9 \times 4 + 7$	**c**	$17 - 7 \times 2$
d	$6 \times 7 - 18$	**e**	$36 - 6 \times 5$	**f**	$19 - 7 \times 0$
g	$3 \times 6 - 6$	**h**	$70 - 5 \times 4 \times 3$	**i**	$45 \div 3 - 9$
j	$8 \times 5 - 6 \times 4$	**k**	$7 + 3 + 5 \times 2$	**l**	$17 - 6 \times 4 + 9$

Example 7   🔊 **Self Tutor**

Simplify:
$3 + (11 - 7) \times 2$

$\qquad 3 + (11 - 7) \times 2$
$\quad = 3 + 4 \times 2 \qquad$ {work the brackets first}
$\quad = 3 + 8 \qquad\quad$ {$\times$ before $+$}
$\quad = 11$

---

7 Simplify:

a	$14 + (8 - 5)$	**b**	$(19 + 7) - 13$	**c**	$(18 \div 6) - 2$
d	$18 \div (6 - 4)$	**e**	$72 - (18 \div 6)$	**f**	$(72 - 18) \div 6$
g	$36 + (14 \div 2)$	**h**	$36 - (7 + 13) - 9$	**i**	$(22 - 5) + (15 - 11)$
j	$(18 \div 3) \div 2$	**k**	$32 \div (4 \div 2)$	**l**	$28 - (7 \times 3) - 9$

Example 8   🔊 **Self Tutor**

Simplify:
$[12 + (9 \div 3)] - 11$

$\qquad [12 + (9 \div 3)] - 11$
$\quad = [12 + 3] - 11 \qquad$ {work the inner brackets first}
$\quad = 15 - 11 \qquad\quad$ {outer brackets next}
$\quad = 4$

---

8 Simplify:

a	$8 - [(4 - 6) + 3 \times 2]$	**b**	$[22 - (11 + 4)] \times 3$
c	$25 - [(11 - 7) + 8]$	**d**	$[28 - (15 \div 3)] \times 4$
e	$300 \div [6 \times (15 \div 3)]$	**f**	$[(14 \times 5) \div (28 \div 2)] \times 3$

Example 9   🔊 **Self Tutor**

Simplify: $\dfrac{12 + (5 - 7)}{18 \div (6 + 3)}$

$\qquad \dfrac{12 + (5 - 7)}{18 \div (6 + 3)}$

$\quad = \dfrac{12 + (-2)}{18 \div 9} \qquad$ {working the brackets first}

$\quad = \dfrac{10}{2} \qquad\qquad$ {simplifying numerator and denominator}

$\quad = 5$

9 Simplify:

a $\dfrac{240}{8 \times 6}$ b $\dfrac{27}{17 - 8}$ c $\dfrac{39 \div 3}{14 + 12}$ d $\dfrac{18 + 7}{7 - 2}$

e $\dfrac{58 - 16}{11 - 5}$ f $\dfrac{6 \times 7 + 7}{7}$ g $\dfrac{54}{11 - (2 \times 4)}$ h $\dfrac{(6 + 9) - 5}{7 + (9 - 6)}$

USING YOUR CALCULATOR WITH INTEGERS

Most modern calculators have the **Order of Operations** rules built into them.

For example, consider $5 \times 3 + 2 \times 5$.

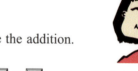

Try to remember BEDMAS!

If you key in 5 $\times$ 3 $+$ 2 $\times$ 5 $=$ the calculator gives an answer of 25, which is **correct**.

The calculator has performed the two multiplications before the addition.

However, if we consider $\dfrac{12}{4 + 2}$ and key in 12 $\div$ 4 $+$ 2 $=$ the calculator gives an answer of 5, which is **incorrect**.

The calculator has divided 12 by 4 to give 3, and then added on 2 to give 5.

To fix this problem we use brackets.

We need to evaluate the denominator first before performing the division.

If we key in 12 $\div$ $($ 4 $+$ 2 $)$ $=$ we obtain the answer 2, which is correct.

In this case the calculator has divided 12 by the sum of 4 and 2.

Example 10   🔊 **Self Tutor**

Calculate: **a** $12 + 32 \div (8 - 6)$ **b** $\dfrac{75}{7 + 8}$

a   12 $+$ 32 $\div$ $($ 8 $-$ 6 $)$ $=$ *Answer:* 28

b   75 $\div$ $($ 7 $+$ 8 $)$ $=$ *Answer:* 5

THE SIGN CHANGE KEY

The $(-)$ (or $+/-$)   key is used to enter negative numbers into the calculator.

To enter -5 into the calculator, key in $(-)$ 5   or   5 $+/-$ and -5 will appear on the display.

Example 11   Calculate: **a** 41×-7 **b** -18×23 🔊 **Self Tutor**

    a Key in   41 $\boxed{\times}$ $\boxed{(-)}$ 7 $\boxed{=}$ *Answer:* -287

    b Key in $\boxed{(-)}$ 18 $\boxed{\times}$ 23 $\boxed{=}$ *Answer:* -414

---

10 Evaluate each of the following using your calculator:

    a $87 + 27 \times 13$ **b** $(29 + 17) \times 19$ **c** $136 \div 8 + 16$

    d $136 \div (8 + 9)$ **e** 39×-27 **f** $-128 \div -32$

    g $\dfrac{97 + -7}{-5 \times 3}$ **h** $-67 + 64 \div -4$ **i** $\dfrac{-25 - 15}{9 - (16 \div 4)}$

B   OPERATIONS WITH FRACTIONS

A **common fraction** consists of two whole numbers, a **numerator** and a **denominator**, separated by a bar symbol.

$$\dfrac{4}{5} \quad \begin{matrix} \leftarrow \text{numerator} \\ \leftarrow \text{bar (which also means } divide \text{)} \\ \leftarrow \text{denominator} \end{matrix}$$

TYPES OF FRACTIONS

    $\frac{4}{5}$ is a **proper fraction**   {as the numerator is less than the denominator}

    $\frac{7}{6}$ is an **improper fraction**   {as the numerator is greater than the denominator}

    $2\frac{3}{4}$ is a **mixed number**   {as it is really $2 + \frac{3}{4}$}

    $\frac{1}{2}, \frac{3}{6}$ are **equivalent fractions**   {as both fractions represent equivalent portions}

ADDITION AND SUBTRACTION

To **add** (or **subtract**) two fractions we convert them to equivalent fractions with a common denominator. We then add (or subtract) the new numerators.

Example 12   🔊 **Self Tutor**

    Find: $\frac{3}{4} + \frac{5}{6}$

$$\frac{3}{4} + \frac{5}{6} \qquad \{\text{LCD} = 12\}$$

$$= \frac{3 \times 3}{4 \times 3} + \frac{5 \times 2}{6 \times 2} \quad \{\text{to achieve a common denominator of 12}\}$$

$$= \frac{9}{12} + \frac{10}{12}$$

$$= \frac{19}{12}$$

$$= 1\frac{7}{12}$$

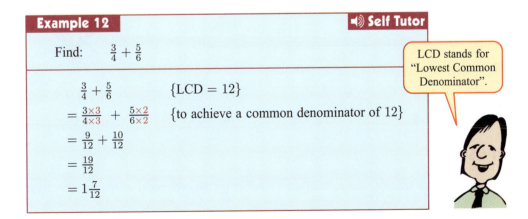

LCD stands for "Lowest Common Denominator".

Example 13   Find: $1\frac{2}{3} - 1\frac{2}{5}$ ◄⬤ **Self Tutor**

$1\frac{2}{3} - 1\frac{2}{5}$

$= \frac{5}{3} - \frac{7}{5}$ {write as improper fractions}

$= \frac{5 \times 5}{3 \times 5} - \frac{7 \times 3}{5 \times 3}$ {to achieve a common denominator of 15}

$= \frac{25}{15} - \frac{21}{15}$

$= \frac{4}{15}$

EXERCISE 2B

1 Find:

a $\frac{5}{13} + \frac{7}{13}$ **b** $\frac{9}{16} + \frac{2}{16}$ **c** $\frac{3}{8} + \frac{1}{4}$ **d** $\frac{2}{5} + \frac{1}{6}$

e $\frac{3}{7} + 4$ **f** $1\frac{1}{3} + \frac{5}{6}$ **g** $2\frac{1}{3} + 1\frac{1}{6}$ **h** $1\frac{1}{2} + 4\frac{2}{3}$

2 Find:

a $\frac{7}{11} - \frac{3}{11}$ **b** $\frac{5}{6} - \frac{2}{3}$ **c** $\frac{4}{9} - \frac{1}{3}$ **d** $1 - \frac{3}{8}$

e $4 - 2\frac{1}{4}$ **f** $2\frac{3}{5} - 1\frac{1}{2}$ **g** $3\frac{1}{3} - 1\frac{1}{2}$ **h** $4\frac{3}{7} - 2\frac{1}{3}$

MULTIPLICATION

To **multiply** two fractions, we first cancel any common factors in the numerator and denominator. We then multiply the numerators together and the denominators together.

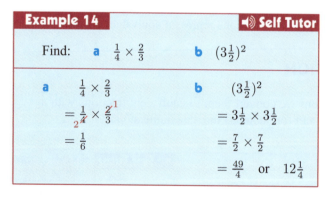

Example 14   ◄⬤ **Self Tutor**

Find: **a** $\frac{1}{4} \times \frac{2}{3}$ **b** $(3\frac{1}{2})^2$

a $\frac{1}{4} \times \frac{2}{3}$

$= \frac{1}{\underset{2}{4}} \times \frac{\overset{1}{2}}{3}$

$= \frac{1}{6}$

b $(3\frac{1}{2})^2$

$= 3\frac{1}{2} \times 3\frac{1}{2}$

$= \frac{7}{2} \times \frac{7}{2}$

$= \frac{49}{4}$ or $12\frac{1}{4}$

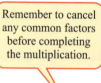

Remember to cancel any common factors before completing the multiplication.

3 Calculate:

a $\frac{2}{15} \times \frac{5}{6}$ **b** $\frac{6}{7} \times \frac{1}{3}$ **c** $3 \times \frac{3}{6}$ **d** $\frac{2}{3} \times 7$

e $1\frac{1}{3} \times \frac{6}{7}$ **f** $1\frac{1}{8} \times \frac{4}{9}$ **g** $(2\frac{1}{2})^2$ **h** $(1\frac{1}{3})^3$

DIVISION

To **divide** by a fraction, we multiply the number by the reciprocal of the fraction we are dividing by.

Example 15 🔊 **Self Tutor**

Find: **a** $3 \div \frac{2}{3}$ **b** $2\frac{1}{3} \div \frac{2}{3}$

a $\quad 3 \div \frac{2}{3}$

$= \frac{3}{1} \div \frac{2}{3}$

$= \frac{3}{1} \times \frac{3}{2}$

$= \frac{9}{2}$

$= 4\frac{1}{2}$

b $\quad 2\frac{1}{3} \div \frac{2}{3}$

$= \frac{7}{3} \div \frac{2}{3}$

$= \frac{7}{\overset{1}{\cancel{3}}} \times \frac{\cancel{3}^{1}}{2}$

$= \frac{7}{2}$

$= 3\frac{1}{2}$

The reciprocal of $\frac{c}{d}$ is $\frac{d}{c}$!

4 Evaluate:

a $\frac{3}{5} \div \frac{7}{10}$ **b** $\frac{3}{8} \div \frac{6}{11}$ **c** $\frac{4}{15} \div \frac{2}{5}$ **d** $\frac{2}{5} \div 4$

e $1 \div \frac{3}{5}$ **f** $1\frac{1}{3} \div \frac{3}{8}$ **g** $\frac{2}{3} \div 1\frac{1}{2}$ **h** $2\frac{1}{4} \div 1\frac{2}{3}$

5 Calculate:

a $3\frac{3}{7} + 1\frac{4}{5}$ **b** $\left(\frac{3}{4}\right)^4$ **c** $7 - 6 \times \frac{3}{4}$

d $\frac{4}{5} \times 1\frac{1}{2} \div 3$ **e** $\dfrac{8 \times 3 \times \frac{1}{3}}{\frac{2}{3}}$ **f** $1 \div \left(\frac{1}{4} + \frac{2}{3}\right)$

g $1 \div \frac{1}{4} + \frac{2}{3}$ **h** $\dfrac{3 - \frac{1}{2}}{3 \times \frac{5}{3}}$ **i** $\frac{2}{3} + \frac{1}{3} \times 1\frac{1}{2}$

j $\frac{5}{6} \times \frac{4}{5} - \frac{1}{15}$ **k** $\frac{1}{3} + \frac{1}{3} \div \frac{1}{5} + \frac{3}{5}$ **l** $1\frac{1}{2} - 2\frac{1}{3} \div 1\frac{2}{3}$

m $12 - \frac{2}{7} \times 3\frac{1}{2}$ **n** $1\frac{1}{3} + \frac{5}{6} - \frac{11}{12}$ **o** $6\frac{2}{5} - \frac{1}{4} \times 1\frac{1}{3} \div \frac{1}{6}$

Example 16 🔊 **Self Tutor**

Anna scores $\frac{3}{5}$ of her team's goals in a netball match.
How many goals did she shoot if the team shot 70 goals?

Remember that 'of' means '×'.

Anna shoots $\quad \frac{3}{5}$ of $70 = \frac{3}{5} \times 70$

$= \dfrac{3 \times \overset{14}{\cancel{70}}}{\underset{1}{\cancel{5}}}$

$= 42$ goals.

6 Solve the following problems:

a Colin eats $\frac{1}{3}$ of a pie and later eats $\frac{2}{5}$ of the pie. What fraction remains?

b The price of a skirt is $\frac{3}{7}$ of the price of a matching jacket. What does the skirt cost if the jacket sells for $105?

c A family spends $\frac{1}{4}$ of its weekly budget on rent, $\frac{1}{4}$ on food, $\frac{1}{10}$ on clothes, $\frac{1}{12}$ on entertainment, and the remainder is banked.
How much is banked if the weekly income is $859.00?

d Yukhi spent $\frac{1}{3}$ of his pocket money, and later spent $\frac{2}{3}$ of what remained.
What fraction of the original amount was left?

e A farmer has 268 cows and each cow has either one or two calves. If there are 335 calves in total, what fraction of the cows have two calves?

7 Isabella had a big bag of sweets. She ate two fifths of them on Monday, two fifths of those remaining on Tuesday, and two thirds of what remained on Wednesday. She then had 12 sweets. How many were in the bag originally?

FRACTIONS ON A CALCULATOR

Most scientific calculators and the **Casio fx-9860G** have a fraction key $\boxed{\text{a b/c}}$ that is used to enter common fractions.

There is no such key for the **TI-83**, so fractions need to be entered differently. You should consult the calculator section on page **11**.

Remember that although you may perform operations on fractions using your calculator, you **must not rely** on your calculator and forget how to manually perform operations with fractions.

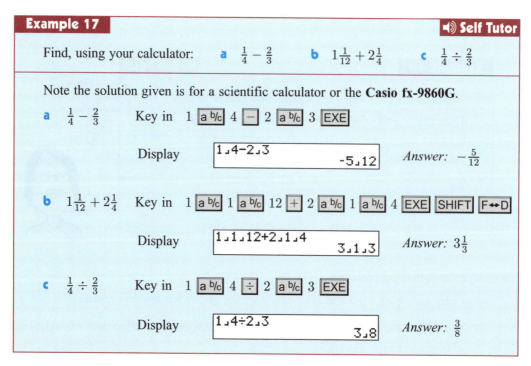

8 Find, using your calculator:

a $\frac{1}{5} + \frac{1}{3}$

b $\frac{1}{3} + \frac{2}{7}$

c $\frac{5}{8} - \frac{2}{7}$

d $\frac{3}{4} - \frac{1}{3}$

e $\frac{2}{5} \times \frac{3}{2}$

f $\frac{4}{7} \times \frac{2}{3}$

g $\frac{6}{7} \times \frac{2}{5}$

h $\frac{3}{5} \div \frac{2}{9}$

i $2\frac{1}{4} + 2\frac{1}{2} \times \frac{3}{4}$

j $1\frac{3}{7} \times 2\frac{1}{8} + 1\frac{1}{7}$

k $2\frac{3}{7} \div (2\frac{3}{4} \times \frac{4}{7})$

C   INDEX NOTATION

Rather than write

$2 \times 2 \times 2 \times 2 \times 2$,   we write such a product as 2^5.

2^5 reads "two to the power of five" or "two with index five".

Thus $5^3 = 5 \times 5 \times 5$ and $3^6 = 3 \times 3 \times 3 \times 3 \times 3 \times 3$.

2^5 — power, index or exponent — base

Example 18   ◀)) Self Tutor

Find the integer equal to: a 3^4 b $2^4 \times 3^2 \times 7$

a 3^4
  $= 3 \times 3 \times 3 \times 3$
  $= 9 \times 9$
  $= 81$

b $2^4 \times 3^2 \times 7$
  $= 2 \times 2 \times 2 \times 2 \times 3 \times 3 \times 7$
  $= 16 \times 9 \times 7$
  $= 1008$

Example 19   ◀)) Self Tutor

Write as a product of prime factors in index form:

a 144   b 4312

a

2	144
2	72
2	36
2	18
3	9
	3

b

2	4312
2	2156
2	1078
7	539
7	77
	11

$\therefore$ $144 = 2^4 \times 3^2$ $\therefore$ $4312 = 2^3 \times 7^2 \times 11$

EXERCISE 2C

1 Find the integer equal to:

a 2^3

b 3^3

c 2^5

d 5^3

e $2^2 \times 3^3 \times 5$

f $2^3 \times 3 \times 7^2$

g $3^2 \times 5^2 \times 13$

h $2^4 \times 5^2 \times 11$

2 By dividing continuously by the primes 2, 3, 5, 7, ..., write as a product of prime factors in index form:

a 50

b 98

c 108

d 360

e 1128

f 784

g 952

h 6500

3 Copy and complete the values of these common powers. Try to memorise them.

   a $2^1 = ...,$ $2^2 = ...,$ $2^3 = ...,$ $2^4 = ...,$ $2^5 = ...,$ $2^6 = ...$

   b $3^1 = ...,$ $3^2 = ...,$ $3^3 = ...,$ $3^4 = ...$

   c $5^1 = ...,$ $5^2 = ...,$ $5^3 = ...,$ $5^4 = ...$

   d $7^1 = ...,$ $7^2 = ...,$ $7^3 = ...$

4 The following numbers can be written as 2^n. Find n.

   a   32   **b**   256   **c**   4096

5 The following numbers can be written as 3^n. Find n.

   a   27   **b**   729   **c**   59 049

6 By considering $3^1, 3^2, 3^3, 3^4, 3^5$ .... and looking for a pattern, find the last digit of 3^{33}.

7 What is the last digit of 7^{77}?

HISTORICAL NOTE

Nicomachus, who lived around 100 AD, discovered an interesting number pattern involving cubes and sums of odd numbers.

$$1 = 1^3$$
$$3 + 5 = 8 = 2^3$$
$$7 + 9 + 11 = 27 = 3^3 \quad \text{etc.}$$

NEGATIVE BASES

So far we have only considered **positive** bases raised to a power.

We will now briefly look at **negative** bases. Consider the statements below:

$(-1)^1 = -1$ $(-2)^1 = -2$

$(-1)^2 = -1 \times -1 = 1$ $(-2)^2 = -2 \times -2 = 4$

$(-1)^3 = -1 \times -1 \times -1 = -1$ $(-2)^3 = -2 \times -2 \times -2 = -8$

$(-1)^4 = -1 \times -1 \times -1 \times -1 = 1$ $(-2)^4 = -2 \times -2 \times -2 \times -2 = 16$

From the pattern above it can be seen that:

       •   a **negative** base raised to an **odd** power is **negative**

       •   a **negative** base raised to an **even** power is **positive**.

Example 20   🔊 Self Tutor

Evaluate:

  a $(-2)^4$ **b** -2^4 **c** $(-2)^5$ **d** $-(-2)^5$

> Notice the effect of the brackets in these examples.

  a $(-2)^4$ **b** -2^4 **c** $(-2)^5$ **d** $-(-2)^5$

      $= 16$ $= -1 \times 2^4$ $= -32$ $= -1 \times (-2)^5$

                         $= -16$ $= -1 \times -32$

                                                       $= 32$

8 Simplify:

a $(-1)^4$ b $(-1)^5$ c $(-1)^{10}$ d $(-1)^{15}$

e $(-1)^8$ f -1^8 g $-(-1)^8$ h $(-3)^3$

i -3^3 j $-(-3)^3$ k $-(-6)^2$ l $-(-4)^3$

CALCULATOR USE

Just like for other operations, different calculators have different keys for entering powers. In general, however, they all perform raising to powers in a similar manner.

Power keys

$\boxed{x^2}$ squares the number in the display.

$\boxed{\wedge}$ raises the number in the display to whater power is required. On some calculators this key is $\boxed{y^x}$, $\boxed{a^x}$ or $\boxed{x^y}$.

> Not all calculators will use these key sequences. If you have problems, refer to the calculator instructions on page **12**.

Example 21 ◀) Self Tutor

Find, using your calculator: **a** 6^5 **b** $(-5)^4$ **c** -7^4

		Answer
a	Press: 6 $\boxed{\wedge}$ 5 $\boxed{\text{ENTER}}$	7776
b	Press: $\boxed{(}$ $\boxed{(-)}$ 5 $\boxed{)}$ $\boxed{\wedge}$ 4 $\boxed{\text{ENTER}}$	625
c	Press: $\boxed{(-)}$ 7 $\boxed{\wedge}$ 4 $\boxed{\text{ENTER}}$	-2401

9 Use your calculator to find the value of the following, recording the entire display:

a 2^8 b $(-5)^4$ c -3^5 d 7^4 e 8^3

f $(-7)^6$ g -7^6 h 1.05^{12} i -0.623^{11} j $(-2.11)^{17}$

10 To find 5^{-2} you could key in: 5 $\boxed{\wedge}$ $\boxed{(-)}$ 2 $\boxed{\text{ENTER}}$. The answer is 0.04.

Use your calculator to find the values of the following:

a 9^{-1} b $\dfrac{1}{9^1}$ c 4^{-2} d $\dfrac{1}{4^2}$

e 3^{-4} f $\dfrac{1}{3^4}$ g 15^0 h 97^0

What do you notice?

Summary:

- $x^0 = 1$ for any x except $x = 0$

- $x^{-n} = \dfrac{1}{x^n}$ i.e., x^{-n} is the reciprocal of x^n.

Example 22   ◄» Self Tutor

Simplify:

a 3^{-1} b 5^{-2} c 10^{-4}

> The negative index indicates the **reciprocal**!

a 3^{-1}

$= \dfrac{1}{3^1}$

$= \dfrac{1}{3}$

b 5^{-2}

$= \dfrac{1}{5^2}$

$= \dfrac{1}{25}$

c 10^{-4}

$= \dfrac{1}{10^4}$

$= \dfrac{1}{10\,000}$

11 Simplify, giving answers in simplest rational form:

a 4^{-1} b 2^{-1} c 6^{-1} d 8^{-1} e 2^{-2}

f 3^{-2} g 7^{-2} h 9^{-2} i 3^{-3} j 10^{-5}

Example 23   ◄» Self Tutor

Simplify, giving answers in simplest rational form:

a $\left(\dfrac{2}{3}\right)^{-1}$ b $\left(\dfrac{3}{5}\right)^{-2}$ c $8^0 - 8^{-1}$

a $\left(\dfrac{2}{3}\right)^{-1}$

$= \left(\dfrac{3}{2}\right)^1$

$= \dfrac{3}{2}$

b $\left(\dfrac{3}{5}\right)^{-2}$

$= \left(\dfrac{5}{3}\right)^2$

$= \dfrac{5^2}{3^2}$

$= \dfrac{25}{9}$

c $8^0 - 8^{-1}$

$= 1 - \dfrac{1}{8}$

$= \dfrac{7}{8}$

12 Simplify, giving answers in simplest rational form:

a $\left(\dfrac{1}{3}\right)^{-1}$ b $\left(\dfrac{2}{5}\right)^{-1}$ c $\left(\dfrac{4}{3}\right)^{-1}$ d $\left(\dfrac{1}{12}\right)^{-1}$ e $\left(\dfrac{2}{7}\right)^{-1}$

f $5^0 - 5^{-1}$ g $\left(\dfrac{3}{4}\right)^{-2}$ h $\left(2\dfrac{1}{4}\right)^{-2}$ i $\left(1\dfrac{1}{2}\right)^{-3}$ j $2^0 + 2^1 + 2^{-1}$

13 Write as powers of 10:

a $1\,000$ b $1\,000\,000$ c 0.001 d $0.000\,000\,01$

14 Write as powers of 2, 3 or 5:

a 8 b $\dfrac{1}{8}$ c 9 d $\dfrac{1}{9}$

e 125 f $\dfrac{1}{125}$ g 32 h $\dfrac{1}{32}$

i 81 j $\dfrac{1}{81}$ k $\dfrac{1}{25}$ l 1

15 The following can be written in the form $2^p \times 3^q \times 5^r$.   Find p, q and r in each case.

a 60 b 300 c $\dfrac{100}{9}$ d 250 e $\dfrac{3}{8000}$ f $2\dfrac{2}{5}$

g $\dfrac{25}{72}$ h 1 i $9\dfrac{3}{8}$ j $\dfrac{1}{15}$ k $1\dfrac{11}{25}$ l $\dfrac{27}{500}$

LAWS OF INDICES

Notice that:
- $2^3 \times 2^4 = 2 \times 2 \times 2 \ \times \ 2 \times 2 \times 2 \times 2 = 2^7$

- $\dfrac{2^5}{2^2} = \dfrac{2 \times 2 \times 2 \times 2 \times 2^{\cancel{1}}}{2 \times 2^{\ 1}} = 2^3$

- $(2^3)^2 = 2 \times 2 \times 2 \ \times \ 2 \times 2 \times 2 = 2^6$

This suggests that:

- $a^m \times a^n = a^{m+n}$ — To **multiply** numbers with the **same base**, keep the base and **add** the indices.

- $\dfrac{a^m}{a^n} = a^{m-n}, \quad a \neq 0$ — To **divide** numbers with the **same base**, keep the base and **subtract** the indices.

- $(a^m)^n = a^{m \times n}$ — When **raising** a **power** to a **power**, keep the base and **multiply** the indices.

Example 24 ◀⦚ Self Tutor

Simplify the following using the laws of indices:

  a $\quad 2^3 \times 2^2$ **b** $\quad x^4 \times x^5$

a $\quad 2^3 \times 2^2 = 2^{3+2}$
$= 2^5$
$= 32$

b $\quad x^4 \times x^5 = x^{4+5}$
$= x^9$

> To multiply, keep the base and add the indices.

EXERCISE 2D

1 Simplify using the index laws:

  a $\quad 2^3 \times 2^1$ **b** $\quad 2^2 \times 2^2$ **c** $\quad 3^5 \times 3^4$ **d** $\quad 5^2 \times 5^3$

  e $\quad x^2 \times x^4$ **f** $\quad a^3 \times a$ **g** $\quad n^4 \times n^6$ **h** $\quad b^3 \times b^5$

Example 25 ◀⦚ Self Tutor

Simplify using the index laws: **a** $\dfrac{3^5}{3^3}$ **b** $\dfrac{p^7}{p^3}$

a $\quad \dfrac{3^5}{3^3} = 3^{5-3}$
$= 3^2$
$= 9$

b $\quad \dfrac{p^7}{p^3} = p^{7-3}$
$= p^4$

> To divide, keep the base and subtract the indices.

2 Simplify using the index laws:

a $\dfrac{2^4}{2^3}$ b $\dfrac{3^5}{3^2}$ c $\dfrac{5^7}{5^3}$ d $\dfrac{4^9}{4^5}$

e $\dfrac{x^6}{x^3}$ f $\dfrac{y^7}{y^4}$ g $a^8 \div a^7$ h $b^9 \div b^5$

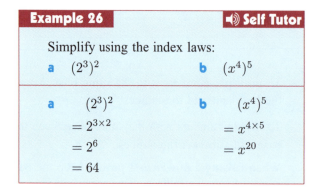

To raise a power to a power, keep the base and multiply the indices.

Example 26   ◀)) **Self Tutor**

Simplify using the index laws:

a $(2^3)^2$ b $(x^4)^5$

a $(2^3)^2$
   $= 2^{3 \times 2}$
   $= 2^6$
   $= 64$

b $(x^4)^5$
   $= x^{4 \times 5}$
   $= x^{20}$

3 Simplify using the index laws:

a $(2^2)^3$ b $(3^4)^3$ c $(2^3)^6$ d $(10^2)^5$

e $(x^3)^2$ f $(x^5)^3$ g $(a^5)^4$ h $(b^6)^4$

4 Simplify using the index laws:

a $a^5 \times a^2$ b $n^3 \times n^5$ c $a^7 \div a^3$ d $a^5 \times a$

e $b^9 \div b^4$ f $(a^3)^6$ g $a^n \times a^5$ h $(b^2)^4$

i $b^6 \div b^3$ j $m^4 \times m^3 \times m^7$ k $(a^3)^3 \times a$ l $(g^2)^4 \times g^3$

FRACTIONAL INDICES

Notice that $9^{\frac{1}{2}} \times 9^{\frac{1}{2}} = 9^{\frac{1}{2}+\frac{1}{2}}$ {using an index law}

$$\therefore \quad 9^{\frac{1}{2}} \times 9^{\frac{1}{2}} = 9^1$$

$$\therefore \quad 9^{\frac{1}{2}} \times 9^{\frac{1}{2}} = 9$$

But $3 \times 3 = 9$ and this suggests that $9^{\frac{1}{2}} = \sqrt{9} = 3$.

In general, $a^{\frac{1}{2}} = \sqrt{a}$.

Also note that $8^{\frac{1}{3}} \times 8^{\frac{1}{3}} \times 8^{\frac{1}{3}} = 8^{\frac{1}{3}+\frac{1}{3}+\frac{1}{3}} = 8^1 = 8$

This suggests that $8^{\frac{1}{3}} = \sqrt[3]{8}$.

In general, $a^{\frac{1}{3}} = \sqrt[3]{a}$ and $a^{\frac{1}{n}} = \sqrt[n]{a}$.

Example 27   🔊 **Self Tutor**

Simplify: **a** $16^{\frac{1}{2}}$ **b** $125^{\frac{1}{3}}$ **c** $16^{\frac{1}{4}}$

a $16^{\frac{1}{2}}$	**b** $125^{\frac{1}{3}}$	**c** $16^{\frac{1}{4}}$
$= \sqrt{16}$	$= \sqrt[3]{125}$	$= \sqrt[4]{16}$
$= 4$	$= 5$	$= 2$

Note: In **b** we ask, 'What number multiplied by itself three times gives 125?'
What question do we ask in **c**?

5 Simplify:

   a $4^{\frac{1}{2}}$ **b** $25^{\frac{1}{2}}$ **c** $64^{\frac{1}{2}}$ **d** $100^{\frac{1}{2}}$ **e** $225^{\frac{1}{2}}$

   f $27^{\frac{1}{3}}$ **g** $64^{\frac{1}{3}}$ **h** $1000^{\frac{1}{3}}$ **i** $81^{\frac{1}{4}}$ **j** $32^{\frac{1}{5}}$

   k $64^{\frac{1}{6}}$ **l** $4^{-\frac{1}{2}}$ **m** $16^{-\frac{1}{2}}$ **n** $8^{-\frac{1}{3}}$ **o** $32^{-\frac{1}{5}}$

6 $a^{\frac{m}{n}} = \left(a^{\frac{1}{n}}\right)^m = \left(\sqrt[n]{a}\right)^m$, so $8^{\frac{2}{3}} = \left(\sqrt[3]{8}\right)^2 = 2^2 = 4$

   Use the above rule to find:

   a $16^{\frac{3}{4}}$ **b** $27^{\frac{2}{3}}$ **c** $32^{\frac{3}{5}}$ **d** $27^{-\frac{2}{3}}$ **e** $32^{-\frac{4}{5}}$

7 Find the value of:

   a $\left(1\frac{1}{2}\right)^2$ **b** $\left(1\frac{1}{2}\right)^{-2}$ **c** $\left(\frac{5}{6}\right)^2$ **d** $\left(\frac{5}{6}\right)^{-2}$

   e $\left(2\frac{1}{4}\right)^{\frac{1}{2}}$ **f** $\left(2\frac{1}{4}\right)^{-\frac{1}{2}}$ **g** $\left(\frac{1}{4}\right)^{-3}$ **h** $\left(3\frac{3}{8}\right)^{-\frac{2}{3}}$

REVIEW SET 2A

1 Find the value of:

   a $16 - 7$ **b** $-16 + -7$ **c** -3×7

   d -3^2 **e** $-(-1)^2$ **f** $-42 \div -6$

2 Simplify:

   a $10 - 5 - 2$ **b** $12 + 3 \times 5$ **c** $12 \div 4 - 1$

3 Simplify:

   a $20 \div (3 + 2)$ **b** $14 + [(12 - 2) \times 5]$ **c** $\dfrac{9 + 7 - 6}{18 - 4 \times 2}$

4 Find the value of:

   a $1\frac{1}{2} + \frac{3}{5}$ **b** $2\frac{1}{5} - \frac{3}{4}$ **c** $4\frac{1}{2} - 1\frac{1}{4} \div 2$

5 Before he leaves for the airport, Jorg weighs his luggage. He has a case, a laptop
computer and a backpack with total weight 19.2 kg. $\frac{2}{3}$ of the 19.2 kg is the weight
of the case and $\frac{3}{5}$ of the remainder is the weight of his laptop. How much does the
backpack weigh?

6 Find the integer equal to: **a** 3^4 **b** 5×2^3

7 Write as a product of primes in index form: **a** 36   **b** 242

8 Simplify, giving your answers in simplest rational form:

     a 3^{-3} **b** $\left(\frac{4}{3}\right)^{-2}$ **c** $3^0 - 3^1$

9 Write $\frac{1}{16}$ as a power of 2.

10 Simplify, using the index laws:

     a $5^6 \times 5$ **b** $b^7 \div b^2$ **c** $(x^4)^3$

11 Simplify: **a** $16^{\frac{1}{2}}$ **b** $27^{-\frac{1}{3}}$

REVIEW SET 2B

1 Find the value of:

     a $-9 + 17$ **b** $12 - -7$ **c** -3×-5

     d $(-3)^3$ **e** $-2^2 \times (-3)^2$ **f** $24 \div -3$

2 Simplify:

     a $3 \times 4 \div 2$ **b** $7 - 2 \times 6$ **c** $4 \times 6 - 8 \div 2$

3 Simplify:

     a $24 \div (6 \div 2)$ **b** $18 - (2 \times 7) - 4$ **c** $\dfrac{22 + 5}{9 - (3 \times 2)}$

4 Find the value of:

     a $2\frac{3}{4} + 3\frac{1}{3}$ **b** $5 - 1\frac{2}{3}$ **c** $6\frac{1}{2} - 5 \times \frac{3}{4}$

5 Gabriella had to drive 260 km to visit her best friend.
She decided to drive $\frac{2}{5}$ of the distance before stopping for lunch, then $\frac{2}{3}$ of the remaining distance before stopping again for a cup of coffee.

     a What fraction of the journey was left to drive?

     b How far had Gabriella travelled when she stopped the second time?

6 Find the integer equal to: **a** 7^3 **b** $3^2 \times 5^2$

7 Write as a product of primes in index form: **a** 42   **b** 144

8 Simplify, giving your answers in simplest rational form:

     a 6^{-2} **b** $\left(1\frac{1}{2}\right)^{-1}$ **c** $\left(\frac{3}{5}\right)^{-2}$

9 125 can be written as 5^n. Find n.

10 Simplify, using the index laws:

     a $3^2 \times 3^6$ **b** $a^5 \div a^5$ **c** $(y^3)^5$

11 Simplify: **a** $25^{\frac{1}{2}}$ **b** $16^{-\frac{1}{4}}$

Chapter 3

Sets, sequences and logic

Contents:

A   Set notation
B   Important number sets
C   Constructing sets (Interval notation)
D   Venn diagrams
E   Union and intersection
F   Simple set problems
G   Number sequences
H   Introduction to logic

OPENING PROBLEM

A city has two newspapers, The Sun and The Advertiser.

56% of the people read The Sun and 71% of the people read The Advertiser.

18% read neither of these newspapers.

What percentage of the people read:

- both of the newspapers
- at least one of the newspapers
- The Sun, but not The Advertiser
- exactly one of the two newspapers?

A   SET NOTATION

A **set** is a collection of objects or things.

For example, we might have:

- the set of all boys in a class
- the set of all girls who play a musical instrument
- the set of all books in a library
- the set of vowels a, e, i, o and u
- the set of even numbers.

We usually use a capital letter to represent a set.

We may describe the set in words or using a formula, or else list each member of the set. The description is placed in curly brackets.

The members of a set are also called **elements**.

For example, $V = \{\text{vowels}\} = \{a, e, i, o, u\}$

$E = \{\text{even numbers}\} = \{2, 4, 6, 8, 10, 12, \ldots\}$

These dots indicate the set continues endlessly.

We say that V is a **finite set** as it has a finite number of elements (5).

E is an **infinite set** as it has infinitely many elements.

We use the symbol $\in$ to mean 'is a member of' or 'is in'.

and $\notin$ to mean 'is not a member of' or 'is not in'.

So, in the above sets $a \in V$,   but $w \notin V$

$28 \in E$,   but $117 \notin E$.

The number of elements in set S is represented by $n(S)$.

Using this notation, $n(V) = 5$ whereas $n(E)$ is infinite.

EXERCISE 3A

1 If $A = \{1, 2, 3, 4, 5, 6, 7, 8, 9\}$

    a use $\in$ or $\notin$ to complete: **i** $7 \ldots\ldots A$ **ii** $17 \ldots\ldots A$

    b find $n(A)$.

2 If M_3 is the set of all multiples of 3, list the first 8 elements of M_3 in set notation.

3 If F_8 is the set of all factors of 8, list the members of F_8 in set notation. What is $n(F_8)$?

4 If $B = \{$Mohammed, Abdul, Samira$\}$:

    a use $\in$ or $\notin$ to complete   Fahran $\ldots\ldots B$ **b** find $n(B)$.

5 List the following sets in set notation:

    a the set of all multiples of 6   **b** the set of all multiples of 11

    c the set of all factors of 3   **d** the set of all factors of 9

    e the set of all factors of 24   **f** the set of all factors of 32

    g the set of all factors common to 12 and 15

6 A *prime* number is a positive whole number which has exactly 2 factors, itself and 1.

    a   **i** List the set of all prime numbers less than 20.

        ii If this set is represented by P_{20}, what is $n(P_{20})$?

    b   **i** List the set of all prime numbers between 30 and 50.

        ii If this set is represented by Y, what is $n(Y)$?

    c What are the prime factors of   **i** 3   **ii** 8   **iii** 77   **iv** 60?

7 A *composite* number is a positive whole number which has more than two factors.

    a Explain why 6 is a composite number.

    b List the set of all prime numbers less than 13.

    c List the set of all composite numbers less than 13.

    d What set is made up of all primes and composites less than 13?

B   IMPORTANT NUMBER SETS

We use:

- $\mathbb{N}$ to represent the set of all **natural numbers** $\{0, 1, 2, 3, 4, 5, 6 \ldots\ldots\}$

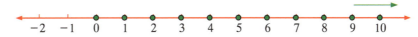

- $\mathbb{Z}$ to represent the set of all **integers** $\{0, \pm1, \pm2, \pm3, \pm4, \pm5, \pm6 \ldots\ldots\}$

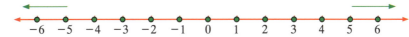

- $\mathbb{Z}^+$ to represent the set of all **positive integers** $\{1, 2, 3, 4, 5, 6 \ldots\ldots\}$

- $\mathbb{Q}$ to represent the set of all **rational numbers**

> **Rational numbers** have the form $\dfrac{p}{q}$ where p and q are integers and $q \neq 0$.

For example: $\frac{15}{4}$, $10 \ (= \frac{10}{1})$, $0.5 \ (= \frac{1}{2})$, $-\frac{3}{8}$ are all rational numbers.

> Numbers which cannot be written in rational form are called **irrational numbers**.

For example: Radicals (or surds) such as $\sqrt{2}$ and $\sqrt{7}$ are irrational.

π which is $3.14159265......$ is an irrational number.

Non-recurring decimal numbers and numbers such as $0.12233344445......$ are irrationals.

- $\mathbb{R}$ to represent the set of all **real numbers**

Real numbers include all numbers which can be placed on the number line.

For example, $\frac{1}{8} = 0.125$, $\sqrt{2} = 1.41421356....$, $\pi = 3.14159265....$

are all real numbers.

$\frac{2}{0}$ and $\sqrt{-2}$ are not real numbers because we cannot write them in decimal form.

EXERCISE 3B

1 True or false?

   a $3 \in \mathbb{Z}^+$ **b** $6 \in \mathbb{Z}$ **c** $\frac{3}{4} \in \mathbb{Q}$ **d** $\sqrt{2} \notin \mathbb{Q}$

   e $-\frac{1}{4} \notin \mathbb{Q}$ **f** $2\frac{1}{3} \in \mathbb{Z}$ **g** $0.3684 \in \mathbb{R}$ **h** $\dfrac{1}{0.1} \in \mathbb{Z}$

2 Which of these are rational?

   a 8 **b** -8 **c** $2\frac{1}{3}$ **d** $-3\frac{1}{4}$

   e $\sqrt{3}$ **f** $\sqrt{400}$ **g** 9.176 **h** $\pi - \pi$

All terminating and recurring decimal numbers can be shown to be rational numbers.

For example, $0.\overline{3} = \frac{1}{3}$, $0.53 = \frac{53}{100}$, $0.\overline{17} = \frac{17}{99}$.

Example 1   ◀)) **Self Tutor**

Show that $0.\overline{36}$, which is $0.36363636....$, is a rational number.

Let $x = 0.\overline{36} = 0.36363636....$

$\therefore \quad 100x = 36.363636.... = 36 + x$

$\therefore \quad 99x = 36$ and so $x = \frac{36}{99} = \frac{4}{11}$

So, $0.\overline{36}$ is actually the rational number $\frac{4}{11}$.

3 Show that these numbers are rational: **a** $0.\overline{7}$ **b** $0.\overline{41}$ **c** $0.\overline{324}$

4 Why is 0.527 a rational number?

5 $0.\overline{9}$ is a rational number. In fact, $0.\overline{9} \in \mathbb{Z}$. Give evidence to support this statement.

6 Explain why these statements are false:

    a The sum of two irrationals is irrational.

    b The product of two irrationals is irrational.

    Note: You only have to find one counter-example to show that a statement is untrue.

UNIVERSAL SETS

> A **universal set** is the set of all elements under consideration.

For example, we may be considering all of the positive integers less than 20.

The universal set in this case is:

$$U = \{1, 2, 3, 4, 5, 6, 7, 8, 9, 10, 11, 12, 13, 14, 15, 16, 17, 18, 19\}.$$

We could also consider **subsets** of U, such as:

$$M_6 = \{\text{all multiples of 6 less than 20}\}$$
$$= \{6, 12, 18\}$$

or $\quad P_{20} = \{\text{primes less than 20}\}$
$$= \{2, 3, 5, 7, 11, 13, 17, 19\}$$

SUBSETS

Consider two sets A and B.

> A is a **subset** of B, written $\quad A \subseteq B, \quad$ if every element of A is also in B.

For example,   for $\quad A = \{2, 3, 5\}, \quad B = \{1, 2, 3, 4, 5, 6, 7\} \quad$ and $\quad C = \{3, 5, 8\}$

we see that $\quad A \subseteq B \quad$ as every element of A is also in B,   but

C is not a subset of B as C contains 8 which is not in B.

THE COMPLEMENT OF A SET

> S', the **complement** of S, consists of all the members of U which are not in S.

For example,   if $\quad U = \{1, 2, 3, 4, 5, 6, 7\} \quad$ and $\quad S = \{1, 3, 5, 7\}$

then $\quad S' = \{2, 4, 6\}$.

THE EMPTY SET

> An **empty set** has no elements. It is represented by $\varnothing$ or $\{\ \}$.

7 For the universal set $U = \{1, 2, 3, 4, 5, 6, 7, 8, 9, 10, 11, 12\}$:

    a List S, the set of factors of 12.   **b** List S'.

    c Why is $S \subseteq U$?   **d** List P, the set of all primes in U.

    e List P'.   **f** Why is $P' \subseteq U$?

8 If $U = \mathbb{Z}^+$ and $E = \{\text{even integers}\}$, describe E'.

9 If $U = \mathbb{Z}$ and $E = \mathbb{Z}^+$, describe the set E'.

10 If $U = \mathbb{Z}^+$ and $P = \{\text{primes}\}$, describe the set P'.

11 The empty set $\varnothing$ is a subset of any other set.

    a Explain why this statement is true.

    b List all the subsets of:

        i $\{a\}$, the set containing the one symbol, a

        ii $\{a, b\}$

        iii $\{a, b, c\}$

C   CONSTRUCTING SETS (INTERVAL NOTATION)

Consider the set of numbers on the number line from 1 to 4 inclusive, i.e., including 1 and 4. We will call this set S.

Now S is not $\{1, 2, 3, 4\}$ since we also need to include the non-integer numbers between 1 and 4.

Instead we can describe the set as $S = \{x \mid 1 \leqslant x \leqslant 4, \quad x \in \mathbb{R}\}$.

                      the set x such that x is real

                      of all

x is represented by $\{x \mid -2 < x < 7, \quad x \in \mathbb{R}\}$

x is represented by $\{x \mid x \geqslant 5, \quad x \in \mathbb{R}\}$

Note: $\{x \mid -2 < x < 4, \quad x \in \mathbb{Z}\}$ is read as:

        "the set of all x such that x is an integer between -2 and 4".

        So, this set would simplify to $\{-1, 0, 1, 2, 3\}$.

EXERCISE 3C

1 Write verbal statements for the meaning of:

    a $\{x \mid x > 4\}$ **b** $\{x \mid x \leqslant 5\}$ **c** $\{y \mid 0 < y < 8\}$

    d $\{x \mid 1 \leqslant x \leqslant 4\}$ **e** $\{t \mid 2 < t < 7\}$ **f** $\{n \mid n \leqslant 3 \text{ or } n > 6\}$

Example 2   ◀») **Self Tutor**

Write in set notation:

a

b   included   not included

a $\{x \mid 1 \leqslant x \leqslant 5, \quad x \in \mathbb{Z}\}$

b $\{x \mid -3 \leqslant x < 6, \quad x \in \mathbb{R}\}$

2 Write in set notation:

a

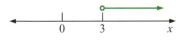

b

c

d

e

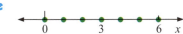

f

3 Sketch the following number sets:

a $\{x \mid 4 \leqslant x < 8, \quad x \in \mathbb{N}\}$

b $\{x \mid -5 < x \leqslant 4, \quad x \in \mathbb{Z}\}$

c $\{x \mid -3 < x \leqslant 5, \quad x \in \mathbb{R}\}$

d $\{x \mid x > -5, \quad x \in \mathbb{Z}\}$

e $\{x \mid x \leqslant 6, \quad x \in \mathbb{R}\}$

f $\{x \mid -5 \leqslant x \leqslant 0, \quad x \in \mathbb{R}\}$

Note: Unless stated otherwise, we assume that we are dealing with *real* numbers.
So, $\{x \mid -3 < x < 2\}$ is really $\{x \mid -3 < x < 2, \quad x \in \mathbb{R}\}$.

D   **VENN DIAGRAMS**

A **Venn diagram** consists of a universal set U represented by a rectangle, and
sets within it that are generally represented by circles.

Example 3   ◀») **Self Tutor**

Draw a Venn diagram to show the set
$S = \{2, 4, 6, 7\}$ within the universal set
$U = \{x \mid x \leqslant 10, \quad x \in \mathbb{Z}^+\}$.

$U = \{1, 2, 3, 4, 5, 6, 7, 8, 9, 10\}$

Example 4   🔊 **Self Tutor**

If $U = \{0, 1, 2, 3, 4, 5, 6, 7\}$ and $E = \{2, 3, 5, 7\}$,
list the set E' and illustrate E and E' on a Venn diagram.

$E' = \{0, 1, 4, 6\}$

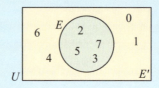

EXERCISE 3D

1 If $U = \{x \mid x \leqslant 8, \ x \in \mathbb{Z}^+\}$ and $A = \{\text{prime numbers} \leqslant 8\}$:

   a Show set A on a Venn diagram.   **b** List the set A'.

2 Suppose $U = \{\text{letters of the English alphabet}\}$ and
               $V = \{\text{letters of the English alphabet which are vowels}\}$.

   a Show these two sets on a Venn diagram.   **b** List the set V'.

3

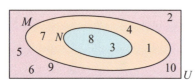

   a List the elements of:
       i U **ii** N **iii** M
   b What are $n(N)$ and $n(M)$?
   c Is $M \subseteq N$?

4 **a** $U = \{1, 2, 3, 4, 5, 6, 7, 8\}$, $A = \{2, 4, 6, 8\}$ and $B = \{2, 6\}$
      Illustrate these sets on a Venn diagram.

   b Copy and complete: If $S \subseteq T$ then on a Venn diagram the circle representing S
      lies ....

Example 5   🔊 **Self Tutor**

If $U = \{x \mid 0 \leqslant x \leqslant 12, \ x \in \mathbb{Z}\}$, $A = \{2, 3, 5, 7, 11\}$
and $B = \{1, 3, 6, 7, 8\}$, show A and B on a Venn diagram.

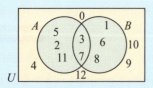

We notice that 3 and 7 are in both A and B so
the circles representing A and B must overlap.

We place 3 and 7 in the overlap, then fill in the
rest of A, then fill in the rest of B.

The remaining elements of U go outside the two
circles.

5 Show A and B on a Venn diagram if:

   a $U = \{1, 2, 3, 4, 5, 6\}$, $A = \{1, 2, 3, 4\}$, $B = \{3, 4, 5, 6\}$
   b $U = \{4, 5, 6, 7, 8, 9, 10\}$, $A = \{6, 7, 9, 10\}$, $B = \{5, 6, 8, 9\}$
   c $U = \{3, 4, 5, 6, 7, 8, 9\}$, $A = \{3, 5, 7, 9\}$, $B = \{4, 6, 8\}$

6 Suppose the universal set is $U = \mathbb{R}$, the set of all real numbers.

$\mathbb{Q}$, $\mathbb{Z}$, and $\mathbb{N}$ are all subsets of $\mathbb{R}$.

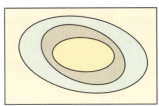

a Copy the given Venn diagram and label the sets U, $\mathbb{Q}$, $\mathbb{Z}$, and $\mathbb{N}$ on it.

b Place these numbers on the Venn diagram:
$\frac{1}{2}$, $\sqrt{2}$, $0.\overline{3}$, -5, $-5\frac{1}{4}$, 0, 10, and
$0.2137005618.....$ which does not terminate or recur.

c True or false?   **i** $\mathbb{N} \subseteq \mathbb{Z}$ **ii** $\mathbb{Z} \subseteq \mathbb{Q}$ **iii** $\mathbb{N} \subseteq \mathbb{Q}$

d Shade the region representing the set of irrationals $\mathbb{Q}'$.

E   UNION AND INTERSECTION

THE UNION OF TWO SETS

$A \cup B$ denotes the **union** of sets A and B. This set contains all elements belonging to A **or** B **or both** A and B.

$A \cup B = \{x \mid x \in A \ \textbf{or} \ x \in B\}$

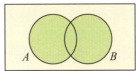

$A \cup B$ is shaded green.

THE INTERSECTION OF TWO SETS

$A \cap B$ denotes the **intersection** of sets A and B. This is the set of all elements common to both sets.

$A \cap B = \{x \mid x \in A \ \textbf{and} \ x \in B\}$

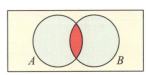

$A \cap B$ is shaded red.

In the Venn diagram alongside,
$A = \{2, 3, 4, 7\}$ and $B = \{1, 3, 7, 8, 10\}$.
We can see that $A \cap B = \{3, 7\}$
and $A \cup B = \{1, 2, 3, 4, 7, 8, 10\}$

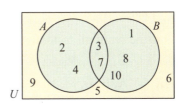

Example 6   ◀)) **Self Tutor**

If $U = \{$whole numbers $\leqslant 12\}$, $A = \{$primes $\leqslant 12\}$ and $B = \{$factors of $12\}$:

a List the elements of the sets A and B.

b Show the sets A, B and U on a Venn diagram.

c List the elements in   **i** A' **ii** $A \cap B$ **iii** $A \cup B$

d Find: **i** $n(A \cap B)$ **ii** $n(A \cup B)$ **iii** $n(B')$

a $A = \{2, 3, 5, 7, 11\}$ and $B = \{1, 2, 3, 4, 6, 12\}$

b

Write the elements in the intersection of the circles first.

c **i** $A' = \{1, 4, 6, 8, 9, 10, 12\}$

   ii $A \cap B = \{2, 3\}$

   iii $A \cup B = \{1, 2, 3, 4, 5, 6, 7, 11, 12\}$

d **i** $n(A \cap B) = 2$ **ii** $n(A \cup B) = 9$

   iii $B' = \{5, 7, 8, 9, 10, 11\}$,   so $n(B') = 6$

EXERCISE 3E

1

a List: **i** set C **ii** set D **iii** set U
   iv set $C \cap D$ **v** set $C \cup D$

b Find: **i** $n(C)$ **ii** $n(D)$ **iii** $n(U)$
   iv $n(C \cap D)$ **v** $n(C \cup D)$

2

a List: **i** set A **ii** set B **iii** set U
   iv set $A \cap B$ **v** set $A \cup B$

b Find: **i** $n(A)$ **ii** $n(B)$ **iii** $n(U)$
   iv $n(A \cap B)$ **v** $n(A \cup B)$

3 Consider $U = \{x \mid x \leqslant 12, \ x \in \mathbb{Z}^+\}$,
   $A = \{2, 7, 9, 10, 11\}$ and $B = \{1, 2, 9, 11, 12\}$.

a Show these sets on a Venn diagram.

b List the elements of: **i** $A \cap B$ **ii** $A \cup B$ **iii** B'

c Find: **i** $n(A)$ **ii** $n(B')$ **iii** $n(A \cap B)$ **iv** $n(A \cup B)$

4 If A is the set of all factors of 36 and B is the set of all factors of 63, find:

   a $A \cap B$ **b** $A \cup B$

5 If $X = \{A, B, D, M, N, P, R, T, Z\}$ and $Y = \{B, C, M, T, W, Z\}$, find:

   a $X \cap Y$ **b** $X \cup Y$

6 If $U = \{x \mid x \leqslant 30, \ x \in \mathbb{Z}^+\}$,
   $A = \{$factors of 30$\}$ and $B = \{$prime numbers $\leqslant 30\}$:

   a Find: **i** $n(A)$ **ii** $n(B)$ **iii** $n(A \cap B)$ **iv** $n(A \cup B)$

   b Use **a** to verify that $n(A \cup B) = n(A) + n(B) - n(A \cap B)$

7

Use the Venn diagram given to prove that:

$n(A \cup B) = n(A) + n(B) - n(A \cap B)$.

Note: (a) means there are a elements in this region, so $n(A) = a + b$

Example 7   ◀ **Self Tutor**

On separate Venn diagrams shade the region representing

a in A or in B but not in both   **b** $A' \cap B$

a   **b** We look for where the outside of
                                                    A intersects (overlaps) with B.

8 On separate Venn diagrams like the one given, shade the region representing:

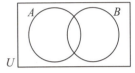

a not in A **b** in both A and B

c $A \cap B'$ **d** in either A or B

e $A \cup B'$ **f** $(A \cup B)'$

g $(A \cap B)'$ **h** in exactly one of A or B

9 **a** For $U = \{1, 2, 3, 4, 5, 6, 7, 8\}$, $X = \{1, 3, 5, 7\}$, $Y = \{2, 4, 6, 8\}$

  find   **i** $X \cup Y$ **ii** $X \cap Y$.

  b Find   **i** $A \cup A'$ **ii** $A \cap A'$ for any set A in universal set U.

A **set identity** is an equation involving sets which is true for *all* sets.

Examples of set identities include: $A \cup A' = U$ $A \cap A' = \varnothing$

$(A \cup B)' = A' \cap B'$ $(A \cap B)' = A' \cup B'$

Set identities can be verified using Venn diagrams.

Example 8   ◀ **Self Tutor**

Verify that $(A \cup B)' = A' \cap B'$.

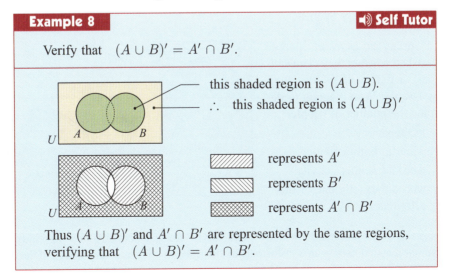

this shaded region is $(A \cup B)$.

∴   this shaded region is $(A \cup B)'$

⬛ represents A'

⬛ represents B'

⬛ represents $A' \cap B'$

Thus $(A \cup B)'$ and $A' \cap B'$ are represented by the same regions,
verifying that $(A \cup B)' = A' \cap B'$.

COMPUTER DEMO

10 Verify that $(A \cap B)' = A' \cup B'$.

F   # SIMPLE SET PROBLEMS

Example 9    **Self Tutor**

The Venn diagram alongside illustrates
the number of people in a sporting club
who play tennis (T) and hockey (H).

Determine the number of people:

a   in the club
b   who play hockey
c   who play both sports
d   who play neither sport
e   who play at least one sport

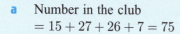

a   Number in the club
    $= 15 + 27 + 26 + 7 = 75$

b   Number who play hockey
    $= 27 + 26 = 53$

c   Number who play both sports $= 27$

d   Number who play neither sport $= 7$

e   Number who play at least one sport
    $= 15 + 27 + 26 = 68$

EXERCISE 3F

1   The Venn diagram alongside illustrates the number
of students in a particular class who study French
(F) and Spanish (S). Determine the number of
students:

   a   in the class
   b   who study both subjects
   c   who study at least one of the subjects
   d   who only study Spanish.

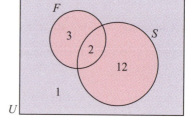

2   In a survey at a resort, people
were asked whether they went sailing (S) or fishing (F) during their
stay. Use the Venn diagram to determine the number of people:

   a   in the survey
   b   who did both activities
   c   who did neither activity
   d   who did exactly one of the
activities.

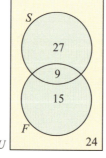

3   In a class of 30 students, 19 study Physics, 17 study Chemistry and 15 study both of
these subjects. Display this information on a Venn diagram and hence determine the
number of students who study:

   a   at least one of the subjects
   b   Physics, but not Chemistry
   c   exactly one of the subjects
   d   neither subject.

4 In a class of 40 students, 19 play tennis, 20 play netball and 8 play neither of these sports. Determine the number of students in the class who:

    a play tennis   **b** do not play netball

    c play at least one of the sports   **d** play one and only one of the sports

    e play netball, but not tennis

5 In a class of 25 students, 15 play hockey and 16 play basketball. If there are 4 students who play neither sport, determine the number of students who play both hockey and basketball.

6 In a class of 40, 34 like bananas, 22 like pineapples and 2 dislike both fruits. Find the number of students who:

    a like both fruits   **b** like at least one fruit

7 In a group of 50 students, 40 study Mathematics and 32 study Physics. Each student studies at least one of these subjects. From a Venn diagram, find how many students:

    a study both subjects   **b** study Mathematics but not Physics

8 In a class of 40 students, 23 have dark hair, 18 have brown eyes, and 26 have dark hair, brown eyes, or both. How many students have:

    a dark hair and brown eyes   **b** neither dark hair nor brown eyes

    c dark hair but not brown eyes?

9 400 families were surveyed. It was found that 90% had a TV set and 60% had a computer. Every family had at least one of these items. How many of the families had both a TV set and a computer?

G   NUMBER SEQUENCES

A **number sequence** is a set of numbers connected by some kind of rule or pattern.

For example, 1, 3, 9, 27, ... is the number sequence of the powers of 3.

Number sequences have a **rule** which can be used to generate the **terms** of the sequence.

For 1, 3, 9, 27, ... the rule could be 'start with 1 and multiply by 3 each time'.
Often a formula can be used to construct the sequence.

For 1, 3, 9, 27, ... the formula $u_n = 3^{n-1}$ could be used.

Notice that: u_1, the first term, is $3^{1-1} = 3^0 = 1$

                 u_2, the second term, is $3^{2-1} = 3^1 = 3$

               ...... and so on.

               u_n is called the **n^{th} term** of the sequence.

If we are given a formula for u_n then we can use a graphics calculator to generate the terms of the sequence. You should consult the calculator instructions section on **Lists**, beginning on page **18**. You will first need to learn how to create a list on your calculator, and then proceed to the specific section on **Number Sequences**.

EXERCISE 3G

1 Find the next *two* terms and write a rule in words to describe these number sequences:

  a   2, 3, 4, 5, 6, ...   **b**   29, 27, 25, 23, 21, ...

  c   1, 2, 4, 8, 16, ...   **d**   48, 24, 12, 6, ...

  e   2, 5, 8, 11, 14, ...   **f**   100, 93, 86, 79, 72, ...

  g   1, 8, 27, 64, ...   **h**   1, 1, 2, 3, 5, 8, ...

2 Use the rules to list the first six terms of the sequence:

  a   start with 1 and add 2 each time

  b   start with 3 and multiply by 2 each time

  c   start with 24 and subtract 8 each time

  d   start with 32 and divide by 2 each time

  e   start with 5 and double each time

  f   start with 1 and 2 and add the previous two numbers to get the next one.

3 Write down the first *five* terms of the sequence given by:

  a $u_n = 2n$ **b** $u_n = 2n + 1$ **c** $u_n = 2n - 1$ **d** $u_n = 2n + 5$

  e $u_n = 3n$ **f** $u_n = 3n + 2$ **g** $u_n = 5n + 1$ **h** $u_n = 7n + 2$

  i $u_n = -n$ **j** $u_n = -n + 3$ **k** $u_n = -2n + 5$ **l** $u_n = -3n + 4$

4 All of the sequences in question **3** are of the form $u_n = an + b$.

  For example: in **f**, $u_n = 3n + 2$ has $a = 3$ and $b = 2$.
  in **k**, $u_n = -2n + 5$ has $a = -2$ and $b = 5$.

  In what way does the value of a affect the terms of the sequence?

You should have noticed in **3** and **4** that:

> For a sequence where we are adding on a each time, the rule generating the sequence has form $u_n = an + b$.

Example 10   ◀ᴗ **Self Tutor**

Find the rule which will generate the sequence:

  a   3, 7, 11, 15, 19, ...   **b**   92, 88, 84, 80, 76, ...

---

  a   We are adding on 4, $\therefore$ $u_n = 4n + b$

  $\therefore$ $u_1 = 4(1) + b = 4 + b$

  But $u_1 = 3$,   so $b = -1$

  $\therefore$ $u_n = 4n - 1$

  b   We are adding on -4, $\therefore$ $u_n = -4n + b$

  $\therefore$ $u_1 = -4(1) + b = -4 + b$

  But $u_1 = 92$,   so $b = 96$

  $\therefore$ $u_n = -4n + 96$

5 Find the rule which will generate the sequence:

a 4, 7, 10, 13, 16, ...

b −2, 3, 8, 13, 18, ...

c 1, 7, 13, 19, 25, ...

d 3, 10, 17, 24, 31, ...

e 40, 37, 34, 31, ...

f 76, 72, 68, 64, ...

g 8, 3, −2, −7, ...

h 127, 121, 115, 109, ...

i $\frac{1}{3}, \frac{2}{5}, \frac{3}{7}, \frac{4}{9}, \frac{5}{11}$, ...

j $\frac{1}{4}, \frac{3}{7}, \frac{5}{10}, \frac{7}{13}, \frac{9}{16}$, ...

6 a Write down the first *five* terms of the sequence given by:

    i $u_n = 3^{n-1}$ ii $u_n = 2 \times 3^{n-1}$ iii $u_n = 5 \times 3^{n-1}$

  b State in words how the next term is found from the previous one in each part of **a**.

  c What part of each formula causes this to happen?

7 If $u_n = n^2 + 1$:   find   a u_1 b u_9 c u_{57}.

8 Suppose D_n is the number of diagonals of an n-sided polygon.

For example,   for a pentagon, $n = 5$

        and $D_5 = 5$.

  a Find D_3, D_4, D_6, D_7 and D_8.

  b Jian stated that a 10-sided polygon has 70 diagonals. She said 'Consider the number of diagonals from one vertex. There are 7 of them. Since there are 10 vertices there must be $7 \times 10 = 70$ diagonals'.

    Toshi drew a diagram of a 10-sided polygon and its diagonals. He counted 35 diagonals. So why is Jian's reasoning incorrect?

  c How many diagonals has:

    i a 20-sided polygon   ii an n-sided polygon?

9 This is a 2 by 2 chess board. We can see 5 squares: 4 small ones and one large one.

Notice that $5 = 1^2 + 2^2$.

  a Show that a 3 by 3 chess board contains $1^2 + 2^2 + 3^2$ squares.

  b How many squares can be seen on a 4 by 4 chess board?

  c How many squares can be seen on a real chess board which is 8 by 8?

H INTRODUCTION TO LOGIC

Logic is a topic connected with **Pure Mathematics**. Much of its theory was devised by **Aristotle** some 2300 years ago. In this introduction to the topic we will learn what is meant by a proposition, negation, conjuction, and disjunction.

> A **proposition** is a statement which can only be true (T) or false (F).
> Whether it is true or false is the **truth value** of the proposition.

An example of a proposition is "A square has four equal sides". It is a proposition because it is a statement and it is always true.

Questions and opinions are not propositions.

For example:

"I think it will rain tomorrow" is an opinion and not everyone will agree. It is therefore not a proposition.

"It will rain tomorrow" *is* a proposition, because although we do not yet know if the statement is true or false, it will definitely be one or the other.

NEGATION

The **negation** of a proposition is the exact opposite to the proposition.

For example, the negation of "It will rain today" is "It will not rain today". Notice that if the statement is true its negation is false, and vice versa.

CONJUNCTION

When two propositions are combined using the word **and**, the new proposition is the **conjunction** of the original propositions.

For example, for the propositions "It will be sunny today" and "I will go swimming today", the conjunction is "It will be sunny today and I will go swimming".

A **conjunction** is true (T) only when both propositions are true.

DISJUNCTION

When two propositions are combined using the word **or**, the new proposition is the **disjunction** of the original propositions.

For example, for the propositions "I will go to the movies today" and "I will go swimming today", the disjunction is "I will go to the movies or I will go swimming today".

A **disjunction** is true (T) when either or both propositions are true.

EXERCISE 3H

1   Which of these statements is a proposition?

   a   Is there sugar in my coffee?
   b   It will be warm enough to go swimming.
   c   Is it sunny this morning?
   d   I understand this exercise.
   e   Where are my brown socks?
   f   I will get a top grade in my next test.
   g   The train will be on time.
   h   Today is Monday.

2   Write down the negation of these propositions:

   a   I will go skiing today.
   b   Today is Saturday.
   c   I enjoy Art lessons.
   d   The train will not be on time.
   e   It will be sunny today.
   f   This exercise is difficult.

3 Write the negations of these propositions without using the word *not*.

   a Wendy likes mathematics.
   b He owns at least three cats.
   c A student in my class snores
   d My brother is taller than me.

4 Write down the conjunction of:

   a "The train will be late today", "I will miss the first lesson".
   b "There is hot weather forecast", "We will go to the beach"
   c "I will go to the café", "I will go to the cinema".

5 Write down the disjunction of:

   a "We will have eggs for breakfast", "We will have porridge for breakfast".
   b "We will play tennis", "We will ride horses".
   c "x is a factor of 8", "x is a factor of 12".

NOTATION AND TRUTH TABLES

Propositions are usually represented by lower case letters such as p, q and r.

For example, p could be the proposition "Jon snores when sleeping"
              q could be the proposition "Jon sleeps poorly".

Symbols: $\neg$ is used for negation, $\wedge$ for conjunction, $\vee$ for disjunction.

   $\neg p$ is the proposition "Jon does not snore when sleeping"
   $\neg q$ is the proposition "Jon does not sleep poorly"
   $p \wedge q$ is the proposition "Jon snores when sleeping **and** Jon sleeps poorly"
   $p \vee q$ is the proposition "Jon snores when sleeping **or** Jon sleeps poorly"

A **truth table** for a compound proposition is a table which lists all possibilities for the truth values of the original propositions.

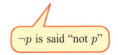

$\neg p$ is said "not p"

Consider **negation**.

Clearly if p is true then $\neg p$ is false and vice versa.

These are the only possibilities, so the truth table is:

p	$\neg p$
T	F
F	T

For the **conjunction** and **disjunction** of two propositions p and q there are four possibilities to consider: both p and q are true, p is true and q is false, p is false and q is true, both p and q are false.

The conjunction $p \wedge q$ is true if both p and q are true; otherwise it is false.

The disjunction $p \vee q$ is true if either or both p and q are true; otherwise it is false.

The truth tables are:

Conjunction

p	q	$p \wedge q$
T	T	T
T	F	F
F	T	F
F	F	F

Disjunction

p	q	$p \vee q$
T	T	T
T	F	T
F	T	T
F	F	F

Example 11   ◀)) **Self Tutor**

For propositions p and q construct truth tables for: **a** $\neg p \lor q$ **b** $\neg(p \land \neg q)$

a

p	q	$\neg p$	$\neg p \lor q$
T	T	F	T
T	F	F	F
F	T	T	T
F	F	T	T

b

p	q	$\neg q$	$p \land \neg q$	$\neg(p \land \neg q)$
T	T	F	F	T
T	F	T	T	F
F	T	F	F	T
F	F	T	F	T

identical

Note:

The truth tables are identical for $\neg p \lor q$ and $\neg(p \land \neg q)$.

This means that $\neg(p \land \neg q)$ and $\neg p \lor q$ are **logically equivalent**.

6 For the propositions p and q draw truth tables for:

    a $\neg(\neg q)$ **b** $\neg(p \land q)$ **c** $\neg q \lor \neg p$ **d** $p \land \neg q$

7 From **6a**, what statement is logically equivalent to:

    a I will not not go to the beach.

    b He is not not the best mathematician in the class.

8 Show that:

    a $\neg p \land \neg q$ and $\neg(p \lor q)$ are logically equivalent.

    b $\neg p \lor \neg q$ and $\neg(p \land q)$ are logically equivalent.

9 Write down the negations of these compound statements using your observations in **8**.

    a It will be sunny today and I will go to the beach.

    b I will go shopping or I will go to the cinema.

    c I like football and I like basketball.

    d I like skiing and I do not like swimming.

    e I will walk to school or I will cycle to school.

    f It will not rain today or it will not snow today.

DISCUSSION   **SETS AND LOGIC**

1 Compare:

    • $(A')'$ in sets with $\neg(\neg p)$ in logic

    • $A \cap B$ in sets with $p \land q$ in logic

    • $A \cup B$ in sets with $p \lor q$ in logic.

2 In **Example 8** we used a Venn diagram to show that $(A \cup B)' = A' \cap B'$ and in the following question we showed that $(A \cap B)' = A' \cup B'$.

Use what you have learnt from the discussion in **1** to predict logic rules for $\neg(p \lor q)$ and $\neg(p \land q)$.

REVIEW SET 3A

1 If F_{12} is the set of all factors of 12:

   a List the members of F_{12} using set notation.

   b Copy and complete using $\in$ or $\notin$: **i** 4 .... F_{12} **ii** 9 .... F_{12}

   c Find $n(F_{12})$.

2 **a** If P is the set of prime numbers between 20 and 30, list P using set notation.

   b Find $n(P)$.

3 **a** Answer true or false:

     i $5 \in \mathbb{Z}$ **ii** $0 \in \mathbb{Z}^+$ **iii** $1\frac{1}{4} \in \mathbb{Q}$ **iv** $0 \in \mathbb{Q}$

   b Which of these numbers are rational:

     i $\sqrt{3}$ **ii** $\frac{1}{3}$ **iii** $0.\overline{7}$ **iv** 9.8?

4 For the universal set $U = \{1, 2, 3, 4, 5, 6, 7, 8, 9, 10\}$:

   a List F, the set of factors of 10.   **b** Why is $F \subseteq U$?

   c List E, the set of even numbers in U.   **d** List E'.

   e List O, the set of odd numbers in U.   **f** Comment on your answers to **d** and **e**.

5 Write in set notation:

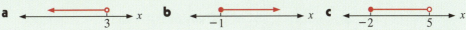

a   **b**   **c**

6 If $U = \{x \mid x \leqslant 5, \ x \in \mathbb{Z}^+\}$ and $A = \{\text{prime numbers} \leqslant 5\}$:

   a show set A on a Venn diagram   **b** list the set A'.

7

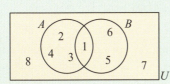

   a List **i** U **ii** A **iii** B

   b Find **i** $n(U)$ **ii** $n(A)$

           iii $n(A \cap B)$ **iv** $n(A \cup B)$

   c List the elements of $A \cup B$.

8 On diagrams like the one shown, shade the region representing:

   a A' **b** $A \cap B'$ **c** $A \cup B'$

9 63 office workers were surveyed to find how they travelled to work. 23 used a car, 49 used public transport, and 3 used neither.

   a Draw a Venn diagram to illustrate this situation.

   b How many workers only used public transport to go to work?

10 **a** Write a rule in words to describe the number sequence   3, 9, 15, 21, ...

   b From the rule 'start with 17 and subtract 3 each time' list the first six terms of the sequence.

   c Write down the first 5 terms of the sequence given by $u_n = -2n + 5$.

   d Find the rule that will generate the sequence $\frac{1}{2}, \frac{2}{3}, \frac{3}{4}, \frac{4}{5}, \frac{5}{6}, \ldots$

11 **a** Write the negation of the proposition: 'My room is tidy'.

   b Write the conjunction of: 'Sally has brown hair', 'Sally wears glasses'.

   c Write the disjunction of: 'I will go to a football match', 'I will go to the movies'.

REVIEW SET 3B

1 **a** List, in set notation, the set M of multiples of 3 less than 20.

 b Find $n(M)$.

 c List the set N of multiples of 9 less than 20.

 d Is $N \subseteq M$? Explain your answer.

2 **a** Answer true or false: **i** $0.151 \in \mathbb{R}$ **ii** $\frac{1}{0} \in \mathbb{Q}$

 b Show that $0.\overline{1}$ is rational.

3 If $U = \mathbb{Z}^+$ and $O = \{$odd integers$\}$, describe O'.

4 **a** Write in words: $\{x \mid x \leqslant -5 \text{ or } x > 2\}$

 b Write in set notation: **i** ![number line with x] **ii** ![number line with x]

 c Sketch $\{x \mid x \leqslant 8, \ x \in \mathbb{Z}\}$.

5 **a** Draw a Venn diagram to show the sets $A = \{2, 3, 5, 7\}$ and
      $B = \{2, 4, 6, 8\}$ within the universal set $U = \{x \mid x \leqslant 8, \ x \in \mathbb{Z}^+\}$.

 b List: **i** A' **ii** $A \cup B$ **iii** $A \cap B$

 c Find $n(B')$.

6 $U = \{x \mid x \leqslant 20, \ x \in \mathbb{Z}^+\}$, $A = \{$factors of 20$\}$ and
   $B = \{$multiples of $4 \leqslant 20\}$.

 a Find: **i** $n(A)$ **ii** $n(B)$ **iii** $n(A \cap B)$ **iv** $n(A \cup B)$

 b Use **a** to verify that $n(A \cup B) = n(A) + n(B) - n(A \cap B)$

7 In a class of 25 students, 9 are left handed and 7 wear glasses. 3 students are left handed *and* wear glasses. Display this information on a Venn diagram and hence determine the number of students who:

 a are not left handed and wear glasses

 b are left handed and do not wear glasses

 c are neither left handed nor wear glasses.

8 **a** Find the rule that will generate the sequence $1, 2, 4, 8, 16, \ ......$

 b Write the first *five* terms of: **i** $u_n = 5n - 8$ **ii** $u_n = 3 \times 2^{n+1}$

 c If $u_n = 100 - n^2$, find: **i** u_1 **ii** u_5 **iii** u_{10}.

9 **a** Write the negation of the propositions:
   i It is not raining.   **ii** Sarah is playing her flute.

 b Write the conjunction of the propositions:
       'Raphael plays tennis', 'Raphael plays best on clay courts'.

 c Write the disjunction of the propositions:
       'I will ride my bike to school', 'I will go to school by bus'.

10 Construct truth tables for $\neg(p \wedge q)$ and $\neg p \vee \neg q$ using the following headings:

p	q	$p \wedge q$	$\neg(p \wedge q)$

p	q	$\neg p$	$\neg q$	$\neg p \vee \neg q$

What do you notice from your results?

Chapter 4

Rounding and estimation

Contents:

A   Rounding numbers
B   Rounding money
C   One figure approximations
D   Rounding decimal numbers
E   Using a calculator to round off
F   Significant figure rounding
G   Rounding time

Often we are not really interested in the exact value of a number. We only want a reasonable estimate of it.

For example, there may be 58 students in the library or 515 competitors at the athletics carnival or 48 948 spectators at the football match.

If we are only interested in approximate numbers then 60 students, 500 competitors and 49 000 spectators would be good approximations.

OPENING PROBLEM

What are sensible approximations for:

- There are 229 students in Year 10.
- This school has a student body of 2788.
- 387 066 spectators attended the tennis championships this year.
- The population of our state was 6 277 168 at the last census.

A   ROUNDING NUMBERS

If there are 58 students in the library then we can say this is approximately 6 lots of 10, or 60 students. We have *rounded* the number 58 to the nearest ten.

Notice that 468 is roughly 47 tens or 470,   whereas   463 is roughly 46 tens or 460.

We say 468 is *rounded up* to 470 and 463 is *rounded down* to 460.

Rules for rounding off are:

- If the digit after the one being rounded off is **less than** 5   (i.e., 0, 1, 2, 3 or 4) we round **down**.

- If the digit after the one being rounded off is 5 **or more**   (i.e., 5, 6, 7, 8, 9) we round **up**.

Example 1   ◀⦚ Self Tutor

Round off the following to the nearest 10:

a 38   **b** 483   **c** 8605

a   38 is approximately 40   {Round up as 8 is greater than 5}

b   483 is approximately 480   {Round down as 3 is less than 5}

c   8605 is approximately 8610   {Round up as 5 is rounded up}

EXERCISE 4A

1 Round off to the nearest 10:

a	23	**b**	65	**c**	68	**d**	97
e	347	**f**	561	**g**	409	**h**	598
i	3015	**j**	2856	**k**	3094	**l**	8885
m	2895	**n**	9995	**o**	30 905	**p**	49 895

Example 2   ◀)) Self Tutor

Round off the following to the nearest 100:
    a   89   **b**   152   **c**   19 439

a   89 is approximately 100
     {Round up as 8 is greater than 5}

b   152 is approximately 200
     {Round up for 5 or more}

c   19 439 is approximately 19 400
     {Round down as 3 is less than 5}

Look first at the digit **after** the one being rounded off. This is the first one to the right.

---

2 Round off to the nearest 100:

a	81	**b**	671	**c**	617	**d**	850
e	349	**f**	982	**g**	2111	**h**	3949
i	999	**j**	13 484	**k**	99 199	**l**	10 074

3 Round off to the accuracy given:

    a   €187 (to nearest €10)   **b**   £18 745 (to nearest £1000)

    c   375 km (to nearest 10 km)   **d**   785 Ft (to nearest 100 Ft)

    e   the population of a town is 29 295   (to nearest one thousand)

    f   995 cm   (to nearest metre)

    g   8945   litres (to nearest kilolitre)

    h   the cost of a house was $274 950   (to nearest $10 000)

    i   the number of sheep on a farm is 491 560   (nearest 100 000)

B   ROUNDING MONEY

Three double beef burgers and fries... $175 thanks!

Not likely!

People operating computers and calculators sometimes make mistakes when typing in the information.

So, it is very important when we use calculators that we can make an **estimate** of what the answer should be. An estimate is not a guess. It is a quick and easy **approximation** to the correct answer.

By making an estimate we can tell if our calculated answer is **reasonable**.

ROUNDING TO THE NEAREST 5 CENTS

Some countries no longer use smaller denominations of currency such as 1 cent and 2 cent coins. Amounts of money to be paid in cash must therefore be rounded to the nearest 5 cents.

For example, a supermarket bill and the bill for fuel at a service station must be rounded to the nearest 5 cents.

> If the number of cents ends in
>
> - 0 or 5, the amount remains unchanged
> - 1 or 2, the amount is rounded down to 0
> - 3 or 4, the amount is rounded up to 5
> - 6 or 7, the amount is rounded down to 5
> - 8 or 9, the amount is rounded up to 10.

Have you noticed that petrol pumps show prices such as $51.82, $51.83, $51.86?

These prices have not been rounded to the nearest 5 cents.

When you pay cash for the petrol, however, you may have to pay to the nearest 5 cents.

For example, $51.82 would be $51.80
$51.83 would be $51.85
$51.86 would be $51.85
$51.88 would be $51.90

Example 3   ◀) Self Tutor

Round the following amounts to the nearest 5 cents:
a $1.42   b $12.63   c $24.99

a $1.42   would be rounded down to $1.40

2 is rounded down

b $12.63   would be rounded up to $12.65

3 is rounded up to 5

c $24.99   would be rounded up to $25.00

9 is rounded up to 10,   so   99 becomes 100   and $24.99   becomes $25.00

EXERCISE 4B

1   Round these amounts to the nearest 5 cents:

a 99 cents	b $2.74	c $1.87	d $1.84
e $34.00	f $25.05	g $16.77	h $4.98
i $13.01	j $102.23	k $430.84	l $93.92

2 **a** Xingfeng paid cash for her supermarket bill of $84.72. How much did she pay?

   b Rolando filled his car with petrol and the amount shown at the petrol pump was $31.66. How much did he pay in cash?

   c Marcel used the special dry-cleaning offer of '3 items for $9.99'. How much money did he pay?

ROUNDING IN DECIMAL CURRENCIES

The term **decimal currency** is used to describe any currency for which one basic unit is made up of 100 (or sometimes 1000) sub-units.

For example: 100 cents make one dollar ($)

100 euro cents make one euro (€)

100 pence make one pound (£)

100 Russian kopecks make one ruble (R)

100 Indian paise make one rupee (Rs)

To estimate money in these currencies, we often round to the nearest whole unit:

- If the decimal is from 0.01 to 0.49 then we round *down*.
- If the decimal is from 0.50 to 0.99 then we round *up*.

Example 4　　　　　　　　　　　　　　　　　　　　🔊 **Self Tutor**

Approximate: **a** Rs 4.37 to the nearest rupee   **b** €16.85 to the nearest euro.

a Rs 4.37 is rounded down to Rs 4.00   {37 paise is less than 50 paise}

b €16.85 is rounded up to €17.00   {85 euro cents is greater than 50 euro cents}

---

3 Round to the nearest whole unit of currency:

a £3.87	**b** €9.28	**c** 4.39 rubles	**d** ¥511.05	**e** $7.55
f Fr 19.45	**g** $19.55	**h** €39.45	**i** £39.50	**j** Rs 61.19

4

Ice block $0.85

Cheese snacks $1.30

300mL drink $1.15

Crisps $1.05

Jelly snakes $1.80

Licorice rope $0.75

Icecream $2.10

Jubes $1.20

Honeycomb bar $0.95

Health bar $1.95

Chocolate bar $1.30

Estimate the total cost (by rounding the prices to the nearest dollar) of:

    a one icecream, a packet of crisps, a health bar and a drink

    b 5 licorice ropes, 4 icecreams, 2 honeycomb bars and 4 drinks

    c 3 ice blocks, 2 packets of jelly snakes, 4 chocolate bars and 3 cheese snacks

    d 10 health bars, 4 icecreams, 6 jubes and 3 licorice ropes

    e 19 ice blocks, 11 drinks, 12 packets of cheese snacks and 9 packets of jelly snakes

    f 21 packets of crisps, 18 chocolate bars, 28 health bars and 45 drinks

    g 4 dozen drinks, half a dozen packets of jelly snakes and a dozen health bars

    h 192 honeycomb bars, 115 icecreams, 189 packets of crisps and 237 drinks

    i 225 licorice ropes, 269 drinks, 324 honeycomb bars and 209 ice blocks.

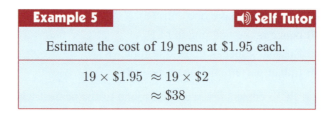

Example 5	◀ **Self Tutor**

Estimate the cost of 19 pens at \$1.95 each.

$$19 \times \$1.95 \approx 19 \times \$2$$
$$\approx \$38$$

5 Estimate the cost of:

    a 195 exercise books at 98 pence each   **b** 27 sweets packets at ¥21.80 a packet

    c 18 show bags at \$3.45 each   **d** 12 bottles of drink at \$2.95 a bottle

    e 4 dozen iceblocks at RM 1.20 each   **f** 3850 football tickets at €6.50 each.

C   ONE FIGURE APPROXIMATIONS

A fast way of estimating a calculation is to perform a **one figure approximation**. We round each number in the calculation to one significant figure, then perform the calculation with these approximations.

Rules:
- Leave single digit numbers as they are.
- Round all other numbers to one figure approximations.
- Perform the calculation.

For example, 3785×7
$$\approx 4000 \times 7$$
$$\approx 28\,000$$

Example 6	◀ **Self Tutor**

Estimate the product: **a** 57×8 **b** 537×6

  a Round off to the nearest 10.   **b** Round off to the nearest 100.

$$57 \times 8 \qquad\qquad 537 \times 6$$
$$\approx 60 \times 8 \qquad\qquad \approx 500 \times 6$$
$$\approx 480 \qquad\qquad\quad \approx 3000$$

EXERCISE 4C

1   Estimate the products:

    a 79×4 **b** 47×8 **c** 62×7

    d 88×6 **e** 55×3 **f** 37×5

2   Estimate the products:

    a 284×3 **b** 617×7 **c** 408×9

    d 494×6 **e** 817×8 **f** 2094×7

Example 7 ◄ﮞ **Self Tutor**

Estimate the product: 623×69

Round 623 to the nearest 100 and round 69 to the nearest 10.

$$623 \times 69$$
$$\approx 600 \times 70$$
$$\approx 42\,000$$

The estimate tells us the correct answer should have
5 digits in it.

---

3   Estimate the products using one figure approximations:

    a 57×42 **b** 73×59 **c** 85×98

    d 275×54 **e** 389×73 **f** 4971×32

    g 3079×29 **h** $40\,989 \times 9$ **i** 880×750

DEMO

Example 8 ◄ﮞ **Self Tutor**

Find the approximate value of $3946 \div 79$.

$$3946 \div 79 \approx 4000 \div 80$$
$$\approx 400 \div 8$$
$$\approx 50$$

---

4   Estimate using one figure approximations:

    a $397 \div 4$ **b** $6849 \div 7$ **c** $79\,095 \div 8$

    d $6000 \div 19$ **e** $80\,000 \div 37$ **f** $18\,700 \div 97$

    g $2780 \div 41$ **h** $48\,097 \div 243$ **i** $798\,450 \div 399$

5   Use estimation only to find which of these calculator answers is reasonable:

    a 489×19 $\boxed{9291}$ $\boxed{96\,081}$ $\boxed{92\,901}$

    b 843×74 $\boxed{62\,382}$ $\boxed{562\,382}$ $\boxed{6238}$

    c 3907×89 $\boxed{347\,723}$ $\boxed{5\,361\,243}$ $\boxed{35\,723}$

    d $3132 \div 87$ $\boxed{3600}$ $\boxed{36}$ $\boxed{306}$

6 In the following questions, round to one figure to find the approximate value asked for.

a In her bookcase Lynda has 12 shelves. Estimate the number of books in the bookcase if there are approximately 40 books on each shelf.

b Miki reads 217 words in a minute. Estimate the number of words she can read in one hour.

c A bricklayer lays 115 bricks each hour. If he works a $37\frac{1}{2}$ hour week, approximately how many bricks will he lay in one month?

d If Joe can type at 52 words per minute, find an approximate time for him to type a document of 3820 words.

e In a vineyard there are 189 vines in each row. There are 54 rows. Find the approximate number of vines in the vineyard.

f A winery bottles 480 000 cases of wine each year. If each case holds one dozen bottles, approximately how many bottles of wine are produced each year?

g A trip of 1023 km from Adelaide to Sydney took 19 hours. Find the approximate average speed in kilometres per hour.

h An electricity supply company employs 19 people to read meters.

Each meter takes approximately 3 minutes to read. Estimate how many meters are read each hour.

AREA AND VOLUME ERRORS

LINKS
click here

Areas of interaction:
Approaches to learning

D   ROUNDING DECIMAL NUMBERS

In many situations we may be given a measurement as a decimal number. Stating the *exact* value of the measurement may not be particularly important; what we want is a good *approximation* of the measurement.

For example:

Since 1924 the Olympic marathon has been measured as exactly 42.195 km or 26.2187 miles. The exact value is rarely quoted, however, since most people use approximations; they commonly say 42 km, 42.2 km, 26 miles, or 26.2 miles.

RULES FOR ROUNDING

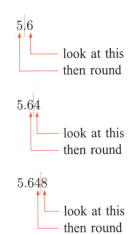

- **Rounding to the nearest whole number**

  Look at the *first* decimal place.
  If the digit is   5, 6, 7, 8 or 9,   round **up**.
  If the digit is   0, 1, 2, 3 or 4,   round **down**.

- **Rounding to the nearest one decimal place**

  Look at the *second* decimal place.
  If the digit is   5, 6, 7, 8 or 9,   round **up**.
  If the digit is   0, 1, 2, 3 or 4,   round **down**.

- **Rounding to the nearest two decimal places**

  Look at the *third* decimal place.
  If the digit is   5, 6, 7, 8 or 9,   round **up**.
  If the digit is   0, 1, 2, 3 or 4,   round **down**.

Example 9   ◀ᴺ **Self Tutor**

Round 39.748 to the nearest:

a   whole number   **b**   one decimal place   **c**   two decimal places

a $39.748 \approx 40$ to the nearest whole number

b $39.748 \approx 39.7$ to one decimal place

c $39.748 \approx 39.75$ to two decimal places

Notice that: $0.5864 \approx 0.586$ (to 3 decimal places)

≈ 0.59 (to 2 decimal places)

≈ 0.6 (to 1 decimal place)

ANOTHER APPROACH

Consider rounding 37.1485 to 1 decimal place. Use these steps if you find rounding difficult.

Step 1:	Circle the digit in the place to be rounded.	37.①485
Step 2:	Look at the next digit to the right of the circled digit and underline it.	37.①485
Step 3:	Remove all digits to the right of the underlined digit.	37.①4
Step 4:	• If the underlined digit is 0, 1, 2, 3 or 4, remove it. • If the underlined digit is 5, 6, 7, 8 or 9, remove it and add 1 to the circled digit.	37.1

Example 10   ◀ᴺ **Self Tutor**

Write 265.417 correct to: **a** 1 decimal place   **b** 2 decimal places.

a   265.④17   {to 1 d.p.}

$\approx 265.④17$

≈ 265.4

b   265.4①7   {to 2 d.p.}

≈ 265.42

EXERCISE 4D

1 Round to the nearest whole number:
  a 0.813   **b** 7.499   **c** 7.500   **d** 11.674   **e** 128.437

2 Write these numbers correct to 1 decimal place:
  a 2.43   **b** 3.57   **c** 4.92   **d** 6.38   **e** 4.275

3 Write these numbers correct to 2 decimal places:
  a 4.236   **b** 2.731   **c** 5.625   **d** 4.377   **e** 6.5237

4 Write 0.486 correct to:
  a 1 decimal place   **b** 2 decimal places

5 Write 3.789 correct to: **a** 1 decimal place   **b** 2 decimal places

6 Write 0.183 75   **a** 1 decimal place   **b** 2 decimal places
  correct to: **c** 3 decimal places   **d** 4 decimal places

7 Find approximations for:
  a 3.87 to the nearest tenth   **b** 4.3 to the nearest whole number
  c 6.09 to one decimal place   **d** 0.4617 to 3 decimal places
  e 2.946 to 2 decimal places   **f** 0.175 61 to 4 decimal places

Example 11	◀ッ **Self Tutor**
Find $\frac{2}{7}$ correct to 3 decimal places.	$0.2\ 8\ 5\ 7$ $7\ \overline{\smash{\big)}\ 2\ .\ 0\ ^6 0\ ^4 0\ ^5 0}$ $\qquad \therefore\ \frac{2}{7} \approx 0.286$

8 Find the answer correct to the number of decimal places shown in square brackets:
  a $\frac{17}{4}$ [1]   **b** $\frac{73}{8}$ [2]   **c** 4.3×2.6 [1]

  d 0.12×0.4 [2]   **e** $\frac{8}{11}$ [2]   **f** 0.08×0.31 [3]

  g $(0.7)^2$ [1]   **h** $\frac{37}{6}$ [2]   **i** $\frac{17}{7}$ [3]

9 In her maths exam Julie was asked to round 7.45 cm to one decimal place and to the nearest whole integer.

Julie's answer was that 7.45 cm $\approx$ 7.5 cm (to one decimal place), and that 7.5 cm $\approx$ 8 cm (to the nearest whole number).

Explain what Julie has done wrong and why we need to be careful when we make approximations.

E   USING A CALCULATOR TO ROUND OFF

If you have several calculations to do and must give your answers to a certain fixed number of decimal places, it is convenient to get your calculator to do this for you. Instructions for fixing the number of decimal places in the calculator display can be found on page **13**.

Example 12   ◄)) Self Tutor

a Calculate to two decimal places the value of 38.26×53.07

b Calculate to one decimal place the value of $8.179 \div 0.0138$

Using a Texas Instruments **TI-83**:

a Change the number of decimal places to 2, then press 38.26 $\boxed{\times}$ 53.07 $\boxed{\text{ENTER}}$.

Answer: 2030.46

b Change the number of decimal places to 1, then press 8.179 $\boxed{\div}$ 0.0138 $\boxed{\text{ENTER}}$.

Answer: 592.7

```
38.26*53.07
           2030.46
8.179/0.0138
             592.7
```

Using a **Casio fx-9860G**:

a Change the number of decimal places to 2, press $\boxed{\text{EXIT}}$ to return to the **RUN·MAT** screen, then 38.26 $\boxed{\times}$ 53.07 $\boxed{\text{EXE}}$.

Answer: 2030.46

b Change the number of decimal places to 1, press $\boxed{\text{EXIT}}$ to return to the **RUN·MAT** screen, then 8.179 $\boxed{\div}$ 0.0138 $\boxed{\text{EXE}}$.

Answer: 592.7

```
38.26×53.07
             2030.46
8.179÷0.0138
              592.7

►MAT
```

EXERCISE 4E

1 When denominators are not a single number we must take great care.

Consider these attempts at finding $\dfrac{20}{2 \times 5}$ and $\dfrac{36}{12 - 3}$:

For $\dfrac{20}{2 \times 5}$ Yan pressed   20 $\boxed{\div}$ 2 $\boxed{\times}$ 5 $\boxed{=}$

Frank pressed   20 $\boxed{\div}$ $\boxed{(}$ 2 $\boxed{\times}$ 5 $\boxed{)}$ $\boxed{=}$

For $\dfrac{36}{12 - 3}$ Yasuka pressed   36 $\boxed{\div}$ 12 $\boxed{-}$ 3 $\boxed{=}$

Melanie pressed   36 $\boxed{\div}$ $\boxed{(}$ 12 $\boxed{-}$ 3 $\boxed{)}$ $\boxed{=}$

a Without using a calculator, find the values of $\dfrac{20}{2 \times 5}$ and $\dfrac{36}{12 - 3}$.

b Which of Yan and Frank is correct?

c Which of Yasuka and Melanie is correct?

d Explain in your own words what you have learnt from **a**, **b** and **c**.

2 Give the order in which the calculator keys should be pressed to calculate:

a $8.704 + \dfrac{6.93}{0.74}$

b $\dfrac{8.704 + 6.93}{0.74}$

c $\dfrac{0.74}{8.704 + 6.93}$

3 Set your calculator to give answers to 1 decimal place. Then find:

    a $\dfrac{3.675 + 11.291}{5.67}$ **b** $\dfrac{17.65}{3 - 0.271}$ **c** $\pi \times (5.67)^2$

4 Set your calculator to give answers correct to 2 decimal places. Then find:

    a 21.7×18.29 **b** $\dfrac{21.7}{18.29}$ **c** $(13.29)^2 \times 15.67$

    d $\dfrac{(16.2)^3}{5.71 \times 3.68}$ **e** $\frac{1}{3} \times \pi \times (6.92)^2$ **f** $\sqrt{\dfrac{11}{2.77}}$

5 Solve the following problems:

    a A petrol tank holds exactly 64 litres. Find the cost of filling an empty tank at 122.7 cents per litre.

    b A courier receives 37 cents per kilometre travelled. What does the courier receive for a trip of 1079 km?

    c Cindy averages 39.43 seconds for each lap of a 50 m pool. Find the total time taken, in minutes and seconds, by Cindy if she swam 1500 m.

    d

A gold nugget weighs 1.389 kg. If it is sold for 43 607 Swiss francs, how much was one gram of gold worth on the day of sale?

F   SIGNIFICANT FIGURE ROUNDING

The first **significant figure** of a decimal number is the first (left-most) non-zero digit.

For example:

- the first significant figure of 1234 is 1
- the first significant figure of 0.023 45 is 2.

Every digit to the right of the first significant figure is regarded as another significant figure.

Procedure for rounding off to significant figures:

Count off the specified number of significant figures then look at the next digit.
- If the digit is less than 5, do not change the last significant figure.
- If the digit is 5 or more then increase the last significant figure by 1.

Delete all figures following the significant figures, replacing with 0s where necessary.

Notice that if 13.238 is rounded to 13.24, then it has been rounded to 2 decimal places or to 4 significant figures.

Example 13   🔊 **Self Tutor**

Round: **a**   5.371 to 2 significant figures   **b**   0.0086 to 1 significant figure
          c   423 to 1 significant figure

a $5.371 \approx 5.4$ (2 s.f.)

This is the 2nd significant figure, so we look at the next digit which is 7.
The 7 tells us to round the 3 to a 4 and leave off the remaining digits.

b $0.0086 \approx 0.009$ (1 s.f.)

These zeros at the front are place holders and so must stay. The first significant
figure is the 8. The next digit is 6, which tells us to round the 8 to a 9 and leave
off the remaining digits.

c $423 \approx 400$ (1 s.f.)

4 is the first significant figure so it has to be rounded. The second digit, 2, tells
us to keep the original 4. We convert the 23 into 00. These two zeros are place
holders; they are not 'significant figures' but need to be there to make sure the
4 still represents 4 hundreds.

EXERCISE 4F

1   Round correct to the number of significant figures shown in brackets.

a	42.3	[2]	**b**	6.237	[3]	**c**	0.0462	[2]
d	0.2461	[2]	**e**	437	[2]	**f**	2064	[2]
g	31 009	[3]	**h**	10.27	[3]	**i**	0.999	[1]
j	0.999	[2]	**k**	264 003	[4]	**l**	0.037 642	[4]
m	3699.231	[4]	**n**	0.007 639	[2]	**o**	29 999	[3]
p	69.7003	[2]						

2   The crowd at a football match was officially
        26 247 people.

    a   Round the crowd size to:
        i   1 significant figure
        ii   2 significant figures.

    b   Which of these figures might be used
        by the media to indicate crowd size?

3   The newspaper stated that 2500 people attended a protest march in Paris.

    If this figure had been rounded to two significant figures, what was the largest number
    of people that could have attended the protest?

4   During a rabbit plague there were 132 709 rabbits in South Australia. What figure would
    you expect to see in a newspaper headline for an article on these rabbits?

Solve these problems by rounding each quantity to a sensible number of significant figures.

5 Andy wants to build a 480 m long post and wire fence. Posts will be 9 m apart and cost $8.75 each. A coil of wire is 100 m long and costs $42.50. Estimate the cost of a seven wire fence.

6 To paint and wallpaper a bedroom Bronwyn needs five rolls of paper at $19.50 each and one 10 litre tin of paint that costs $88.70 on special. Estimate the total cost of the paint and paper.

7 Fertiliser costs $250 per tonne to buy and spread. It is spread on fields at a rate of 0.5 tonne per hectare. Estimate the cost to spread fertiliser on a 324.6 ha farm.

G   ROUNDING TIME

Example 14   ◀ᵕ Self Tutor

Change 3 hours 45 minutes and 33 seconds into hours, correct to 4 decimal places.

33 seconds $= \frac{33}{60}$ minutes $= 0.55$ minutes

$\therefore$ 45 minutes 33 seconds $= 45.55$ minutes

Now   45.55 minutes $= \dfrac{45.55}{60}$ hours ≈ 0.7592 hours

So, 3 hours 45 minutes and 33 seconds ≈ 3.7592 hours.

Example 15   ◀ᵕ Self Tutor

Change 12.8967 hours into hours, minutes and seconds, to the nearest second.

We have 12 whole hours which we can immediately record in the answer.
The remaining   0.8967 hours $= 0.8967 \times 60 = 53.802$ minutes
We can hence record the 53 whole minutes in the answer.
The remaining   0.802 minutes $= 0.802 \times 60 = 48.12$ seconds
                                          which rounds to 48 seconds.
So, 12.8967 hours $\approx$ 12 hours, 53 minutes, 48 seconds.

EXERCISE 4G

1 Convert:

a 3.567 minutes into minutes and seconds to the nearest second

b 24 921 seconds into hours, minutes and seconds

c 4.835 hours into hours, minutes and seconds

d 5 minutes 23 seconds into minutes, to 3 decimal places

   e 1 hour 17 minutes 47 seconds into hours, to 2 decimal places

   f 8.005 79 hours into hours, minutes and seconds to the nearest second

   g 4.833 weeks into weeks, days and hours to the nearest hour

   h 2 days, 17 hours and 55 minutes into days to 3 significant figures.

2 Chris leaves home at 0755 and takes 2.72 hours to complete a journey. Find the arrival time, to the nearest minute.

3 A train travels 200 km in 1 hour 5 minutes. Calculate its speed, in $km\,h^{-1}$.

   Remember that $speed = \dfrac{distance}{time}$.

REVIEW SET 4A

1 Round 3579 to the: **a** nearest 10   **b** nearest 100   **c** nearest 1000

2 Round off:

   a 388 km to the nearest 10 km   **b** 3501 L to the nearest kL

   c 74 821 sheep to the nearest 10 000 sheep

3 Round: **a** $13.68 to the nearest 5 cents   **b** £13.68 to the nearest pound.

4 Estimate the cost of the following using sensible rounding:

   a 78 notepads at €1.95 each   **b** 6 dozen icecreams at RM 0.95 each.

5 Using 1 figure approximations, find estimates of:

   a 148×6 **b** 804×29 **c** $3016 \div 58$

6 A tiler can lay 72 tiles each hour and works a 42 hour week.

   a Estimate the number of tiles laid in a week using 1 figure approximations.

   b What is the actual number laid in a week?

   c What is the error made when the estimation is used?

7 Chen walks 31 729 metres in 5 hours 58 min. Find a 1 figure estimate of Chen's average speed in metres per minute.

8 Round 28.907 to: **a** the nearest whole   **b** 1 dec. place   **c** 2 dec. places.

9 Find $\frac{22}{7}$ correct to: **a** 1 decimal place   **b** 2 decimal places.

10 Use a calculator to find, correct to 2 decimal places, the value of:

   a $\pi \times 3.68^2$ **b** $\dfrac{48.67}{314.72 \times 0.0766}$ **c** $\dfrac{21.66 - 18.79}{21.66 + 18.79}$

11 Kerosene is sold in drums of capacity 48 litres. Estimate the cost of 97 drums of kerosene costing $0.62 per litre.

12 At the football match on Sunday the crowd was 43 768. Round the crowd size to:
    a 1 significant figure   **b** 2 significant figures.

13 Change 2 hours 43 minutes 27 seconds into hours, correct to 4 decimal places.

REVIEW SET 4B

1 Round 4608 to the nearest: **a** 10   **b** 100   **c** 1000

2 Round off:
    a 659 km to the nearest 100 km
    b 20 144 tonnes to the nearest 1000 tonnes
    c 156 797 people to the nearest 10 000 people.

3 Round:
    a \$69.73 to the nearest 5 cents   **b** €172.62 to the nearest euro.

4 Estimate the cost of the following using sensible rounding:
    a 6 magazines at ¥25.85 each   **b** 32 kg of apples at \$3.15 per kg.

5 Estimate using 1 figure approximations:
    a 63×9 **b** 198×4 **c** $1989 \div 42$

6 A company wants to mail advertising to 3065 clients. Each package of advertising takes 2 minutes to prepare for mailing. Estimate how long it would take to prepare the mailing if 3 people were working at once on this task.

7 Round 55.039 to:
    a the nearest whole number   **b** 1 decimal place   **c** 2 decimal places.

8 **a** Find $\frac{8}{11}$ correct to 3 decimal places.
    b Find 6.8×0.0253 correct to 2 decimal places.

9 Use a calculator to find, correct to 2 decimal places, the value of:
    a $\dfrac{12.37 + 63.85}{15.2 \times 1.09}$ **b** $\frac{1}{3} \times \pi \times (46.73)^2$

10 Laszlo drives 876 km at an average speed of 75.4 km h^{-1}. Use your calculator to find the time he takes to drive this distance, correct to the nearest minute.

11 The profit for 2007 for a business is Rs 5 683 422. Round this amount to:
    a 1 significant figure   **b** 2 significant figures.

12 Calculate to 3 significant figures: **a** 2367×0.8621 **b** $\dfrac{268.7}{21.73}$

13 Change 8.4679 hours into hours, minutes and seconds, to the nearest second.

Chapter 5

The Rule of Pythagoras

Contents:

- **A** The Rule of Pythagoras (Review)
- **B** Further problem solving
- **C** Testing for right angles
- **D** Navigation

Right angles (90° angles) are used when constructing buildings and dividing areas of land into rectangular regions.

The ancient **Egyptians** used a rope with 12 equally spaced knots to form a triangle with sides in the ratio $3 : 4 : 5$.

This triangle had a right angle between the sides of length 3 and 4 units.

In fact, this is the simplest right angled triangle with sides that are whole numbers.

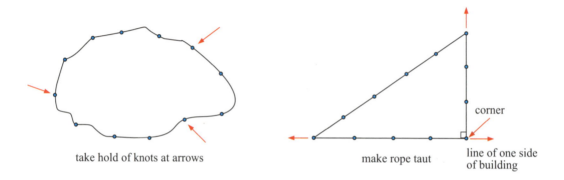

take hold of knots at arrows

make rope taut

corner

line of one side of building

OPENING PROBLEM

Karrie is playing golf in the British Open. She hits a poor tee shot on the opening hole. Her caddy paces out some distances and finds that Karrie has hit the ball 250 m, but 70 m from the centre of the fairway. A marker which is 150 m from the hole is further up the fairway as shown.

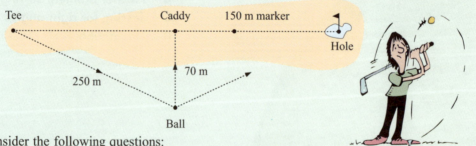

Consider the following questions:

1 From where he stands on the fairway, how far would the caddy have to walk back to retrieve Karrie's putter if he left it on the tee?

2 From where the caddy stands on the fairway, what distance is left to the 150 m marker if he knows the hole is 430 m long?

3 How far does Karrie need to hit her ball with her second shot to reach the hole?

A   THE RULE OF PYTHAGORAS (REVIEW)

A **right angled triangle** is a triangle which has a right angle as one of its angles.

The side **opposite** the **right angle** is called the **hypotenuse** and is the **longest** side of the triangle.

The other two sides are called the **legs** of the triangle.

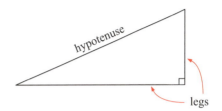

Around 500 BC, the Greek mathematician **Pythagoras** discovered a rule. It connects the lengths of the sides of all right angled triangles.

It is thought that he discovered the rule while studying tessellations of tiles on bathroom floors. Such patterns, like the one illustrated, were common on the walls and floors of bathrooms in ancient **Greece**.

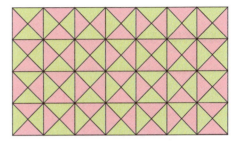

THE RULE OF PYTHAGORAS

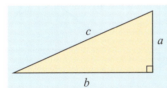

In a right angled triangle, with hypotenuse c and legs a and b,

$$c^2 = a^2 + b^2.$$

In geometric form, the **Rule of Pythagoras** is:

In any right angled triangle, the area of the square on the hypotenuse is equal to the sum of the areas of the squares on the other two sides.

VIDEO CLIP

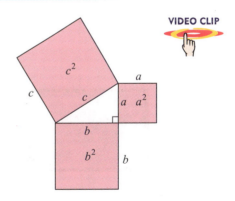

LINKS
click here

PYTHAGORAS

Areas of interaction:
Human ingenuity

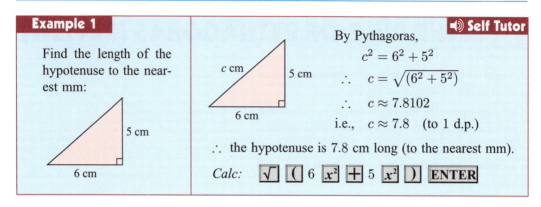

Example 1   ◀)) **Self Tutor**

Find the length of the hypotenuse to the nearest mm:

By Pythagoras,
$$c^2 = 6^2 + 5^2$$
$$\therefore \quad c = \sqrt{(6^2 + 5^2)}$$
$$\therefore \quad c \approx 7.8102$$
i.e., $c \approx 7.8$ (to 1 d.p.)

$\therefore$ the hypotenuse is 7.8 cm long (to the nearest mm).

Calc: $\sqrt{}$ $($ 6 x^2 $+$ 5 x^2 $)$ **ENTER**

EXERCISE 5A

1 Find the length of the hypotenuse to the nearest mm:

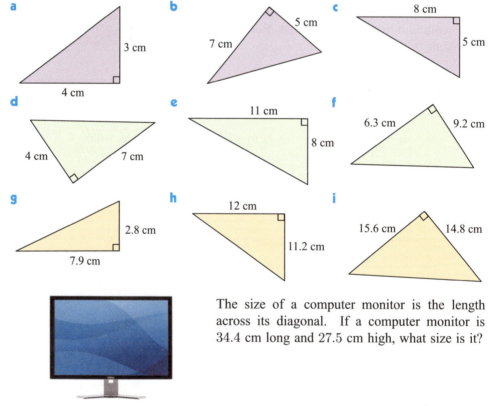

a   3 cm, 4 cm

b   5 cm, 7 cm

c   8 cm, 5 cm

d   4 cm, 7 cm

e   11 cm, 8 cm

f   6.3 cm, 9.2 cm

g   2.8 cm, 7.9 cm

h   12 cm, 11.2 cm

i   15.6 cm, 14.8 cm

2   The size of a computer monitor is the length across its diagonal. If a computer monitor is 34.4 cm long and 27.5 cm high, what size is it?

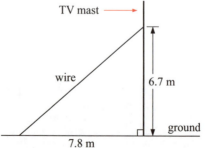

3   a Find the length of the wire shown supporting the TV mast.

b There are six wires which support the mast.

   i Find their total length.

   ii If 3% extra wire is needed for tying, how many metres of wire need to be purchased? The wire must be purchased in a whole number of metres.

TV mast ⟶

wire

6.7 m

ground

7.8 m

4 Metal supports are made as shown. They are fitted from the lower edge of the table top to the legs. The flat ends of the supports are 2 cm long. Find the length of the metal needed to make the 8 supports used to stabilise the table.

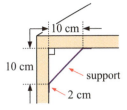

  🔊 **Self Tutor**

Find, to the nearest mm, the length of the third side.

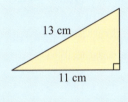

By Pythagoras:

$a^2 + 11^2 = 13^2$

$\therefore \quad a^2 = 13^2 - 11^2$

$\therefore \quad a = \sqrt{(13^2 - 11^2)}$

$\therefore \quad a \approx 6.9282$

$\therefore$ the third side is 6.9 cm long (to the nearest mm)

Calc: $\sqrt{}$ $($ 13 x^2 $-$ 11 x^2 $)$ **ENTER**

---

5 Find, to the nearest mm, the length of the third side of the triangle:

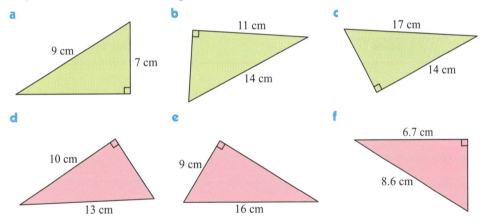

6 A radio mast has a support wire tied 8.1 m above ground level. The other end is tied to a peg in the ground. How far is the peg from the base of the mast?

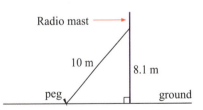

7

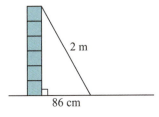

A ladder is 2 metres long. It leans against a wall so the base is 86 cm from the wall.

a Write 86 cm in metres.

b How far up the wall does the ladder reach?

8 Heidi has made a rectangular cushion cover which measures 36 cm long by 32 cm wide. She wants to put lace across one diagonal on each side.

  a Find the length of the diagonal.

  b Find the total length of lace required, if 4 cm extra is allowed for finishing off the ends.

  c Calculate the cost of the lace at $2.30 per metre.

Example 3
🔊 **Self Tutor**

Find, to the nearest mm, the length of the unknown side.

a

10.3 cm

b

14 cm

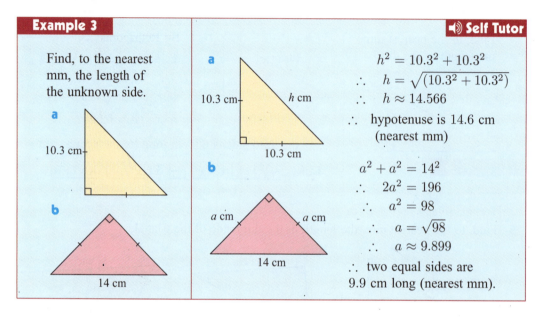

a

10.3 cm h cm

10.3 cm

$$h^2 = 10.3^2 + 10.3^2$$
$$\therefore \quad h = \sqrt{(10.3^2 + 10.3^2)}$$
$$\therefore \quad h \approx 14.566$$

$\therefore$ hypotenuse is 14.6 cm (nearest mm)

b

a cm a cm

14 cm

$$a^2 + a^2 = 14^2$$
$$\therefore \quad 2a^2 = 196$$
$$\therefore \quad a^2 = 98$$
$$\therefore \quad a = \sqrt{98}$$
$$\therefore \quad a \approx 9.899$$

$\therefore$ two equal sides are 9.9 cm long (nearest mm).

---

9 Find, to the nearest mm, the length of the unknown side:

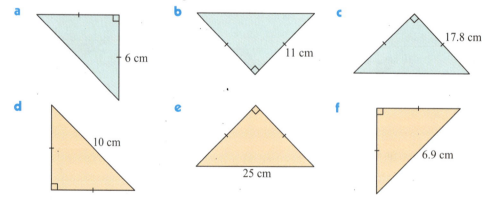

a

6 cm

b

11 cm

c

17.8 cm

d

10 cm

e

25 cm

f

6.9 cm

10 A square garden with sides 100 m is divided into two triangular plots by a fence along one diagonal.

  a What is the length of the fence in metres (to 1 decimal place)?

  b If the fence costs $15.50 per metre, what is the total cost?

11 A 160 m long water pipe runs along the diagonal of a square paddock. What are the lengths of the sides of the paddock?

12 A garden gate is 1.2 metres wide and 1.2 metres high.
The gate is strengthened by a diagonal strut.

   a How long is the strut?

   b Calculate the length of steel needed for the frame
of the gate, including the strut.

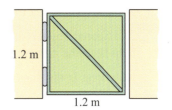

13 A knitting needle is 24 cm long. It just fits across the diagonal of the base of a square
tin. How long are the sides of the tin? Answer to the next millimetre.

B   FURTHER PROBLEM SOLVING

Right angled triangles are used constantly in the building industry for houses, industrial
sites, bridges, and more. The Rule of Pythagoras is used to find unknown lengths on these
triangles.

Example 4   ◀)) **Self Tutor**

Find the length of the truss AB
for the given roof structure.

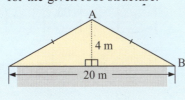

By Pythagoras,

$$h^2 = 4^2 + 10^2$$
$$\therefore \quad h = \sqrt{(4^2 + 10^2)}$$
$$\therefore \quad h \approx 10.7703$$
$$\therefore \quad AB \approx 10.77 \text{ m long}$$
(nearest cm)

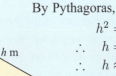

EXERCISE 5B

1 Find the length
of the truss AB
for the
following roof
structures:

  a

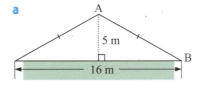

  b

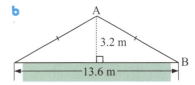

2 How high is the
roof above the
walls in the
following roof
structures?

  a

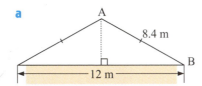

  b

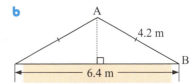

3 A 5 m long ladder leans against a brick wall.

If it reaches 4.8 m up the wall, how far are the
feet of the ladder from the base of the wall?

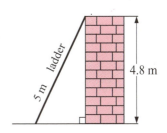

4 A metal gate is 3.4 m wide and 1.2 m high.

A diagonal support is added for strength to help keep the corners right angled.

How long is the diagonal support?

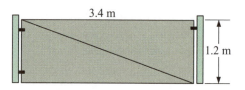

5

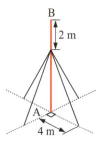

A pole AB is 10 m tall above the ground. At a point 2 m below B, four wires are connected from the pole to the ground.

Each wire is pegged to the ground 4 m from the base of the pole. What is the total length of the wire needed given that a total of 2 m extra is needed for tying?

6 On a triangular property a farmer erects a 4 strand wire fence. The fence is along all three sides of the property.

   a Find the length of side AC.
   b Find the perimeter of the property.
   c Find the total length of wire required.
   d If the wire costs $29.50 for 100 m, find the total cost of the wire for the fence.

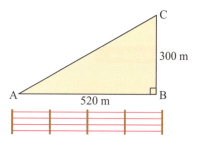

Example 5   ◀)) **Self Tutor**

Find the total length of metal to make 15 000 right angled brackets like the one shown.

By Pythagoras,
$$x^2 = 14^2 + 20^2$$
$$\therefore \quad x = \sqrt{(14^2 + 20^2)}$$
$$\therefore \quad x \approx 24.4 \text{ cm}$$

Sketch of a bracket (measurements in cm)

Length needed for one bracket
$$= 30 + 18 + 24.4 \text{ cm}$$
$$= 72.4 \text{ cm}$$
$$\therefore \quad \text{total length needed} = 15\,000 \times 0.724 \text{ m}$$
$$= 10\,860 \text{ m}$$

---

7 Find the total length of metal required to make these right angled brackets:

a

3 cm   8 cm   3 cm
20 cm

Number required: 2500

b

3 cm
16 cm
4 cm   5 cm
12 cm

Number required: 8450

8 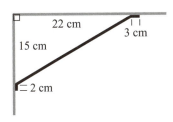 Six steel brackets like the one shown are used to support a shelf for books. The steel weighs 2.4 kg per metre. Find:

   a the length of metal in one bracket

   b the total length of metal for the 6 brackets

   c the total weight of the 6 brackets.

9 A mirror with dimensions as shown has a timber frame. Find:

   a the length of AB

   b the total length of timber required to make the frame.

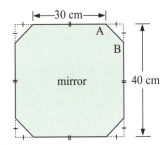

10 Three metal trusses are used to make the roof of a shed. Find:

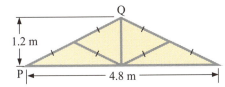

   a the length of PQ

   b the total length of metal to make one truss

   c the total length of metal to make all three trusses.

ISOSCELES AND EQUILATERAL TRIANGLES

Isosceles triangles have *two* equal sides. Equilateral triangles have *three* equal sides.

In both cases, a perpendicular line from the base to the apex *bisects* the base.

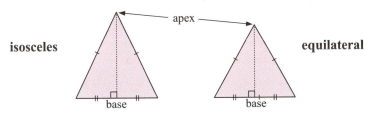

Example 6	◀)) Self Tutor

An isosceles triangular garden bed has equal sides 12 m long. The third side has length 10 m. Find:

   a the altitude of the triangle

   b the area of the triangle.

a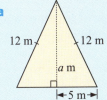

The altitude bisects the base at right angles. So,

$$a^2 + 5^2 = 12^2$$
$$\therefore \quad a^2 = 12^2 - 5^2$$
$$\therefore \quad a = \sqrt{(12^2 - 5^2)}$$
$$\therefore \quad a \approx 10.91$$

$\therefore$ the altitude is 10.9 m

b The area $= \frac{1}{2}$ base $\times$ height

$$= \frac{1}{2} \times 10 \times 10.91$$
$$\approx 54.6 \text{ m}^2$$

Note: Always sketch a diagram of the situation. Show all given lengths and other information.

11 An equilateral triangle has sides of length 12 cm.
    a Find the length of one of its altitudes.
    b Find the area of the triangle.

12 An isosceles triangle has equal sides of length 8 cm and a base of length 6 cm.
    a Find the altitude of the triangle.
    b Find the area of the triangle.

13 A new park is an equilateral triangle with sides 200 m. It will be surfaced with instant turf.
    a Find the length of an altitude of the triangle (to 2 d.p.).
    b Find the area of turf needed to grass it.
    c If the turf costs \$4.25 per m² fully laid, find the total cost of grassing the park.

C   TESTING FOR RIGHT ANGLES

In the construction of houses and other buildings it is essential that the corners are 'square'. In other words, they need to meet each other at right angles.

The following diagram shows a typical frame for the wall of a house:

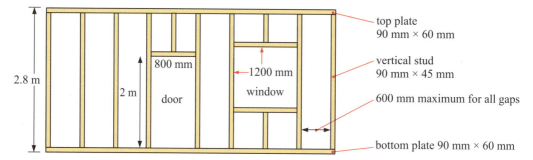

top plate
90 mm × 60 mm

vertical stud
90 mm × 45 mm

600 mm maximum for all gaps

bottom plate 90 mm × 60 mm

How do the workers make sure that they have right angled corners?

One method is to use the Rule of Pythagoras in reverse.

We call this the **right angled triangle test**:

GEOMETRY PACKAGE

> If a triangle has sides of length a, b and c units and $a^2 + b^2 = c^2$, then the triangle is right angled.

Example 7	🔊 Self Tutor
Is the triangle with sides 6 cm, 8 cm and 5 cm right angled?	The two shorter sides have lengths 5 cm and 6 cm, and $\begin{aligned} 5^2 + 6^2 &= 25 + 36 \\ &= 61 \end{aligned}$ But $8^2 = 64$, $\therefore$ $5^2 + 6^2 \neq 8^2$ So, the triangle is not right angled.

EXERCISE 5C

1   The following figures *are not drawn accurately.* Which of the triangles are right angled?

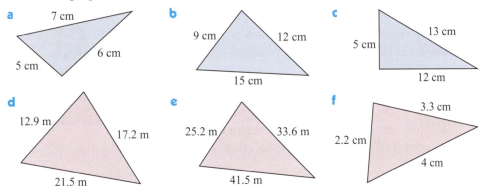

a 7 cm, 6 cm, 5 cm

b 9 cm, 12 cm, 15 cm

c 5 cm, 13 cm, 12 cm

d 12.9 m, 17.2 m, 21.5 m

e 25.2 m, 33.6 m, 41.5 m

f 3.3 cm, 2.2 cm, 4 cm

2   Colin believes he has cut out a perfect rectangular canvas covering which has adjacent sides 8.6 m and 5.4 m. The opposite sides are equal. He measures a diagonal to be 10.155 m. Is Colin's rectangle right angled?

3   Julie has just cut out a triangular sail for her boat. The lengths of the sides are 6.23 m, 3.87 m and 4.88 m. The sail is supposed to be right angled. Is it?

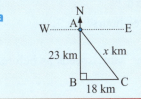

Due to rounding, $a^2 + b^2$ and c^2 may not be *exactly* equal. However, if they are very close we might still say that the triangle is right angled.

D   NAVIGATION

The problems in this section involve navigation and compass bearings, including some problems where we test for right angles. Remember that drawing a diagram of the situation may be very helpful in solving the problem.

| **Example 8** | ◄⟩ **Self Tutor** |

A yacht sails 23 km south and then 18 km east.

a   Draw a fully labelled diagram of the yacht's course.

b   How far is the yacht from its starting point?

a

b   By Pythagoras,
$$x^2 = 23^2 + 18^2$$
$$\therefore \; x = \sqrt{(23^2 + 18^2)} \quad \therefore \; x \approx 29.2$$
$\therefore$ the yacht is 29.2 km from the start.

EXERCISE 5D

1 A yacht sails 9 km due west and then 7 km due south. How far is it from its starting point?

2 A cyclist rides 8 km due west and then 10 km due north. How far is he from his starting point?

3 A runner is 9 km west and 6 km south of her starting point.

    a How far is she from her starting point?

    b How long would it take her to return to her starting point in a direct line if she can run at 10 km h^{-1}?

4 Two ships X and Y leave port P at the same time. X travels due east at a constant speed of 15 km h^{-1}. Y travels due north at a constant speed of 20 km h^{-1}.

    a How far have X and Y each travelled after three hours?

    b Find the distance between them after three hours.

5 Hayato and Yuki are sailing at sea. From a particular buoy they sail for 240 m in one direction, then turn and sail for 100 m in another. They are now 260 m from the buoy. Was the angle they turned a right angle?

6 Pirate Captain William Hawk left his hat on Treasure Island. He sailed 18 km northeast through the Forbidden Straight, then 11 km southeast to his home before realising it was missing. If he sent his parrot to fetch the hat, how far did the bird need to fly?

7 Town A is 80 km south of town B. Town C is 150 km east of town B.

    a Find how long it takes to travel directly from A to C by car at 90 km h^{-1}.

    b Find how long it takes to travel from A to C via B in a train travelling at 130 km h^{-1}.

    c Comparing **a** and **b**, which is faster?

8  Two runners set off from town A at the same time. One ran due east to town B while the other ran due south to town C at twice the speed of the first. They arrived at B and C two hours later. If B and C are 60 km apart, find the speed at which each runner travelled.

9 Max and Kyle leave home at the same time, both riding their bicycles. Max travels due east at 12 km h^{-1}, while Kyle travels due south at 15 km h^{-1}.

    a How far have Max and Kyle each travelled after three hours?

    b How far apart are they after three hours?

    c If they start to ride directly towards each other at the same speeds as before, how long will it take for them to meet?

REVIEW SET 5A

1 A young tree has a 2 m support rope tied to a peg in the ground 1.2 m from its base. How high up the tree is the rope tied?

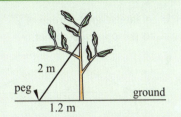

2 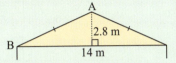 Find the length of the truss AB for the roof structure shown.

3 A television screen size is advertised as 34 cm. If the screen is 20 cm high, how wide must it be?

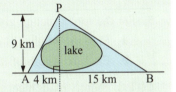

4 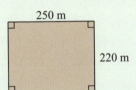 A farmer has a paddock which is 250 m long and 220 m wide. She walks along two sides checking the electric fence then returns by walking diagonally across the paddock. How far has she walked?

5 A new industrial park is built at P, 9 km across the lake from the straight road connecting towns A and B. New roads have been made from A to P and B to P to allow quick access to the park for workers from these towns.

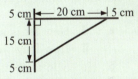

Find the distances AP and BP to the nearest 100 m.

6 A bracket for hanging flower baskets is shown in the diagram. Find the length of steel needed to make this bracket.

7 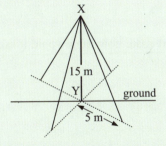 A pole XY is 15 metres tall. Four wires from the top of the pole X connect it to the ground.

Each wire is pegged 5 metres from the base of the pole. Find the total length of wire needed if a total of 2 m extra is needed for tying.

8 Mia and Yvette leave home at the same time. Mia walks east at 5 km h^{-1} and Yvette walks at 4 km h^{-1} in another direction.

  a How far do they each walk in $1\frac{1}{2}$ hours?

  b If they are now approximately 9.6 km apart, show that Yvette travelled at right angles to Mia.

  c What directions might Yvette have walked in?

REVIEW SET 5B

1 A landscaped garden is 25 metres square. Find the length of a path from one corner to the opposite corner.

2 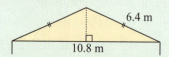 How high is the roof above the walls in the roof structure shown?

3 A ladder is 2 m long. It leans against a wall so that it reaches 1.8 m up the wall.

How far from the wall is the foot of the ladder?

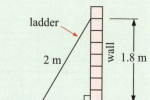

4  A fishing boat leaves port and sails 8 km west then 15 km south. How far must it sail if it returns to port by the shortest distance?

5 For the roof structure given:

a Find the height QS of the roof above the walls.

b Find the length of the roof truss PQ.

6 Two country roads meet at right angles at X. A motorist can travel from P to X to Q on a sealed road, travelling at 90 km h^{-1}.

a **i** How far is it from P to X to Q?

ii How long would it take him (in minutes)?

b He could also travel in a straight line from P to Q along a dirt road.

i Find the distance along the dirt road.

ii If he can travel at 60 km h^{-1} on the dirt road, how long would it take him to reach Q?

c Which is the quicker route?

7 An equilateral triangle has sides 6 m long.

a Find the length of a perpendicular from a vertex to the opposite side.

b Find the area of the triangle.

8 Kim has made a rectangular wooden frame for a photograph. It measures 59 cm long and 41 cm wide. The diagonal measures 71.85 cm. Check that the frame is rectangular.

Chapter  6

Algebra

Contents:

A   Changing words into symbols

B   Generalising arithmetic

C   Converting into algebraic form

D   Formula construction

E   Number patterns and rules

F   The value of an expression

OPENING PROBLEM

A fencing contractor builds fences made from termite resistant timber. The posts and the rails are identical in size and length.

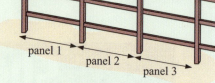

panel 1   panel 2   panel 3

- Can you find how many lengths of timber are needed to make

  a a one-panel fence   **b** a two-panel fence

  c a three-panel fence   **d** a ten-panel fence

  e a one hundred-panel fence **f** a one thousand-panel fence?

- Clearly we do not wish to draw fences with large numbers of panels in order to answer **e** and **f** above. How else could we find exact answers to **e** and **f**?

A | CHANGING WORDS INTO SYMBOLS

In algebra we can convert sentences into **algebraic expressions** or **equations**.

We can use letters or *pronumerals* such as n or x to represent unknown numbers.

For example,

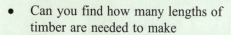

Three times a number,   less 2   is   7 more than the number

becomes $3x$ $- 2$ $=$ $x + 7.$

Many algebraic statements use words such as sum, difference, product, and quotient.

Word	Meaning	Examples
sum	The sum of two or more numbers is obtained by **adding** them.	$4 + 5$, $x + 7$, $r + s + t$ are sums.
difference	The difference between two numbers is the larger one **minus** the smaller one.	$8 - 3$, $n - 11$ (if $n > 11$) are differences.
product	The product of two or more numbers is obtained by **multiplying** them.	2×7, $4b$, pqr are products.
quotient	The quotient of two numbers is the first one mentioned **divided** by the second.	The quotient of a and b is $\dfrac{a}{b}$.
mean	The **mean** of a set of numbers is their sum divided by the number of numbers.	The mean of x, y and z is $\dfrac{x + y + z}{3}$.

Example 1

🔊 **Self Tutor**

a State the sum of 6 and a.
b State the difference between c and d $(d > c)$.
c State the mean of p, q and r.

a The sum of 6 and a is $6 + a$.

b The difference is $d - c$.   {as d is larger than c}

c The mean is $\dfrac{p + q + r}{3}$.

When writing products we leave out the multiplication sign between unknowns and write them in alphabetical order.

EXERCISE 6A

1 Write expressions for the sum of:
   a 9 and 2   **b** 5 and a **c** m and $3n$ **d** d, e and f

2 Write expressions for the product of:
   a 8 and 6   **b** 6 and p **c** n and $4m$ **d** b, d and e

3 Write expressions for the quotient of:
   a 6 and 5   **b** d and 3   **c** m and $5n$ **d** $p + q$ and x

4 Write expressions for the mean of:
   a 6 and 10   **b** 9 and d **c** k and $4v$ **d** d, e and f

5 Write expressions for the difference between:
   a 5 and 8   **b** 6 and s if $6 < s$ **c** 8 and p if $8 > p$

6 Write down algebraic expressions for:
   a seven times a is subtracted from m **b** the product of x and the square of y
   c the sum of d and three times e **d** 5 less than a
   e b more than 2   **f** the product of the square of 4 and c
   g the square of the product of a and b **h** the sum of the squares of p and q

---

B   GENERALISING ARITHMETIC

To find algebraic expressions for many real world situations we first think in terms of numbers.

For example, suppose we are asked to find the total cost of p pens where each pen costs $\$x$.

We could first find the total cost of 4 pens where each pen costs $\$5$. In this case the total cost is $4 \times \$5 = \$20$.

We *multiplied* the two quantities, and so the total cost of p pens at $\$x$ each is $p \times \$x = \$px$.

First work out how to do the problem using numbers.

Example 2

Self Tutor

Find: **a**   the cost of x bananas at 30 cents each

   b   the change from \$50 when buying y books at \$6 each.

a   Suppose we were buying 7 bananas at 30 cents each.

The cost of 7 bananas at 30 cents each would be 7×30 cents.

$\therefore$ the cost of x bananas at 30 cents each is $x \times 30 = 30x$ cents.

b   Suppose we were buying 5 books at \$6 each.

The change when buying 5 books at \$6 each would be $50 - (5 \times 6)$ dollars.

$\therefore$ the change when buying y books at \$6 each is $50 - (y \times 6)$ dollars

$$= 50 - 6y \text{ dollars.}$$

EXERCISE 6B

1   Find the total cost (in cents) of buying:

   a   4 apples at 50 cents each   **b** x apples at 50 cents each

   c x apples at c cents each

2   Find the total cost (in pounds) of buying:

   a   6 apples at 20 pence each   **b** y apples at 20 pence each

   c d apples at c pence each

3   Find the change from CHF 100 when buying:

   a   6 books at CHF 10 each   **b** n books at CHF 10 each

   c n books at CHF p each

4   Yuri has €30 in his pocket. How much would he have if:

   a   he spends €8   **b**   he spends €m **c**   he is given €t?

5   Brian went on a journey to see his friends. He travelled 6 km to see Jonas, then another k km to see Susan. He travelled another n km to see James, then drove the 8 km directly home. How far did he travel on his journey?

6   Carlos is now 16 years old. How old will he be in b years time?

7   Peta can run at 12 km h^{-1}. How far can she run in h hours?

8   You have a 9 m length of string. If you cut 4 lengths of x m from it, what length remains?

9   Graham buys p pencils and b books. Find the total cost in cents, if each pencil costs 60 cents and each book costs 95 cents.

10   **a**   A cyclist travels at an average speed of 24 km h^{-1} for 4 hours. How far does the cyclist travel?

   b   How far does the cyclist travel if he rides at an average speed of k km h^{-1} for h hours?

C CONVERTING INTO ALGEBRAIC FORM

Example 3
🔊 **Self Tutor**

Convert into algebraic form:
- **a** 18 more than a number
- **b** 7 less than a number
- **c** double a number
- **d** double the sum of a number and 7

a 18 more than a number is   the number plus 18   i.e., $x + 18$

b 7 less than a number is   the number minus 7   i.e., $x - 7$

c double a number is   the number multiplied by 2   i.e., $2 \times x$ or $2x$

d The sum of a number and 7 is $x + 7$,
so double this sum is $2 \times (x + 7)$ i.e., $2(x + 7)$

double ⟍ sum of the number and 7

Note: Any pronumeral, for example, y, could have been used here.

EXERCISE 6C

1 Translate the following into algebraic expressions:
- **a** 8 more than p
- **b** g is decreased by 3
- **c** n is increased by 2
- **d** the sum of c and 4
- **e** 3 less than x
- **f** the product of 4 and f
- **g** h is divided by 3
- **h** 4 more than 2 times a
- **i** double p and add 14

2 Translate the following into algebraic expressions:
- **a** 3 more than a certain number
- **b** 5 less than a number
- **c** one half of a number
- **d** treble a certain number
- **e** one quarter of a number
- **f** 12 minus a number
- **g** 1 more than double a number
- **h** 6 less than five times a number

3 Copy and complete:
- **a** Two numbers have a sum of 4. If one of them is s then the other is ......
- **b** Two numbers are in the ratio $1:2$. If the smaller one is a then the larger one is ......
- **c** Two numbers in the ratio $2:3$ can be represented by $2c$ and ......
- **d** If there are 27 students in a class and b are boys, then there are ...... girls.
- **e** If the smaller of two consecutive integers is y, then the larger is ......
- **f** Three consecutive integers in ascending order are x, ..., ...
- **g** Two consecutive odd integers in ascending order are d and ......
- **h** Three consecutive integers in descending order are a, ..., ...
- **i** If the middle integer of three consecutive integers is m, then the other two are ...... and ......
- **j** Two numbers differ by 3. If the smaller one is s then the other is ......

4 Write each of the following quantities as an algebraic expression in terms of the given pronumeral:

    a The sum of two numbers is 13. One of the numbers is x. What is the other number?

    b The larger of two consecutive integers is k. What is the smaller integer?

    c n is the smallest of three consecutive integers. What are the other two integers?

    d The larger of two consecutive odd integers is v. What is the smaller one?

    e The middle integer of three consecutive even integers is m. What are the other two integers?

    f There are s students in a class. If g of them are girls, how many of them are boys?

Example 4   ◀) **Self Tutor**

Translate into an algebraic expression:

a the sum of three consecutive odd numbers, where the smallest is n

b the total value of x 43-cent stamps and $(7 - x)$ 75-cent stamps.

a If n is the smallest number then the others are $n + 2$ and $n + 4$

    $\therefore$ sum is $n + (n + 2) + (n + 4)$.

b The x stamps each costing 43 cents have total value $43x$ cents.

    The $(7 - x)$ stamps each costing 75 cents have total value $75(7 - x)$ cents

    $\therefore$ total value $= 43x + 75(7 - x)$ cents.

---

5 Translate into an algebraic expression:

    a the sum of two consecutive whole numbers

    b the sum of two consecutive even numbers

    c the total value of x ¥50 coins and $(x + 4)$ ¥20 coins

    d the total value of x €5 notes and $(8 - x)$ €20 notes

D   FORMULA CONSTRUCTION

Formulae are often constructed as the generalisation of numerical observations. To construct a formula, we reduce the problem to a specific numeric situation to understand it, and then generalise the result.

For example,

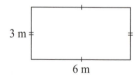

the perimeter of the rectangle is given by

    $P = 3 + 6 + 3 + 6$ metres

$\therefore$ $P = (2 \times 3) + (2 \times 6)$ metres

$\therefore$ P is double the width plus double the length.

Thus for

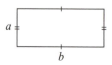

            $P = 2a + 2b$

or $P = 2(a + b)$.

Example 5   ◀》 **Self Tutor**

Write the formula for the total cost C of a taxi trip given a fixed charge of:

a $3 and $0.55 per km for 12 km
b $3 and $0.55 per km for k km
c $3 and $d per km for k km
d $F and $d per km for k km

a $C = 3 + (0.55 \times 12)$

b $C = 3 + (0.55 \times k)$
    i.e., $C = 3 + 0.55k$

c $C = 3 + d \times k$
    i.e., $C = 3 + dk$

d $C = F + dk$

EXERCISE 6D

1   Write a formula for the amount €A in a new savings account given monthly deposits of:

  a   €300 over 15 months   b   €300 over m months   c   €d over m months

2   Write a formula for the amount £A in a bank account if initially the balance was:

  a   £3000, and then £200 was deposited each week for 6 weeks
  b   £3000, and then £200 was deposited each week for w weeks
  c   £3000, and then £m was deposited each week for w weeks
  d   £P, and then £m was deposited each week for w weeks.

3   Write the formula for the total cost C of hiring a plumber given a fixed call-out fee of:

  a $60 plus $50 per hour for 5 hours work
  b $60 plus $50 per hour for t hours work
  c $60 plus $d per hour for t hours work
  d $F plus $d per hour for t hours work.

Example 6   ◀》 **Self Tutor**

Write the formula for the amount A in a person's bank account if initially the balance was:

a $5000 and $200 was withdrawn each week for 10 weeks
b $5000 and $200 was withdrawn each week for w weeks
c $5000 and $x was withdrawn each week for w weeks
d $B and $x was withdrawn each week for w weeks.

a $A = 5000 - 200 \times 10$

b $A = 5000 - 200 \times w$
    i.e., $A = 5000 - 200w$

c $A = 5000 - x \times w$
    i.e., $A = 5000 - xw$

d $A = B - x \times w$
    i.e., $A = B - xw$

4   Write the formula for the amount A in Leon's wallet if initially he had:

  a $300 and he bought 10 $6 presents
  b $300 and he bought x $6 presents
  c $300 and he bought x $b presents
  d $P and he bought x $b presents

5 Write a formula for the capacity, C litres, of a tank if initially the tank held:

  a 6000 litres and 20 litres per minute for 100 minutes have run out of it through a tap

  b 6000 litres and d litres per minute for 100 minutes have run out of it through a tap

  c 6000 litres and d litres per minute for m minutes have run out of it through a tap

  d L litres and d litres per minute for m minutes have run out of it.

E   NUMBER PATTERNS AND RULES

Consider the pattern of matchstick triangles:

 , ... etc.

It starts with *one* triangle made from 3 matchsticks.

The second diagram has *two* triangles made from 5 matchsticks.

The third diagram has *three* triangles made from 7 matchsticks, and so on.

These results can be placed in a table:

Number of triangles (t)	1	2	3	4	5	....
Number of matchsticks (M)	3	5	7	9	11	....

$+2 \quad +2 \quad +2 \quad +2$

Notice that when $t = 1$, $M = 2 \times 1 + 1 = 3$

        when $t = 2$, $M = 2 \times 2 + 1 = 5$

        when $t = 3$, $M = 2 \times 3 + 1 = 7$

        when $t = 4$, $M = 2 \times 4 + 1 = 9$

        etc.

What part of the table shows the constant addition of 2?

Is this where the 2 of the number pattern comes from?

We see that $M = 2t + 1$ is the formula which allows us to find the number of matchsticks M for the figure made up of t triangles.

Example 7 🔊 **Self Tutor**

Consider this matchstick pattern:

∧ , ∧‿ , ∧‿‿∧ , ∧‿‿‿ , ...

  a Draw the next diagram.

  b Copy and complete the table:

Diagram number (n)	1	2	3	4	5
Number of matchsticks (M)	2	5			

  c Complete the sentence:

  As the diagram number increases by 1, the number of matchsticks needed ...... by ......

  d Find the rule that relates the diagram number (n) to the number of matchsticks (M).

  e Use the rule to find:

  i the number of matchsticks in the 10th diagram of the pattern

  ii which diagram number is made from 152 matchsticks.

a

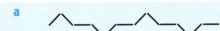

b

Diagram number (n)	1	2	3	4	5
Number of matchsticks (M)	2	5	8	11	14

+3   +3   +3   +3

c .... increases by 3.

d $M = 3n - 1$

e **i** If $n = 10$, $M = 3 \times 10 - 1 = 29$

So, 29 matchsticks are used in the 10th diagram.

ii If $M = 152$, $152 = 3n - 1$

$\therefore \quad 153 = 3n$ {adding 1 to both sides}

$\therefore \quad n = 51$ {dividing both sides by 3}

So, the 51st diagram is made from 152 matchsticks.

EXERCISE 6E

1 **a** Draw the *next two* diagrams in the pattern , ...

b Copy and complete this table:

Diagram number (n)	1	2	3	4	5	6
Number of squares (S)	1	3	5			

c Which of these possible rules fits the given pattern?

   i $S = 2n + 1$ **ii** $S = \dfrac{n+1}{2}$ **iii** $S = 2n - 1$

d Use the rule found in **c** to find the number of squares when:
   i $n = 11$ **ii** $n = 67$

2 A restaurant table seats 4 people.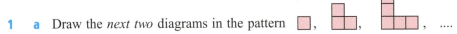

If two tables are pushed together, 6 people can be seated.

a How many people can be seated if:
   i three tables are used   **ii** four tables are used?

b Copy and complete this table:

Number of tables (n)	1	2	3	4	5	6
Number of people (P)	4	6				

c Write down the rule that connects P and n.

3 A weaving pattern can be made from crosses:

a Draw the next diagram in the pattern.

b Copy and complete:

Diagram number (n)	1	2	3	4	5	6
Number of crosses (C)	1	5	9			

c Find the rule which relates the diagram number n to the number of crosses C.

d Use the rule to find:

   i the number of crosses in the 10th diagram

   ii the diagram number which is made up from 97 crosses.

4 A pattern is formed by starting with a square, then adding another square each time as shown:

We will count the number of triangles shown in each diagram.

a Draw the next diagram in the pattern.

b Copy and complete:

Number of squares (n)	1	2	3	4
Number of triangles (t)	0	4		

c Find the rule which relates the number of squares n to the number of triangles t.

d Use the rule to find:

   i the number of triangles in a diagram made from 10 squares

   ii the number of squares needed to make a diagram which shows 56 triangles.

5 **a** Draw the *next two* diagrams in the matchstick pattern.

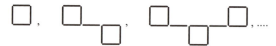

b Copy and complete:

Diagram number (n)	1	2	3	4	5
Number of matchsticks (M)	4	9			

c Find the rule which relates the diagram number n to number of matchsticks M.

d Use the rule to find:

   i the number of matchsticks used to make the 30th diagram

   ii the diagram number which uses 314 matchsticks.

F   THE VALUE OF AN EXPRESSION

In **Exercise 6D** we found algebraic expressions for many real world situations.

For example, the total cost of buying five apples at a cents each and three bananas at b cents each would be $5a + 3b$ cents.

If an apple cost 10 cents and a banana cost 15 cents, the total cost would be

$$5 \times 10 + 3 \times 15 = 50 + 45 = 95 \text{ cents.}$$

In this way we can **evaluate** (find the value of) the **expression** for particular **numerical** values of a and b. In this case we substitute $a = 10$ and $b = 15$.

To **evaluate** a mathematical expression we find its value for particular numerical substitutions of the pronumerals (unknowns).

For example,   when $a = -2$ and $b = -7$ then

$3a - b$

$= 3 \times (-2) - (-7)$ {replacing a by -2 and b by -7}

$= -6 + 7$

$= 1$

> You may find it useful to place substitutions inside brackets.

Example 8   ◀)) **Self Tutor**

For $a = 3$, $b = 2$ and $c = -4$, evaluate:

a $2a + 5b$

b $-2c^2$

a $2a + 5b$

$= 2 \times 3 \ + \ 5 \times 2$

$= 6 + 10$

$= 16$

b $-2c^2$

$= -2 \times (-4)^2$

$= -2 \times 16$

$= -32$

EXERCISE 6F

1 If $a = 4$, $b = 3$, $c = 6$,   and $d = 3$,   find the value of:

a $a + b$	**b** $2a$	**c** $a + 2b$	**d** $3c + d$
e $c - d$	**f** ab	**g** $3bc$	**h** $2c^2$
i $2(a + b)$	**j** $3(c - b)$	**k** $4a^2$	**l** $(4a)^2$

2 If $m = 5$, $n = 3$, $g = 8$,   and $h = 4$,   evaluate:

a $3m + n$	**b** $11 + 2h$	**c** $mn - g$	**d** $3n^2$
e $(3n)^2$	**f** $2h^3$	**g** $(2h)^3$	**h** $3m - 5n$
i $m^2 - 3m$	**j** $m(m - 3)$	**k** $2(g + h)$	**l** $2g + 2h$

3 If $p = 3$, $q = -2$, $r = -1$,   and $s = 2$,   evaluate:

a q^2	**b** q^3	**c** $p^2 q$	**d** qrs
e r^{11}	**f** $q^2 + s^2$	**g** $pq + rs$	**h** $p^2 + r^2 - 3$
i $p^2 - r^2$	**j** $(p - r)(p + r)$	**k** $p + q^2$	**l** $(p + q)^2$

Example 9   ◀)) Self Tutor

If $a = 2$, $b = -3$ and $c = -5$,   evaluate:

a $\dfrac{a - b}{c}$

b $\dfrac{a - c - b}{b - a}$

You should write all negative substitutions in brackets.

a $\dfrac{a - b}{c}$

$= \dfrac{2 - (-3)}{-5}$

$= \dfrac{2 + 3}{-5}$

$= \dfrac{5}{-5}$

$= -1$

b $\dfrac{a - c - b}{b - a}$

$= \dfrac{2 - (-5) - (-3)}{-3 - 2}$

$= \dfrac{2 + 5 + 3}{-3 - 2}$

$= \dfrac{10}{-5}$

$= -2$

4   If $a = 3$, $b = -2$, $c = 10$, $d = 7$, $e = -3$,   and $f = -5$,   find the value of:

a $\dfrac{c}{f}$

b $\dfrac{c}{b}$

c $\dfrac{a}{e}$

d $\dfrac{e - d}{f}$

e $\dfrac{a - b}{a + b}$

f $\dfrac{2c}{-b}$

g $\dfrac{-3b}{e}$

h $\dfrac{e - f}{b}$

i $\dfrac{c + f}{a - b}$

j $\dfrac{c - f}{-f}$

k $\dfrac{d - c}{e}$

l $\dfrac{5e - a}{b}$

5   For

m	n	p	q	r
2	-2	-5	1	-4

find the value of:

a $\dfrac{m}{n}$

b $\dfrac{p + q}{r}$

c $\dfrac{m + r}{q}$

d $\dfrac{p - q}{m}$

e $\dfrac{-5m}{n}$

f $\dfrac{2r}{n - m}$

g $\dfrac{m^2}{2n}$

h $\dfrac{m + n}{m - n}$

i $\dfrac{3m^2}{r}$

j $\dfrac{q^2 - p^2}{r}$

k $\dfrac{qr}{4}$

l $\dfrac{p - q}{-mq}$

INVESTIGATION   "TO BE OR NOT TO BE" EQUAL

Testing by substitution can help us find whether two different looking algebraic expressions are equal or not.

For example:

$2(x + 3)$ and $2x + 6$ are **equal expressions** because no matter what value of x is substituted, both expressions are equal for this value of x.

$2(x + 3)$ and $2x + 3$ cannot be equal, because for $x = 1$

$$2(x+3) \quad = 2(1+3) \qquad \text{whereas} \qquad 2x+3 \quad = 2 \times 1 + 3$$
$$= 2 \times 4 \qquad\qquad\qquad\qquad\qquad = 2 + 3$$
$$= 8 \qquad\qquad\qquad\qquad\qquad\qquad = 5$$

One **counter example** is sufficient to show that two expressions are not equal.

What to do:

Copy and complete the following table of values:

a	b	$a + \dfrac{b}{4}$	$\dfrac{a+b}{4}$	$\dfrac{a}{4} + b$	$\dfrac{a}{4} + \dfrac{b}{4}$
8	4				
3	5				
6	-2				

From the table, which of the four expressions are likely to be equal and which are definitely not equal?

6 **a** If $G = 3P - 7$, find G when $P = 8$.

   b If $M = 4x + 3$, find M when $x = 13$.

   c If $A = \frac{4}{3}d + 3$, find A when $d = 6$.

   d If $T = \dfrac{3g+2}{4}$, find T when $g = 14$.

   e If $S = \sqrt{2n+5}$, find S when $n = 10$.

   f If $P = 2a + 2b$, find P when $a = 9$ and $b = 13$.

   g If $M = \sqrt{a^2 + b^2}$, find M when $a = 4$ and $b = 3$.

7 When visiting the USA last year, Jacob noticed that the forecast temperatures for the next day were given in $^\circ$F rather than in $^\circ$C.

His travel documents gave the formula $C = \dfrac{5F - 160}{9}$ to convert $^\circ$F into $^\circ$C.

What are the $^\circ$C temperatures when the forecast temperatures are:

   a 38°F **b** 65°F **c** 100°F?

8 The depth of a well can be measured using the formula $d = 4.9t^2$ metres where t is the time (in seconds) it takes for a stone to hit the bottom.

   a How deep is a well if it takes a stone 3.6 seconds to hit the bottom?

   b How high is a cliff if it takes a stone 7.2 seconds to reach the sea below?

9 The formula $D = 3.56\sqrt{h}$ gives the approximate distance (D km) to the horizon which can be seen by a person with eye level h metres above the level of the sea. Find the distance to the horizon when a person's eye level is:

   a 5 m above sea level **b** 20 m above sea level.

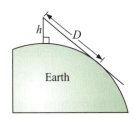

10 The total surface area of a rectangular prism can be found using the formula $S = 2(ab + bc + ac)$.

Find the total surface area of these rectangular prisms:

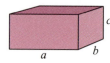

a

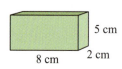

5 cm

8 cm   2 cm

b

4 cm

2 cm

11 If the three sides of a triangle are a, b and c units long we can find the area of the triangle by first finding $s = \dfrac{a + b + c}{2}$ and then using

Heron's formula $A = \sqrt{s(s - a)(s - b)(s - c)}$

a Find the area of

5 cm   3 cm

4 cm

using area $= \frac{1}{2} \times$ base $\times$ height.

b Use Heron's formula to find the area of the triangle in **a**.

c Use Heron's formula to find the area of the triangle with sides 5 cm, 6 cm and 7 cm.

d A triangular paddock has sides 213 m, 318 m and 271 m. Find its area using Heron's formula.

REVIEW SET 6A

1 Write expressions for:

   a the sum of a and b **b** the product of c and d

   c the mean of x and y **d** the difference between m and n if $m < n$

2 What number is:

   a 5 less than b **b** 5 more than a?

3 Find the total cost of:

   a x oranges at 40 cents each   **b** n books at €b each

4 **a** Jason has £50 and buys five items costing £n each. How much has he left?

   b Chong walks for h hours at an average speed of 5 km h^{-1}. How far does he walk?

5 Complete the following:

   a Two numbers have a sum of 11. If one of them is a then the other is ......

   b If x is the smaller of two consecutive *odd* integers, the other integer is ......

6 Find the total value of y \$1 coins and $(7 - y)$ \$2 coins.

7 Write a formula for the cost, C dollars, of delivering a parcel if the courier charges:

    a $4 plus $1 per kilogram given the parcel weighs 5 kg

    b $4 plus $1 per kilogram given the parcel weighs k kg

    c $F plus $1 per kilogram given the parcel weighs k kg

    d $F plus $d per kilogram given the parcel weighs k kg

8   ⬚, ⬚⬚, ⬚⬚⬚, ... is a matchstick pattern.

     (1)   (2)   (3)

    a Draw the fourth diagram.

    b Complete the table:

Diagram number (n)	1	2	3	4	5
Matches needed (M)	5	8			

    c Find the rule connecting M and n.

    d Use the rule to find the number of matches needed to make the 12th diagram.

9 If $a = 5$, $b = 6$, $c = 2$ and $d = -4$, find the value of:

    a $3a - 2b$ **b** $3d^2$ **c** $\dfrac{3d}{b - c}$

10   **a** If $C = 1250 + 3x$, find C when $x = 100$.

     b If $A = \sqrt{x - 2y}$, find A when $x = 15$ and $y = 3$.

11   **a** If $P = 4x + 3y$, find x when $P = 38$ and $y = 6$.

     b If $S = 2.6r + 1.4s$, find s when $S = 31.08$ and $r = 10.5$

REVIEW SET 6B

1 Write algebraic expressions for:

    a 8 less than t **b** the product of p and $2q$

    c the sum of the square of x and 6   **d** the square of the sum of x and 6

2   **a** List 3 consecutive numbers if a is the smallest of them.

     b If two numbers differ by 4 and b is the larger number, what is the smaller number?

3 Write as an algebraic expression:

    a the square of a number   **b** 1 more than half a number

    c 3 less than double a number   **d** double the sum of a number and 5

4 Henri has $20.

    a How much would he have if he spent: **i** $6   **ii** x?

    b How much would he have if he was given: **i** $10   **ii** y?

5 Hannah is x years old and her sister Rachel is 2 years older.

    a How old is Rachel now?

    b Give **i** Hannah's age in 3 years' time   **ii** Rachel's age last year.

6 Find the total mass of x books weighing 2 kg each and twice that number of books weighing 3 kg each.

7 Write a formula for the charge, C dollars, made by an electrician:

   a who charges a call-out fee of $50 plus $60 for each hour spent, if his work takes $1\frac{1}{2}$ hours

   b who charges a call-out fee of D plus x for each hour spent, if his work takes t hours.

8 |_ , □⌐ , □□|_ , ...   is a matchstick pattern.

   a Draw the 4th diagram.

   b Copy and complete the table:

Diagram number (n)	1	2	3	4	5
Matches needed (M)	2	5			

   c Find the rule connecting M and n.

   d Use the rule to find:

   i the number of matches needed to make the 20th diagram

   ii the diagram number which uses 122 matches.

9 If $a = -1$, $b = 2$, $c = -3$ and $d = 4$, find the value of:

   a $8a - c$ **b** $2c^3$ **c** $\dfrac{8b - d}{a + c}$

10 **a** The length of the diagonal in the rectangular prism shown is given by $L = \sqrt{a^2 + b^2 + c^2}$.

   Find the length of the diagonal if $a = 2$ cm, $b = 6$ cm and $c = 9$ cm.

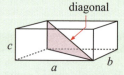

diagonal

   b The surface area of the prism is given by $A = 2ab + 2bc + 2ac$.

   Find c if $a = 5$ cm, $b = 7$ cm, and the surface area is 310 cm^2.

Chapter **7**

Length and area

Contents:

A Perimeter and length
B Area
C Surface area
D Problem solving

OPENING PROBLEM

A grain silo consists of a concrete cylinder with a conical roof. The entire outside of the silo is to be painted white. The paint costs €70 for each 10 litre can, and each litre covers an area of 12 square metres.

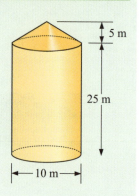

- What must you calculate in order to find the number of cans of paint needed to give the silo two coats of paint?

- How much would the paint cost?

- What other costs would have to be considered to complete the project?

A   PERIMETER AND LENGTH

The **perimeter** of a figure is the measurement of the distance around its boundary.

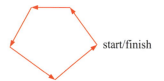

start/finish

One way of thinking about perimeter is to imagine walking around a property. Start at one corner and walk around the boundary. When you arrive back at your starting point the **perimeter** is the distance you have walked.

For a **polygon**, the perimeter is obtained by adding the lengths of all sides.

For a **circle**, the perimeter has a special name, the **circumference**.

DEMO

Following is a summary of some **perimeter formulae**:

Shape	Formula	Shape	Formula
square	$P = 4l$	rectangle	$P = 2l + 2w$ or $P = 2(l + w)$
polygon	$P = a + b + c + d + e$	circle	$C = \pi d$ or $C = 2\pi r$

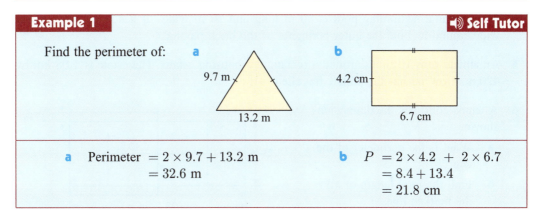

Example 1   ◀) **Self Tutor**

Find the perimeter of: **a**   **b**

9.7 m   4.2 cm

13.2 m   6.7 cm

    a   Perimeter $= 2 \times 9.7 + 13.2$ m   **b** $P = 2 \times 4.2 + 2 \times 6.7$
                   $= 32.6$ m $= 8.4 + 13.4$
                                                             $= 21.8$ cm

EXERCISE 7A

1   Measure with your ruler the lengths of the sides of each given figure and then find its perimeter.

   a   **b**   **c**

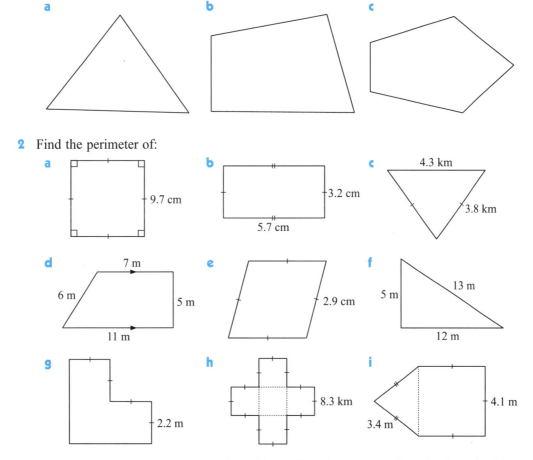

2   Find the perimeter of:

   a   **b**   **c**   4.3 km

          9.7 cm   3.2 cm   3.8 km
                        5.7 cm

   d   7 m   **e**   **f**
    6 m   13 m
           5 m   2.9 cm   5 m
      11 m   12 m

   g   **h**   **i**
                             8.3 km   4.1 m
          2.2 m   3.4 m

3   An equilateral triangular paddock has sides of length 450 m. It is to be fenced with 3 strands of wire where the wire costs $0.28 per metre. Find:

   a   the perimeter of the paddock   **b**   the total length of wire needed
   c   the total cost of the wire.

4 A rectangular swimming pool is 50 m long and 20 m wide. It has brick paving 3 m wide around it. Find the outer perimeter of the brick paving.

5 An athlete runs 10 times around a rectangular housing estate. The estate is 1.08 km by 420 m. How far has the athlete travelled?

6 A tennis court has the dimensions shown.

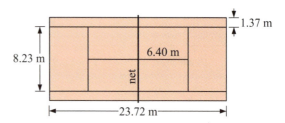

- **a** What is the perimeter of the court?
- **b** Find the total length of all the marked lines.

Example 2   ◀️)) Self Tutor

Find, to 2 decimal places, the circumference of a circle of:
- **a** diameter 13.8 m
- **b** radius 3.7 km

a $C = \pi d$	**b** $C = 2\pi r$
$\quad = \pi \times 13.8$	$\quad = 2 \times \pi \times 3.7$
$\quad \approx 43.35$ m	$\quad \approx 23.25$ km

---

7 Find, to 2 decimal places, the circumference of a circle of:
- **a** diameter 13.2 cm
- **b** radius 8.6 m
- **c** diameter 115 m

8 Find, to 3 decimal places, the circumference of a circle of:
- **a** radius 0.85 km
- **b** diameter 7.2 m
- **c** radius 235 cm

Example 3   ◀️)) Self Tutor

Find, correct to 1 decimal place, the perimeter of:

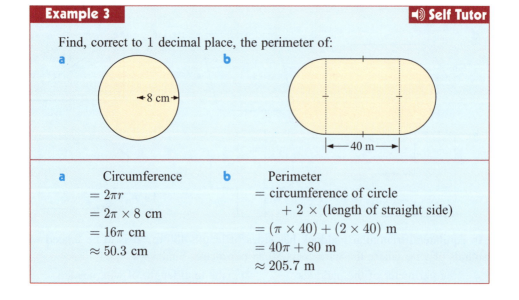

a Circumference	**b** Perimeter
$= 2\pi r$	$=$ circumference of circle
$= 2\pi \times 8$ cm	$\quad + \ 2 \times$ (length of straight side)
$= 16\pi$ cm	$= (\pi \times 40) + (2 \times 40)$ m
≈ 50.3 cm	$= 40\pi + 80$ m
	≈ 205.7 m

9 Find, correct to 1 decimal place, the perimeter of:

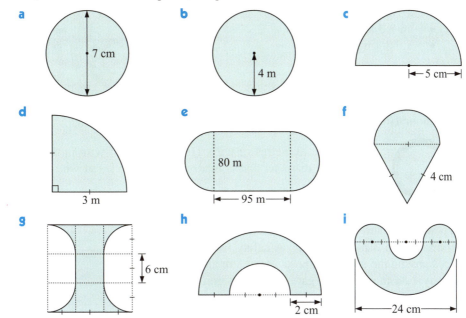

a   7 cm

b   4 m

c   5 cm

d   3 m

e   80 m   95 m

f   4 cm

g   6 cm

h   2 cm

i   24 cm

10 Katy's landscape gardening business makes odd shaped lawns which usually include semi-circles. Find the length of the edging material needed to border these lawn designs:

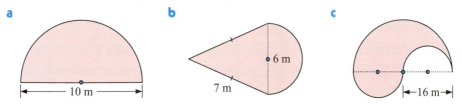

a   10 m

b   6 m   7 m

c   16 m

11 A housing block is 40 m by 16 m and can be fenced for $18.75 per metre. Find the cost of the fence.

12 You have recently purchased an industrial block of land which is 120 m long and 90 m wide. You decide to use fence panels which are 1.2 m wide to enclose your property. The gate is also made of two of these panels.

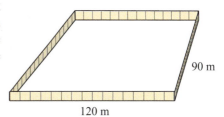

90 m

120 m

   a Find the total perimeter of the block.
   b Find the number of panels required.
   c If each panel costs $12.25, find the cost of the panelling for the fence.

13 The local council needs to build a retaining wall along a 1.5 km long embankment on the high side of a road.

The wall is to be made of old railway sleepers and is three sleepers high.

   a What total length of sleepers is required?
   b If each sleeper weighs (on average) 63 kg and is 2.5 m long, how many tonnes of sleepers are needed?
   c If a truck can carry 15 tonnes of sleepers, how many truckloads are needed?

14 A triathlon course has 3 stages:

- a 1.2 km swim
- an 8.3 km bicycle ride
- a 6.3 km run.

Find:

a the total distance around the course

b the average speed of a contestant who took 1 hour 10 minutes to complete the course.

15 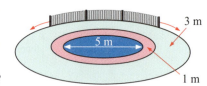 Al needs 30 metres of wire. He has a coil of wire in the shed. It is 35 cm in diameter and is made up of 29 circles of wire. Will this be enough?

16 At Bushby Park there is a 5 m diameter circular pond which is surrounded by a 1 m wide garden bed and then a 3 m wide lawn. A safety fence is placed around the lawn with posts every 3 m and a gateway 1.84 m wide. The gate is wrought iron.

a How many metres of safety fence are needed?

b How many posts are needed?

c If the posts cost \$15.75 and the safety fence costs \$18.35 per metre, calculate the total cost of the fence (excluding the gate).

17 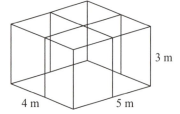 Vincenzo grows vines on a trellis made from 4 strands of wire, as shown. He has 12 rows of trellis, each 150 metres long, and he allows an extra 1 metre of wire for each length for tying. Find the total cost of the wire required given that single strand wire costs 11.8 pence per metre.

18 Find the total length of ribbon used to tie a box as illustrated. 25 cm extra is required for the knot and bow.

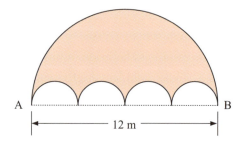

12 cm

16 cm

25 cm

19 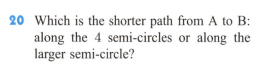 Steel framing for a house extension costs \$8.85 per metre. Find the total cost of the steel necessary to make the framing of the extension illustrated.

3 m

4 m   5 m

20 Which is the shorter path from A to B: along the 4 semi-circles or along the larger semi-circle?

A ⋯⋯⋯⋯ B

12 m

B **AREA**

All around us we see surfaces such as walls, ceilings, paths and ovals. All of these surfaces have boundaries that help to define the surface.

An **area** is the amount of *surface* within specified boundaries.

The **area** of the surface of a closed figure is measured in terms of the number of square units it encloses.

AREA FORMULAE

The following area formulae have been used previously:

RECTANGLES

width

length

Area = length × width

TRIANGLES

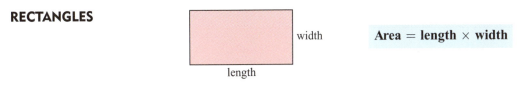

height

base   base   base

COMPUTER DEMO

$$\textbf{Area} = \tfrac{1}{2} \textbf{ (base × height)}$$

PARALLELOGRAMS

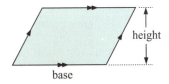

height

base

Area = base × height

COMPUTER DEMO

TRAPEZIA

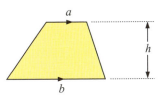

a

h

b

$$\textbf{Area} = \left[\begin{array}{c} \textbf{The average of the lengths} \\ \textbf{of the two parallel sides} \end{array} \right] \times \left[\begin{array}{c} \textbf{the distance between} \\ \textbf{the parallel sides} \end{array} \right]$$

i.e., $A = \left(\dfrac{a+b}{2} \right) \times h$ or $A = \tfrac{1}{2}(a+b) \times h$

COMPUTER DEMO

Example 4   ◀)) **Self Tutor**

Find the area of:

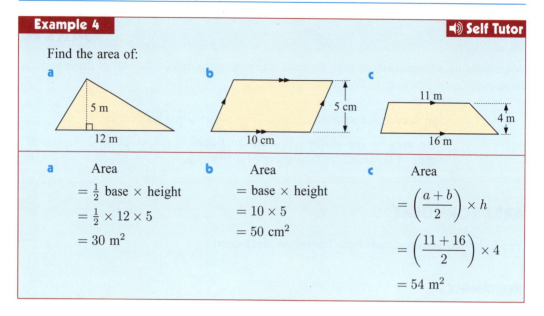

a	Area	**b**	Area	**c**	Area
	$= \frac{1}{2}$ base $\times$ height		$=$ base $\times$ height		$= \left(\dfrac{a+b}{2}\right) \times h$
	$= \frac{1}{2} \times 12 \times 5$		$= 10 \times 5$		
	$= 30 \text{ m}^2$		$= 50 \text{ cm}^2$		$= \left(\dfrac{11+16}{2}\right) \times 4$
					$= 54 \text{ m}^2$

EXERCISE 7B

1 Find the area of the shaded region:

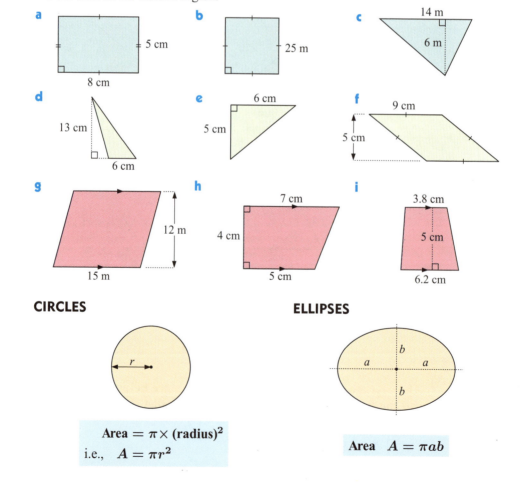

CIRCLES

Area $= \pi \times$ (radius)^2

i.e., $A = \pi r^2$

ELLIPSES

Area $A = \pi ab$

Example 5   ◀ﻪ) **Self Tutor**

Find, to 1 decimal place, the shaded area:

a 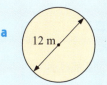 12 m

b 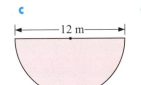 10 m 16 m

a	Area $= \pi r^2$	**b**	Area $= \pi ab$
	$= \pi \times 6^2$		$= \pi \times 8 \times 5$
	$= 36\pi$		$= 40\pi$
	≈ 113.1 m^2		≈ 125.7 m^2

2 Find the area shaded:

a 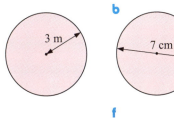 3 m   **b** 7 cm   **c** 12 m   **d** 4 cm

e 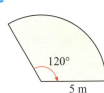 120° 5 m   **f** 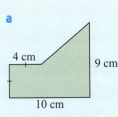 6 cm 11 cm   **g** 36° 9.8 cm   **h** 3.5 m 5.7 m quarter ellipse

Example 6   ◀ﻪ) **Self Tutor**

Find the green shaded area:

a 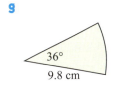 4 cm 9 cm 10 cm

b 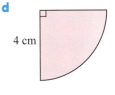 2 m 4 m 6 m 12 m

a We divide the figure into a rectangle and a triangle as shown alongside:

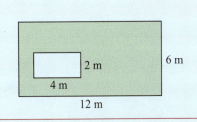
4 cm 4 cm 5 cm 6 cm 4 cm 10 cm

Area $=$ area of rectangle $+$ area of triangle
$= 10 \times 4 + \frac{1}{2} \times 6 \times 5$
$= 40 + 15$
$= 55$ cm^2

b Area $=$ area large rectangle $-$ area small rectangle
$= 12 \times 6 - 4 \times 2$ m^2
$= 64$ m^2

3 Find the area shaded:

a
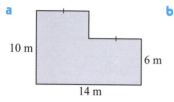
10 m

14 m

6 m

b
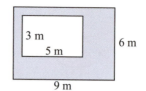
3 m

5 m

6 m

9 m

c
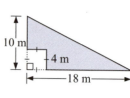
10 m

4 m

18 m

d
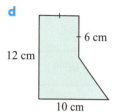
6 cm

12 cm

10 cm

e
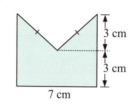
3 cm

3 cm

7 cm

f
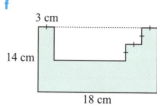
3 cm

14 cm

18 cm

Example 7   ◀) Self Tutor

Find, correct to 1 decimal place, the pink shaded area:

a
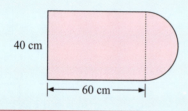
40 cm

60 cm

b
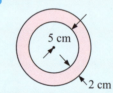
5 cm

2 cm

a   Area = area of rectangle + area of semi-circle
$$= 40 \times 60 + \tfrac{1}{2} \times (\pi \times 20^2) \qquad \{\text{area of circle} = \pi r^2\}$$
$$\approx 3028.3 \text{ cm}^2$$

b   Area = area large circle − area small circle
$$= \pi \times 7^2 - \pi \times 5^2$$
$$\approx 75.4 \text{ cm}^2$$

---

4 Find the area of the shaded regions, giving your answers correct to 2 decimal places:

a
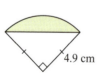
4.9 cm

b
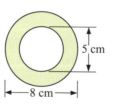
5 cm

8 cm

c
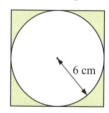
6 cm

d
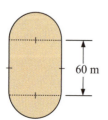
60 m

e
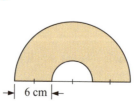
6 cm

f
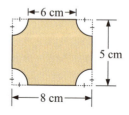
6 cm

5 cm

8 cm

Example 8

🔊 **Self Tutor**

A farmer wishes to seed and fertilise a 1200 m by 750 m paddock.
If it costs \$35.80 per hectare, how much will it cost altogether?

Area of paddock $= $ length $\times$ width
$$= 1200 \times 750 \text{ m}^2$$
$$= \frac{1200 \times 750}{10\,000} \text{ ha}$$
$$= 90 \text{ ha}$$

$\therefore$ total cost $= 90 \times \$35.80$
$$= \$3222.00$$

5

A farmer wishes to spread 150 kg of superphosphate per hectare.

What amount of superphosphate is required to fertilise a 550 m by 300 m paddock?

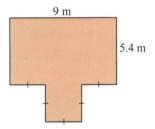

9 m

5.4 m

6 The diagram shows the dimensions of a courtyard. It is to be paved with 60 cm square tiles. How many tiles would be needed?

7 A square tile has an area of 256 cm^2. How many tiles are needed for a floor 4 m $\times$ 2.4 m?

8 A gravel path 1 m wide is placed around a circular garden bed of diameter 2 m. Find the area of the path.

9

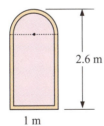

2.6 m

1 m

A door with dimensions as shown has a timber frame 10 cm wide surrounding a glass panel. Find the area of the glass panel.

10 A rectangle is 15 cm by 9 cm. If the length of the rectangle is increased by 3 cm, by how much must the width be changed so that the area remains the same?

LINKS
click here

ESTIMATING AREAS

Areas of interaction:
Approaches to learning/Human ingenuity

INVESTIGATION 1   MAXIMUM AREA BY SPREADSHEET

The following spreadsheet is used to examine the area of a rectangle with a perimeter of 20 cm. The length l and width w may vary.

We notice that

$$2l + 2w = \text{perimeter} = 20$$
$$\therefore \quad l + w = 10$$
$$\therefore \quad w = 10 - l$$

SPREADSHEET

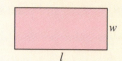

What to do:

1 On a new spreadsheet, enter the information as shown. Use the **fill down** command to complete it to the row where the length is 10 cm.

2 Describe what happens to the width and area as the length increases.

3 Use the **charting** facility to draw a graph of *length* vs *area* as shown alongside.

4 What length gives the largest possible area?

5 What shape is the rectangle when the area is a maximum?

6 Alter the spreadsheet to examine rectangles of perimeter 30 cm. Use smaller changes in length, for example 0.5 cm instead of 1 cm. What is the maximum area now, and what shape is the rectangle?

7 Can you draw any conclusions from your observations?

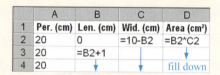

	A	B	C	D
1	Per. (cm)	Len. (cm)	Wid. (cm)	Area (cm²)
2	20	0	=10-B2	=B2*C2
3	20	=B2+1		
4	20			fill down

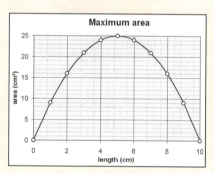

INVESTIGATION 2   SAM THE SHEEP

When Sam the sheep was tethered to a pole P on the back lawn, he was restricted to eating the grass within a circular region as shown:

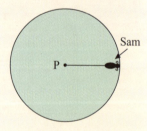

What to do:

1 For the following situations, draw scale diagrams with a scale of 1 cm representing 1 m that show the exact region from which Sam may feed. The rope is 3 m long in each case. You *must* use a 'compass' and a ruler.

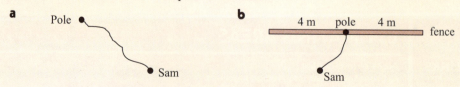

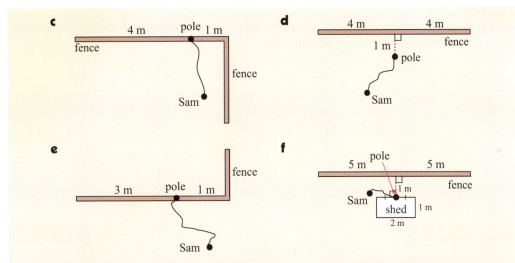

2 For each of the six situations above, use your scale diagram to calculate the area of grass that Sam can feed on. Use appropriate area formulae.

C   SURFACE AREA

SOLIDS WITH PLANE FACES

The **surface area** of a three-dimensional figure with plane faces is the sum of the areas of the faces.

It is often helpful to draw the **net** of a solid before calculating the total surface area.

A net is formed by unfolding the surfaces of the solid to form a two-dimensional figure.

Software that demonstrates **nets** can be found at http://www.peda.com/poly/

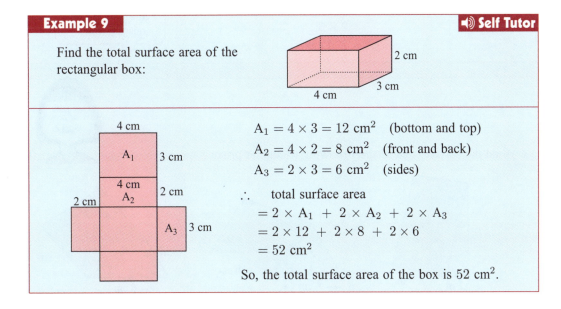

Example 9   ◀)) **Self Tutor**

Find the total surface area of the rectangular box:

$A_1 = 4 \times 3 = 12$ cm^2 (bottom and top)

$A_2 = 4 \times 2 = 8$ cm^2 (front and back)

$A_3 = 2 \times 3 = 6$ cm^2 (sides)

∴   total surface area

$= 2 \times A_1 + 2 \times A_2 + 2 \times A_3$

$= 2 \times 12 + 2 \times 8 + 2 \times 6$

$= 52$ cm^2

So, the total surface area of the box is 52 cm^2.

EXERCISE 7C

1 Find the surface area of a cube with sides:

   a   3 cm   **b**   4.5 cm   **c**   9.8 mm

2 Find the surface area of the following rectangular prisms:

   a   **b**   **c**

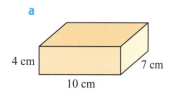

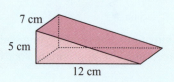

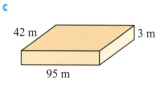

Example 10   🔊 **Self Tutor**

What is the total surface area of this wedge?

(wedge diagram: 7 cm, 5 cm, 12 cm)

We draw a net of the solid:

We next find h using Pythagoras:
$$h^2 = 12^2 + 5^2$$
$$\therefore \ \ h^2 = 169$$
$$\therefore \ \ h = \sqrt{169} = 13 \quad \{\text{as} \ \ h > 0\}$$

Now, $A_1 = \tfrac{1}{2}bh$ $A_2 = 7 \times 5$ $A_3 = 12 \times 7$ $A_4 = 13 \times 7$

           $= \tfrac{1}{2} \times 12 \times 5$ $= 35 \text{ cm}^2$ $= 84 \text{ cm}^2$ $= 91 \text{ cm}^2$

           $= 30 \text{ cm}^2$

$\therefore$ total surface area $= 2 \times A_1 + A_2 + A_3 + A_4$
                        $= 2 \times 30 + 35 + 84 + 91$
                        $= 270 \text{ cm}^2$

> Sometimes we need to use the Rule of Pythagoras to find a missing length.

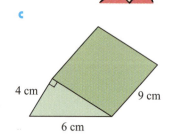

3 Find the surface area of the following triangular prisms:

   a   **b**   **c**

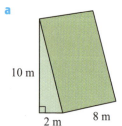

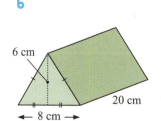

4 Find the surface area of the following prisms:

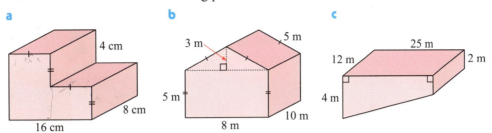

a

b

c

Example 11   ◀) **Self Tutor**

Find the cost of erecting a 6 m by 4 m rectangular garden shed that is 2 m high if the metal sheeting costs $15 per square metre.

The shed: Net:

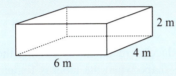

$A_1 = 6 \times 4$ $A_2 = 4 \times 2$ $A_3 = 6 \times 2$

$\quad = 24 \text{ m}^2$ $\quad = 8 \text{ m}^2$ $\quad = 12 \text{ m}^2$

$\therefore$ total surface area $= A_1 + 2 \times A_2 + 2 \times A_3$

$\quad\quad\quad\quad\quad\quad\quad\quad\quad = 24 + 2 \times 8 + 2 \times 12$

$\quad\quad\quad\quad\quad\quad\quad\quad\quad = 64 \text{ m}^2$

$\therefore$ cost $= 64 \times \$15$

$\quad\quad\quad = \$960$

---

5 Find the cost of painting the outside of a rectangular garage 6 m by 3 m by 3 m high if 1 litre of paint costs €9.65 and each litre covers 4 square metres. Assume that the paint can only be bought in whole litres.

6 A marquee with the dimensions as shown is made from canvas. Find the total cost of the canvas if it costs $21.50 per square metre.

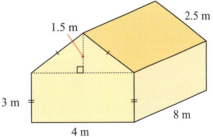

7

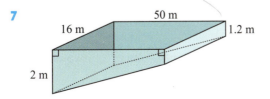

The base and walls of the swimming pool shown are to be tiled.

Determine the total area of tiles required.

SOLIDS WITH CURVED SURFACES

We will consider the outer surface area of two types of object with curved surfaces. These are **cylinders** and **spheres**.

CYLINDERS

Consider the cylinder shown alongside. If the cylinder is cut, opened out and flattened onto a plane, it takes the shape of a rectangle.

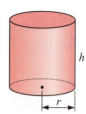

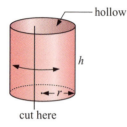

cut here

open out

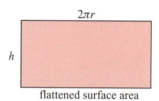

flattened surface area

Note: • You can verify that the curved surface produces a rectangle by peeling the label off a cylindrical can and noticing the shape when the label is flattened.

• The length of the rectangle is the same as the circumference of the cylinder.

So, for a hollow cylinder, the outer surface area A = area of rectangle

$$\therefore \quad A = \text{length} \times \text{width}$$
$$\therefore \quad A = 2\pi r \times h$$
$$\therefore \quad A = 2\pi rh$$

Object	Figure	Outer surface area
Hollow cylinder	hollow / h / r / hollow	$A = 2\pi rh$ (no ends)
Hollow can	hollow / h / r / solid	$A = 2\pi rh + \pi r^2$ (one end)
Solid cylinder	solid / h / r / solid	$A = 2\pi rh + 2\pi r^2$ (two ends)

Example 12

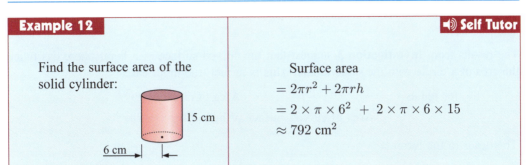

Find the surface area of the solid cylinder:

15 cm

6 cm

Surface area
$$= 2\pi r^2 + 2\pi rh$$
$$= 2 \times \pi \times 6^2 + 2 \times \pi \times 6 \times 15$$
$$\approx 792 \text{ cm}^2$$

8 Find the outer surface area of the following:

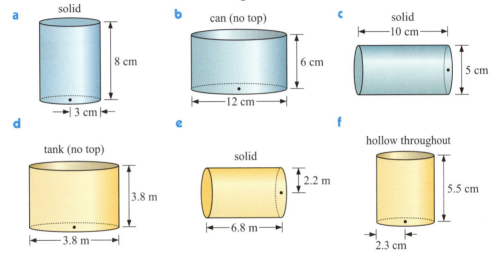

a solid

8 cm

3 cm

b can (no top)

6 cm

12 cm

c solid

10 cm

5 cm

d tank (no top)

3.8 m

3.8 m

e solid

2.2 m

6.8 m

f hollow throughout

5.5 cm

2.3 cm

INVESTIGATION 3   SURFACE AREA OF A SPHERE

You will need:

a solid sphere (e.g., orange or foam ball), cord, nail, scissors.

What to do:

1 Take your model of a sphere and cut it exactly in half to obtain two hemispheres.

2 Insert a nail in the centre of the flat circular surface of one hemisphere and wind a length of cord around the nail in a spiral until the flat surface is completely covered. Cut the length of cord required and put aside.

3 Now insert the nail in the centre of the curved surface of the hemisphere. Wind cord around the nail until the curved surface of the hemisphere is completely covered.

4 Compare the lengths of the cord in both cases. As measured by the cord, is the area of the curved surface twice the area of the flat circular surface?

SPHERES

The results from **Investigation 3** suggest that the curved surface of a hemisphere has twice the area of a circle with the same radius. This is in fact true in all cases.

So, for radius r :

$$\text{Area of circle} = \pi r^2$$
$$\text{Area of curved surface of hemisphere} = 2\pi r^2$$

This leads to the formula:

Surface area of a sphere, $A = 4\pi r^2$

Note: The mathematics required to prove this formula is beyond the scope of this course.

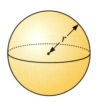

Example 13   ◀)) **Self Tutor**

Calculate the surface area of the sphere:

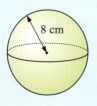

8 cm

Surface area
$= 4\pi r^2$
$= 4 \times \pi \times 8^2 \text{ cm}^2$
$\approx 804 \text{ cm}^2$

---

9 Find the total surface area of the following:

a
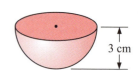
20 cm

b
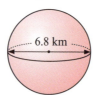
6.8 km

c
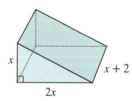
3 cm

10 Find a formula for the surface area A, in terms of x, for the following solids:

a
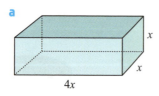
x
x
$4x$

b
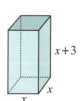
$x+3$
x
x

c

x
$x+2$
$2x$

d
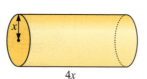
x
$4x$

e
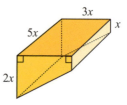
$2x+1$
$2x$

f

$3x$
x
$5x$
$2x$

D ## PROBLEM SOLVING

To solve the problems in this section you will need to select and apply the appropriate formulae from any of the previous sections.

There are simple **steps** to follow when **solving problems**:

- Read the question carefully.
- Draw a diagram with the information clearly marked on it.
- Label the unknowns.
- Choose the correct formula or formulae.
- Work step by step through the problem, making sure the units are correct.
- Answer the original question in words.

Example 14 ◀) Self Tutor

The Highways Department orders 25 road signs that warn motorists to watch out for moose along a 10 km stretch of road.

a What area of metal sheeting (in m^2) is required for the 25 signs?

b How far apart should the signs be placed if they are to be equally spaced?

a

$$\text{Area} = \tfrac{1}{2} b \times h$$
$$= \tfrac{1}{2} \times 1.16 \times 1 \qquad (116 \text{ cm} = 1.16 \text{ m})$$
$$= 0.58 \text{ m}^2$$

$\therefore$ total area $= 25 \times 0.58 \text{ m}^2 = 14.5 \text{ m}^2$

$\therefore$ 14.5 m^2 of metal sheeting is required.

b 25 signs need to cover 10 km $\therefore$ spacing $= 10 \text{ km} \div 25$
$$= 0.4 \text{ km}$$
$$= 400 \text{ m}$$

$\therefore$ the signs should be placed 400 m apart.

EXERCISE 7D

1 6 identical metal discs are stamped out of an 18 cm by 12 cm sheet of copper as illustrated. What percentage of the copper is wasted?

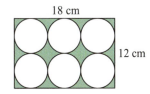

2 A rectangular lawn 12 m by 4 m is surrounded by a concrete path which is 1.5 m wide. Find the area of the path.

3 A 15 cm by 20 cm rectangle has the same perimeter as a square. Which figure has the greater area? By how much?

4 A table-top is shaped as illustrated. A cloth to protect the table-top from stains and heat is cut exactly the same size as the table-top. It is made from fabric 1.6 m wide and costs $18.40 per metre of length.

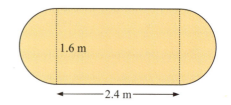

  a What length of fabric must be purchased?

  b Calculate the cost of the fabric.

  c Find the area of the cloth.

  d Calculate the amount of fabric that is wasted.

5 How many spherical balls of diameter 13 cm can be covered by 20 square metres of material?

Example 15   ◄)) Self Tutor

Jane is painting cylindrical tin cans of height 12 cm and diameter 8 cm. If she has enough paint to cover an area of 5 square metres, how many cans is she able to paint including the top and the bottom?

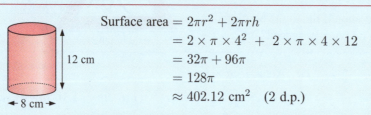

We need to convert m² to cm².

$$\text{Surface area} = 2\pi r^2 + 2\pi rh$$
$$= 2 \times \pi \times 4^2 + 2 \times \pi \times 4 \times 12$$
$$= 32\pi + 96\pi$$
$$= 128\pi$$
$$\approx 402.12 \text{ cm}^2 \quad \text{(2 d.p.)}$$

$\therefore$ the number of cans $= 5 \text{ m}^2 \div 402.12 \text{ cm}^2$
$$= (5 \times 100^2) \text{ cm}^2 \div 402.12 \text{ cm}^2$$
$$= 50\,000 \text{ cm}^2 \div 402.12 \text{ cm}^2$$
$$\approx 124.34$$

$\therefore$ 124 cans could be painted.

---

6 **a** Determine how much paint is required to paint the outside of a cylindrical tank 6 m long with diameter 8 m if each litre of paint covers 12 square metres.

  b If the paint is bought in 5 litre cans costing $82.70 each, find the cost of the paint.

7 Which has the greater surface area: a cylinder of length 17 cm and radius 9 cm or a sphere of radius 13 cm?

8 We commonly use a sphere to model the Earth although it is not a *perfect* sphere. The Earth has a radius of approximately 6400 km.

  a Use the formula for the surface area of a sphere to find the approximate surface area of the Earth.

  b 71% of the Earth's surface is covered by water. Find the area covered by water.

REVIEW SET 7A

1 Find the perimeter of:

a
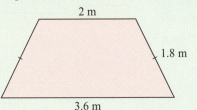

b
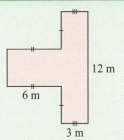

2 A rectangular bathroom measuring 3 m by 2 m is to be decorated on all walls with a single row of patterned tiles. There is a doorway measuring 90 cm wide. Find:

  a the total length of patterned tiles required

  b the total cost if each patterned tile is 15 cm long and costs \$5.

3 Find the circumference of a circle with diameter 3 cm, correct to 2 decimal places.

4 Find the perimeter of:

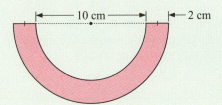

5 Find the area of:

a
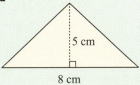

b
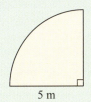

c
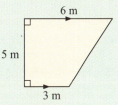

6 A circular area within a square courtyard will be paved, and the remainder will be landscaped, as shown alongside.

  a Find the area to be paved.

  b Find the cost of paving at \$28 per square metre.

  c Find the area to be landscaped.

7 Find the surface area of the following solids:

a
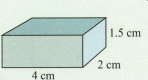

b
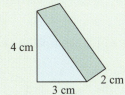

c
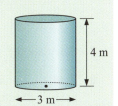

8 Using the formula $A = 4\pi r^2$, calculate the area of a sphere of radius 3 cm to 3 significant figures.

REVIEW SET 7B

1 New guttering is to be installed around the perimeter of the house with floorplan shown.

    a What is the total perimeter of the house?

    b If the guttering costs $30 per metre installed, find the total cost.

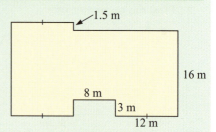

2 Competitors in a mountain-biking race complete four laps of an 8.5 km circuit. If the winning time is 1 h 33 min, find the average speed of the winner.

3 A security-conscious man builds himself a round fort of radius 50 m. He surrounds it with a moat 3 m wide. A large dog patrols on the other side of the moat to deter anyone who may attempt to cross the moat. The dog makes 15 complete circuits of the moat every day. How far in km does the dog walk every day? Answer correct to 1 decimal place.

4 Find the area of:

    a   **b**   **c**

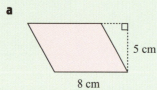 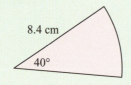 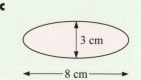

5 Find the shaded area correct to 2 decimal places.

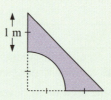

6 **a** For the building shown find the surface area of:

        i all vertical walls

        ii the flat roof section

        iii the sloping roof sections.

    b Find the number of litres of paint needed to paint the walls if each litre covers 5 square metres.

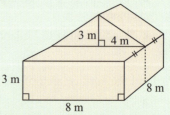

7 Calculate the surface area of a hemisphere of radius 4 cm.

8 Find a formula for the surface area A, in terms of x, of the following solids:

    a   **b**

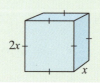 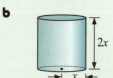

Chapter **8**

Decimals and percentage

Contents:

A   Decimal numbers
B   Percentage
C   Working with percentages
D   Unitary method in percentage
E   Percentage increase and decrease
F   Scientific notation (Standard form)

OPENING PROBLEM

Asif bought a car for $7500. He repaired and refitted the car and then repainted it. This work cost $2700. Asif then sold the car for $13 800.

- What were Asif's total costs?
- What profit did he make?
- What was his percentage profit on selling the car?

A   DECIMAL NUMBERS

The number 4.63 is a quick way of writing $4 + \frac{6}{10} + \frac{3}{100}$,

which can also be written as an **improper fraction** $\frac{463}{100}$ or as a **mixed number** $4\frac{63}{100}$.

Likewise, 14.062 is the quick way of writing $14 + \frac{6}{100} + \frac{2}{1000}$.

Numbers such as 4.63 and 14.062 are commonly called **decimal numbers**.

Example 1   ◀) Self Tutor

a   Write 5.704 in expanded fractional form.

b   Write $3 + \frac{2}{10} + \frac{4}{100} + \frac{1}{10\,000}$ in decimal form.

a 5.704

$\quad = 5 + \frac{7}{10} + \frac{4}{1000}$

b $3 + \frac{2}{10} + \frac{4}{100} + \frac{1}{10\,000}$

$\quad = 3.2401$

EXERCISE 8A

1   Write the following in expanded fractional form:

   a   3.4   **b**   3.04   **c**   3.0407   **d**   5.0018   **e**   0.0706

2   Write the following in decimal form:

   a $2 + \frac{4}{10}$ **b** $\frac{6}{10} + \frac{2}{100}$ **c** $\frac{3}{10} + \frac{5}{1000}$

   d $\frac{8}{100} + \frac{1}{1000}$ **e** $3 + \frac{2}{10\,000}$ **f** $2 + \frac{1}{100} + \frac{7}{10\,000}$

3   Evaluate:

   a $6.53 + 4.9$ **b** $12.87 + 10.76$ **c** $19.08 - 12.84$

   d $3.4 - 0.7$ **e** $13 - 6.158$ **f** $0.17 + 0.789 + 2.34$

   g $0.307 + 0.0098$ **h** $6.8 - 7.9$ **i** $0.45 + 0.062 - 0.374$

   j $0.648 - 1$ **k** $-0.713 + 2$ **l** $-3.3 - 4.81$

Example 2   ◀) **Self Tutor**

Evaluate: **a** 24×0.8 **b** $3.6 \div 0.02$

a $24 \times 8 = 192$
         $\therefore \quad 24 \times 0.8 = 19.2$ {÷10 by shifting decimal 1 place left}

b $3.6 \div 0.02$
         $= 3.\overset{\frown}{6}0 \div 0.\overset{\frown}{0}2$ {shift both decimal points the same
         $= 360 \div 2$ number of places to the right}
         $= 180$

---

4 Evaluate:

a 25.4×100	**b** $0.6 \div 100$	**c** $17 \div 0.5$
d 0.4×9	**e** 0.4×0.09	**f** 2000×0.7
g 2.4×0.7	**h** $1 \div 0.04$	**i** $(0.4)^3$
j $300 \times (0.3)^2$	**k** $0.48 \div 120$	**l** $0.5075 \div 2.5$
m $0.5 \times 0.4 + 0.1$	**n** $0.5 + 0.4 \times 0.1$	**o** $1.2 + 2.4 \times 2 + 1.9$
p $1.4 + 1.2^2$	**q** $5.5 - 2 \div 0.5$	**r** $(5.5 - 2) \div 0.5$
s $4.8 + 3.6 \div 3$	**t** $6.9 - 5.6 \div 0.7 - 3.1$	

Example 3   ◀) **Self Tutor**

Jon bought four drinks for $1.30 each. How much
change did he get from a $10 note?

$\text{cost} = \$1.30 \times 4$ $\therefore$ $\text{change} = \$10 - \$5.20$
    $= \$5.20$ $= \$4.80$

---

5 Solve the following problems:

a Sally has used 30 litres of petrol in the last week. What did it cost her if petrol was
selling at 126.9 cents per litre?

b Sliced ham sells at €5.60 per kg. How much would 400 g of ham cost?

c Gravel costs $3.95 per bag. How much would 6 bags cost?

d The cost of electricity is 53.8 cents per kilowatt
for each hour. What would

   i   400 kilowatts of electricity cost for one hour
   ii it cost to burn an 80 watt globe for 6 hours?

© iStockphoto

e At a perfume factory, bottles are filled from large tanks that each hold 2400 litres.
How many bottles can be filled from one tank if each bottle holds 60 mL?

f Norbert Raimes is a professional pastry chef. Each day he mixes 22.5 kg of pastry for use with his various creations. If they require an average 115 g of pastry each, how many items does Norbert make in a day?

g A juicing plant uses machines to crush fruit and then filter out seeds and other solids. The processed juice is collected in a 7000 L vat before bottling. How many 600 mL bottles can be filled from each vat?

h A manufacturer has 160 kg of metal to be made into ball bearings. If each bearing is to have mass 4.5 g, how many can be made?

6 Find, giving your answers correct to 2 decimal places where necessary:

a $(4.9 + 7.6) \times 12.3$

b $4.9 + 7.6 \times 12.3$

c $93 \div 9 - 6$

d $93 \div (9 - 6)$

e $\dfrac{13.27}{6.4 + 12.8}$

f $\dfrac{11.4}{3.1} - \dfrac{12.5}{7.7}$

g $\dfrac{68.7 - 35.5}{2.8} + 11.3$

h $\dfrac{6.208 - 0.97}{16.41 + 4.232}$

B   PERCENTAGE

Percentages are comparisons of a portion with the whole amount (which we call 100%).

% reads **percent** which means **out of every hundred**.

So, 10% means 10 out of every 100 or $\frac{10}{100}$.

Likewise, 25% means $\frac{25}{100}$.

So, $x\% = \dfrac{x}{100}$.

For help with fractions on the TI-83, consult the section on page **11**.

CONVERTING A PERCENTAGE TO A FRACTION

Example 4   ◀) Self Tutor

Express as a fraction in simplest form: **a** 40% **b** 150% **c** $12\frac{1}{2}\%$

a   40%
$= \frac{40}{100}$
$= \frac{40 \div 20}{100 \div 20}$
$= \frac{2}{5}$

Calculator:

40 [a b/c] 100 [EXE]

b   150%
$= \frac{150}{100}$
$= \frac{150 \div 50}{100 \div 50}$
$= \frac{3}{2}$
$= 1\frac{1}{2}$

c $12\frac{1}{2}\%$
$= \frac{12\frac{1}{2} \times 2}{100 \times 2}$
$= \frac{25 \div 25}{200 \div 25}$
$= \frac{1}{8}$

Calculator:

12 [a b/c] 1 [a b/c] 2 [÷] 100 [EXE]

EXERCISE 8B

1 Copy and complete:

   a $6\% = \dfrac{\square}{100}$ **b** $51\% = \dfrac{\square}{100}$ **c** $27\% = \dfrac{\square}{100}$ **d** $86\% = \dfrac{\square}{100}$

2 Express as a fraction in simplest form:

   a 25% **b** 130% **c** 65% **d** 40%

   e 210% **f** 100% **g** 12% **h** 2%

   i $22\frac{1}{2}\%$ **j** 2.5% **k** $77\frac{1}{2}\%$ **l** $62\frac{1}{4}\%$

CONVERTING A PERCENTAGE TO A DECIMAL

Example 5	◀)) Self Tutor

Express as a decimal:

a 43%

b $12\frac{1}{2}\%$

   a 43%

       $= \dfrac{43}{100}$

       $= 0.43$

   b $12\frac{1}{2}\%$

       $= \dfrac{12.5}{100}$

       $= 0.125$

Calculator: 43 ÷ 100 ENTER

> Shifting the decimal point 2 places to the left divides by 100.

3 Express as a decimal:

   a 66% **b** 29% **c** 50% **d** 75%

   e 180% **f** 205% **g** 300% **h** 128%

   i 0.01% **j** 0.3% **k** $10\frac{1}{2}\%$ **l** $56\frac{1}{4}\%$

CONVERTING DECIMALS AND FRACTIONS TO PERCENTAGES

Example 6	◀)) Self Tutor

Convert to a percentage:

   a 0.46

   b 1.35

   a 0.46

       $= \dfrac{46}{100}$

       $= 46\%$

   b 1.35

       $= \dfrac{135}{100}$

       $= 135\%$

> Remember that $\dfrac{x}{100} = x\%$.

4 Write as a percentage:

   a 0.17 **b** 0.55 **c** 0.09 **d** 0.8

   e 0.04 **f** 2 **g** 0.4 **h** 3.5

   i 2.05 **j** 3.64 **k** 0.088 **l** 1.409

Another method of converting fractions and decimals to percentages is to multiply the fraction or decimal by 100%.

Example 7   ◀)) **Self Tutor**

Convert to percentages by multiplying by 100%:

a $\frac{3}{5}$ b   0.042

a $\frac{3}{5}$

$= \frac{3}{5} \times 100\%$ {100% = 1}

$= 60\%$

Calculator:

3 ÷ 5 × 100 ENTER

b   0.042

$= 0.042 \times 100\%$ {100% = 1}

$= 4.2\%$ {shift decimal point
2 places to the right}

Calculator:

0.042 × 100 ENTER

5   Convert to percentages:

a $\frac{1}{4}$ b $\frac{3}{10}$ c $\frac{7}{20}$ d $\frac{11}{25}$

e   1   f $\frac{16}{10}$ g $\frac{27}{50}$ h $\frac{19}{40}$

i   0.04   j   0.375   k   2.4   l   3.76

C   WORKING WITH PERCENTAGES

ONE QUANTITY AS A PERCENTAGE OF ANOTHER

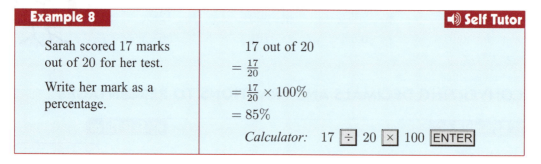

Example 8   ◀)) **Self Tutor**

Sarah scored 17 marks out of 20 for her test.

Write her mark as a percentage.

17 out of 20

$= \frac{17}{20}$

$= \frac{17}{20} \times 100\%$

$= 85\%$

Calculator: 17 ÷ 20 × 100 ENTER

EXERCISE 8C

1   Express as a percentage:

a   30 cm out of 60 cm   b   14 minutes out of 25 minutes

c   36 marks out of 40 marks   d   21 kg out of 30 kg

2   On the practice green Tiger sank 13 putts out of 20. Write this as a percentage.

3   Mohammed scored 66 marks out of 70 for his chemistry test. What was his percentage?

4   Erika was late for her bus 3 days out of 22 last month. What percentage of the days was she on time?

5   Phyllis sells new cars. Her sales quota for last month was 35 cars. If she sold 43 cars during the month, write this as a percentage of the quota.

Example 9
🔊 Self Tutor

Express as a percentage: Rani spent 5 months of the last two years overseas.

5 months of the last two years

$= 5$ months out of 24 months   {write with the *same* units}

$= \frac{5}{24} \times 100\%$ {*Calculator:* 5 ÷ 24 × 100 ENTER }

$\approx 20.8\%$ So, Rani spent 20.8% of the last 2 years overseas.

6 Write as a percentage:

    a 48 cm out of 2 m

    b 26 seconds out of 5 minutes

    c 298 g out of 1.4 kg

    d 9 months out of 2.5 years

7 Pierre had €5 in his pocket until he spent 85 euro cents on some sweets. What percentage of his money did Pierre spend?

8 Sven walks 475 metres to the underground station, then makes a 3.5 km journey by train. What percentage of the *total* distance travelled was on foot?

9 Leah ate 250 grams of cake from a cake weighing $1\frac{1}{2}$ kg. What percentage of the cake did she eat?

FINDING A PERCENTAGE OF A QUANTITY

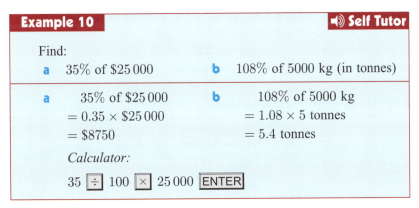

Example 10
🔊 Self Tutor

Find:

    a 35% of $25 000

    b 108% of 5000 kg (in tonnes)

    a 35% of $25 000

      $= 0.35 \times \$25\,000$

      $= \$8750$

    b 108% of 5000 kg

      $= 1.08 \times 5$ tonnes

      $= 5.4$ tonnes

Calculator:

35 ÷ 100 × 25 000 ENTER

The word 'of' indicates that we should multiply the numbers.

10 Find:

    a 60% of €8

    b 25% of $64

    c 40% of 12 L

    d 150% of 35 kg

    e 7% of 3 tonnes

    f $12\frac{1}{2}\%$ of 800 m

    g 76% of 3 hours (in minutes)

Example 11
🔊 Self Tutor

Sandra scored 86% in her exam out of 150. What mark did she score?

Sandra scored   86% of 150

      $= 0.86 \times 150$

      $= 129$ i.e.,   Sandra scored 129 marks.

Calculator: 86 ÷ 100 × 150 ENTER

11 Li scored 75% in her test out of 32. What mark did she score?

12 John scored 70% for an examination marked out of 120. How many marks did he actually get?

13 A petroleum company claims that cars using their new premium unleaded fuel will travel 112% of the distance travelled on regular un-leaded. If Geoff can travel 584 miles on a tank of regular fuel, how far should he be able to travel on the premium unleaded?

14 Paula receives $7\frac{1}{2}$% of the nett profits on a book she helped to write. If the nett profits this year are £38 700, how much will she receive in royalties?

15 Nicki is part of a syndicate that owns racehorses. He owns 28% of Peter Pan, who last week won $18 600 in the derby. How much should Nicki receive?

16 A restaurant charges $7\frac{1}{2}$% service on the total bill. If Jack and Jill buy food and wine to the value of €54, how much will they have to pay

    a   for service   **b**   in total?

D   UNITARY METHOD IN PERCENTAGE

Michelle and Brigette own a business. Brigette receives 25% of the profits each month. How can Brigette work out the total profit made by the business in a month when her share was $2080?

The **unitary method** can be used to solve this problem.

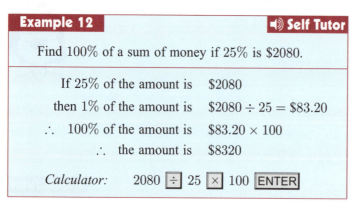

Example 12   ◄)) **Self Tutor**

Find 100% of a sum of money if 25% is $2080.

If 25% of the amount is $2080

then 1% of the amount is $2080 ÷ 25 = $83.20

∴ 100% of the amount is $83.20 × 100

∴ the amount is $8320

Calculator: 2080 ÷ 25 × 100 ENTER

The final answer can be found in one step by multiplying $2080 by $\frac{100}{25}$.

EXERCISE 8D

1 Find 100% if:

    a   30% is CHF 48   **b**   16% is 2.56 L   **c**   11% is 143 mL

    d   13% is 416 kg   **e**   87% is £1131   **f**   95% is 399 km

    g   22% is 77 L   **h**   36% is 252 kg   **i**   63% is €1323

Example 13

Find 60% of a sum of money if 14% is ¥7280.

If 14% is   ¥7280

then 1% is $\dfrac{¥7280}{14} = ¥520$

∴   60% is   ¥520 × 60   *Calculator:*

∴   60% is   ¥31 200

7280 ÷ 14 × 60 ENTER

2   Find:

a   40% if 9% is $117

b   72% if 6% is 96 kg

c   6% if 48% is €630

d   8% if 95% is 1235 mL

e   90% if 6% is 14 kg

f   4% if 75% is $465

Example 14

82% of fans at a basketball match support the Lakers. If there are 24 026 Lakers fans at the match, how many people are in attendance?

If 82% is   24 026 fans

then 1% is $\dfrac{24\,026}{82} = 293$ fans

∴   100% is $293 \times 100 = 29\,300$ *Calculator:*

∴   29 300 fans attend the match.

24 026 ÷ 82 × 100 ENTER

3   A survey showed that 39% of cars passing through a city intersection had only one occupant. If this was 663 cars, how many cars were surveyed?

4   35% of the proceeds of a concert was given to charity. If $26 425 was given to charity, find the total of the proceeds.

5   144 girls attend a country school. If 48% of the students are girls, find the total number of students who attend the school.

E   PERCENTAGE INCREASE AND DECREASE

If we *increase* an amount by 20% then we have   the amount + 20% of the amount.

If we *decrease* an amount by 20% then we have   the amount − 20% of the amount.

Example 15
🔊 **Self Tutor**

A fruit grower picked 1720 kg of apples last year. This year she expects her crop to be 20% bigger. How many kilograms of apples does she expect to pick this year?

$$\begin{aligned} \text{New crop} \;&= 1720 + 20\% \text{ of } 1720 \text{ kg} \\ &= 1720 + 0.2 \times 1720 \text{ kg} \\ &= 1720 + 344 \text{ kg} \\ &= 2064 \text{ kg} \end{aligned}$$

She expects to pick 2064 kg.

Calculator: 1720 $\boxed{+}$ 0.2 $\boxed{\times}$ 1720 $\boxed{\text{ENTER}}$

EXERCISE 8E

1 The price of vegetables has risen by 20% because of the dry season. How much does Justine need to spend for tomatoes that usually cost $3.50 per kilogram?

2 Kurt's business is expanding. He has increased the number of staff by 25%. If he previously employed 64 people, how many does he employ now?

3 Juliet studied hard and increased her Mathematics marks by 6% from last term's result. If she scored 54 last term, what did she score this term (to the nearest whole mark)?

4 In 2005 Su-Lin's salary was $48 000. In 2006 it increased by 35% when she was promoted to manager. What was her salary in 2006?

Example 16
🔊 **Self Tutor**

Stefan grows cherries and expected to harvest 2000 kg of them. If bad storms damaged 60% of his crop, what weight of cherries can he expect to harvest now?

$$\begin{aligned} \text{New weight} \;&= 2000 - 60\% \text{ of } 2000 \text{ kg} \\ &= 2000 - 0.6 \times 2000 \text{ kg} \\ &= 2000 - 1200 \text{ kg} \\ &= 800 \text{ kg} \end{aligned}$$

He can expect to harvest 800 kg.

Calculator: 2000 $\boxed{-}$ 0.6 $\boxed{\times}$ 2000 $\boxed{\text{ENTER}}$

5 Marius found that travelling on the new free-way decreased his travelling time to work by 12%. He used to take 50 minutes to get to work. How long does he take now?

6 In a clearance sale, the price of a new car was decreased by 35%. If it would normally cost \$14 960, what was the new price?

7 If Claudia walked to school following the footpaths, she would walk 920 metres. If she walked across the park she could reduce this distance by 16%. How far would she walk then?

8 Every day for 2 months Dimitri walked 5 km. At first he took 80 minutes, but by the end of 2 months he had reduced his time by 24%. How long does he take now?

F | SCIENTIFIC NOTATION (STANDARD FORM)

Observe the pattern:

$$\begin{aligned}
\div 10 \left(\begin{aligned} 10\,000 &= 10^4 \\ 1000 &= 10^3 \\ 100 &= 10^2 \\ 10 &= 10^1 \end{aligned}\right) \end{aligned}$$

As we divide by 10, the **exponent** or **power** of 10 decreases by one. If we continue this pattern, we get:

$$\begin{aligned}
\div 10 \left(\begin{aligned} 1 &= 10^0 \\ \tfrac{1}{10} &= 10^{-1} \\ \tfrac{1}{100} &= 10^{-2} \\ \tfrac{1}{1000} &= 10^{-3}, \end{aligned}\right) \text{........etc.} \end{aligned}$$

We can use this pattern to simplify the writing of very large and very small numbers.

For example,

$$\begin{aligned}
& 5\,000\,000 \\
&= 5 \times 1\,000\,000 \\
&= 5 \times 10^6
\end{aligned}$$

and

$$\begin{aligned}
& 0.000\,003 \\
&= \frac{3}{1\,000\,000} \\
&= \frac{3}{1} \times \frac{1}{1\,000\,000} \\
&= 3 \times 10^{-6}
\end{aligned}$$

SCIENTIFIC NOTATION

Scientific notation (or **standard form**) involves writing any given number as *a number between 1 and 10*, multiplied by a *power of 10*,

i.e., $a \times 10^k$ where $1 \leqslant a < 10$ and k is an integer.

Example 17

> **◄)) Self Tutor**
>
> Write in scientific notation: **a** 37 600   **b** 0.000 86
>
> ---
>
> **a** $\overset{\frown}{37\,600} = 3.76 \times 10\,000$ {shift decimal point 4 places to the
> $= 3.76 \times 10^4$ left and $\times\ 10\,000$}
>
> **b** $0.00086 = 8.6 \div 10^4$ {shift decimal point 4 places to the
> $= 8.6 \times 10^{-4}$ right and $\div\ 10\,000$}

Note:
- If the original number is > 10, the power of 10 is **positive** $(+)$.
- If the original number is < 1, the power of 10 is **negative** $(-)$.
- If the original number is between 1 and 10, leave it as it is and multiply it by 10^0.

EXERCISE 8F

1 Write the following as powers of 10:

a	100	**b**	1000	**c**	10	**d**	100 000
e	0.1	**f**	0.01	**g**	0.0001	**h**	100 000 000

2 Express the following in scientific notation (standard form):

a	387	**b**	38 700	**c**	3.87	**d**	0.0387
e	0.003 87	**f**	20.5	**g**	205	**h**	0.205
i	20 500	**j**	20 500 000	**k**	0.000 205		

3 Express the following in scientific notation (standard form):

a The circumference of the Earth is approximately 40 075 kilometres.

b The distance from the Earth to the Sun is 149 500 000 000 m.

c Bacteria are single cell organisms, some of which have a diameter of 0.0004 mm.

d There are typically 40 million bacteria in a gram of soil.

e The probability that your six numbers will be selected for Lotto on Saturday night is 0.000 000 141 62.

f Superfine sheep have wool fibres as low as 0.01 mm in diameter.

Example 18

> **◄)) Self Tutor**
>
> Write as an ordinary number:
> **a** 3.2×10^2 **b** 5.76×10^{-5}
>
> ---
>
> **a** 3.2×10^2 **b** 5.76×10^{-5}
>
> $= \overset{\frown}{3.20} \times 100$ $= \overset{\frown}{000005.76} \div 10^5$
>
> $= 320$ $= 0.000\,057\,6$

4 Write as an ordinary decimal number:

    a 3×10^2 **b** 2×10^3 **c** 3.6×10^4 **d** 9.2×10^5

    e 5.6×10^6 **f** 3.4×10^1 **g** 7.85×10^6 **h** 9×10^8

5 Write as an ordinary decimal number:

    a 3×10^{-2} **b** 2×10^{-3} **c** 4.7×10^{-4} **d** 6.3×10^{-5}

    e 1.7×10^0 **f** 9.5×10^{-4} **g** 3.49×10^{-1} **h** 7×10^{-6}

6 Write as an ordinary decimal number:

    a The wavelength of visible light is 9×10^{-7} m.

    b In 2007, the world population was approximately 6.606×10^9.

    c The diameter of our galaxy, the Milky Way, is 1×10^5 light years.

    d The smallest viruses are 1×10^{-5} mm in size.

    e 1 atomic mass unit is approximately 1.66×10^{-27} kg.

Example 19 🔊 **Self Tutor**

Simplify the following, giving your answer in scientific notation (standard form):

    a $(5 \times 10^4) \times (4 \times 10^5)$ **b** $(8 \times 10^5) \div (2 \times 10^3)$

    a $(5 \times 10^4) \times (4 \times 10^5)$

        $= 5 \times 4 \times 10^4 \times 10^5$

        $= 20 \times 10^{4+5}$

        $= 2 \times 10^1 \times 10^9$

        $= 2 \times 10^{10}$

    b $(8 \times 10^5) \div (2 \times 10^3)$

        $= \dfrac{8 \times 10^5}{2 \times 10^3}$

        $= \frac{8}{2} \times 10^{5-3}$

        $= 4 \times 10^2$

---

7 Simplify the following, giving your answer in scientific notation (standard form):

    a $(8 \times 10^3) \times (2 \times 10^4)$ **b** $(8 \times 10^3) \times (4 \times 10^5)$

    c $(5 \times 10^4) \times (3 \times 10^5)$ **d** $(2 \times 10^3)^3$

    e $(6 \times 10^3)^2$ **f** $(7 \times 10^{-2})^2$

    g $(9 \times 10^4) \div (3 \times 10^3)$ **h** $(8 \times 10^5) \div (4 \times 10^6)$

SCIENTIFIC NOTATION ON A CALCULATOR

Scientific and graphics calculators are able to display very large and very small numbers in scientific notation.

If you perform $2\,300\,000 \times 400\,000$ your calculator might display $\boxed{9.2^{11}}$ or $\boxed{9.2\, \varepsilon\, 11}$

or $\boxed{9.2\, \varepsilon + 11}$, all of which actually represent 9.2×10^{11}.

Likewise, if you perform $0.0024 \div 10\,000\,000$ your calculator might display $\boxed{2.4^{-10}}$

or $\boxed{2.4\, \varepsilon\, -10}$, which actually represent 2.4×10^{-10}.

8 Write each of the following as it would appear on the display of *your* calculator in scientific notation:

    a $4\,650\,000$ **b** $0.000\,051\,2$ **c** 5.99×10^{-4}

    d 3.761×10^{10} **e** $49\,500\,000$ **f** $0.000\,008\,44$

9 Calculate each of the following, giving your answers in scientific notation. The decimal part should be correct to 2 decimal places:

    a $0.06 \times 0.002 \div 4000$ **b** $426 \times 760 \times 42\,000$ **c** $627\,000 \times 74\,000$

    d $320 \times 600 \times 51\,400$ **e** $0.004\,28 \div 120\,000$ **f** $0.026 \times 0.00\,42 \times 0.08$

Numbers which are already represented in scientific notation can be entered into the calculator using $\boxed{\text{EE}}$ or $\boxed{\text{EXP}}$.

We enter 4.022×10^4 on a scientific calculator by pressing 4.022 $\boxed{\text{EE}}$ 4 and it will appear on the display as $\boxed{4.022 \varepsilon 4}$ or $\boxed{4.022^{04}}$.

Likewise, 5.446×10^{-11} can be entered as: 5.446 $\boxed{\text{EE}}$ 11 $\boxed{+/-}$ and it will appear as $\boxed{5.446 \varepsilon \text{-}11}$ or $\boxed{5.446^{\text{-}11}}$.

Instructions for graphics calculators can be found on page **14**.

Example 20   ◀ঠ **Self Tutor**

Use your calculator to find:

    a $(1.42 \times 10^4) \times (2.56 \times 10^8)$ **b** $(4.75 \times 10^{-4}) \div (2.5 \times 10^7)$

Instructions are given for the **Casio fx-6890G** :   *Answer:*

    a 1.42 $\boxed{\text{EXP}}$ 4 $\boxed{\times}$ 2.56 $\boxed{\text{EXP}}$ 8 $\boxed{\text{EXE}}$ 3.6352×10^{12}

    b 4.75 $\boxed{\text{EXP}}$ $\boxed{(-)}$ 4 $\boxed{\div}$ 2.5 $\boxed{\text{EXP}}$ 7 $\boxed{\text{EXE}}$ 1.9×10^{-11}

---

10 Find, in scientific notation, with decimal part correct to 2 places:

    a $(5.31 \times 10^4) \times (4.8 \times 10^3)$ **b** $(2.75 \times 10^{-3})^2$ **c** $\dfrac{8.24 \times 10^{-6}}{3 \times 10^4}$

    d $(7.2 \times 10^{-5}) \div (2.4 \times 10^{-6})$ **e** $\dfrac{1}{4.1 \times 10^4}$ **f** $(3.2 \times 10^3)^2$

11 For the following give answers in scientific notation correct to 3 significant figures:

    a   How many millimetres are there in 479.8 kilometres?

    b   How many seconds are there in one year?

    c   How many seconds are there in a millennium?

    d   How many kilograms are there in 0.5 milligrams?

12 If a missile travels at 3600 km h^{-1}, how far will it travel in:

    a 1 day   **b** 1 week   **c** 2 years?

Give your answers in scientific notation with decimal part correct to 2 places. Assume that 1 year = 365.25 days.

13 Light travels at a speed of 3×10^8 metres per second. How far will light travel in:

    a 1 minute   **b** 1 day   **c** 1 year?

Give your answers in scientific notation with decimal part correct to 2 decimal places. Assume that 1 year = 365.25 days.

REVIEW SET 8A

1 Write the following in expanded fractional form:

    a 4.2   **b** 4.025   **c** 4.2005   **d** 0.0105

2 Write as decimal numbers: **a** $5 + \frac{1}{10} + \frac{7}{1000}$ **b** $\frac{4}{100} + \frac{9}{1000}$

3 Find the value of:

    a $86.204 - 3.779$ **b** 34.7×1000 **c** 3×2.1

    d $5.6 \div 7$ **e** 2000×0.09 **f** $(0.4)^2$

4 How much did Karl earn if he worked for 7 hours and was paid $18.25 per hour?

5 Kate deposited $124.95 in a new bank account. The next week she deposited $132.75, then she withdrew $103.20 the following week. What was the balance then?

6 Use your calculator to find, correct to 2 decimal places where necessary:

    a $58.31 - 1.72 \times 14.9$ **b** $\dfrac{62.97}{16.88 - 4.59}$

7 **a** Express as a fraction in simplest form:

        i 75%   **ii** $6\frac{1}{4}\%$ **iii** 120%

    b Express as a decimal:

        i 25%   **ii** $6\frac{1}{4}\%$ **iii** 120%

8 Convert to a percentage:

    a $\frac{7}{10}$ **b** $1\frac{3}{8}$ **c** 0.53   **d** 4.03

9 Adam drank 220 mL of milk from a 600 mL carton. What percentage of the full carton did he drink?

10 An examination paper out of 150 marks was made up of short answer questions and problem solving questions. If the short answer questions were worth 40% of the marks, find how many marks the problem solving questions were worth.

11 When 92% of the children at a school ordered lunches from the canteen, 552 lunches were ordered. How many lunches would be ordered if 95% of the students ordered lunches from the canteen?

12 Stavros decreased his household water consumption of 326 kL for the year by 10%. What was his new consumption?

13 Write in scientific notation: **a** 9   **b** 34 900   **c** 0.0075

14 Write as an ordinary decimal number:

   a 2.81×10^6 **b** 2.81×10^0 **c** 2.81×10^{-3}

15 Simplify, giving your answer in scientific notation:

   a $(6 \times 10^3) \times (7.1 \times 10^4)$ **b** $(2.4 \times 10^6) \div (4 \times 10^2)$

REVIEW SET 8B

1 Write the following in expanded fractional form:

   a   6.81   **b**   6.081   **c**   6.0801   **d**   6.0081

2 Write as decimal numbers: **a** $1 + \frac{4}{10} + \frac{5}{100} + \frac{6}{10\,000}$ **b** $9 + \frac{1}{100} + \frac{2}{1000}$

3 Find the value of:

   a $46.802 + 20.05$ **b** $25.8 \div 1000$ **c** $0.147 \div 7$

   d 0.6×1.2 **e** $(0.01)^2$ **f** 300×0.03

4 **a** How many 4 kg packets of birdseed can be packed from 364.8 kg of birdseed?

   b What weight of birdseed remains?

5 Alberto had $25.50. Find how much money was left if he bought 6 cartons of iced coffee costing $2.35 each.

6 Use your calculator to find, correct to 1 decimal place where necesary:

   a $\dfrac{31.5}{63.86 \div 4.1}$ **b** $(11.7)^2 - \dfrac{18.6}{14.7}$

7 **a** Express as a fraction in simplest form:

   i   80%   **ii**   0.2%   **iii**   255%

   b Express as a decimal:

   i   46%   **ii** $12\frac{1}{2}\%$ **iii**   105%

8 Convert to a percentage:

   a $\frac{2}{5}$ **b** $1\frac{1}{20}$ **c**   0.97   **d**   0.021

9 Leslie has saved $33 out of the $60 that she needs for a concert ticket. What percentage of the money has she saved?

10 An item is advertised at '15% off the marked price'. If the marked price is ¥3500, how much would you need to pay for the item?

11 Julie received a 3% salary increase. If Julie was previously paid £18 000 per year, find her new salary.

12 When Mount Bold reservoir is 40% full it holds 18 472 megalitres of water. How much water would it hold if it was 90% full?

13 Write in scientific notation:

    a 263.57
    b 0.000 511
    c 863 400 000

14 Write as an ordinary decimal number:

    a 2.78×10^0
    b 3.99×10^7
    c 2.081×10^{-3}

15 Simplify, giving your answer in scientific notation:

    a $(8 \times 10^3)^2$
    b $(3.6 \times 10^5) \div (6 \times 10^{-2})$

HISTORICAL NOTE   WOMEN IN MATHEMATICS

Over the centuries women have made enormous contributions to mathematics, though their part has often been unheralded. Following are brief statements about two women who have been recognised for their achievements:

SOFYA KOVALEVSKAYA (1850 - 1891)

Sofya was born in Moscow in 1850. As a girl she studied three languages, music, art and mathematics. She was a very fast learner, but unfortunately many universities refused to allow women to study mathematics and science. She therefore moved to Heidelberg University in Germany, but even there she had to dress in an unfeminine manner to be accepted by the male-dominated mathematics department.

In 1874 she obtained a degree at the University of Gottingen, but as she was a women she was unable to obtain work as a teacher or researcher at any university.

In 1888 she went to Paris to continue her study. Following the death of her husband and a bad lapse in health she wrote hundreds of important mathematical formulae. She became a lecturer at the University of Stockholm and was awarded the Bordin Prize by the French Academy of Sciences on her research on *The rotation of a solid body about a fixed point*. Her work was so impressive the prize money was increased from 3000 francs to 5000 francs.

Unfortunately Sofya died two years later at the age of 41 after being struck down in an influenza epidemic sweeping through Europe.

ÉMILIE DU CHÂTELET (1706 - 1749)

Émilie was born in France in 1706. As a student she learned several languages and was an expert sword fighter. Her main passion in life, however, was the study of science and mathematics. She once entered a cafe which was the gathering place of mathematicians and scientists but was turned away because she was a woman. Undaunted she returned dressed as a man and was admitted.

Émilie is well remembered for her ability to clarify the works of other famous people of her time. Her best known work was her translation of Newton's *Principia Mathematica*. She was highly regarded as a scholar by her peers but was not treated seriously by the upper classes. In fact Frederick the Great of Prussia said, "Without wishing to flatter you, I can assure you that I should never have believed your sex, usually so delightfully gifted with all the graces, capable also of such deep knowledge, minute research, and solid discovery as appears in your fine work." Having done a great deal for the cause of the intellect of women, Émilie died at the young age of 43.

Chapter 9

Algebraic simplification and expansion

Contents:

A   Collecting like terms
B   Product notation
C   The distributive law
D   The expansion of $(a+b)(c+d)$
E   The expansion rules
F   Perimeters and areas

OPENING PROBLEM

Alf decides to put a 7 m by 3 m rectangular swimming pool in his back yard. A concrete path is to be laid around the pool with a border of lawn planted *double* the width of the path. The whole area needs to be fenced and Alf has 50 m of beautiful and expensive fencing available. What should the dimensions of the pool area be if Alf wants to use all available fencing?

Think about the following:

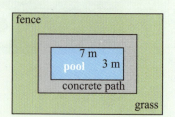

- What unknown lengths are there in Alf's plan?

- How are the unknown lengths connected?

- If you were to solve the problem using *algebra*, what unknown length would you choose to be represented by the *pronumeral* x?

- What is the *length* of the fence in terms of x?

- Can you find x by *trial and error* substitution, by using a *spreadsheet*, or by *solving an equation*?

- Can you draw a complete dimensioned *plan* of the enclosed pool area?

- If Alf had 68 m of fencing available, how would this affect the answer?

A   COLLECTING LIKE TERMS

Like terms are algebraic terms which contain the same pronumerals to the same indices.

For example:
- $3bc$ and $-2bc$ are **like terms**
- $-x^2$ and $5x$ are **unlike terms** because the indices of x are not the same.

Algebraic expressions can often be simplified by adding or subtracting like terms. This is sometimes called **collecting like terms**.

Consider $3x + 2x = \underbrace{x + x + x}_{\text{"3 lots of } x\text{"}} + \underbrace{x + x}_{\text{"2 lots of } x\text{"}}$.

In total we have 5 lots of x, and so $3x + 2x = 5x$.

Example 1   ◀) Self Tutor

Simplify, where possible, by collecting like terms:

a $3a + 4a$ **b** $11b - b$ **c** $5 + x + 2$ **d** $2ab + 3ab$ **e** $3x^2 + 2x$

a $3a + 4a$
   $= 7a$

b $11b - b$
   $= 11b - 1b$
   $= 10b$

c $5 + x + 2$
   $= 5 + 2 + x$
   $= 7 + x$ $\{5 \text{ and } 2 \text{ are like terms}\}$

d $2ab + 3ab$
   $= 5ab$

e $3x^2 + 2x$ is in simplest form.
   $\{3x^2 \text{ and } 2x \text{ are unlike terms}\}$

EXERCISE 9A

1 Simplify, where possible, by collecting like terms:

    a $6 + x + 2$ **b** $5 + 6 + a$ **c** $t + 2 - 5$ **d** $b + 5 + b$

    e $d + d + 6$ **f** $q + q + q$ **g** $3x + x$ **h** $c - 3 + 6 + c$

    i $4a + 2a$ **j** $5y - 3y$ **k** $4z - 2z$ **l** $c^2 + c^2$

    m $3a + 8$ **n** $x^2 + 4x^2$ **o** $12a - 9$ **p** $12a - a$

    q $5v^2 - 2v^2$ **r** $3bc + 3bc$ **s** $z + 2z - 4z$ **t** $6b - 5b - 4$

2 Simplify, where possible:

    a $5x - 5x$ **b** $5x - x$ **c** $5x - 5$

    d $2xy + yx$ **e** $ab + 3ab$ **f** $3p^2 - p^2$

    g $3 + 2a + 5a - 6$ **h** $x + 3x + 2x$ **i** $1 + b + 5b - 4$

    j $3bc + 2cb$ **k** $2b - a + 3a + b$ **l** $2n^2 + 3n - n^2 + 4n$

    m $8x + 2x - 3x$ **n** $3m + 2m - 5m$ **o** $2ab + b^2 - ab + 2b^2$

    p $8x + 7x - 9$ **q** $4x + 2x - 6x$ **r** $2y + 9y - y$

Example 2   ◀⬥ **Self Tutor**

Simplify, where possible: **a** $3a - 5a$ **b** $-4x - 6x$ **c** $-2b - -5b$

    a $3a - 5a$ **b** $-4x - 6x$ **c** $-2b - -5b$

        $= -2a$ $= -10x$ $= -2b + 5b$

       $\{$since $3 - 5 = -2\}$ $\{$since $-4 - 6 = -10\}$ $= 3b$

---

3 Simplify, by collecting like terms:

    a $4a + 6a$ **b** $4a - 6a$ **c** $-4a + 6a$ **d** $-4a - 6a$

    e $7x + x$ **f** $7x - x$ **g** $-7x + x$ **h** $-7x - x$

    i $3n + n^2$ **j** $-8d - 5d$ **k** $-8d + 5d$ **l** $8d - 5d$

    m $b + 2 - 3b$ **n** $2t - 3t - t$ **o** $-6g + g$ **p** $2m - 7 - 3m$

    q $2a + 4 - 5a$ **r** $-3c - -5c$ **s** $4b - b$ **t** $4b - -b$

Example 3   ◀⬥ **Self Tutor**

Simplify, by collecting like terms:

    a $3x - 4 - 5x - 2$ **b** $2y^2 - y - -3y^2 + 5y$

    a $3x - 4 - 5x - 2$ **b** $2y^2 - y - -3y^2 + 5y$

        $= 3x - 5x - 4 - 2$ $= 2y^2 - y + 3y^2 + 5y$

        $= -2x - 6$ $= 2y^2 + 3y^2 - y + 5y$

                                      $= 5y^2 - y + 5y$

       $\{3x$ and $-5x$ are like terms $= 5y^2 + 4y$

          -4 and -2 are like terms.$\}$ $\{2y^2$ and $3y^2$ are like terms,

                                          $-y$ and $5y$ are like terms.$\}$

4 Simplify, where possible:

a	$3a + 1 - 2a - 6$	**b** $c - b + 4c + 2b$	**c** $3xy + 3 - 2ab - 1$
d	$-ab + 2ba - 5ab$	**e** $2x - 6 + 6 - 7x$	**f** $m^2 - 5 + 2m^2 - 4$
g	$-2n + 5 + 3n - 6$	**h** $2a + 5b - 3a - 6b$	**i** $4uv - 2uv + 2$
j	$2i^2 + 2i - 4i^2 - 3i$	**k** $-a^2 - a^3 + a^3 - 2a^2$	**l** $4x + 2y - -x - y$
m	$2xy + y - 4xy - 2y$	**n** $-3x - 5 - 3x - 5$	

B   PRODUCT NOTATION

In algebra we agree:

- to **leave out** the "×" **signs** between any multiplied quantities provided that at least one of them is an unknown (letter)
- to write **numerals (numbers) first** in any product
- where products contain two or more letters, we write them in **alphabetical order**.

For example: • $3b$ is used rather than $3 \times b$ or $b3$
              • $3bc$ is used rather than $3cb$.

WRITING SUMS AS PRODUCTS

Sums of identical terms can be easily written using **product notation**.

For example, $5 + 5 + 5 + 5 = 4 \times 5$ {4 lots of 5}

∴ $a + a + a + a = 4 \times a = 4a$ {4 lots of a}

and likewise $b + b + b = 3b$ and $x + x + x + x + x + x = 6x$.

WRITING PRODUCTS USING INDICES (EXPONENTS)

When the same number is multiplied two or more times we use **index notation** as a quick way of writing the product.

For example, $2 \times 2 \times 2 = 2^3$

and $x \times x \times x \times x \times x = x^5$ where x^5 is read as "x to the fifth".

Note: • In 2^3, the 2 is called the **base** and the 3 is called the **index** or **power** or **exponent**.

  • x^2 is read "x squared"   and x^3 is read "x cubed".

SIMPLIFYING ALGEBRAIC PRODUCTS

$3 \times 2x$ and $a^2 \times 2ab$ are **algebraic products**.

Algebraic products can often be simplified using these steps:

- **Expand** out any brackets.
- Calculate the **coefficient** of the final product by multiplying all the numbers.
- **Simplify** the unknowns using index notation where appropriate. The unknowns should be written in alphabetical order.

Example 4   ◄)) **Self Tutor**

Simplify: **a** $a + a + b + b + b$ **b** $a \times a + b + c + c$

a $a + a + b + b + b$

$= 2a + 3b$

b $a \times a + b + c + c$

$= a^2 + b + 2c$

Example 5   ◄)) **Self Tutor**

Simplify: **a** $x^2 \times x^3$ **b** $2a \times 5a^2$

a $x^2 \times x^3$

$= x \times x \times x \times x \times x$

$= x^5$

b $2a \times 5a^2$

$= 2 \times a \times 5 \times a \times a$

$= 10a^3$

EXERCISE 9B

1 Simplify:

a $a + b + b + b$ **b** $a + a \times a + a$ **c** $2 \times b + b \times b$

d $6 \times a + a \times 2$ **e** $3 \times a - a \times a$ **f** $a \times 2 + a + 3 \times a$

g $4 \times x \times x - x$ **h** $b \times b \times b - b$ **i** $3 \times a \times a - a - a$

2 Simplify:

a $2 \times x \times x - 3$ **b** $b \times b \times b \times b$ **c** $a \times a \times a - a \times a$

d $6 \times t \times t$ **e** $m \times m \times 4 \times m \times m$ **f** $4 \times y \times y \times 3 \times y$

g $5 \times b \times b - 2 \times b$ **h** $s \times s - s \times s$ **i** $3 \times a \times b + 2 \times a \times a$

3 Simplify:

a $a^2 \times a$ **b** $b \times b^2$ **c** $c^2 \times c^2$

d $n \times n^3$ **e** $6a \times 3b$ **f** $5c \times 4a$

g $m^2 \times m^3$ **h** $k^3 \times k^2$ **i** $p^3 \times p^3$

Example 6   ◄)) **Self Tutor**

Simplify: $(x^2)^2$

$(x^2)^2$

$= x^2 \times x^2$

$= x \times x \times x \times x$

$= x^4$

4 Simplify:

a $(a^2)^2$ **b** $(m^2)^3$ **c** $(r^3)^2$

d $(ab)^2$ **e** $(s^4)^2$ **f** $(3x^3)^2$

g $(2mn)^2$ **h** $(3y^2)^3$ **i** $(5ab^2)^2$

j $(4x^3)^2$ **k** $(2m^3)^3$ **l** $(ac)^2 \times 2c^3$

Example 7   ◀)) **Self Tutor**

Simplify: **a** $2x \times 5$ **b** $4x \times 3x^2$ **c** $6x^2 \times 5x^2$

a $2x \times 5$

$= 2 \times x \times 5$

$= 10x$

b $4x \times 3x^2$

$= 4 \times x \times 3 \times x \times x$

$= 12x^3$

c $6x^2 \times 5x^2$

$= 6 \times x \times x \times 5 \times x \times x$

$= 30x^4$

With practice, you should be able to do these without the middle step.

5 Simplify the following:

a $2y \times 3$	**b** $6x \times 2x$	**c** $3ac \times 4a$	**d** $(3d)^2$
e $2st \times 3st$	**f** $a^2 \times 2a^2$	**g** $4y \times (2y)^2$	**h** $3g \times g \times 4$
i $3a \times (2a)^2$	**j** $9b^3 \times 4b^2$	**k** $(-x) \times 3x$	**l** $(-2x) \times x^2$
m $(-2x) \times (-x)$	**n** $(-3x) \times 4x^2$	**o** $(-x^2) \times 5x^2$	**p** $4x^2 \times (-2x)$
q $8x \times (-x^3)$	**r** $3x^2 \times (-x)^3$	**s** $2d^2 \times (-d)^2$	**t** $(3x)^3$

C   THE DISTRIBUTIVE LAW

Consider the large rectangle which has been split into two smaller rectangles:

The large rectangle has   area $=$ width $\times$ length

$= a \times (b + c)$

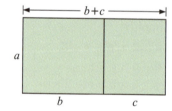

and the two smaller rectangles have area ab and ac

$\therefore \quad a(b + c) = ab + ac.$

This suggests that the factor outside the brackets is multiplied by each term within the bracket.

i.e., $a(b + c) = ab + ac$ and $a(b + c + d) = ab + ac + ad$.

This process of removing the brackets in a product is known as **expansion**, and

$a(b + c) = ab + ac$ is called the **distributive law**.

> Remember to multiply each term inside the brackets with the quantity outside the brackets.

Example 8   ◀)) **Self Tutor**

Expand and simplify: **a** $5(x + 4)$ **b** $4(y - 3)$

a $5(x + 4)$

$= 5 \times x + 5 \times 4$

$= 5x + 20$

b $4(y - 3)$

$= 4(y + -3)$

$= 4 \times y + 4 \times (-3)$

$= 4y - 12$

EXERCISE 9C

1 Expand and simplify:

a $3(x+2)$	**b** $4(x-1)$	**c** $5(a+4)$	**d** $6(a+b)$
e $2(b-4)$	**f** $9(m+3)$	**g** $3(n-m)$	**h** $2(s-t)$
i $5(4+x)$	**j** $2(x-y)$	**k** $3(t-7)$	**l** $7(3+p)$
m $9(b+c)$	**n** $4(x-5)$	**o** $2(6+j)$	**p** $8(q-p)$
q $2(5-k)$	**r** $6(y-z)$	**s** $4(k-5)$	**t** $5(10-x)$

Example 9 🔊 **Self Tutor**

Expand and simplify:

a $3(2a+7)$

b $2(3x-4)$

a $3(2a+7)$

$= 3 \times 2a + 3 \times 7$

$= 6a + 21$

b $2(3x-4)$

$= 2 \times 3x + 2 \times (-4)$

$= 6x - 8$

---

2 Expand and simplify:

a $4(3x+1)$	**b** $3(2a+7)$	**c** $2(1-2x)$	**d** $6(2-3n)$
e $5(2m+n)$	**f** $7(2x-y)$	**g** $3(b+3c)$	**h** $4(2a-b)$
i $2(a-6b)$	**j** $3(5+3d)$	**k** $7(4-2k)$	**l** $2(b+8a)$
m $11(4x+y)$	**n** $2(m-7n)$	**o** $6(3g-2h)$	**p** $3(4+3x)$
q $2(3x+z)$	**r** $6(c-3d)$	**s** $5(p+6q)$	**t** $4(3a-bc)$

Example 10 🔊 **Self Tutor**

Expand and simplify:

a $2y(3y+5)$

b $2x(3-2x)$

a $2y(3y+5)$

$= 2y \times 3y + 2y \times 5$

$= 6y^2 + 10y$

b $2x(3-2x)$

$= 2x \times 3 + 2x \times (-2x)$

$= 6x - 4x^2$

---

3 Expand and simplify:

a $a(a+4)$	**b** $b(3-b)$	**c** $c(3c+1)$	**d** $d(5-4d)$
e $a(2b+c)$	**f** $g(g^2-1)$	**g** $a^2(7-2a)$	**h** $3x(2x-3)$
i $2x(5-x)$	**j** $3x(5-x)$	**k** $4a^2(a-3)$	**l** $7n(4+2n)$
m $(3x-2)x$	**n** $(4+2x)x$	**o** $pq(q-p)$	**p** $ab^2(b-1)$
q $m^2n(3+n)$	**r** $ab(2b-a)$	**s** $5p(1-4pq)$	**t** $(7k^2+2l)l$
u $(3a^2-5)b^2$	**v** $2xy(x+6y)$	**w** $(3-4x^2)xy$	**x** $(4t^2-3s)s$

Example 11 ◀)) Self Tutor

Expand and simplify:

a $-4(x+3)$ **b** $-3(2x-4)$ **c** $-(3-2x)$

a $-4(x+3)$
$= -4 \times x \; + \; -4 \times 3$ $\{-4$ is multiplied by x and by $3.\}$
$= -4x - 12$

b $-3(2x-4)$
$= -3 \times 2x \; + \; -3 \times (-4)$ $\{-3$ is multiplied by $2x$ and by $-4.\}$
$= -6x - -12$
$= -6x + 12$

c $-(3-2x)$
$= -1(3-2x)$ $\{-1$ is multiplied by 3 and by $-2x.\}$
$= -1 \times 3 \; + \; -1 \times (-2x)$
$= -3 + 2x$

4   Expand and simplify:

    a $\;-3(x+1)$ **b** $\;-2(x+3)$ **c** $\;-5(x-2)$ **d** $\;-6(3-x)$

    e $\;-(a+4)$ **f** $\;-(x-2)$ **g** $\;-(6-x)$ **h** $\;-(3x+2)$

    i $\;-5(3-x)$ **j** $\;-9(3x-4)$ **k** $\;-2(5-2c)$ **l** $\;-(x-9)$

Example 12 ◀)) Self Tutor

Expand and simplify:

a $\;-a(a+7)$ **b** $\;-4b(2b-3)$

a $-a(a+7)$ **b** $-4b(2b-3)$
$= -a \times a \; + \; -a \times 7$ $= -4b \times 2b \; + \; -4b \times (-3)$
$= -a^2 - 7a$ $= -8b^2 + 12b$

> Remember that the quantity in front of the brackets is multiplied by every term inside the brackets.

5   Expand and simplify:

    a $\;-a(2+a)$ **b** $\;-b(b-4)$

    c $\;-c(2+c)$ **d** $\;-x(-x+7)$

    e $\;-3n(2-n)$ **f** $\;-4y(y+3)$

    g $\;-6a(3-a)$ **h** $\;-2b(2-5b)$

Example 13   ◀)) **Self Tutor**

Expand and simplify:

a $3(x+5) + 2(4-x)$ **b** $5(3-x) - 2(x+1)$

a $3(x+5) + 2(4-x)$
$= 3 \times x + 3 \times 5 + 2 \times 4 + 2 \times (-x)$
$= 3x + 15 + 8 - 2x$
$= 3x - 2x + 15 + 8$
$= x + 23$

b $5(3-x) - 2(x+1)$
$= 5 \times 3 + 5 \times (-x) + -2 \times x + -2 \times 1$
$= 15 - 5x - 2x - 2$
$= 15 - 2 - 5x - 2x$
$= 13 - 7x$

In practice the second line of working is often left out.

6 Expand and simplify:

a $4(x+1) + 2(x+2)$ **b** $4(x+2) + 4(x+2)$

c $5(x-1) + 2(x-3)$ **d** $2(2x-3) + 3(2-x)$

e $3(m+2) - 2(m-6)$ **f** $2(m-1) - 5(m+2)$

g $2(x+1) - 2(2x+3)$ **h** $8(2+x) - (5x+3)$

i $9(x-2) + 3(7-4x)$ **j** $9(2-5x) - 2(3x+2)$

k $-4(2n-3) - 3(3n-5)$ **l** $7(3y-4) + 5(1-2y)$

m $7(x-1) + 2(2x+3) - 11x$ **n** $5(3t-2) - 2(3t-1) + 3$

Example 14   ◀)) **Self Tutor**

Expand and simplify:

a $4 - 2(x+3)$ **b** $8 - 3(2y-1)$

a $4 - 2(x+3)$
$= 4 + -2(x+3)$
$= 4 + -2 \times x + -2 \times 3$
$= 4 - 2x - 6$
$= -2x - 2$

b $8 - 3(2y-1)$
$= 8 + -3(2y-1)$
$= 8 + -3 \times 2y + -3 \times (-1)$
$= 8 - 6y + 3$
$= 11 - 6y$

7 Expand and simplify:

a $4x - (1+2x)$ **b** $5 - 4(2x+1)$ **c** $9 - 6(2x-4)$

d $9x - (6-2x)$ **e** $5 - 3(2-5x)$ **f** $12 - (3+4x)$

g $5 - 6(2+3x)$ **h** $x - 7 + 2(3-4x)$ **i** $7x + 5 - 3(2-3x)$

j $8 - (5-2x)$ **k** $5x - (3-4x) + 4$ **l** $7 - 3(8-4x)$

Example 15   ◀) **Self Tutor**

Expand and simplify:
  a $a(a+2) + 2a(3a-2)$ **b** $y(3y-1) - 3y(2y-5)$

a $a(a+2) + 2a(3a-2)$
$$= a \times a \; + \; a \times 2 \; + \; 2a \times 3a \; + \; 2a \times (-2)$$
$$= a^2 + 2a + 6a^2 - 4a$$
$$= 7a^2 - 2a$$

b $y(3y-1) - 3y(2y-5)$
$$= y \times 3y \; + \; y \times (-1) \; + \; -3y \times 2y \; + \; -3y \times (-5)$$
$$= 3y^2 - y - 6y^2 + 15y$$
$$= 14y - 3y^2$$

8 Expand and simplify:
  a $3(x+2) + 4x(x-1)$ **b** $a(a-2) - a(4+a)$
  c $2(p+q) - 3(q-p)$ **d** $x(x^2+1) - 3x^2(1-2x)$
  e $x^2(x-8) - 3x(2+x^2)$ **f** $6(a-b+3) - 2(2+a-3b)$

Example 16   ◀) **Self Tutor**

Expand and simplify:
  a $3(x^2+4x-5)$ **b** $2a(a^2-3a+1)$

a $3(x^2+4x-5)$ **b** $2a(a^2-3a+1)$
$$= 3 \times x^2 \; + \; 3 \times 4x \; + \; 3 \times (-5) \qquad\qquad = 2a \times a^2 \; + \; 2a \times (-3a) \; + \; 2a \times 1$$
$$= 3x^2 + 12x - 15 \qquad\qquad\qquad\qquad\qquad = 2a^3 - 6a^2 + 2a$$

9 Expand and simplify:
  a $3(a^2+3a+1)$ **b** $3(b^2-3b+2)$ **c** $4(2c^2-3c-7)$
  d $d(-d^2-2d+1)$ **e** $2e(e^2+3e-5)$ **f** $3a(2a^2-3a+1)$
  g $3x(-4x^2-2x+5)$ **h** $-2b(5b+2b^2-1)$ **i** $-7y(3-y+5y^2)$

INVESTIGATION   **"THINK OF A NUMBER"**

Algebra is a powerful tool in mathematical problem solving.

Algebra can help us to describe problems in general terms and often gives us an insight into *why* something works.

What to do:

1 Play the following 'think of a number' game with a partner:

Think of a number.

Add 4.

Double the result.

Subtract 2.

Halve the result.

Subtract your original number.

Repeat the game choosing different numbers. You should find that the answer is always 3. Why is this so?

2 Algebra can provide an insight into why the answer to this game is always 3.

Let x represent the starting number.

Copy and complete the following argument by writing down each step in terms of x:

Think of a number:		x
Add 4	gives	$x + 4$
Double the result	gives	$2(x + 4) = ... + ...$
Subtract 2	gives	$.... + ... - 2 = ... + ...$
Halve the result	gives	$\frac{1}{2}(.... + ...) = ... + ...$
Subtract your original number	gives	$.... + ... - x = ...$

3 Try the following 'think of a number' game:

Think of a number.

Double it.

Add 8.

Halve the result.

Subtract 4.

What is your answer? Repeat the game using different numbers.

4 For the game above, let x be the starting number. Use algebra to show how the game works.

5 Make up your own 'think of a number' game. Test it with algebra before you try it on others.

D   THE EXPANSION OF $(a+b)(c+d)$

Products like $(a + b)(c + d)$ can be expanded by **repeated use** of the **distributive law**.

For example,

$$(x + 3)(x + 2) \quad (1)$$
$$= (x + 3)x \; + \; (x + 3)2 \quad (2)$$
$$= x(x + 3) \; + \; 2(x + 3) \quad (3)$$
$$= x^2 + 3x + 2x + 6 \quad (4)$$
$$= x^2 + 5x + 6$$

Compare:

$$\square(x + 2)$$
$$= \square \times x \; + \; \square \times 2$$

Notice that the distributive law for bracket expansion was used three times: once to get line (2) and twice to get line (4).

Example 17   ◀) Self Tutor

Expand and simplify by repeated use of the distributive law:

a $(x+5)(x+4)$ **b** $(x-2)(2x-1)$

a $(x+5)(x+4)$
$= (x+5)x + (x+5)4$
$= x(x+5) + 4(x+5)$
$= x^2 + 5x + 4x + 20$
$= x^2 + 9x + 20$

b $(x-2)(2x-1)$
$= (x-2)2x + (x-2)(-1)$
$= 2x(x-2) - (x-2)$
$= 2x^2 - 4x - x + 2$
$= 2x^2 - 5x + 2$

EXERCISE 9D

1 Expand and simplify by repeated use of the distributive law:

a $(x+1)(x+4)$ **b** $(a+3)(a+2)$ **c** $(c+1)(c-4)$

d $(a-2)(a-5)$ **e** $(w+x)(y+z)$ **f** $(p+q)(a+b)$

g $(x-1)(3x+2)$ **h** $(1-x)(2x+3)$ **i** $(2x+5)(x-3)$

j $(3x-2)(x+4)$ **k** $(4x-3)(3x-5)$ **l** $(x-1)(x^2+5)$

Example 18   ◀) Self Tutor

Expand using the distributive law repeatedly: **a** $(x+5)^2$ **b** $(x-5)^2$

a $(x+5)^2$
$= (x+5)(x+5)$
$= (x+5)x + (x+5)5$
$= x(x+5) + 5(x+5)$
$= x^2 + 5x + 5x + 25$
$= x^2 + 10x + 25$

b $(x-5)^2$
$= (x-5)(x-5)$
$= (x-5)x + (x-5)(-5)$
$= x(x-5) - 5(x-5)$
$= x^2 - 5x - 5x + 25$
$= x^2 - 10x + 25$

2 Expand using repeated use of the distributive law:

a $(x+2)^2$ **b** $(x-2)^2$ **c** $(5+x)^2$ **d** $(5-x)^2$

e $(2x+3)^2$ **f** $(2x-3)^2$ **g** $(a+b)^2$ **h** $(a-b)^2$

i $(x-6)^2$ **j** $(11+z)^2$ **k** $(3-5x)^2$ **l** $(2+7x)^2$

Example 19   ◀) Self Tutor

Use the distributive law
to expand and simplify:

$(x+2)(x^2+2x-3)$

$(x+2)(x^2+2x-3)$
$= (x+2)x^2 + (x+2)2x + (x+2)(-3)$
$= x^2(x+2) + 2x(x+2) - 3(x+2)$
$= x^3 + 2x^2 + 2x^2 + 4x - 3x - 6$
$= x^3 + 4x^2 + x - 6$

3 Use the distributive law to expand and simplify:

    a $(x+2)(x^2+2x+4)$

    b $(x+1)(2x^2-x+3)$

    c $(x-3)(x^2-2x+1)$

    d $(x^2-x+3)(x+5)$

    e $(x^2-2x-4)(3x-5)$

    f $(3x^2+2x+1)(2x-7)$

    g $(2x-5)(3-x^2+x)$

    h $(x+8)(x^2+1-3x)$

E   THE EXPANSION RULES

Consider the following rectangle which is 8 units long and 6 units wide.

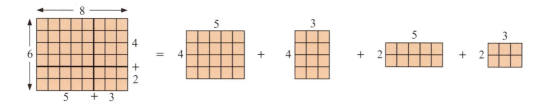

Comparing the total number of squares on each side of the $=$ sign, we notice that:

$$(4+2)(5+3) \quad = \quad 4 \times 5 \quad + \quad 4 \times 3 \quad + \quad 2 \times 5 \quad + \quad 2 \times 3.$$

We generalise this result by considering a rectangle with sides $(a+b)$ and $(c+d)$.

The original rectangle has area $= (a+b)(c+d)$.   {length $\times$ width}

The sum of the areas of the smaller rectangles $= ac+ad+bc+bd$.

$$\therefore \quad (a+b)(c+d) \ = \ ac+ad+bc+bd.$$

This expansion rule is called the **FOIL** rule as:

$$(a+b)(c+d) \ = \ ac \ + \ ad \ + \ bc \ + \ bd$$

inners

outers

                              Firsts   **O**uters   **I**nners   **L**asts

Example 20

🔊 **Self Tutor**

Expand and simplify: **a** $(x + 3)(x + 7)$ **b** $(x - 2)(x + 4)$

a $(x + 3)(x + 7)$

$= x \times x + x \times 7 + 3 \times x + 3 \times 7$

$= x^2 + 7x + 3x + 21$

$= x^2 + 10x + 21$

b $(x - 2)(x + 4)$

$= x \times x + x \times 4 - 2 \times x - 2 \times 4$

$= x^2 + 4x - 2x - 8$

$= x^2 + 2x - 8$

> The second line is often done mentally and so not written down.

EXERCISE 9E

1 Use the rule $(a + b)(c + d) = ac + ad + bc + bd$ to expand, and then simplify if possible:

a $(p + q)(x + y)$	**b** $(q + r)(s + t)$	**c** $(x + 3)(x + 6)$
d $(x + 4)(x + 2)$	**e** $(a + 5)(a + 1)$	**f** $(y + 6)(y + 5)$
g $(b + 3)(b - 3)$	**h** $(x - 5)(x + 3)$	**i** $(x + 8)(x - 4)$
j $(x - 1)(x + 4)$	**k** $(k + 4)(k - 3)$	**l** $(x + 2)(x - 6)$
m $(x + 5)(x - 2)$	**n** $(x - 3)(x - 6)$	**o** $(z - 9)(2z - 3)$
p $(3n - 1)(n + 2)$	**q** $(x - 7)(2x + 5)$	**r** $(3x + 5)(4x - 3)$

PERFECT SQUARES

> Notice that the middle two terms are identical.

Example 21

🔊 **Self Tutor**

Expand and simplify:

a $(x + 7)^2$

b $(3x - 2)^2$

a $(x + 7)^2$

$= (x + 7)(x + 7)$

$= x^2 + 7x + 7x + 49$

$= x^2 + 14x + 49$

b $(3x - 2)^2$

$= (3x - 2)(3x - 2)$

$= 9x^2 - 6x - 6x + 4$

$= 9x^2 - 12x + 4$

2 Expand and simplify using the rule $(a + b)(c + d) = ac + ad + bc + bd$:

a $(x + 1)^2$	**b** $(x + 3)^2$	**c** $(x - 3)^2$	**d** $(x - 8)^2$
e $(4 + y)^2$	**f** $(4 - y)^2$	**g** $(3x + 1)^2$	**h** $(3x - 1)^2$
i $(1 + 2a)^2$	**j** $(1 - 2a)^2$	**k** $(a + b)^2$	**l** $(a - b)^2$
m $(4x + 1)^2$	**n** $(3x - 4)^2$	**o** $(8x - 3)^2$	**p** $(6x + 3)^2$

The expressions in question **2** are known as **perfect squares**.

Perfect squares have form $(a + b)^2$ or $(a - b)^2$, and because we see them often in algebraic expressions we use the following rule for writing down their expansions:

$$(a + b)^2 = a^2 + 2ab + b^2$$

This rule is easily established by repeated use of the distributive law.

$(a+b)^2 = a^2 + 2ab + b^2$ can be demonstrated using areas.

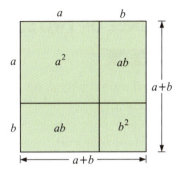

The following is a useful way of remembering the perfect square rules:

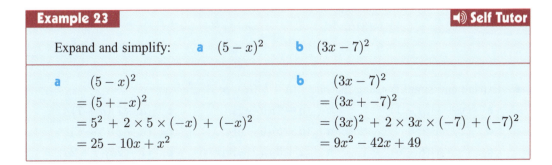

$(a + b)^2$	$=$	a^2	$+$	$2ab$	$+$	b^2
1st term 2nd term		square of first term		twice product of 2 terms		square of 2nd term

---

Example 22   ◀ﹱ **Self Tutor**

Expand and simplify: **a** $(x + 6)^2$ **b** $(2x + 5)^2$

a $(x + 6)^2$
$= x^2 + 2 \times x \times 6 + 6^2$
$= x^2 + 12x + 36$

b $(2x + 5)^2$
$= (2x)^2 + 2 \times 2x \times 5 + 5^2$
$= 4x^2 + 20x + 25$

---

3 Expand and simplify using the rule $(a + b)^2 = a^2 + 2ab + b^2$:

a $(c + d)^2$	**b** $(x + y)^2$	**c** $(p + q)^2$	**d** $(a + 2)^2$
e $(x + 7)^2$	**f** $(x + 9)^2$	**g** $(3a + 1)^2$	**h** $(1 + 2b)^2$
i $(2x + 5)^2$	**j** $(6 + 5x)^2$	**k** $(x^2 + 2)^2$	**l** $(x + x^2)^2$

Example 23   ◀ﹱ **Self Tutor**

Expand and simplify: **a** $(5 - x)^2$ **b** $(3x - 7)^2$

a $(5 - x)^2$
$= (5 + -x)^2$
$= 5^2 + 2 \times 5 \times (-x) + (-x)^2$
$= 25 - 10x + x^2$

b $(3x - 7)^2$
$= (3x + -7)^2$
$= (3x)^2 + 2 \times 3x \times (-7) + (-7)^2$
$= 9x^2 - 42x + 49$

4 Expand and simplify using the rule $(a+b)^2 = a^2 + 2ab + b^2$:

a	$(m-n)^2$	**b**	$(p-q)^2$	**c**	$(c-d)^2$	**d**	$(h-2)^2$
e	$(3-n)^2$	**f**	$(6-x)^2$	**g**	$(2x-5)^2$	**h**	$(7-2z)^2$
i	$(3x-2)^2$	**j**	$(4-3a)^2$	**k**	$(2x-3y)^2$	**l**	$(x^2-3)^2$

DIFFERENCE OF TWO SQUARES

Notice that the middle two terms add to zero!

Example 24   ◀)) **Self Tutor**

Expand and simplify using $(a+b)(c+d) = ac + ad + bc + bd$:

a $(x+3)(x-3)$ **b** $(2x-5)(2x+5)$

a $\quad (x+3)(x-3)$
$\quad = x^2 - 3x + 3x - 9$
$\quad = x^2 - 9$

b $\quad (2x-5)(2x+5)$
$\quad = 4x^2 + 10x - 10x - 25$
$\quad = 4x^2 - 25$

5 Expand and simplify using the rule $(a+b)(c+d) = ac + ad + bc + bd$:

a	$(x+1)(x-1)$	**b**	$(a-2)(a+2)$	**c**	$(b+5)(b-5)$
d	$(c-3)(c+3)$	**e**	$(4+x)(4-x)$	**f**	$(7-x)(7+x)$
g	$(1+y)(1-y)$	**h**	$(8-b)(8+b)$	**i**	$(2x+3)(2x-3)$
j	$(4a-5)(4a+5)$	**k**	$(2+3x)(2-3x)$	**l**	$(1-6y)(1+6y)$

In question **5** above we noticed that when we expand expressions of the form $(a+b)(a-b)$
we get $a^2 - ab + ab - b^2 = a^2 - b^2$

Since a^2 and b^2 are perfect squares, $a^2 - b^2$ is called the **difference of two squares**.

In general, $\qquad\qquad \boldsymbol{(a+b)(a-b) = a^2 - b^2}.$

Example 25   ◀)) **Self Tutor**

Expand and simplify using the rule $(a+b)(a-b) = a^2 - b^2$:

a $(x+3)(x-3)$ **b** $(2x-5)(2x+5)$

a $\quad (x+3)(x-3)$
$\quad = (x)^2 - (3)^2$
$\quad = x^2 - 9$

b $\quad (2x-5)(2x+5)$
$\quad = (2x)^2 - (-5)^2$
$\quad = 4x^2 - 25$

6 Expand and simplify using the rule $(a+b)(a-b) = a^2 - b^2$:

a	$(y+1)(y-1)$	**b**	$(b+2)(b-2)$	**c**	$(a-7)(a+7)$
d	$(x-4)(x+4)$	**e**	$(6-b)(6+b)$	**f**	$(5-x)(5+x)$
g	$(8+a)(8-a)$	**h**	$(2+3y)(2-3y)$	**i**	$(7-2a)(7+2a)$
j	$(3x+1)(3x-1)$	**k**	$(5-3y)(5+3y)$	**l**	$(-x+2)(-x-2)$

7 Expand and simplify using the appropriate expansion rule:

a	$(x+7)(x-3)$	**b**	$(x+3)(x+5)$	**c**	$(x+4)^2$
d	$(3-x)(5-x)$	**e**	$(1-x)(x-3)$	**f**	$(x-11)^2$
g	$(a+8)(a-8)$	**h**	$(h+9)^2$	**i**	$(2x+13)(2x-13)$
j	$(x+3)(2x-5)$	**k**	$(3x+5)^2$	**l**	$(m+n)(m-n)$
m	$(3x-2)(x+5)$	**n**	$(5x-2)^2$	**o**	$(7x+1)(7x-1)$
p	$(4x+1)(5-x)$	**q**	$(3-2r)^2$	**r**	$(-2+3x)(4x-3)$

F   PERIMETERS AND AREAS

Sometimes in problem solving we are required to find perimeters and areas in terms of one or more variables.

Reminder:
- The **perimeter** of a closed figure is the distance around its boundary.
- The **area** of a closed figure is the number of square units contained within the boundary.

Example 26   ◀)) Self Tutor

Find the perimeter P of:

a

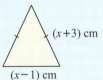
$(x+3)$ cm

$(x-1)$ cm

b

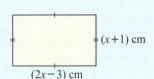
$(x+1)$ cm

$(2x-3)$ cm

a $P =$ two lots of $(x+3)$ + one lot of $(x-1)$
$P = 2(x+3) + (x-1)$
$P = 2x + 6 + x - 1$
$\therefore \quad P = 3x + 5$ cm

b $P =$ two lots of $(x+1)$ + two lots of $(2x-3)$
$P = 2(x+1) + 2(2x-3)$
$P = 2x + 2 + 4x - 6$
$\therefore \quad P = 6x - 4$ cm

EXERCISE 9F

1 Find the perimeter P of the following if all measurements are in cm:

a

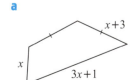
$x+3$

x

$3x+1$

b

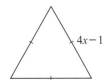
$4x-1$

c

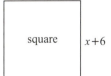
square

$x+6$

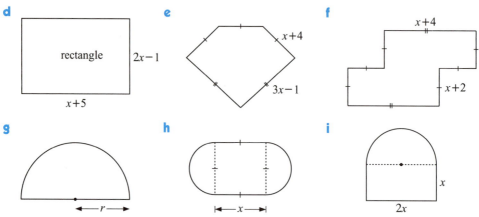

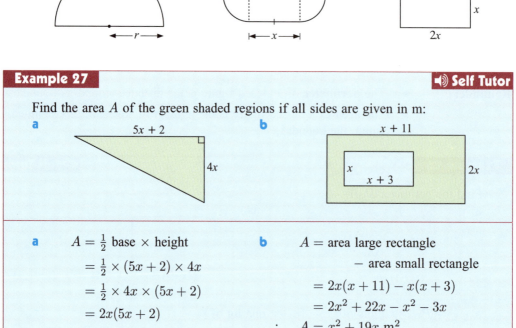

Example 27

Find the area A of the green shaded regions if all sides are given in m:

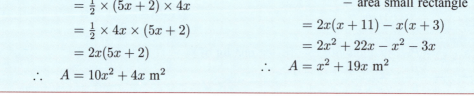

a
$A = \frac{1}{2}$ base $\times$ height

$= \frac{1}{2} \times (5x + 2) \times 4x$

$= \frac{1}{2} \times 4x \times (5x + 2)$

$= 2x(5x + 2)$

$\therefore \quad A = 10x^2 + 4x$ m^2

b
$A = $ area large rectangle

$\qquad - $ area small rectangle

$= 2x(x + 11) - x(x + 3)$

$= 2x^2 + 22x - x^2 - 3x$

$\therefore \quad A = x^2 + 19x$ m^2

2 Find the area A of the shaded regions if all sides are given in m:

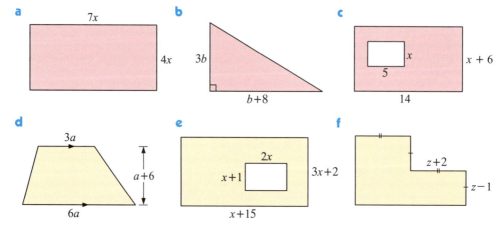

REVIEW SET 9A

1 Simplify where possible, by collecting like terms:

   a $2x + 5x$ **b** $7 - 7y$ **c** $x + y - 2x$

   d $4a + ab$ **e** $3xy + 7xy$ **f** $3x^2 + 2 - 2x^2 - 2$

   g $4a - a$ **h** $5y^2 - -2y^2$ **i** $x^2 + x^2 + x^2$

2 Simplify:

   a $c + d + d + d$ **b** $c \times d \times d \times d$ **c** $3 \times d + c \times d$

3 Simplify:

   a $x \times x^3$ **b** $4x^2 \times 2x^2$ **c** $(x^2)^3$

   d $3x \times y^2$ **e** $(-3x) \times (-2x)$ **f** $2ab^2 \times 5a^2$

4 Expand and simplify:

   a $4(y + 2)$ **b** $2(8a - 3b)$ **c** $-(4 - x)$

   d $-2(x + 1)$ **e** $7(x + 1) - 3(x - 1)$ **f** $5 - 4(y + 2) - y$

5 Expand and simplify: $2x(x^2 - 5x + 6)$

6 Expand and simplify:

   a $(x - 6)(x + 3)$ **b** $(2y - 1)^2$ **c** $(3a - 2)(4a - 5)$

   d $(2x + 11)(2x - 11)$ **e** $(3x + 2y)^2$ **f** $(a^2 + a - 2)(a + 5)$

7 Find the perimeter P of the following shapes (all measurements in cm):

   a 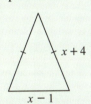   **b** 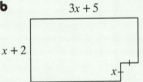   **c**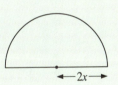

8 Find the area A of the following shapes if all measurements are in cm:

   a 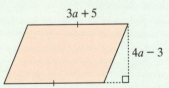   **b**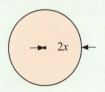

REVIEW SET 9B

1 Simplify where possible, by collecting like terms:

   a $3q - 3q$ **b** $a + 5a - 4a$ **c** $q - p + 3q$

   d $ab + 7ab$ **e** $y^2 - y^2 + y^2$ **f** $2a^2 - -7a^2$

2 Simplify:

   a $a + b + a + b$ **b** $b \times b \times b \times c$ **c** $c \times d - 5 \times c$

3 Simplify:

    a $y^2 \times y$ **b** $2y \times y^2$ **c** $(y^2)^3$

    d $x \times 2y^2$ **e** $(-3y) \times (-5y)$ **f** $5x^2y \times 3xy^2$

4 Expand and simplify:

    a $3(5 - 2x)$ **b** $-3(x - 5)$ **c** $-3x(1 + x)$

    d $7 + 5x(1 - x)$ **e** $4(y + 2) - (1 - y)$ **f** $2a(a - 3) - 3(5 - 2a)$

5 Expand and simplify: $3x(x^2 + 4x + 7)$

6 Expand and simplify:

    a $(x + 12)(x + 5)$ **b** $(3a + 1)^2$ **c** $(2a - 1)(a - 5)$

    d $(x + 7)(x - 7)$ **e** $(4x - 3y)^2$ **f** $(a^2 + 1)(a - 3)$

7 Find the perimeter P of the following shapes (all measured in cm):

    a 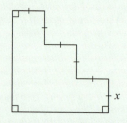   **b** 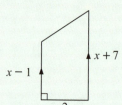   **c**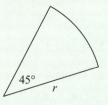

8 Find the areas A of the following shapes (all sides measured in m):

    a 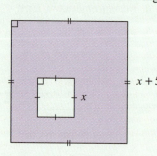   **b**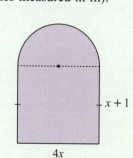

Chapter 10

Statistics

Contents:

A Terminology for the study of statistics
B Quantitative (numerical) data
C Grouped discrete data
D Frequency histograms
E Measuring the centre
F Cumulative data
G Measuring the spread
H Box-and-whisker plots
I Statistics from technology

HISTORICAL NOTE

- Florence Nightingale (1820-1910), the famous "lady with the lamp", developed and used graphs to represent data relating to hospitals and public health.

- Today about 92% of all nations conduct a census at regular intervals. The UN gives assistance to developing countries to help them with census procedures, so that accurate and comparable worldwide statistics can be collected.

OPENING PROBLEM

  Kelly grows pumpkins and wishes to investigate the effect of an organic fertiliser on the number of pumpkins harvested.

She hopes that the fertiliser will significantly increase the number of pumpkins harvested per plant.

In identical soils she has planted many seeds in two patches, one using the fertiliser and the other not. All other factors such as watering have been kept the same for both patches.

Random plants are selected and the number of pumpkins counted. The results are:

Without fertiliser

```
4 7 8 3 9    8 6 5 9 7    8 7 8 4 6
7 6 8 6 7    6 6 7 8 8    4 7 7 7 3
5 5 8 9 7    4 9 6 9 7
```

With fertiliser

```
8 10 4 10 15    4 9 7 11 10    8 8 6 10 10
9 5 9 6 7       5 7 7 9 8       6 5 7 8 7
2 6 9 7 10      6 8 7 10 8
```

For you to consider:

- Can you state clearly the problem that Kelly wants to solve?
- How has Kelly tried to make a fair comparison?
- How could Kelly have made sure that her selection was at random?
- What is the best way of organising this data?
- What are suitable methods for displaying the data?
- Are there any abnormally high or low results, and how should they be treated?
- How can she best indicate the most typical yield per plant?
- How can we best indicate the spread of the data?
- Can a satisfactory conclusion be made?

TERMINOLOGY FOR THE STUDY OF STATISTICS

STATISTICS

> **Statistics** is the art of solving problems and answering questions by collecting and analysing data.

The facts or pieces of information we collect are called **data**. Data is the plural of the word *datum*, which means a single piece of information.

A list of information is called a **data set** and because it is not in an organised form it is called **raw data**.

THE STATISTICAL METHOD

The process of **statistical enquiry** (or **investigation**) includes the following steps:

Step 1:   Examining a problem which may be solved using data and posing the correct question(s).
Step 2:   Collecting data.
Step 3:   Organising the data.
Step 4:   Summarising and displaying the data.
Step 5:   Analysing the data, making a conclusion in the form of a conjecture.
Step 6:   Writing a report.

VARIABLES

There are two types of variables that we commonly deal with:

- A **categorical variable** is one which describes a particular quality or characteristic. It can be divided into **categories**. The information collected is called **categorical data**.

    Examples of categorical variables are:

    Getting to school: the categories could be train, bus, car and walking.
    Colour of eyes: the categories could be blue, brown, hazel, green, and grey.

- A **quantitative variable** is one which has a numerical value, and is often called a **numerical variable**. The information collected is called **numerical data**.

    Quantitative variables can be either discrete or continuous.

    > A **quantitative discrete variable** takes exact number values and is often a result of **counting**.

    Examples of discrete quantitative variables are:

    The number of people in a household: the variable could take the values 1, 2, 3, ...
    The score out of 30 for a test: the variable could take the values 0, 1, 2, 3, ..., 30.

A **quantitative continuous variable** takes numerical values within a certain continuous range. It is usually a result of **measuring**.

Examples of quantitative continuous variables are:

- *The weight of newborn babies:*   the variable could take any positive value on the number line but is likely to be in the range 0.5 kg to 7 kg.
- *The heights of Year 10 students:*   the variable would be measured in centimetres. A student whose height is recorded as 145 cm could have exact height anywhere between 144.5 cm and 145.5 cm.

CENSUS OR SAMPLE

The two types of data collection are by census or sample.

A **census** is a method which involves collecting data about every individual in a *whole population*.

The individuals in a population may be people or objects. A census is detailed and accurate but is expensive, time consuming, and often impractical.

A **sample** is a method which involves collecting data about a *part of the population* only.

A sample is cheaper and quicker than a census but is not as detailed or as accurate. Conclusions drawn from samples always involve some error.

A sample must truly reflect the characteristics of the whole population. It must therefore be **unbiased** and **sufficiently large**.

A **biased sample** is one in which the data has been unfairly influenced by the collection process and is not truly representative of the whole population.

EXERCISE 10A

1   Classify the following variables as either categorical or numerical:
   a   the time taken to travel to school
   b   the number of cousins a person has
   c   voting intention at the next election
   d   the number of cars in a household
   e   the speed of cars on a particular stretch of highway
   f   favourite type of apple
   g   town or city where a person was born
   h   the weight of three-year-old children

2   Write down the possible categories for the following categorical variables:
   a   gender
   b   favourite football code
   c   hair colour
   d   type of fuel used in a car

3 For each of the following possible investigations, classify the variable as categorical, quantitative discrete or quantitative continuous:

    a the number of goals scored each week by a hockey team

    b the weights of the members of a basketball team

    c the most popular TV station

    d the number of kittens in each litter

    e the number of bread rolls bought each week by a family

    f the pets owned by students in your class

    g the number of leaves on a rose plant stem

    h the number of hours of daylight each day in winter

    i the number of people who die from heart attacks each year in a given city

    j the amount of rainfall in each month of the year

    k the countries of origin of refugees

    l the reasons people use public transport

    m the stopping distances of cars doing 80 km h^{-1}

    n the number of cars passing through an intersection per hour

    o the pulse rates of a group of hockey players at rest

4 State whether a census or a sample would be used for these investigations:

    a the reasons for people using taxis

    b the heights of the basketballers at a particular school

    c finding the percentage of people in a city who suffer from asthma

    d the resting pulse rates of members of your favourite sporting team

    e finding the country of origin of immigrants

    f the amount of daylight each month where you live

5 Discuss any possible bias in the following situations:

    a Only Year 12 students are interviewed about changes to the school uniform.

    b Motorists stopped in peak hour are interviewed about traffic problems.

    c Real estate agents are interviewed about the prices of houses.

    d A 'who will you vote for' survey at an expensive city restaurant.

STATISTICAL GRAPHS

Two variables under consideration are usually linked by one being *dependent* on the other.

For example,   the *total cost of a dinner* depends on *the number of guests present*.

        We say that   *the total cost of a dinner* is the **dependent variable**,   and

                       the number of guests present is the **independent variable**.

In general, when we draw **graphs** involving two variables, the *independent variable* is placed on the **horizontal axis** and the *dependent variable* is placed on the **vertical axis**. An exception to this is when we draw a horizontal bar chart.

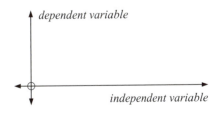

Acceptable graphs to display categorical data are:

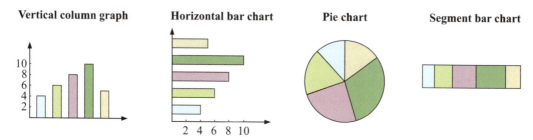

Vertical column graph   **Horizontal bar chart**   **Pie chart**   **Segment bar chart**

For categorical data, the **mode** is the category which occurs most frequently. In the graphs above, the mode is the green category.

INTERNET STATISTICS

There are thousands of sites worldwide which display statistics for everyone to see. Sites which show statistics that are important on a global scale include:

- www.un.org   for the United Nations

- www.who.int   for the World Health Organisation

GRAPHING STATISTICS USING A COMPUTER PACKAGE

Click on the icon to obtain a graphing package for statistics.
Experiment with the different types of graphs it can produce.
Enter some data of your own and print the results.

STATISTICS PACKAGE

6 At a school, children were randomly chosen and asked to nominate their favourite fruit. The following data was collected:

Type of fruit	Frequency
Apple	20
Banana	24
Grapes	3
Orange	11
Mandarin	10
Nectarine	7
Pear	2
Peach	3

a What are the variables in this investigation?

b What is the dependent variable?

c What is the sample size?

d If we are trying to find out the favourite fruit of children, is the sample unbiased?

e If we are only interested in the favourite fruit of 368 children within the school, is the sample unbiased?

f What is the mode?

g Using the computer package, construct a vertical column graph to illustrate the data.

7 55 randomly selected Year 10 students were asked to nominate their favourite subject studied at school. The results of the survey are displayed in the bar chart shown.

a What are the variables in this investigation?

b What are the dependent and independent variables?

c What is the mode?

d What given information indicates that the sample was unbiased?

e If there are 173 Year 10 students at the school, is the sample size sufficient?

f Construct a pie chart for the data. If possible, use a spreadsheet.

8 Warren read the following report from the local paper:

OUR CHANGING POPULATION

A spokesperson from the Statistics Bureau reported today that the number of persons per household has reached an all time low. Some of the reasons suggested for this decline were: women having fewer children and at a later stage in their lives because they want to establish their careers, more couples choosing not to have children at all, and it being more expensive than at any time previously to raise children.

In the past large families were common. It was cheaper to raise children as the 'necessities' of life were basic compared with the current times. Few married women had paid employment outside the home.

Whilst there have been fluctuations in family size over the last hundred years, such as the 'baby boom' following World War II, it is now seen as unlikely that we will ever return to the large families of the past.

Warren decided to put this statement to the test in his local town of Boodernut. He applied for and received census data from the Statistics Bureau, a copy of which is given alongside.

a Find the population sizes of the town in:

   i 1935   **ii** 1960

   iii 1985

Private household size of Boodernut			
Number of persons	*Year*		
	1935	1960	1985
1	9	8	69
2	68	177	184
3	73	162	248
4	109	374	162
5+	178	283	38
Totals			

b Prepare a table of percentages for the town's population data (correct to 1 decimal place).

c Using the data, write a brief discussion and conclusion which compares the changes in the household sizes over the 1935 to 1985 period.

B   QUANTITATIVE (NUMERICAL) DATA

Recall that:

A **quantitative variable** is one which has a numerical value, and is often called a **numerical variable**. The information collected is called **numerical data**.

Quantitative variables can be either discrete or continuous and they each have an appropriate way to organise and display the data collected for them.

A **quantitative discrete variable** takes exact number values and is often a result of **counting**.

Some examples are:

- *The number of pets in a household:*   the variable could take the values of 0, 1, 2, 3, 4, ...

- *Shoe size:*   the variable could take the values of 3, $3\frac{1}{2}$, 4, $4\frac{1}{2}$, 5, $5\frac{1}{2}$, ...

A **quantitative continuous variable** takes numerical values within a certain continuous range. It is usually a result of **measuring**.

Some examples are:

- *The weight of Year 10 students:*   the variable could take any positive value from about 40 kg to 120 kg. Theoretically the variable could take any value on the number line but is very unlikely to take a value outside the range given.

- *The time taken to get to school:*   the variable could take any value from about 1 minute to 80 minutes.

ORGANISATION AND DISPLAY OF DISCRETE DATA

In the **Opening Problem**, the quantitative discrete variable is: *the number of pumpkins per plant*.

To organise the data a **tally-frequency table** could be used. We count the data systematically and use a '|' to indicate each data value. We use $\cancel{||||}$ to represent 5.

Below is the table for *Without fertiliser*:

Number of pumpkins/plant	Tally	Frequency
3	||	2
4	||||	4
5	|||	3
6	ⅢⅠ ||	7
7	Ⅲ Ⅲ |	11
8	Ⅲ |||	8
9	Ⅲ	5

A **column graph** or **dot plot** could be used to display the results.

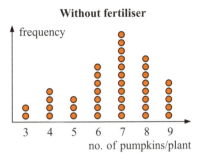

DISCUSSION

Are there any advantages or disadvantages in using a dot plot rather than a column graph?

From both graphs we can make observations and calculations such as:

- 7 pumpkins per plant is the **mode** of the *Without fertiliser* data since this is the value which occurred most frequently.

- 5% of the plants had fewer than 4 pumpkins on them.

DESCRIBING THE DISTRIBUTION OF THE DATA SET

The **mode** of a data set is the most frequently occurring value(s). Many data sets show **symmetry** or **partial symmetry** about the mode.

If we place a curve over the column graph we see that this curve shows symmetry. We say that we have a **symmetrical distribution**.

For the *Without fertiliser* data we have the distribution alongside. It is said to be **negatively skewed** because, by comparison with the symmetrical distribution, it has been 'stretched' on the left (or negative) side of the mode.

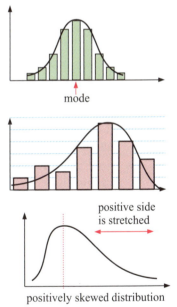

So, we have:

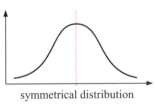

symmetrical distribution

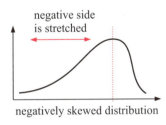

negatively skewed distribution

positively skewed distribution

OUTLIERS

Outliers are data values that are either much larger or much smaller than the general body of data. Outliers appear separated from the body of data on a frequency graph.

For example, in the data set: 3, 1, 7, 6, 8, 18, 2, 6, 7, 7, the data value 18 is an outlier. Some outliers are genuine and must be included in an analysis of the whole data set. However, other outliers may not reflect the truth and should not be considered. These may be due to human error or some other factor.

EXERCISE 10B

1 State whether these quantitative (or numerical) variables are discrete or continuous:
  a the time taken to run 1500 metres
  b the maximum temperature reached on a March day
  c the weight of cargo taken on a ship
  d the time taken for a battery to run down
  e the number of trips made by a taxi
  f the number of people in a theatre
  g the number of minutes spent sending text messages per day

2 20 students were asked "How many TV sets do you have in your household?" and the following data was collected: 2 1 0 3 1 2 1 3 4 0 0 2 2 0 1 1 0 1 0 1
  a What is the variable in this investigation?
  b Is the data discrete or continuous? Why?
  c Construct a dot plot to display the data. Use a heading for the graph, and add an appropriate scale and label to each axis.
  d How would you describe the distribution of the data? Is it symmetrical, positively skewed or negatively skewed? Are there any outliers?
  e What percentage of the households had no TV sets?
  f What percentage of the households had three or more TV sets?

3 A randomly selected sample of shoppers was asked, 'How many times did you shop at a supermarket in the past week?' A column graph was constructed for the results.
  a How many shoppers gave data in the survey?
  b How many of the shoppers shopped once or twice?
  c What percentage of the shoppers shopped more than four times?
  d Describe the distribution of the data.

4 Employees of a company were asked to record the number of times they left the company office on business appointments during one week. The following dot plot was constructed from the data:

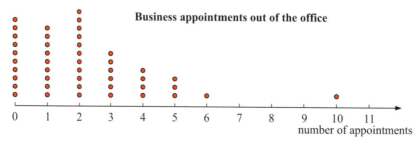

a What is the variable in this investigation?

b Explain why the data is discrete numerical data.

c What percentage of the employees did not leave the office?

d What percentage of the employees left the office more than 5 times?

e What was the most frequent number of business appointments out of the office?

f Describe the distribution of the data.

g How would you describe the data value '10'?

5 The number of toothpicks in a box is stated as 50 but the actual number of toothpicks has been found to vary. To investigate this, the number of toothpicks in a box was counted for a sample of 60 boxes:

50 52 51 50 50 51 52 49 50 48 51 50 47 50 52 48 50 49 51 50
49 50 52 51 50 50 52 50 53 48 50 51 50 50 49 48 51 49 52 50
49 49 50 52 50 51 49 52 52 50 49 50 49 51 50 50 51 50 53 48

a What is the variable in this investigation?

b Is the data continuous or discrete numerical data?

c Construct a frequency table for this data.

d Display the data using a bar chart.

e Describe the distribution of the data.

f What percentage of the boxes contained exactly 50 toothpicks?

6 Revisit the **Opening Problem** on page **188**. Using the *With fertiliser* data:

a Organise the data in a tally-frequency table.

b Draw a column graph of the data.

c Are there any outliers?

d Is the data skewed?

e What evidence is there that the fertiliser increases the number of pumpkins per plant?

f Can it be said that the fertiliser will increase the farmer's pumpkin crop and therefore her profits?

C GROUPED DISCRETE DATA

In situations where there are lots of different numerical values recorded, it may not be practical to use an ordinary tally-frequency table, or to display the data using a dot plot or column graph.

For example, a local hardware store is concerned about the number of people visiting the store at lunch time.

Over 30 consecutive week days they recorded data.

The results were:

37, 30, 17, 13, 46, 23, 40, 28, 38, 24, 23, 22, 18, 29, 16,
35, 24, 18, 24, 44, 32, 54, 31, 39, 32, 38, 41, 38, 24, 32

In situations like this, grouping the data into **class intervals** is appropriate.

It seems sensible to use class intervals of length 10 in this case.

The tally-frequency table is:

Number of people	Tally	Frequency
10 to 19	IIII I	5
20 to 29	IIII IIII	9
30 to 39	IIII IIII I	11
40 to 49	IIII	4
50 to 59	I	1
	Total	30

STEM-AND-LEAF PLOTS

A **stem-and-leaf plot** (often called a stem-plot) is a way of writing down the data in groups and is used for small data sets. It shows actual data values and gives a visual comparison of frequencies.

For numbers with two digits, the first digit forms part of the **stem** and the second digit forms a **leaf**.

For example, for the data value 17,   1 is recorded on the stem, and the 7 is a leaf value.

The **stem-and-leaf plot** is:

Stem	Leaf
1	73868
2	384329444
3	70852192882
4	6041
5	4 **Note:** 1 | 7 means 17

The **ordered stem-and-leaf plot** is:

Stem	Leaf
1	36788
2	233444489
3	01222578889
4	0146
5	4

The ordered stemplot arranges all data from smallest to largest.

Notice the following features:

- all the actual data is shown
- the minimum (smallest) data value is 13
- the maximum (largest) data value is 54
- the 'thirties' interval (30 to 39) occurred most often, and is the **modal class**.

EXERCISE 10C

1   The data set below is the test scores (out of 100) for a Science test for 50 students.

92	29	78	67	68	58	80	89	92
69	66	56	88	81	70	73	63	55
67	64	62	74	56	75	90	56	47
59	64	89	39	51	87	89	76	59
72	80	95	68	80	64	53	43	61
71	38	44	88	62				

a   Construct a tally and frequency table for this data using class intervals 0 - 9, 10 - 19, 20 - 29, ..., 90 - 100.

b   What percentage of the students scored 80 or more for the test?

c What percentage of students scored less than 50 for the test?

d Copy and complete the following:

More students had a test score in the interval .... than in any other interval.

2   a Draw a stem-and-leaf plot using stems 2, 3, 4, and 5 for the following data:

29, 27, 33, 30, 46, 40, 35, 24, 21, 58, 27, 34, 25, 36, 57, 34, 42, 51, 50, 48

b Redraw the stem-and-leaf plot from **a** so that it is ordered.

3 For the ordered stem-and-leaf plot given, find:

Stem	Leaf
0	1 3 7
1	0 3 4 7 8 8 9
2	0 0 1 2 2 3 5 5 6 8 9
3	2 4 4 5 8 9
4	3

a the minimum value

b the maximum value

c the number of data with a value greater than 25

d the number of data with a value of at least 40

e the percentage of the data which is less than 15.

4 A test score out of 60 marks is recorded for a group of 45 students:

34 37 44 51 53 39 33 58 40 42 43 43 47 37 35
41 43 48 50 55 44 44 52 54 59 39 31 29 44 57
45 34 29 27 18 49 41 42 37 42 43 43 45 34 51

a Construct a stem-and-leaf plot for this data using 0, 1, 2, 3, 4, and 5 as the stems.

b Redraw the stem-and-leaf plot so that it is ordered.

c What advantage does a stem-and-leaf plot have over a frequency table?

d What is the **i** highest **ii** lowest   mark scored for the test?

e If an 'A' is awarded to students who scored 50 or more for the test, what percentage of students scored an 'A'?

f What percentage of students scored less than half marks for the test?

g Describe the distribution of the data.

D   FREQUENCY HISTOGRAMS

A **continuous numerical variable** can theoretically take any value on part of the number line. A continuous variable often has to be **measured** so that data can be recorded.

Examples of continuous numerical variables are:

The height of Year 10 students: the variable can take any value from about 100 cm to 200 cm.

The speed of cars on a stretch of highway: the variable can take any value from 0 km h^{-1} to the fastest speed that a car can travel, but is most likely to be in the range 30 km h^{-1} to 240 km h^{-1}.

ORGANISATION AND DISPLAY OF CONTINUOUS DATA

When data is recorded for a continuous variable there are likely to be many different values. This data is therefore organised using **class intervals**. A special type of graph called a **frequency histogram** is used to display the data.

A histogram is similar to a column graph but, to account for the continuous nature of the variable, the 'columns' are joined together.

An example is given alongside:

The **modal class**, which is the class of values that appears most often, is easy to identify from a histogram.

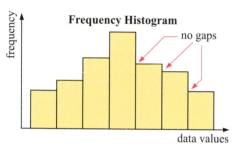

Frequency Histogram

no gaps

SUMMARY OF COLUMN GRAPHS AND FREQUENCY HISTOGRAMS

Column graphs and frequency histograms both have the following features:

- on the **vertical axis** we have the **frequency** of occurrence
- on the **horizontal axis** we have the range of scores
- **column widths are equal** and the height varies according to frequency.

Histograms have no gaps between the columns because they are used for **continuous** data.

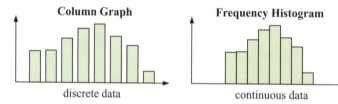

Column Graph	Frequency Histogram
discrete data	continuous data

Example 1   ◆) Self Tutor

The weights of parcels sent on a given day from a post office were, in kilograms:

2.9, 4.0, 1.6, 3.5, 2.9, 3.4, 3.2, 5.2, 4.6, 3.1, 2.8, 3.7, 4.9, 3.4, 1.3, 2.5, 2.2

Organise the data using a frequency table and graph the data.

The data is *continuous* since the weight could be any value from 0.1 kg up to 6 kg. The lowest weight recorded is 1.3 kg and the highest is 5.2 kg so we will use class intervals of 1 kg. The class interval $2 - < 3$ includes all weights from 2 kg up to, but not including, 3 kg.

Weight (kg)	Frequency
$1 - < 2$	2
$2 - < 3$	5
$3 - < 4$	6
$4 - < 5$	3
$5 - < 6$	1

A frequency histogram is used to graph this continuous data.

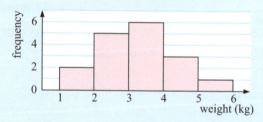

A stemplot could also be used to organise the data:

Note: The modal class is $(3 - < 4)$ kg as this occurred most frequently.

Stem	Leaf
1	3 6
2	2 5 8 9 9
3	1 2 4 4 5 7
4	0 6 9
5	2

Scale: 2 | 9 means 2.9 kg.

EXERCISE 10D

1 A frequency table for the weights of a volleyball squad is given below.

Weight (kg)	Frequency
75 - < 80	2
80 - < 85	5
85 - < 90	8
90 - < 95	7
95 - < 100	5
100 - < 105	1

a Explain why 'weight' is a continuous variable.

b Construct a frequency histogram for the data. The axes should be carefully marked and labelled, and you should include a heading for the graph.

c What is the modal class? Explain what this means.

d Describe the distribution of the data.

2 A school has conducted a survey of 50 students to investigate the time it takes for them to travel to school. The following data gives the travel times to the nearest minute:

```
16    8   10   17   25   34   42   18   24   18   45   33   40
 3   20   12   10   10   27   16   37   45   15   16   26   16
14   18   15   27   19   32    6   12   14   20   10   16
21   25    8   32   46   14   15   20   18    8   10   25
```

a Is travel time a discrete or continuous variable?

b Construct an ordered stemplot for the data using stems 0, 1, 2, ...

c Describe the distribution of the data.

d Copy and complete:
"The modal travelling time was between ..... and ..... minutes."

3 For the following data, state whether a frequency histogram or a column graph should be used and draw the appropriate graph.

a Most appealing car colour:

Colour	white	red	blue	black	other
Frequency	47	44	31	23	18

b The number of students in classes:

Number of students	21	22	23	24	25	26	27
Frequency	1	4	7	9	15	8	2

> Notice in **d** that the interval 140 - 149 is really
> 139.5 - < 149.5
> and your graph must show this.
>
> 139.5   149.5   159.5

c The time taken to make a pizza (to the nearest min):

Time (min)	5	6	7	8	9	10	11
Frequency	1	2	3	7	10	8	5

d The heights of 25 netball players (to the nearest cm):

Height (cm)	140 - 149	150 - 159	160 - 169	170 - 179	180 - 189
Frequency	2	3	7	9	4

e 45 swimmers have 'best times':

Time (sec)	50 - < 60	60 - < 70	70 - < 80	80 - < 90	90 - < 100
Frequency	8	23	7	4	3

4   A plant inspector takes a random sample of ten week old plants from a nursery and measures their height to the nearest mm.

height (mm)	frequency
20 - 39	4
40 - 59	17
60 - 79	15
80 - 99	8
100 - 119	2
120 - 139	4

The results are shown in the table alongside.

a   Represent the data on a frequency histogram.

b   How many of the seedlings are 40 mm or more?

c   What percentage of the seedlings are between 60 and 79 mm?

d   The total number of seedlings in the nursery is 857. Estimate the number of seedlings which measure: **i**   less than 100 mm   **ii**   between 40 and 99 mm.

E   MEASURING THE CENTRE

We can get a better understanding of a data set if we can locate the **middle** or **centre** of the data and get an indication of its **spread**. Knowing one of these without the other is often of little use.

There are *three statistics* that are used to measure the **centre** of a data set. These are: the **mean**, the **median** and the **mode**.

THE MEAN

> The **mean** of a data set is the statistical name for the arithmetic average.
>
> $$\text{mean} = \frac{\textbf{the sum of all data values}}{\textbf{the number of data values}}$$
>
> or $\overline{x} = \dfrac{\sum x}{n}$ {where $\sum x$ is the sum of the data values}

The mean gives us a single number which indicates a centre of the data set. It is not necessarily a member of the data set.

For example, a mean test mark of 67% tells us that there are several marks below 67% and several above it. 67% is at the centre, but it does not mean that one of the students scored 67%.

THE MEDIAN

> The **median** is the *middle value* of an ordered data set.

An ordered data set is obtained by listing the data, usually from smallest to largest. The median splits the data in halves. Half of the data are less than or equal to the median and half are greater than or equal to it.

For example, if the median mark for a test is 67% then you know that half the class scored less than or equal to 67% and half scored greater than or equal to 67%.

Note: For an **odd number** of data, the median is one of the data.

For an **even number** of data, the median is the average of the two middle values and may not be one of the original data.

Here is a **rule for finding the median**:

> If there are n data values, find the value of $\dfrac{n+1}{2}$.
>
> The median is the $\left(\dfrac{n+1}{2}\right)$th data value.

For example:

If $n = 13$, $\dfrac{13+1}{2} = 7$, so the median = 7th ordered data value.

If $n = 14$, $\dfrac{14+1}{2} = 7.5$, so the median = average of 7th and 8th ordered data values.

THE MODE

> The **mode** is the most frequently occurring value in the data set.

Example 2   ◀) **Self Tutor**

The number of heavy transport vehicles using a road over a 13-day period
is 4 6 3 2 7 8 3 5 5 7 6 6 4. For this data set, find:

a the mean   **b** the median   **c** the mode.

a mean $= \dfrac{4+6+3+2+7+8+3+5+5+7+6+6+4}{13}$ ◀— sum of the data

$\phantom{\text{mean}}$ 13 data values

$= \dfrac{66}{13}$

≈ 5.08 trucks

b The ordered data set is: 2 3 3 4 4 5 5 6 6 6 7 7 8 $\{$as $n = 13$, $\frac{n+1}{2} = 7\}$
∴ median = 5 trucks

c 6 is the score which occurs the most often ∴ mode = 6 trucks

---

For the heavy transport vehicle data of **Example 2**, how are the measures of the middle
affected if on the 14th day the number of trucks was 7?

We expect the mean to *increase* because the new data value is greater than the old mean.

In fact,   new mean $= \dfrac{66+7}{14} = \dfrac{73}{14} \approx 5.21$ trucks

The new ordered data set would be: 2 3 3 4 4 5 5 6 6 6 7 7 7 8

 two middle scores

∴ median $= \dfrac{5+6}{2} = 5.5$ trucks

This new data set has two modes, 6 and 7 trucks, and we say that the data set is **bimodal**.

Note: • If a data set has three or more modes, we do not use the mode as a measure of the middle.

• Consider the data: 4 2 5 6 7 4 5 3 5 4 7 6 3 5 8 6 5

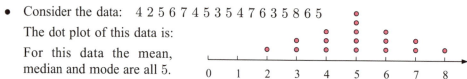

The dot plot of this data is:

For this data the mean, median and mode are all 5.

Equal or approximately equal values of the mean, mode and median *may* indicate a *symmetrical distribution* of data. However, we should always check using a graph before calling a data set symmetric.

EXERCISE 10E

1 Find the **i** mean **ii** median **iii** mode for each of the following data sets:

   a 12, 17, 20, 24, 25, 30, 40

   b 8, 8, 8, 10, 11, 11, 12, 12, 16, 20, 20, 24

   c 7.9, 8.5, 9.1, 9.2, 9.9, 10.0, 11.1, 11.2, 11.2, 12.6, 12.9

   d 427, 423, 415, 405, 445, 433, 442, 415, 435, 448, 429, 427, 403, 430, 446, 440, 425, 424, 419, 428, 441

2 Consider the two data sets: *Data set A:*   5, 6, 6, 7, 7, 7, 8, 8, 9, 10, 12
                                  Data set B: 5, 6, 6, 7, 7, 7, 8, 8, 9, 10, 20

   a Find the mean for both *Data set A* and *Data set B*.

   b Find the median of both *Data set A* and *Data set B*.

   c Explain why the mean of *Data set A* is less than the mean of *Data set B*.

   d Explain why the median of *Data set A* is the same as the median of *Data set B*.

3 The selling price of nine houses are: $158 000, $290 000, $290 000, $1.1 million, $900 000, $395 000, $925 000, $420 000, $760 000

   a Find the mean, median and modal selling prices.

   b Explain why the mode is an unsatisfactory measure of the middle in this case.

   c Is the median a satisfactory measure of the middle of this data set?

4 The following raw data is the daily rainfall (to the nearest millimetre) for the month of February 2007 in a city in China:

   0, 4, 1, 0, 0, 0, 2, 9, 3, 0, 0, 0, 8, 27, 5, 0, 0, 0, 0, 8, 1, 3, 0, 0, 15, 1, 0, 0

   a Find the mean, median and mode for the data.

   b Give a reason why the median is not the most suitable measure of centre for this set of data.

   c Give a reason why the mode is not the most suitable measure of centre for this set of data.

   d Are there any outliers in this data set?

   e On some occasions outliers are removed because they are not typical of the rest of the data and may be errors in observation and/or calculation. If the outliers in this data set were accurately found, should they be removed before finding the measures of the middle?

5 A basketball team scored 38, 52, 43, 54, 41 and 36 points in their first six matches.

  a What is the mean number of points scored for the first six matches?

  b What score will the team need to shoot in the next match so that they maintain the same mean score?

  c The team scores only 20 points in the seventh match. What is the mean number of points scored for the seven matches?

  d The team scores 42 points in their eighth and final match. Will this increase or decrease their previous mean score? What is the mean score for all eight matches?

Example 3   ◀)) **Self Tutor**

The mean of five scores is 12.2. What is the sum of the scores?

Let $S =$ sum of scores $\therefore$ $\dfrac{S}{5} = 12.2$

$\therefore$ $S = 12.2 \times 5 = 61$

$\therefore$ the sum of the scores is 61.

---

6 The mean of 12 scores is 8.8. What is the sum of the scores?

7 While on a camping holiday, Daffyd drove an average of 325 km per day for a period of 7 days. How far did Daffyd drive in total while on holiday?

8 The mean monthly sales for a CD store are $216 000. Calculate the total sales for the store for the year.

9 Over a semester, Jamie did 8 science tests. Each was marked out of 30 and Jamie averaged 25. However, when checking his files, he could only find 7 of the 8 tests. For these he scored 29, 26, 18, 20, 27, 24 and 29. Determine how many marks out of 30 he scored for the eighth test.

10 On the first four days of her holiday, Benita drove an average of 424 kilometres per day. On the next three days she drove an average of 544 kilometres per day.

  a What is the total distance that Benita drove in the first four days?

  b What is the total distance that Benita drove in the next three days?

  c What is the mean distance Benita travelled per day over the seven day period?

DISCUSSION

Which of the measures of the middle is more affected by the presence of an outlier? Develop at least two examples to show how the measures of the middle can be altered by outliers.

MEASURES OF THE CENTRE FROM OTHER SOURCES

When the same data appears several times we often summarise the data in table form.

Consider the data in the given table:

We can find the measures of the centre directly from the table.

Data value	Frequency	Product
3	1	$1 \times 3 = 3$
4	2	$2 \times 4 = 8$
5	4	$4 \times 5 = 20$
6	14	$14 \times 6 = 84$
7	11	$11 \times 7 = 77$
8	6	$6 \times 8 = 48$
9	2	$2 \times 9 = 18$
Total	40	258

The mode

There are 14 of data value 6 which is more than any other data value.
The mode is therefore 6.

The mean

Adding a 'Product' column to the table helps to add all scores.

For example, there are 14 data of value 6 and these add to $14 \times 6 = 84$.

So,   mean $= \dfrac{258}{40} = 6.45$

The median

There are 40 data values, an even number, so there are *two* *middle* data values.

As the sample size $n = 40$, $\dfrac{n+1}{2} = \dfrac{41}{2} = 20.5$

Remember that the median is the middle of the *ordered* data set.

∴   the median is the average of the 20th and 21st data values.

In the table, the blue numbers show us accumulated values.

Data Value	Frequency	
3	1	1 ← one number is 3
4	2	3 ← 3 numbers are 4 or less
5	4	7 ← 7 numbers are 5 or less
6	14	21 ← 21 numbers are 6 or less
7	11	32 ← 32 numbers are 7 or less
8	6	
9	2	
Total	40	

We can see that the 20th and 21st data values (in order) are both 6's.

∴   median $= \dfrac{6+6}{2} = 6$

Notice that we have a skewed distribution for which the mean, median and mode are nearly equal. This is why we need to be careful when we use measures of the middle to call distributions symmetric.

Example 4

◄)) **Self Tutor**

Each student in a class of 20 is assigned a number between 1 and 10 to indicate his or her fitness.

Calculate the: **a**   mean
                   b   median
                   c   mode

of the scores.

Score	Number of students
5	1
6	2
7	4
8	7
9	4
10	2
Total	20

a

Score	Number of students	Product
5	1	$5 \times 1 = 5$
6	2	$6 \times 2 = 12$
7	4	$7 \times 4 = 28$
8	7	$8 \times 7 = 56$
9	4	$9 \times 4 = 36$
10	2	$10 \times 2 = 20$
Total	20	157

The mean score

$= \dfrac{\text{total of scores}}{\text{number of scores}}$

$= \dfrac{157}{20}$

$= 7.85$

b   There are 20 scores, and so the median is the average of the 10th and 11th.

Score	Number of Students
5	1
6	2
7	4
8	7
9	4
10	2

1st student
2nd and 3rd student
4th, 5th, 6th and 7th student
8th, 9th, **10th**, **11th**, 12th, 13th, 14th student

STATISTICS PACKAGE

The 10th and 11th students both scored 8   ∴   median = 8.

c   Looking down the 'number of students' column, the highest frequency is 7. This corresponds to a score of 8, so the mode = 8.

11   The table given shows the results when 3 coins were tossed simultaneously 40 times. The number of heads appearing was recorded.

Number of heads	Number of times occurred
0	6
1	16
2	14
3	4
Total	40

Calculate the: **a**   mode   **b**   median   **c**   mean.

12 The following frequency table records the number of text messages sent in a day by 50 fifteen-year-olds.

No. of messages	Frequency
0	2
1	4
2	7
3	4
4	2
5	0
6	1
7	8
8	13
9	7
10	2

a For this data, find the:
  i mean **ii** median **iii** mode.

b Construct a column graph for the data and show the position of the measures of centre (mean, median and mode) on the horizontal axis.

c Describe the distribution of the data.

d Why is the mean smaller than the median for this data?

e Which measure of centre would be the most suitable for this data set?

13 The frequency column graph alongside gives the value of donations for an overseas aid organisation, collected in a particular street.

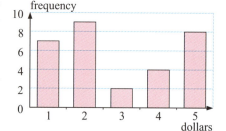

a Construct a frequency table from the graph.
b Determine the total number of donations.
c For the donations find the:
  i mean **ii** median **iii** mode.

d Which of the measures of central tendency can be found easily from the graph only?

14 Families at a school in Canada were surveyed and the number of children in each family recorded. The results of the survey are shown alongside.

Number of children	Frequencies
1	5
2	28
3	15
4	8
5	2
6	1
Total	59

a Calculate the:
  i mean **ii** mode **iii** median.

b If the average Canadian family has 2.2 children, how does this school compare to the national average?

c The data set is skewed. Is the skewness positive or negative?

d How has the skewness of the data affected the measures of the middle?

F   CUMULATIVE DATA

Sometimes it is useful to know the number of scores that lie above or below a particular value. In such situations it is convenient to construct a **cumulative frequency distribution table** and a **cumulative frequency graph** to represent the data.

The cumulative frequency gives a *running total* of the scores up to a particular value.

Example 5

🔊 **Self Tutor**

The data shown gives the weights of 80 male basketball players.

a Construct a cumulative frequency distribution table.

b Represent the data on a cumulative frequency graph.

c Use your graph to estimate the:
   i median weight
   ii number of men weighing less than 84 kg
   iii number of men weighing more than 93 kg.

Weight (w kg)	frequency
$65 \leqslant w < 70$	1
$70 \leqslant w < 75$	2
$75 \leqslant w < 80$	8
$80 \leqslant w < 85$	16
$85 \leqslant w < 90$	21
$90 \leqslant w < 95$	19
$95 \leqslant w < 100$	8
$100 \leqslant w < 105$	3
$105 \leqslant w < 110$	1
$110 \leqslant w < 115$	1

a

Weight (w kg)	frequency	cumulative frequency
$65 \leqslant w < 70$	1	1
$70 \leqslant w < 75$	2	3	← this is $1 + 2$
$75 \leqslant w < 80$	8	11	← this is $1 + 2 + 8$, etc.
$80 \leqslant w < 85$	16	27	
$85 \leqslant w < 90$	21	48	← this 48 means that there are 48 players who weigh less than 90 kg
$90 \leqslant w < 95$	19	67	
$95 \leqslant w < 100$	8	75	
$100 \leqslant w < 105$	3	78	
$105 \leqslant w < 110$	1	79	
$110 \leqslant w < 115$	1	80	

b

STATISTICS PACKAGE

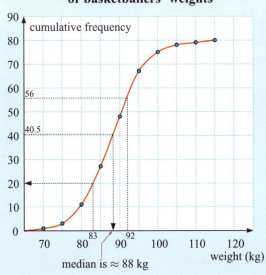

Cumulative frequency graph of basketballers' weights

median is ≈ 88 kg

c
i The median is the average of the 40th and 41st weights. Call it 40.5. Reading from the graph, the median ≈ 88 kg.

ii There are 20 men who weigh less than 83 kg.

iii There are $80 - 56 = 24$ men who weigh more than 92 kg.

EXERCISE 10F

1 The following data shows the lengths, in centimetres, of 40 salmon caught in a lake during a fishing competition.

30 26 38 28 27 31 38 34 40 24 33 30 36 38 32 35 32 36 27 35
36 37 29 31 33 40 34 37 44 38 36 34 33 31 38 35 36 33 33 28

    a Construct a cumulative frequency table for salmon lengths, x cm, using the intervals: $24 \leqslant x < 27$, $27 \leqslant x < 30$, ... etc.

    b Draw a cumulative frequency graph.

    c Use **b** to find the median length.

    d Use the original data to find its median and compare your answer with **c**. Comment!

2 In an examination the following scores were achieved by a group of students:

Draw a cumulative frequency graph of the data and use it to find:

    a the median examination mark

    b how many students scored less than 75 marks

    c how many students scored between 60 and 80 marks

    d how many students failed, given that the pass mark was 55

    e the credit mark, given that the top 16% of students were awarded credits.

Score	frequency
$10 \leqslant x < 20$	2
$20 \leqslant x < 30$	6
$30 \leqslant x < 40$	4
$40 \leqslant x < 50$	8
$50 \leqslant x < 60$	12
$60 \leqslant x < 70$	27
$70 \leqslant x < 80$	34
$80 \leqslant x < 90$	18
$90 \leqslant x < 100$	9

3 The following frequency distribution was obtained by asking 50 randomly selected people the size of their shoes.

Shoe size	5	$5\frac{1}{2}$	6	$6\frac{1}{2}$	7	$7\frac{1}{2}$	8	$8\frac{1}{2}$	9	$9\frac{1}{2}$	10
frequency	2	0	1	4	6	12	11	7	3	2	2

Draw a cumulative frequency graph of the data and use it to find:

    a the median shoe size

    b how many people had a shoe size of: **i** 7 or more   **ii** $8\frac{1}{2}$ or less.

4 In a cross-country race, the times (in minutes) of 160 competitors were recorded as follows:

Draw a cumulative frequency graph of the data and use it to find:

    a the median time

    b the approximate number of runners whose time was not more than 32 minutes

    c the approximate time in which the fastest 40 runners completed the course.

Times (min)	frequency
$20 \leqslant t < 25$	18
$25 \leqslant t < 30$	45
$30 \leqslant t < 35$	37
$35 \leqslant t < 40$	33
$40 \leqslant t < 45$	19
$45 \leqslant t < 50$	8

MEASURING THE SPREAD

Knowing the middle of a data set can be quite useful, but for a more accurate picture of the data set we also need to know its spread.

For example,   2, 3, 4, 5, 6, 7, 8, 9, 10   has a mean value of 6 and so does

4, 5, 5, 6, 6, 6, 7, 7, 8.   However, the first data set is more widely spread than the second one.

Three commonly used statistics that indicate the spread of a set of data are the

- **range**   • **interquartile range**   • **standard deviation**.

Note that the discussion of standard deviation will be left until the IB Studies Diploma course.

THE RANGE

The **range** is the difference between the **maximum** (largest) data value and the **minimum** (smallest) data value.

range = maximum data value − minimum data value

Example 6   ◄)) **Self Tutor**

Find the range of the data set: 6, 4, 7, 5, 3, 4, 2, 6, 5, 7, 5, 3, 8, 9, 3, 6, 5

range = maximum value − minimum value = $9 - 2 = 7$

THE UPPER AND LOWER QUARTILES AND THE INTERQUARTILE RANGE

The median divides an ordered data set into halves, and these halves are divided in half again by the **quartiles**.

The middle value of the lower half is called the **lower quartile**. One quarter, or 25%, of the data have values less than or equal to the lower quartile. 75% of the data have values greater than or equal to the lower quartile.

The middle value of the upper half is called the **upper quartile**. One quarter, or 25%, of the data have values greater than or equal to the upper quartile. 75% of the data have values less than or equal to the upper quartile.

The **interquartile range** is the range of the middle half (50%) of the data.

interquartile range = upper quartile − lower quartile

The data set is thus divided into quarters by the lower quartile (Q_1), the median (Q_2), and the upper quartile (Q_3).

So, the interquartile range,   **$IQR = Q_3 - Q_1$.**

Example 7   ◄) Self Tutor

For the data set: 6, 4, 7, 5, 3, 4, 2, 6, 5, 7, 5, 3, 8, 9, 3, 6, 5   find the

a median **b** lower quartile **c** upper quartile **d** interquartile range

The ordered data set is:

~~2 3 3 3 4 4 5 5~~ 5 ~~5 6 6 6 7 7 8 9~~ (17 of them)

a   As $n = 17$, $\dfrac{n+1}{2} = 9$

The median = 9th score = 5

b/c   As the median is a data value we now ignore it and split the
remaining data into two:

$$\underbrace{2\ 3\ 3\ 3\ 4\ 4\ 5\ 5}_{\text{lower}} \qquad \underbrace{5\ 6\ 6\ 6\ 7\ 7\ 8\ 9}_{\text{upper}}$$

$Q_1 = $ median of lower half $= \dfrac{3+4}{2} = 3.5$

$Q_3 = $ median of upper half $= \dfrac{6+7}{2} = 6.5$

d   IQR $= Q_3 - Q_1 = 6.5 - 3.5 = 3$

Example 8   ◄) Self Tutor

For the data set: 11, 6, 7, 8, 13, 10, 8, 7, 5, 2, 9, 4, 4, 5, 8, 2, 3, 6   find

a   the median   **b**   the lower quartile
c   the upper quartile   **d**   the interquartile range

The ordered data set is:

~~2 2 3 4 4 5 5 6~~ 6 7 ~~7 8 8 8 9 10 11 13~~   (18 of them)

a   As $n = 18$, $\dfrac{n+1}{2} = 9.5$

$\therefore$ median $= \dfrac{\text{9th value } + \text{ 10th value}}{2} = \dfrac{6+7}{2} = 6.5$

b/c   As the median is not a data value we split the data into two:

$$\underbrace{2\ 2\ 3\ 4\ 4\ 5\ 5\ 6\ 6}_{\text{lower}} \qquad \underbrace{7\ 7\ 8\ 8\ 8\ 9\ 10\ 11\ 13}_{\text{upper}}$$

$\therefore$ $Q_1 = 4$, $Q_3 = 8$

d   IQR $= Q_3 - Q_1$
       $= 8 - 4$
       $= 4$

Note: Some computer packages (for example,
MS Excel) calculate quartiles in a different
way from this example.

EXERCISE 10G

1 For each of the following data sets, make sure the data is ordered and then find:

    i the median   **ii** the upper and lower quartiles

    iii the range   **iv** the interquartile range.

  a 5, 6, 6, 6, 7, 7, 7, 8, 8, 8, 8, 9, 9, 9, 9, 9, 10, 10, 11, 11, 11, 12, 12

  b 11, 13, 16, 13, 25, 19, 20, 19, 19, 16, 17, 21, 22, 18, 19, 17, 23, 15

  c 23.8, 24.4, 25.5, 25.5, 26.6, 26.9, 27, 27.3, 28.1, 28.4, 31.5

2 The times spent (in minutes) by 24 people in a queue at a supermarket, waiting to be served at the checkout, were:

  1.4 5.2 2.4 2.8 3.4 3.8 2.2 1.5

  0.8 0.8 3.9 2.3 4.5 1.4 0.5 0.1

  1.6 4.8 1.9 0.2 3.6 5.2 2.7 3.0

  a Find the median waiting time and the upper and lower quartiles.

  b Find the range and interquartile range of the waiting time.

  c Copy and complete the following statements:

    i "50% of the waiting times were greater than .... minutes."

    ii "75% of the waiting times were less than ...... minutes."

    iii "The minimum waiting time was .... minutes and the maximum waiting time was ..... minutes. The waiting times were spread over ...... minutes."

3

Stem	Leaf
2	0 1 2 2
3	0 0 1 4 4 5 8
4	0 2 3 4 6 6 9
5	1 1 4 5 8

For the data set given, find:

  a the minimum value   **b** the maximum value

  c the median   **d** the lower quartile

  e the upper quartile   **f** the range

  g the interquartile range.

H   BOX-AND-WHISKER PLOTS

A **box-and-whisker plot** (or simply a **boxplot**) is a visual display of some of the descriptive statistics of a data set. It shows:

- the minimum value
- the lower quartile (Q_1)
- the median (Q_2)
- the upper quartile (Q_3)
- the maximum value

These five numbers form what is known as the **five-number summary** of a data set.

Here is the boxplot for **Example 7**:

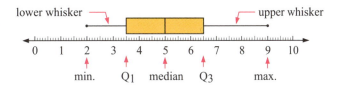

The rectangular box represents the 'middle' half of the data set.

The lower whisker represents the 25% of the data with smallest values.

The upper whisker represents the 25% of the data with greatest values.

Example 9   ◄» **Self Tutor**

For the data set: 4 5 9 5 1 7 8 7 3 5 6 3 4 3 2 5

a   construct the five-number summary   **b**   draw a boxplot

c   find the   **i**   range   **ii**   interquartile range

d   find the percentage of data values less than 7.

a   The ordered data set is

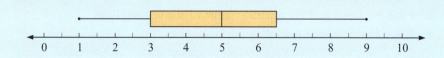

$Q_1 = 3$ median = 5 $Q_3 = 6.5$

So the 5-number summary is: $\begin{cases} \text{min. value} = 1 & Q_1 = 3 \\ \text{median} = 5 & Q_3 = 6.5 \\ \text{max. value} = 9 \end{cases}$

b

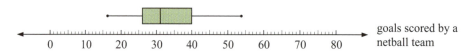

c   **i**   range = max value − min value   **ii**   IQR $= Q_3 - Q_1$

$= 9 - 1$ $= 6.5 - 3$

$= 8$ $= 3.5$

STATISTICS PACKAGE

d   75% of the data values are less than 7.

EXERCISE 10H

1

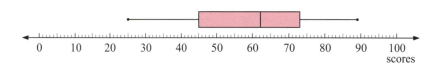

goals scored by a netball team

a   The boxplot given summarises the goals scored by a netball team. Locate:

 i   the median   **ii**   the maximum value   **iii**   the minimum value

 iv   the upper quartile   **v**   the lower quartile

b   Calculate: **i**   the range   **ii**   the interquartile range

2

The boxplot shown summarises the points scored by a basketball team. Copy and complete the following statements about their results:

a   The highest score was ...... points.   **b**   The lowest score was ...... points.

c   Half of the scores were greater than or equal to ..... points.

    d The top 25% of the scores were at least ..... points.

    e The middle half of the scores were between .... and .... points.

    f Find the range of the data set.

    g Find the interquartile range of the data set.

3 For the following data sets:

    i construct a 5-number summary   **ii** draw a boxplot

    iii find the range   **iv** find the interquartile range

    a 5, 5, 10, 9, 4, 2, 8, 6, 5, 8, 6, 7, 9, 6, 10, 3, 11

    b 7, 0, 4, 6, 8, 8, 9, 5, 6, 8, 8, 8, 9, 8, 1, 8, 3, 7, 2, 7, 4, 5, 9, 4

4 The weight, in kilograms, of a particular brand of bags of firewood is stated to be 20 kg. However, some bags weigh more than this and some weigh less. A sample of bags is carefully weighed, and the measurements are given in the ordered stem-and-leaf plot shown.

Stem	Leaf
18	8
19	5 7 7 8 8 9
20	1 1 1 2 2 5 6 8
21	0 1 1 2 4 6
22	3

20 | 5 represents 20.5 kg

    a Locate the median, upper and lower quartiles, and maximum and minimum weights for the sample.

    b Draw a boxplot for the data.

    c Find: **i** the interquartile range   **ii** the range.

    d Copy and complete the following statements about the distribution of weights for the bags of firewood in this sample:

      i Half of the bags of firewood weighed at least .... kg.

      ii .....% of the bags had a weight less than 20 kg.

      iii The weights of the middle 50% of the bags were spread over ...... kg.

      iv The lightest 25% of the bags had a weight of ..... kg or less.

    e Is the distribution of weights in this sample symmetrical, or positively or negatively skewed?

PARALLEL BOXPLOTS

Parallel boxplots enable us to make a *visual comparison* of the distributions of two sets of data and their descriptive statistics (median, range and interquartile range).

Parallel boxplots could be horizontal or vertical.

Example 10   ◄⬤ **Self Tutor**

An office worker has the choice of travelling to work by car or bus and has collected data giving the travel times from recent journeys using both of these types of transport. He is interested to know which type of transport is the quickest to get him to work and which is the most reliable.

Car travel times (min): 13, 14, 18, 18, 19, 21, 22, 22, 24, 25, 27, 28, 30, 33, 43

Bus travel times (min): 16, 16, 16, 17, 17, 18, 18, 18, 20, 20, 21, 21, 23, 28, 30

Prepare parallel boxplots for the data sets and use them to compare the two methods of transport for speed and reliability.

For car travel: min $= 13$ $Q_1 = 18$ median $= 22$ $Q_3 = 28$ max. $= 43$

For bus travel: min $= 16$ $Q_1 = 17$ median $= 18$ $Q_3 = 21$ max. $= 30$

In the data sets we identify some outliers: 28 and 30 mins by bus and 43 mins by car. They are represented as asterisks on the boxplot, and are not included in the whiskers.

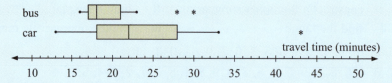

Using the medians, 50% of the time bus travel takes 18 minutes or less, compared with car travel at 22 minutes or less. Bus travel is therefore generally *quicker*.

Comparing spread: range for car $= 43 - 13$ range for bus $= 30 - 16$

$\qquad\qquad\qquad\qquad\qquad\qquad\quad = 30 \qquad\qquad\qquad\qquad\qquad\qquad = 14$

$$IQR = Q_3 - Q_1 \qquad\qquad\qquad\qquad IQR = Q_3 - Q_1$$
$$= 28 - 18 \qquad\qquad\qquad\qquad\qquad = 21 - 17$$
$$= 10 \qquad\qquad\qquad\qquad\qquad\qquad\; = 4$$

Comparing these spread measures, the bus travel times are less 'spread out' than the car travel times. They are *more predictable or reliable.*

5 The following boxplots compare the numbers of students on school buses A and C over a one month period.

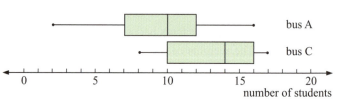

a Find the 5-number summaries for the students on both buses.

b Determine the **i** range **ii** interquartile range   for each group of students.

6 Two classes have completed the same test. Boxplots have been drawn to summarise and display the results. They have been drawn on the same set of axes so that the results can be compared.

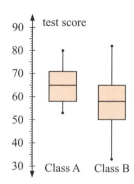

a In which class was:

   i the highest mark   **ii** the lowest mark

   iii there a larger spread of marks?

b Find: **i** the range of marks in class B

   ii the interquartile range for class A.

c If the top 50% of class B passed the test, what percentage of class A passed?

d Describe the distribution of marks in: **i** class A   **ii** class B.

e Copy and complete: The students in class .... generally scored higher marks.

   The marks in class ...... were more varied.

7 The heights (to the nearest centimetre) of boys and girls in a Year 10 class in Norway are as follows:

Boys 165 171 169 169 172 171 171 180 168 168 166 168 170 165 171 173 187
181 175 174 165 167 163 160 169 167 172 174 177 188 177 185 167 160

Girls 162 171 156 166 168 163 170 171 177 169 168 165 156 159 165 164 154
171 172 166 152 169 170 163 162 165 163 168 155 175 176 170 166

a Find the five-number summary for each of the data sets.

b Compare and comment on the distribution of the data.

LINKS
click here

HOW MANY TROUT ARE IN THE LAKE?

Areas of interaction:
Environments/Human ingenuity

I   **STATISTICS FROM TECHNOLOGY**

GRAPHICS CALCULATOR

A **graphics calculator** can be used to find descriptive statistics and to draw some types of graphs.

Consider the data set: 5 2 3 3 6 4 5 3 7 5 7 1 8 9 5

No matter what brand of calculator you use you should be able to:

- Enter the data as a list.

- Enter the statistics calculation part of the menu and obtain the descriptive statistics like these shown.

    $\bar{x}$ is the mean

```
1-Var Stats
x̄=4.866666667
Σx=73
Σx²=427
Sx=2.263583337
σx=2.186829262
↓n=15
```

```
1-Var Stats
↑n=15
 minX=1  ⎫
 Q1=3    ⎪
 Med=5   ⎬  5-number
 Q3=7    ⎪   summary
 maxX=9  ⎭
■
```

- Obtain a box-and-whisker plot such as:

    These screen dumps are from a TI-83.

- Obtain a vertical barchart if required.

- Enter a second data set into another list and obtain a side-by-side boxplot for comparison with the first one.

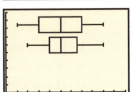

Instructions for these tasks can be found at the front of the book in the **Graphics Calculator Instructions** section.

EXERCISE 10I

1 For your calculator enter the data set: 5 2 3 3 6 4 5 3 7 5 7 1 8 9 5   and obtain the mean and the 5-number summary. This is the first example above and you should check your results from it.

2 Obtain the boxplot for question **1**.

3 Obtain the vertical bar chart for question **1**.

4 Enter the data set: 9 6 2 3 5 5 7 5 6 7 6 3 4 4 5 8 4   into a second list. Find the mean and 5-number summary. Now create a side-by-side boxplot for both sets of data.

COMPUTER PACKAGE

Various statistical packages are available for computer use, but many are expensive and often not easy to use. Click on the icon to use the statistics package on the CD.

Enter data set 1:   5 2 3 3 6 4 5 3 7 5 7 1 8 9 5

Enter data set 2:   9 6 2 3 5 5 7 5 6 7 6 3 4 4 5 8 4

STATISTICS PACKAGE

Examine the side-by-side column graphs.

Click on the Box & whisker tab to view the side-by-side boxplots.

Click on the Statistics tab to obtain the descriptive statistics.

Select Print ... from the File menu to print all of these on one sheet of paper.

5 Enter the **Opening Problem** data, placing the *Without fertiliser* data in Set 1 and the *With fertiliser* data in Set 2. Print the page of graphs, boxplots and descriptive statistics.

6 Enter these grouped continuous data sets:

Set 1:

Value	Frequency
11.6	1
11.7	3
11.8	16
11.9	28
12.0	11
12.1	7
12.2	9

Set 2:

Value	Frequency
11.5	1
11.6	8
11.7	17
11.8	31
11.9	16
12.0	8
12.1	10
12.2	3

Examine the graphs, boxplots and descriptive statistics for each and print the results.

REVIEW SET 10A

1 A randomly selected sample of small businesses has been asked, "How many full-time employees are there in your business?". A column graph has been constructed for the results.

a How many small businesses gave data in the survey?

b How many of the businesses had only one or two full-time employees?

c What percentage of the businesses had five or more full-time employees?

d Describe the distribution of the data.

2 A class of 20 students was asked "How many children are there in your household?" and the following data was collected:

1   2   3   3   2   4   5   4   2   3   8   1   2   1   3   2   1   2   1   2

   a What is the variable in the investigation?

   b Is the data discrete or continuous? Why?

   c Construct a dot plot to display the data showing a heading for the graph, a scale and clearly labelled axes.

   d How would you describe the distribution of the data? Is it symmetrical, or positively or negatively skewed? Are there any outliers?

3 The test score out of 40 marks was recorded for a group of 30 students:

25   18   35   32   34   28   24   39   29   33
22   34   39   31   36   35   36   33   35   40
26   25   20   18   9   40   32   23   28   27

   a Construct a stem-and-leaf plot for this data using 0, 1, 2, 3 and 4 as the stems.

   b Redraw the stem-and-leaf plot so that it is ordered.

   c What advantage does the stem-and-leaf plot have over a frequency table?

   d What was the **i** highest **ii** lowest mark scored for the test?

   e If an 'A' was awarded to students who scored 36 or more for the test, what percentage of students scored an 'A'?

4 A frequency table for the masses of eggs in a carton marked '50 g eggs' is given below.

Mass (g)	Frequency
48 - < 49	1
49 - < 50	1
50 - < 51	16
51 - < 52	4
52 - < 53	3

   a Explain why 'mass' is a continuous variable.

   b Construct a frequency histogram for the data. The axes should be carefully marked and labelled, and you should include a heading for the graph.

   c What is the modal class? Explain what this means.

   d Describe the distribution of the data.

5 For the following data set showing the number of points scored by a rugby team, find:

   a the mean   **b** the mode   **c** the median

   d the range   **e** the upper and lower quartiles   **f** the interquartile range.

28, 24, 16, 6, 46, 34, 43, 16, 36, 49, 30, 28, 4, 31, 47, 41, 26, 25, 20, 29, 42

6

   a From the boxplot that shows the scores out of 100 for an exam, state:

      i the median score   **ii** the maximum score   **iii** the minimum score

      iv the upper quartile   **v** the lower quartile

   b Calculate: **i** the range   **ii** the interquartile range of scores.

REVIEW SET 10B

1 Find the   **a** mean   **b** median   **c** mode   for the following data set:

13   16   15   17   14   13   13   15   16   14   16   14   15   15   15   13   17   14   12   14

2 The data alongside is the scores (out of 100) for a Mathematics examination for 45 students.

58	31	80	69	70	71	82	91	94	60	68	58
90	83	72	75	65	76	69	66	64	57	58	77
92	94	49	61	66	91	64	53	89	91	78	61
74	82	97	70	82	66	55	45	63			

a Construct a stem-and-leaf plot for this data using 3, 4, ... to 9 as the stems.

b Redraw the stem-and-leaf plot so that it is ordered.

c What advantages does a stem-and-leaf plot have over a frequency table?

d What is the **i** highest **ii** lowest mark scored for the examination?

e If an 'A' was awarded to students who scored 85 or more for the examination, what percentage of students scored an 'A'?

f Would you describe this distribution as:

   i symmetric   **ii** skewed   **iii** neither symmetric nor skewed?

3 The given table shows the distribution of scores for a Year 10 spelling test in Australia.

a Calculate the: **i** mean **ii** mode **iii** median
   iv range of the scores

b The average score for all Year 10 students across Australia in this spelling test was 6.2. How does this class compare to the national average?

c The data set is skewed. Is the skewness positive or negative?

Score	Frequency
6	2
7	4
8	7
9	12
10	5
Total	30

4 In a one month period at a particular hospital the lengths of newborn babies were recorded. The results are shown in the table given.

a Represent the data on a frequency histogram.

b How many babies are 52 cm or more?

c What percentage of babies have lengths in the interval $50\,cm \leqslant l < 53\,cm$?

d Construct a cumulative frequency distribution table.

e Represent the data on a cumulative frequency graph.

f Use your graph to estimate the:

   i median length   **ii** number of babies with length less than 51.5 cm.

length (cm)	frequency
$48 \leqslant l < 49$	1
$49 \leqslant l < 50$	3
$50 \leqslant l < 51$	9
$51 \leqslant l < 52$	10
$52 \leqslant l < 53$	16
$53 \leqslant l < 54$	4
$54 \leqslant l < 55$	5
$55 \leqslant l < 56$	2

5 The given parallel boxplots represent the 100-metre swim times for the members of a swimming squad.

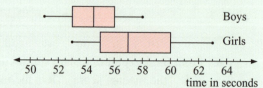

Copy and complete the following:

a Comparing the median swim times for girls and boys shows that, in general, the ...... swim ...... seconds faster than the ......

b The range of the girls' swim times is ...... seconds compared to the range of ...... seconds for the boys.

c The fastest 25% of the boys swim faster than ......% of the girls.

d ......% of the boys swim faster than 60 seconds whereas ......% of the girls swim faster than 60 seconds.

Chapter 11

Equations

Contents:

A   Solution by inspection or trial and error

B   Maintaining balance

C   Formal solution of linear equations

D   Equations with a repeated unknown

E   Fractional equations

F   Unknown in the denominator

G   Forming equations

H   Problem solving using equations

I   Finding an unknown from a formula

J   Formula rearrangement

Many problems in mathematics can be solved by using **equations**. We convert the worded problem into an algebraic equation, then follow a formal procedure to **solve** the equation and hence find the solution to the problem.

> **Algebraic equations** are mathematical sentences which indicate that two expressions have the same value. They always contain the "$=$" sign.

For example, $5x - 2 = 7$ is an equation.

The symbol $=$ is read as 'equals' or 'is equal to'.

LINEAR EQUATIONS

> A **linear equation** is an equation which contains a pronumeral which is not raised to any power other than 1.

For example, $3x + 4 = 2$, $\frac{2}{3}x + 1 = 6$,   and $\dfrac{x - 1}{4} = 8$ are all linear equations

whereas $x^2 + 5x = 7$, $\dfrac{3}{x} = x^3$,   and $\sqrt{x} = 8$ are not linear equations.

OPENING PROBLEM

- Could these equations be solved easily by 'trial and error' methods?

  A $7x + 5 = 35$ **B** $14x + 7 = x + 1$ **C** $\dfrac{3x + 1}{2} - \dfrac{x - 4}{7} = 2$

- Consider the equation $7x + 5 = 35$.   When $x = 1$, $7x + 5 = 12$.

  When $x = 2$, $7x + 5 = 19$.

  When $x = 3$, $7x + 5 = 26$.

  When $x = 4$, $7x + 5 = 33$.

  When $x = 5$, $7x + 5 = 40$.

So if $7x + 5 = 35$, x must be between 4 and 5.

How can we find the exact value of x?

DISCUSSION

Discuss various methods for finding exact solutions when solving algebraic equations.

SIDES OF AN EQUATION

> The **left hand side** (LHS) of an equation is on the left of the $=$ sign.
> The **right hand side** (RHS) of an equation is on the right of the $=$ sign.

For example, $\underbrace{3x + 7}_{\text{LHS}} = \underbrace{13}_{\text{RHS}}$

THE SOLUTIONS OF AN EQUATION

The **solutions** of an equation are the values of the pronumeral which make the equation true, i.e., make the **left hand side (LHS)** equal to the **right hand side (RHS)**.

In the example $3x + 7 = 13$ above, the only value of the pronumeral x which makes the equation true is $x = 2$.

Notice that when $x = 2$, $\begin{aligned} \text{LHS} &= 3x + 7 \\ &= 3 \times 2 + 7 \\ &= 6 + 7 \\ &= 13 \\ &= \text{RHS} \qquad \therefore \quad \text{LHS} = \text{RHS} \end{aligned}$

Simple linear equations involving one unknown may often be solved by:
- inspection *or*
- trial and error.

However, many equations become too difficult to solve mentally. Later in the chapter we will therefore develop a formal method to assist us with this task.

A SOLUTION BY INSPECTION OR TRIAL AND ERROR

Example 1
🔊 **Self Tutor**

Solve by inspection: **a** $b + 7 = -2$ **b** $13 - x = 7$ **c** $\dfrac{x}{5} = -2$

a $\quad b + 7 = -2$
but $\quad -9 + 7 = -2$
$\therefore \quad b = -9$

b $\quad 13 - x = 7$
but $\quad 13 - 6 = 7$
$\therefore \quad x = 6$

c $\quad \dfrac{x}{5} = -2$
but $\quad \dfrac{-10}{5} = -2$
$\therefore \quad x = -10$

EXERCISE 11A

1 Solve by inspection:

    a $\quad n + 4 = 13$ **b** $\quad x + 2 = -6$ **c** $\quad t + 5 = 3$ **d** $\quad x + 3 = 7$

    e $\quad 5 + x = 0$ **f** $\quad y - 11 = 2$ **g** $\quad 10 - a = 4$ **h** $\quad 9 - b = 0$

    i $\quad x - 7 = -4$ **j** $\quad a - 6 = -5$ **k** $\quad \dfrac{x}{2} = 4$ **l** $\quad \dfrac{x}{3} = -5$

    m $\quad \dfrac{y}{-3} = -6$ **n** $\quad \dfrac{15}{a} = 3$ **o** $\quad \dfrac{18}{b} = -3$ **p** $\quad 4a = 36$

    q $\quad y \times 5 = -15$ **r** $\quad -4x = -20$ **s** $\quad -8b = 24$ **t** $\quad 2a = -12$

Example 2

The solution of the equation $3x - 7 = -4$ is one of the integers -1, 1, or 3. Find the solution by trial and error.

We *substitute* each possible solution into the LHS until it equals the RHS -4.

When $x = -1$,	when $x = 1$,	when $x = 3$,
$3x - 7$	$3x - 7$	$3x - 7$
$= 3 \times (-1) - 7$	$= 3 \times 1 - 7$	$= 3 \times 3 - 7$
$= -3 - 7$	$= 3 - 7$	$= 9 - 7$
$= -10$	$= -4$	$= 2$

$\therefore$ the solution is $x = 1$.

2   The solution of each of the following equations is one of the given possibilities. Find the solution by trial and error.

   a $3y + 7 = 13$ $\{-2, 0, \text{ or } 2\}$ **b** $1 - 3b = -8$ $\{2, 3, \text{ or } 4\}$

   c $\dfrac{x - 4}{2} = -3$ $\{-2, 1, \text{ or } 10\}$ **d** $\dfrac{6 - a}{2} = 5$ $\{4, -2, \text{ or } -4\}$

3   Which of the following equations are:

   A   true for *exactly one* value of x **B**   true for *two* values of x

   C   true for *all* values of x **D**   *never* true

   E   true for *all* values of x except 0?

   a $x + 2 = 9$ **b** $x - x = 0$ **c** $4x = 20$

   d $x^2 = 16$ **e** $x \times 1 = x$ **f** $x - x = 2$

   g $17 - 2x = 9$ **h** $x + 3 = x$ **i** $\dfrac{x}{2} = 12$

   j $3x + 4x = 7x$ **k** $x^2 = x$ **l** $\dfrac{x}{x} = 1$

B   MAINTAINING BALANCE

The **balance** of an equation is maintained provided we perform the same operation on **both sides** of the equals sign. We can compare equations to a set of scales.

Adding to, subtracting from, multiplying by, and dividing by the same quantity on **both sides** of an equation will maintain the **balance** or **equality**.

Example 3	◀) Self Tutor

What equation results from:

   a adding 5 to both sides of $2x - 5 = 7$

   b subtracting 3 from both sides of $5x + 3 = 18$?

a $2x - 5 = 7$	**b** $5x + 3 = 18$
$\therefore \quad 2x - 5 + 5 = 7 + 5$	$\therefore \quad 5x + 3 - 3 = 18 - 3$
$\therefore \qquad 2x = 12$	$\therefore \qquad 5x = 15$

EXERCISE 11B

1   What equation results from *adding*:

    a 5 to both sides of $x - 5 = 2$
         b 4 to both sides of $x - 4 = 4$

    c 9 to both sides of $2x - 9 = 1$
         d 11 to both sides of $3x - 11 = -2$?

2   What equation results from *subtracting*:

    a 6 from both sides of $x + 6 = 9$
         b 7 from both sides of $x + 7 = -3$

    c 4 from both sides of $2x + 4 = 0$
         d 8 from both sides of $3x + 8 = -1$?

Example 4	◀) Self Tutor

What equation results when:

   a both sides of $\dfrac{3x - 2}{4} = -1$ are multiplied by 4

   b both sides of $5x = -15$ are divided by 5?

a $\dfrac{3x - 2}{4} = -1$	**b** $5x = -15$
	$\therefore \quad \dfrac{5x}{5} = \dfrac{-15}{5}$
$\therefore \quad 4 \times \dfrac{3x - 2}{4} = 4 \times -1$	$\therefore \quad x = -3$
$\therefore \quad 3x - 2 = -4$	

3   What equation results from *multiplying* both sides of:

    a $x = -2$ by   4
      b $3x = -1$ by   6
      c $\dfrac{x}{3} = 4$ by   3

    d $\dfrac{x}{9} = -1$ by   9
      e $\dfrac{x}{-8} = -2$ by -8
      f $\dfrac{x}{-5} = 4$ by -5?

4   What equation results from *dividing* both sides of:

    a $6x = 12$ by   6
         b $-3x = 30$ by -3

    c $8x + 8 = 0$ by   8
         d $6x - 12 = 24$ by   6

    e $3(x + 2) = -12$ by   3
         f $-5(x - 1) = -25$ by -5?

C ‹ FORMAL SOLUTION OF LINEAR EQUATIONS

When we use the "=" sign between two algebraic expressions we have an equation which is in balance. We have already seen that whatever we do to one side of the equation, we must do the same to the other side to **maintain the balance**.

Compare the balance of weights:

remove 3 from both sides

$2x + 3 = 8$ $\therefore\ 2x = 5$

In this section we perform operations on both sides of each equation in order to **isolate the unknown**. We consider how the expression has been **built up** and then **isolate the unknown** by using **inverse operations** in **reverse order**.

Example 5   ◀》 **Self Tutor**

Solve for x: $3x + 7 = 22$

$$\therefore\quad 3x + 7 = 22$$
$$\therefore\quad 3x + 7 - 7 = 22 - 7 \qquad \text{\{subtract 7 from both sides\}}$$
$$\therefore\quad 3x = 15 \qquad \text{\{simplify\}}$$
$$\therefore\quad \frac{3x}{3} = \frac{15}{3} \qquad \text{\{divide both sides by 3\}}$$
$$\therefore\quad x = 5 \qquad \text{\{simplify\}}$$

Check: LHS $= 3 \times 5 + 7 = 22$ $\therefore$ LHS $=$ RHS ✓

The inverse operation for $+7$ is -7.

EXERCISE 11C

1 Solve for x:

   a $x + 11 = 0$ **b** $4x = -12$ **c** $5x + 35 = 0$

   d $4x - 5 = -17$ **e** $5x + 3 = 28$ **f** $3x - 9 = 18$

   g $8x - 1 = 7$ **h** $3x + 5 = -10$ **i** $13 + 7x = -1$

   j $14 = 3x + 5$ **k** $4x - 7 = -13$ **l** $-3 = 2x + 9$

Example 6   🔊 **Self Tutor**

Solve for x: $11 - 5x = 26$

$$11 - 5x = 26$$
$$\therefore \quad 11 - 5x - 11 = 26 - 11 \qquad \{\text{subtract 11 from both sides}\}$$
$$\therefore \quad -5x = 15 \qquad \{\text{simplify}\}$$
$$\therefore \quad \frac{-5x}{-5} = \frac{15}{-5} \qquad \{\text{divide both sides by } -5\}$$
$$\therefore \quad x = -3 \qquad \{\text{simplify}\}$$

Check: LHS $= 11 - 5 \times -3 = 11 + 15 = 26$ $\therefore$ LHS $=$ RHS ✓

2 Solve for x:

    a $8 - x = -3$ **b** $-4x = 22$ **c** $3 - 2x = 11$

    d $6 - 4x = -8$ **e** $3 - 7x = -4$ **f** $17 - 2x = -5$

    g $15 = 3 - 2x$ **h** $24 - 3x = -9$ **i** $4 = 3 - 2x$

    j $13 = -1 - 7x$ **k** $-21 = 3 - 6x$ **l** $23 = -4 - 3x$

Example 7   🔊 **Self Tutor**

Solve for x: $\dfrac{x}{3} + 2 = -2$

$$\frac{x}{3} + 2 = -2$$
$$\therefore \quad \frac{x}{3} + 2 - 2 = -2 - 2 \qquad \{\text{subtract 2 from both sides}\}$$
$$\therefore \quad \frac{x}{3} = -4 \qquad \{\text{simplify}\}$$
$$\therefore \quad \frac{x}{3} \times 3 = -4 \times 3 \qquad \{\text{multiply both sides by 3}\}$$
$$\therefore \quad x = -12 \qquad \{\text{simplify}\}$$

Check: LHS $= -\frac{12}{3} + 2 = -4 + 2 = -2 =$ RHS. ✓

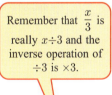

Remember that $\frac{x}{3}$ is really $x \div 3$ and the inverse operation of $\div 3$ is $\times 3$.

3 Solve for x:

    a $\dfrac{x}{4} = 7$ **b** $\dfrac{2x}{5} = -6$ **c** $\dfrac{x}{2} + 3 = -5$

    d $\dfrac{x}{4} - 2 = -5$ **e** $\dfrac{x - 1}{3} = 6$ **f** $\dfrac{x + 5}{6} = -1$

    g $4 = \dfrac{2 + x}{3}$ **h** $-1 + \dfrac{x}{3} = 7$

Example 8   ◀ **Self Tutor**

Solve for x: $\dfrac{4x+3}{5} = -2$

$\dfrac{4x+3}{5} = -2$

$\therefore \ 5 \times \dfrac{(4x+3)}{5} = -2 \times 5$ {multiply both sides by 5}

$\therefore \ 4x+3 = -10$ {simplify}

$\therefore \ 4x+3-3 = -10-3$ {subtract 3 from both sides}

$\therefore \ 4x = -13$ {simplify}

$\therefore \ \dfrac{4x}{4} = -\dfrac{13}{4}$ {divide both sides by 4}

$\therefore \ x = -3\tfrac{1}{4}$ {simplify}

4 Solve for x:

a $\dfrac{2x+11}{3} = 0$ **b** $\tfrac{1}{2}(3x+1) = -4$ **c** $\dfrac{1+2x}{5} = 7$

d $\dfrac{1-2x}{5} = 3$ **e** $\tfrac{1}{4}(1-3x) = -2$ **f** $\tfrac{1}{4}(5-2x) = -3$

D EQUATIONS WITH A REPEATED UNKNOWN

Equations where the unknown appears more than once need to be solved systematically. Generally, we:

- Expand any brackets
- Collect like terms
- Use inverse operations to isolate the unknown while at the same time maintaining the balance of the equation.

Example 9   ◀ **Self Tutor**

Solve for x: $5(x+1)-2x = -7$

$5(x+1)-2x = -7$

$\therefore \ 5x+5-2x = -7$ {expand brackets}

$\therefore \ 3x+5 = -7$ {collect like terms}

$\therefore \ 3x+5-5 = -7-5$ {subtract 5 from both sides}

$\therefore \ 3x = -12$ {simplify}

$\therefore \ \dfrac{3x}{3} = \dfrac{-12}{3}$ {divide both sides by 3}

$\therefore \ x = -4$ {simplify}

EXERCISE 11D

1 Solve for x:

    a $3(x - 2) - x = 12$ **b** $4(x + 2) - 2x = -16$

    c $5(x - 3) + 4x = -6$ **d** $2(3x + 2) - x = -6$

    e $5(2x - 1) - 4x = 11$ **f** $-2(4x + 3) + 2x = 12$

2 Solve for x:

    a $3(x + 2) + 2(x + 4) = -1$ **b** $5(x + 1) - 3(x + 2) = 11$

    c $4(x - 3) - 2(x - 1) = -6$ **d** $3(3x + 1) - 4(x + 1) = 14$

    e $2(3 + 2x) + 3(x - 4) = 8$ **f** $4(5x - 3) - 3(2x - 5) = 17$

When the unknown appears on more than one side of the equation, remove it from one side. Aim to do this so the unknown is left with a **positive** coefficient.

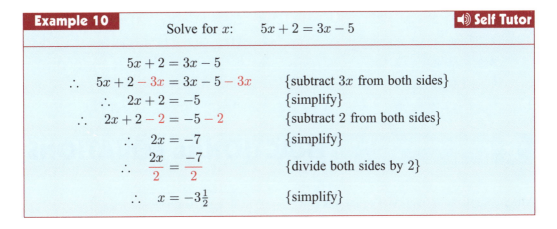

Example 10   Solve for x: $5x + 2 = 3x - 5$ ◀ᴺ **Self Tutor**

$5x + 2 = 3x - 5$

$\therefore \quad 5x + 2 - 3x = 3x - 5 - 3x$ {subtract $3x$ from both sides}

$\therefore \quad 2x + 2 = -5$ {simplify}

$\therefore \quad 2x + 2 - 2 = -5 - 2$ {subtract 2 from both sides}

$\therefore \quad 2x = -7$ {simplify}

$\therefore \quad \dfrac{2x}{2} = \dfrac{-7}{2}$ {divide both sides by 2}

$\therefore \quad x = -3\frac{1}{2}$ {simplify}

3 Solve for x:

    a $5x + 2 = 3x + 14$ **b** $8x + 7 = 4x - 5$ **c** $7x + 3 = 2x + 9$

    d $3x - 8 = 5x - 2$ **e** $x - 3 = 5x + 11$ **f** $3 + x = 15 + 4x$

Example 11   Solve for x: $15 - 2x = 11 + x$ ◀ᴺ **Self Tutor**

$15 - 2x = 11 + x$

$\therefore \quad 15 - 2x + 2x = 11 + x + 2x$ {add $2x$ to both sides}

$\therefore \quad 15 = 11 + 3x$ {simplify}

$\therefore \quad 15 - 11 = 11 + 3x - 11$ {subtract 11 from both sides}

$\therefore \quad 4 = 3x$ {simplify}

$\therefore \quad \dfrac{4}{3} = \dfrac{3x}{3}$ {divide both sides by 3}

$\therefore \quad x = 1\frac{1}{3}$ {simplify}

4 Solve for x:

    a $6 + 2x = 15 - x$ **b** $3x + 7 = 15 - x$ **c** $5 + x = 11 - 2x$

    d $17 - 3x = 4 - x$ **e** $8 - x = x + 6$ **f** $9 - 2x = 3 - x$

SUMMARY

Step 1:   If necessary, **expand** any **brackets** and **collect like terms**.

Step 2:   If necessary, remove the unknown from one side of the equation. Aim to do this so the unknown is left with a **positive** coefficient.

Step 3:   Use inverse operations to **isolate the unknown** and maintain balance.

Step 4:   **Check** that your solution satisfies the equation,   i.e., LHS = RHS.

5 Solve for x:

    a $2(x + 4) - x = 8$ **b** $5(2 - 3x) = -8 - 6x$

    c $3(x + 2) - x = 12$ **d** $2(x + 1) + 3(x - 4) = 5$

    e $4(2x - 1) + 9 = 3x$ **f** $11x - 2(x - 1) = -5$

    g $3x - 2(x + 1) = -7$ **h** $8 - (2 - x) = 2x$

    i $5x - 4(4 - x) = x + 12$ **j** $4(x - 1) = 1 - (3 - x)$

    k $3(x - 6) + 7x = 5(2x - 1)$ **l** $3(2x - 4) = 5x - (12 - x)$

E   FRACTIONAL EQUATIONS

More complicated fractional equations can be solved by:

- writing all fractions with the **lowest common denominator (LCD)** and then

- **equating numerators**.

> To solve equations involving fractions, we make the denominators the same so that we can equate the numerators.

Example 12   ◄) Self Tutor

Solve for x: $\dfrac{x}{3} = \dfrac{2}{5}$

$$\dfrac{x}{3} = \dfrac{2}{5} \qquad \text{has LCD of 15}$$

$$\therefore \quad \dfrac{x \times 5}{3 \times 5} = \dfrac{2 \times 3}{5 \times 3} \qquad \text{\{to achieve a common denominator\}}$$

$$\therefore \quad 5x = 6 \qquad \text{\{equating numerators\}}$$

$$\therefore \quad x = 1\tfrac{1}{5} \qquad \text{\{divide both sides by 5\}}$$

EXERCISE 11E

1 Solve for x:

a $\dfrac{x}{2} = \dfrac{2}{5}$ **b** $\dfrac{7}{2} = \dfrac{x}{4}$ **c** $\dfrac{5x}{2} = \dfrac{2}{3}$ **d** $\dfrac{1}{4} = \dfrac{x}{7}$

e $\dfrac{1}{9} = \dfrac{5x}{2}$ **f** $\dfrac{2x}{3} = \dfrac{1}{7}$ **g** $\dfrac{3}{4} = \dfrac{x}{5}$ **h** $\dfrac{2x}{3} = \dfrac{7}{2}$

Example 13   ◀ঙ **Self Tutor**

Solve for x: $\dfrac{2x+3}{4} = \dfrac{x-2}{3}$

$\dfrac{2x+3}{4} = \dfrac{x-2}{3}$ has LCD of 12

$\therefore \ \dfrac{3 \times (2x+3)}{3 \times 4} = \dfrac{4 \times (x-2)}{4 \times 3}$ {to achieve a common denominator}

$\therefore \quad 3(2x+3) = 4(x-2)$ {equating numerators}

$\therefore \quad 6x + 9 = 4x - 8$ {expanding brackets}

$\therefore \quad 6x + 9 - 4x = 4x - 8 - 4x$ {subtracting $4x$ from both sides}

$\therefore \quad 2x + 9 = -8$ {simplifying}

$\therefore \quad 2x + 9 - 9 = -8 - 9$ {subtracting 9 from both sides}

$\therefore \quad 2x = -17$ {simplifying}

$\therefore \quad \dfrac{2x}{2} = -\dfrac{17}{2}$ {dividing both sides by 2}

$\therefore \quad x = -8\tfrac{1}{2}$

---

2 Solve for x:

a $\dfrac{2x+3}{5} = \dfrac{1}{2}$ **b** $\dfrac{x+6}{2} = \dfrac{x}{3}$ **c** $\dfrac{2x-11}{7} = \dfrac{3x}{5}$

d $\dfrac{x+4}{2} = \dfrac{2x-3}{3}$ **e** $\dfrac{3x+2}{2} = \dfrac{x-1}{4}$ **f** $\dfrac{1-x}{2} = \dfrac{x+2}{3}$

g $\dfrac{x+5}{2} = 1 - x$ **h** $\dfrac{2x+7}{3} = x + 4$ **i** $\dfrac{2x+9}{2} = x - 8$

F   UNKNOWN IN THE DENOMINATOR

If the unknown appears as part of the denominator, we still solve by:

- writing the equations with the **lowest common denominator (LCD)**

and then
- **equating numerators**.

EXERCISE 11F

1 Solve for x:

a $\dfrac{3}{x} = \dfrac{1}{5}$ **b** $\dfrac{3}{x} = \dfrac{2}{3}$ **c** $\dfrac{2}{7} = \dfrac{5}{x}$ **d** $\dfrac{4}{9} = \dfrac{1}{x}$

e $\dfrac{1}{2x} = \dfrac{4}{3}$ **f** $\dfrac{7}{3x} = -4$ **g** $\dfrac{4}{5x} = 3$ **h** $-5 = \dfrac{2}{3x}$

Example 14 ◀⑨ Self Tutor

Solve for x: $\dfrac{3x+1}{x-1} = -2$

$$\dfrac{3x+1}{x-1} = \dfrac{-2}{1} \qquad \text{has LCD of } x-1$$

$$\therefore \quad \dfrac{3x+1}{x-1} = \dfrac{-2 \times (x-1)}{1 \times (x-1)} \qquad \{\text{to achieve a common denominator}\}$$

$$\therefore \quad 3x+1 = -2(x-1) \qquad \{\text{equating numerators}\}$$

$$\therefore \quad 3x+1 = -2x+2 \qquad \{\text{expanding brackets}\}$$

$$\therefore \quad 3x+1 + 2x = -2x+2 + 2x \qquad \{\text{adding } 2x \text{ to both sides}\}$$

$$\therefore \quad 5x+1 = 2 \qquad \{\text{simplifying both sides}\}$$

$$\therefore \quad 5x+1-1 = 2-1 \qquad \{\text{subtracting 1 from both sides}\}$$

$$\therefore \quad 5x = 1 \qquad \{\text{dividing both sides by 5}\}$$

$$\therefore \quad x = \tfrac{1}{5}$$

---

2 Solve for x:

a $\dfrac{3x-11}{4x} = -2$ **b** $\dfrac{2x+7}{x-4} = -1$ **c** $\dfrac{2x+1}{x-4} = 4$

d $\dfrac{2x}{x+4} = 3$ **e** $\dfrac{-3}{2x-1} = 5$ **f** $\dfrac{4x+1}{x+2} = -3$

Example 15 ◀⑨ Self Tutor

Solve for x: $\dfrac{x}{2} = \dfrac{5}{x}$

$$\dfrac{x}{2} = \dfrac{5}{x} \qquad \text{has LCD of } 2x$$

$$\therefore \quad \dfrac{x \times x}{2 \times x} = \dfrac{5 \times 2}{x \times 2} \qquad \{\text{to get a common denominator}\}$$

$$\therefore \quad x^2 = 10 \qquad \{\text{equating numerators}\}$$

$$\therefore \quad x = \pm\sqrt{10}$$

> If $x^2 = k$ then $x = \pm\sqrt{k}$ $(k > 0)$.

3 Solve for x:

a $\dfrac{x}{3} = \dfrac{4}{x}$ **b** $\dfrac{x}{6} = \dfrac{6}{x}$ **c** $\dfrac{1}{x} = \dfrac{x}{3}$ **d** $\dfrac{x}{7} = \dfrac{7}{x}$

e $\dfrac{2}{x} = \dfrac{x}{5}$ **f** $\dfrac{7}{x} = \dfrac{x}{5}$ **g** $\dfrac{x}{2} = \dfrac{8}{x}$ **h** $\dfrac{x}{5} = \dfrac{-2}{x}$

G   FORMING EQUATIONS

Algebraic equations are mathematical sentences which indicate that two expressions have the same value. They always contain the "=" sign.

Many problems we are given are stated in words. Before we can solve a worded problem, we need to translate the given statement into a mathematical equation. We then solve the equation to find the solution to the problem.

The following **steps** should be followed:

Step 1:   Decide what the unknown quantity is and choose a pronumeral such as x to represent it.

Step 2:   Look for the operation(s) involved in the problem.

For example,

Statement	Translation
decreased by	subtract
more than	add
double	multiply by 2
halve	divide by 2

Step 3:   Form the equation with an "=" sign. These phrases indicate equality:
"the answer is",   "will be",   "the result is",   "is equal to",   or simply   "is"

Example 16   ◀ Self Tutor

Translate into an equation:
a   "When a number is added to 6 the result is 15."
b   "Twice a certain number is 7 more than the number."

a   *In words*   *Indicates*

"a number"   We let x be the number

"a number is added to 6" $6 + x$

"the result is" $6 + x =$

So, $6 + x = 15$

b   *In words*   *Indicates*

"a certain number"   Let x be the number

"twice a certain number" $2x$

"7 more than the number" $x + 7$

"is"   So, $2x = x + 7$

In the following exercise, you do not have to set out your answers like those given in the example.

With practice you will find that you can combine the steps, but you should note:

- the mathematical sentence you form must be an accurate translation of the information
- for these types of problems, you must have only one pronumeral in your equation.

EXERCISE 11G

1 Translate into linear equations, but *do not solve*:

    a When a number is increased by 6, the answer is 13.

    b When a number is decreased by 5, the result is -4.

    c A number is doubled and 7 is added. The result is 1.

    d When a number is decreased by 1 and the resulting number is halved, the answer is 45.

    e Three times a number is equal to 17 minus the number.

    f Five times a number is 2 more than the number.

Example 17   ◀⦆ **Self Tutor**

Translate into an equation: "The sum of 2 consecutive even integers is 34."

Let the smaller even integer be x.

$\therefore$ the next even integer is $x + 2$.

So, $x + (x + 2) = 34$ is the equation.

---

2 Translate into equations, but *do not solve:*

    a The sum of two consecutive integers is 33.

    b The sum of 3 consecutive integers is 102.

    c The sum of two consecutive odd integers is 52.

    d The sum of 3 consecutive odd integers is 69.

Example 18   ◀⦆ **Self Tutor**

Apples cost 13 cents each and oranges cost 11 cents each.

If I buy 5 more apples than oranges and the total cost of the apples and oranges is $2.33, write a linear equation involving the total cost.

Type of fruit	Number of pieces of fruit	Cost per piece of fruit	Total cost
oranges	x	11 cents	$11x$ cents
apples	$x + 5$	13 cents	$13(x + 5)$ cents
			233 cents

From the table we know the total cost,   and so $11x + 13(x + 5) = 233$.

3 Write an equation for each of the following:

a Oranges cost 25 pence each and apples cost 30 pence each. If I buy 5 more oranges than apples, the total cost will be £4.55.
(Let the pronumeral a represent the number of apples.)

b Isaac is going to boarding school. He buys school shirts at €35 each and trousers at €49 each. Altogether he buys 9 items, and their total cost is €357.
(Let the number of shirts be s.)

c Jessica has a collection of old 2-cent and 5-cent stamps with a total value of $2.24. She has 7 more 5-cent stamps than 2-cent stamps.
(Let the pronumeral f represent the number of 5-cent stamps.)

H   PROBLEM SOLVING USING EQUATIONS

PROBLEM SOLVING METHOD

- Identify the unknown quantity and allocate a pronumeral to it.
- Decide which operations are involved.
- Translate the problem into a linear equation and check that your translation is correct.
- Solve the linear equation by isolating the pronumeral.
- Check that your solution does satisfy the original problem.
- Write your answer in sentence form.

Example 19   ◄)) **Self Tutor**

The sum of 3 consecutive even integers is 132. Find the smallest integer.

Let x be the smallest even integer
$\therefore$ the next is $x + 2$ and the largest is $x + 4$.

So,
$$x + (x + 2) + (x + 4) = 132 \quad \{\text{their sum is 132}\}$$
$$\therefore \quad 3x + 6 = 132 \quad \{\text{simplifying}\}$$
$$\therefore \quad 3x + 6 - 6 = 132 - 6 \quad \{\text{subtract 6 from both sides}\}$$
$$\therefore \quad 3x = 126$$
$$\therefore \quad \frac{3x}{3} = \frac{126}{3}$$
$$\therefore \quad x = 42 \quad \therefore \text{ the smallest integer is 42.}$$

EXERCISE 11H

1 When a number is trebled and then decreased by 5, the answer is 19. Find the number.

2 If two consecutive integers have a sum of 173, find the numbers.

3 If three consecutive integers add to 108, find the smallest of them.

Example 20

Self Tutor

If twice a number is subtracted from 11, the result is 4 more than the number. What is the number?

Let x be the number,

LHS algebraic expression is $11 - 2x$

RHS algebraic expression is $x + 4$.

$\therefore$	$11 - 2x = x + 4$	{the equation}
$\therefore$	$11 - 2x + 2x = x + 4 + 2x$	{add $2x$ to both sides}
$\therefore$	$11 = 3x + 4$	
$\therefore$	$11 - 4 = 3x + 4 - 4$	{subtract 4 from both sides}
$\therefore$	$7 = 3x$	
$\therefore$	$\dfrac{7}{3} = \dfrac{3x}{3}$	{divide both sides by 3}
$\therefore$	$x = 2\frac{1}{3}$	So, the number is $2\frac{1}{3}$.

4   When a number is subtracted from 35, the result is 11 more than the number. Find the number.

5   When a number is increased by 4 and the result is halved, the answer is equal to the original number. Find the number.

6   When one-third of a number is subtracted from one-half of a number, the answer is 14. Find the number.

Example 21

Self Tutor

Cans of sardines come in two sizes. Small cans cost $2 each and large cans cost $3 each. If 15 cans of sardines are bought for a total of $38, how many small cans were purchased?

Table:

Size	Cost per can	Number bought	Value
small	$2	x	$2x$
large	$3	$15 - x$	$3(15 - x)$
		15	$38

So,	$2x + 3(15 - x) = 38$	
$\therefore$	$2x + 45 - 3x = 38$	{expanding brackets}
$\therefore$	$45 - x = 38$	{simplifying}
$\therefore$	$45 - x - 45 = 38 - 45$	{subtract 45 from both sides}
$\therefore$	$-x = -7$	
$\therefore$	$x = 7$	So, 7 small cans were bought.

7 I have 36 coins in my pocket, all of which are 5-cent or 10-cent coins. If their total value is $3.20, how many 5-cent coins do I have?

8 Bananas cost 95 cents each whereas apples cost 35 cents each. If I buy 4 more bananas than apples and the total bill is $10.30, how many bananas did I buy?

9 Containers of soup come in two sizes; 250 g at $2.95 and 500 g at $4.50. If I buy a total of 12 containers and they cost me $43.15, how many 500 g containers did I buy?

FINDING AN UNKNOWN FROM A FORMULA

A **formula** is an equation which connects two or more variables.

If we wish to find the value of one of the variables in a formula and we know the value(s) of the remaining variables, we **substitute** into the formula and **solve** the resulting equation.

Example 22
🔊 Self Tutor

$A = \frac{1}{2}bh$ is the formula for finding the area, A, of a triangle given its base b and height h. Find the height of a triangle of base 12 cm and area 60 cm^2.

$$b = 12 \quad \text{and} \quad A = 60 \quad \therefore \quad 60 = \frac{1}{2} \times 12 \times h$$

$$\therefore \quad 60 = 6h$$

$$\therefore \quad \frac{60}{6} = h \qquad \{\text{dividing both sides by 6}\}$$

$$\therefore \quad h = 10$$

So, the height is 10 cm.

EXERCISE 11I

1 The area of a triangle with base b and height h is given by the formula $A = \frac{1}{2}bh$.   Find:

  a the base if the area is 84 cm^2 and the height is 12 cm

  b the height if the area is 1 m^2 and the base is 2 m.

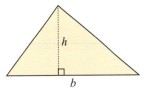

2 The volume of a rectangular box is given by the formula $V = lwd$ where l is its length, w is its width, and d is its depth.   Find:

  a its length if its width is 8 cm, its depth is 3 cm and its volume is 168 cm^3

  b its depth if its volume is 945 cm^3, its length is 9 cm and its width is 15 cm.

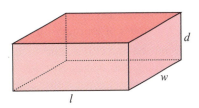

Example 23

When a stone is dropped from a stationary position, the distance s travelled downwards, is given by $s = \frac{1}{2}gt^2$ metres, where g is the gravitational constant of 9.8 m s^{-2} and t is the time in seconds. Find:

a the depth of a well given that a stone takes 1.3 seconds to hit the bottom

b the time taken for a stone to reach the bottom of a 1000 m high vertical cliff.

a
$$s = \tfrac{1}{2}gt^2 \quad \text{where} \quad g = 9.8 \quad \text{and} \quad t = 1.3$$
$$\therefore \quad s = \tfrac{1}{2} \times (9.8) \times (1.3)^2 \qquad \{\text{substituting}\}$$
$$\therefore \quad s = 8.281 \qquad \{\text{calculator}\}$$

So, the well is 8.281 m deep.

b
$$s = \tfrac{1}{2}gt^2 \quad \text{where} \quad g = 9.8 \quad \text{and} \quad s = 1000$$
$$\therefore \quad 1000 = \tfrac{1}{2} \times 9.8 \times t^2 \qquad \{\text{substituting}\}$$
$$\therefore \quad 1000 = 4.9 \times t^2$$
$$\therefore \quad \frac{1000}{4.9} = t^2 \qquad \{\text{dividing both sides by 4.9}\}$$
$$\therefore \quad t = \pm\sqrt{\frac{1000}{4.9}} \qquad \{\text{if } x^2 = k \text{ then } x = \pm\sqrt{k}\}$$
$$\text{i.e.,} \quad t \approx 14.2857 \qquad \{\text{as } t > 0\}$$

The stone would take ≈ 14.3 seconds.

3 The average speed s for an object travelling a distance d in time t is given by $s = \dfrac{d}{t}$.

   a Find the distance travelled by a cyclist whose average speed over a 4 hour period was 23 kilometres per hour (km h^{-1}).

   b Find the time taken to ride a horse 42 km at an average speed of 15 km h^{-1}.

4 The velocity v (in m s^{-1}) of an object dropped from a stationary position is calculated using the formula $v^2 = 2gs$ where g is the gravitational constant of 9.8 m s^{-2} and s is the distance fallen. Find:

   a the velocity (in metres per second) of a boy when he hits the ground after falling from a branch of a tree 8 m above the ground

   b the distance fallen by a base jumper who has reached a velocity of 50 metres per second before opening his parachute.

5 The cost of running a train between two cities is given by the formula $C = wt + ds$ where

   w = wages per hour d = fuel cost per km per hour

   t = hours of journey s = speed of train (in km h^{-1}).

Find the travelling time of a train if the total cost is $\$18\,000$, the wages cost $\$2400$ per hour, the fuel cost is $\$60$ per km per hour, and the speed of the train is 180 km h^{-1}.

© iStockphoto

6 The volume of a cone is given by the formula $V = \frac{1}{3}\pi r^2 h$
where r is the base radius and h is the height. Find:

   a the height of a cone of radius 8 cm and volume 240 cm^3
   b the radius of the base of a cone of volume 96 cm^3 and
height 16 cm.

7

A butcher had 80 kg of steak. He sold
60 kg at a certain price per kg and then
sold the remainder at half price.

His total revenue from the sale of the steak
was \$560. What was the full price per kg?

8 Work colleagues pay €24 each to attend a Christmas luncheon and their employer pays a
fixed booking charge of €50. If the total bill was €722, how many attended the luncheon?

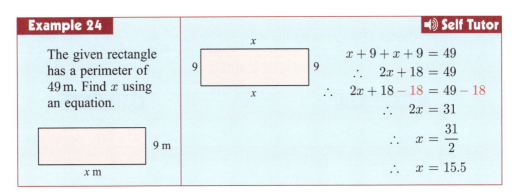

Example 24 ◀》 **Self Tutor**

The given rectangle
has a perimeter of
49 m. Find x using
an equation.

$$x + 9 + x + 9 = 49$$
$$\therefore \quad 2x + 18 = 49$$
$$\therefore \quad 2x + 18 - 18 = 49 - 18$$
$$\therefore \quad 2x = 31$$
$$\therefore \quad x = \frac{31}{2}$$
$$\therefore \quad x = 15.5$$

9 Find x given that:

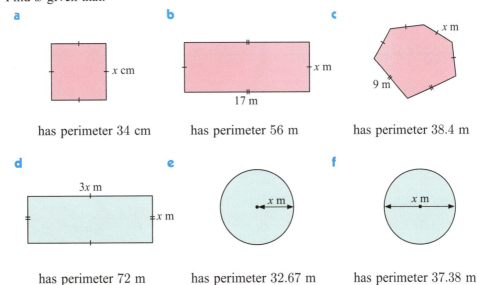

   a has perimeter 34 cm
   b has perimeter 56 m
   c has perimeter 38.4 m
   d has perimeter 72 m
   e has perimeter 32.67 m
   f has perimeter 37.38 m

10 An athletics track is to have a boundary fence of 400 m.

If the straights are to have length 100 m, find what value x, the radius of the *bends*, must have.

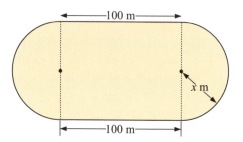

J   FORMULA REARRANGEMENT

For the formula $D = xt + p$ we say that D is the **subject**. This is because D is expressed in terms of the other variables, x, t and p.

We can rearrange formulae to make one of the other variables the subject.

> We **rearrange** formulae using the same processes we use to solve equations. Anything we do to one side we must also do to the other.

Example 25   ◀) Self Tutor

Make y the subject of $2x + 3y = 12$.

$2x + 3y = 12$

$\therefore \ 3y = 12 - 2x$ {subtract $2x$ from both sides}

$\therefore \ y = \dfrac{12 - 2x}{3}$ {divide both sides by 3}

$\therefore \ y = \dfrac{12}{3} - \dfrac{2x}{3} = 4 - \tfrac{2}{3}x$

EXERCISE 11J

1 Make y the subject of:

   a $3x + 5y = 9$ **b** $4x + 3y = 18$ **c** $4x - y = 8$

   d $7x + 2y = 42$ **e** $2x + 3y = 12$ **f** $5x - 3y = -60$

2 Make x the subject of:

   a $a + x = b$ **b** $xy = z$ **c** $2x + p = q$

   d $3x + 2y = r$ **e** $ax + by = c$ **f** $y = mx + c$

   g $7 + px = q$ **h** $a + bx = c$ **i** $7 = p + qx$

Example 26   🔊 **Self Tutor**

Make y the subject of $x = 5 - cy$.

$$x = 5 - cy$$
$$\therefore \quad x + cy = 5 - cy + cy \quad \text{\{add } cy \text{ to both sides\}}$$
$$\therefore \quad x + cy = 5$$
$$\therefore \quad x + cy - x = 5 - x \quad \text{\{subtract } x \text{ from both sides\}}$$
$$\therefore \quad cy = 5 - x$$
$$\therefore \quad \frac{cy}{c} = \frac{5 - x}{c} \quad \text{\{divide both sides by } c\}$$
$$\therefore \quad y = \frac{5 - x}{c}$$

3   Make y the subject of:

   a $mx - y = c$ **b** $a - 3y = b$ **c** $p - 5y = q$

   d $5 - ay = b$ **e** $p - qy = r$ **f** $p = q - ry$

Example 27   🔊 **Self Tutor**

Make z the subject of $c = \dfrac{m}{z}$.

$$c = \frac{m}{z}$$
$$c \times z = \frac{m}{z} \times z \quad \text{\{multiply both sides by } z\}$$
$$\therefore \quad cz = m$$
$$\therefore \quad \frac{cz}{c} = \frac{m}{c} \quad \text{\{divide both sides by } c\}$$
$$\therefore \quad z = \frac{m}{c}$$

4   Make z the subject of:

   a $yz = \dfrac{4}{x}$ **b** $\dfrac{y}{z} = x$ **c** $\dfrac{5}{w} = \dfrac{4}{z}$

   d $\dfrac{z}{3} = \dfrac{y}{z}$ **e** $\dfrac{x}{z} = \dfrac{z}{y}$ **f** $\dfrac{w}{z} = \dfrac{z}{p - q}$

5   Make:

   a m the subject of $F = ma$ **b** r the subject of $C = 2\pi r$

   c l the subject of $V = ldh$ **d** M the subject of $D = \dfrac{M}{V}$

   e b the subject of $A = \dfrac{bh}{2}$ **f** R the subject of $I = \dfrac{PRT}{100}$

6

A housing block has area 800 m^2.

a Write an equation connecting x and y.

b Make y the subject of the formula in **a**.

c Write a formula for the perimeter of the housing block P, in terms of x only.

7

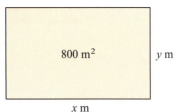

This housing block has perimeter 100 m.

a Write an equation connecting x and y.

b Make y the subject of the formula in **a**.

c Write a formula for the area A, in terms of x only.

Example 28   ◀ᵈ) **Self Tutor**

Find, correct to 2 decimal places, the radius of a circular pond which has a circumference of 30.5 m.

Using $C = 2\pi r$

$\therefore$ $30.5 = 2\pi r$

$\therefore$ $\dfrac{30.5}{2\pi} = r$

$\therefore$ $r \approx 4.85$ {*Calculator:*   30.5 $\boxed{\div}$ $\boxed{(}$ 2 $\boxed{\times}$ $\boxed{\pi}$ $\boxed{)}$ $\boxed{=}$ }

So, the radius is 4.85 m.

---

8 Kirsten has a piece of string 90 cm long which she shapes into a circle. Find the diameter of the circle correct to the nearest mm.

9 The wheel on a barrow is 28 cm in diameter.

a Find the circumference of the wheel to the nearest mm.

b Through how many revolutions must the wheel turn if the barrow is wheeled 200 m?

10 A satellite has a circular orbit 800 km above the surface of the Earth. The radius of the Earth is 6400 km and the satellite must complete exactly 14 orbits in one day.

a What is the circumference of the satellite's orbit, to the nearest km?

b How fast must it be moving?

Example 29 ◄⑴ **Self Tutor**

A circle has the same area as a square with sides 10 cm. Find its radius.

10 cm

10 cm

Area of circle $= \pi r^2$

Area of square $= 10 \text{ cm} \times 10 \text{ cm} = 100 \text{ cm}^2$

So, $\pi r^2 = 100$

$\therefore \quad r^2 = \dfrac{100}{\pi} \quad \{\div \text{ both sides by } \pi\}$

$\therefore \quad r = \sqrt{\dfrac{100}{\pi}} \approx 5.64 \quad \{r > 0\}$

$\therefore$ the radius is 5.64 cm

11 A circular playing field has an area of 4300 m^2. Find its radius.

12 A circle has the same area as a square with sides 15 cm. Find its radius.

13 A cylindrical tank has base radius 1.5 m and total surface area 42.4 m^2. Find its height.

REVIEW SET 11A

1 The solution of the equation $2x - 1 = 13$ is one of the integers 6, 7, or -7. Find the solution by trial and error.

2 What equation results from adding -5 to both sides of $3x + 5 = 17$?

3 Solve for x: **a** $9 + 2x = -11$ **b** $\dfrac{3 - 2x}{7} = -5$

4 Solve for x: **a** $\dfrac{x}{5} = \dfrac{4}{7}$ **b** $\dfrac{4x + 5}{3} = \dfrac{x}{2}$

5 Solve for x: **a** $\dfrac{1}{3x} = 5$ **b** $\dfrac{x + 6}{3 - 2x} = -1$

6 Translate into linear equations but *do not solve*:
  a When a number is increased by 11 and the result is doubled, the answer is 48.
  b The sum of three consecutive integers is 63.

7 When 7 times a certain number is decreased by 11, the result is 31 more than the number. Find the number by solving an equation.

8 I have 25 coins consisting of 5-cent and 50-cent pieces. If the total value is $7.10, how many 5-cent coins do I have?

9 The velocity (v m s^{-1}) of a ball falling from a stationary position is given by $v^2 = 2gs$ where s is the distance fallen in metres and $g = 9.8$ m s^{-2}. Find:
  a the velocity of the ball after falling 25 m
  b the distance fallen when the velocity reaches 40 m s^{-1}.

10 Find x given that the perimeter of the triangle is 56 cm.

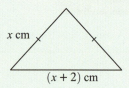

x cm

$(x + 2)$ cm

11 **a** Make y the subject of $5x - 3y = 15$.

   b Make d the subject of $C = \pi d$.

REVIEW SET 11B

1 Is the equation $3x - 2 = 3x + 6$ true:

   A   for all values of x **B**   never   **C**   for exactly one value of x?

2 What equation results from dividing both sides of $4x + 8 = 12$ by 4?

3 Solve for x: **a** $\dfrac{2x}{3} + 11 = -2$ **b** $3(2x - 1) + 9 = 2(x + 7)$

4 Solve for x: **a** $\dfrac{x}{2} = \dfrac{3}{8}$ **b** $\dfrac{1 - 3x}{4} = \dfrac{x - 2}{2}$

5 Solve for x: **a** $\dfrac{5}{3x} = \dfrac{3}{2}$ **b** $\dfrac{2x + 1}{3} - \dfrac{4 - x}{6} = -2$

6 Translate into linear equations, but *do not solve*.

   a Four times a number is equal to the number plus 15.

   b The sum of two consecutive odd integers is 36.

7 Five more than a certain number is nine less than three times the number. Find the number.

8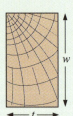

w

t

The strength S of a wooden beam is given by $S = 200w^2 t$ units, where w cm is its width and t cm is its thickness.

Find:

   a the strength of a beam of width 16 cm and thickness 4 cm

   b the width of a 5 cm thick beam of strength 60 000 units.

9 Make V the subject of $D = \dfrac{M}{V}$.

10 **a** Make y the subject of $6x + 5y = 20$.

   b Make r the subject of $C = 2\pi r$.

11 The surface area of a sphere is given by the formula $A = 4\pi r^2$. If the surface area of a sphere is 250 cm^2, find its radius correct to 2 decimal places.

Chapter 12

Ratios and rates

Contents:

A   Ratio
B   Simplifying ratios
C   Equal ratios
D   The unitary method for ratios
E   Using ratios to divide quantities
F   Scale diagrams
G   Rates
H   Rate graphs
I   Travel graphs

OPENING PROBLEMS

Problem A

Jason, Wei and Pauline invest $20 000, $30 000 and $40 000 respectively to start an advertising business. At the end of the first year they split the profits in the same ratio as their investments. If the total profit is $180 000, how much should each receive?

Problem B

Sev's car consumes petrol at the rate of 8.4 litres per hundred kilometres.

a   What does the given rate mean?

b   How much petrol would he need to travel 350 km?

A   RATIO

A **ratio** is a way of comparing two quantities.

If we have 6 apples and 4 bananas, the ratio of the number of apples to the number of bananas is 6 to 4.

We write this as   apples : bananas = 6 : 4
Notice that   bananas : apples = 4 : 6

If measurements are involved we must use the **same units** for each quantity.

For example, the ratio of lengths shown is

20 : 7   {20 mm : 7 mm}   and not   2 : 7.

2 cm   7 mm

Example 1	◀) **Self Tutor**
What is the ratio of the number of squares to the number of triangles? ▫▫▫▫▫▫▫▫ △△△△△△△ △△△	no. of squares : no. of triangles = 8 : 11

EXERCISE 12A

1   a   Find the ratio of squares to triangles in:

b   Find the ratio of ♣s to ♠s   in:

c

Find the ratio of:

i   + signs to × signs

ii   × signs to + signs

iii   •s to × signs

iv   × signs to •s

Example 2   🔊 **Self Tutor**

Write as a ratio, without simplifying your answer:

a   Jack has $5 and Jill has 50 cents.

b   Mix 200 mL of cordial with 1 L of water.

a   Jack : Jill $= \$5 : 50$ cents   {write in the correct order}

              $= 500$ cents : 50 cents   {write in the same units}

              $= 500 : 50$ {express without units}

b   cordial : water $= 200$ mL : 1 L   {write in the correct order}

               $= 200$ mL : 1000 mL   {write in the same units}

               $= 200 : 1000$ {express without units}

---

2   Write as a ratio, without simplifying your answer:

     a $8 is to $3   **b**   3 L is to 7 L   **c**   35 kg is to 45 kg

     d   £3 is to 50 pence   **e**   500 mL is to 3 L   **f**   400 m is to 2.5 km

     g   9 km is to 150 m   **h**   12 m is to 8 km   **i**   4 h is to 40 min

---

B   SIMPLIFYING RATIOS

If we have 6 apples and 4 bananas, we have 3 apples for every 2 bananas.

So, $6 : 4$ is the same as $3 : 2$.

We say that $6 : 4$ and $3 : 2$ are **equal ratios**.

Notice that to get from $6 : 4$ to $3 : 2$ we can divide each number in the first ratio by 2.

Also, to get from $3 : 2$ to $6 : 4$ we can multiply each number in the first ratio by 2.

> To **simplify a ratio** we can multiply or divide each part by the same non-zero number.

Example 3   🔊 **Self Tutor**

Express $45 : 10$ in simplest form.

     $45 : 10$

     $= 45 \div 5 : 10 \div 5$ {5 is the HCF of 45 and 10}

     $= 9 : 2$

EXERCISE 12B

1 Express as a ratio in simplest form:

    a $6 : 8$ **b** $8 : 4$ **c** $4 : 12$ **d** $9 : 15$

    e $3 : 6$ **f** $14 : 8$ **g** $8 : 16$ **h** $18 : 24$

    i $125 : 100$ **j** $2 : 4 : 6$ **k** $1000 : 50$ **l** $6 : 12 : 24$

Example 4	◀ঃ) Self Tutor
Express $0.4 : 1.4$ in simplest form.	$0.4 : 1.4$ $= 0.4 \times 10 : 1.4 \times 10$ $= 4 : 14$ $= 4 \div 2 : 14 \div 2$ $= 2 : 7$

DEMO

2 Express as a ratio in simplest form:

    a $0.5 : 0.2$ **b** $0.3 : 0.7$ **c** $0.6 : 0.4$ **d** $0.4 : 0.2$

    e $0.7 : 1.2$ **f** $0.03 : 0.12$ **g** $2 : 0.5$ **h** $0.05 : 1$

Example 5	◀ঃ) Self Tutor
Write $2\frac{1}{2} : \frac{1}{2}$ as a ratio in simplest form.	$2\frac{1}{2} : \frac{1}{2}$ $= \frac{5}{2} : \frac{1}{2}$ $= \frac{5}{2} \times 2 : \frac{1}{2} \times 2$ $= 5 : 1$

3 Express as a ratio in simplest form:

    a $\frac{1}{3} : \frac{2}{3}$ **b** $\frac{3}{4} : \frac{1}{4}$ **c** $1\frac{1}{2} : \frac{1}{2}$ **d** $1\frac{1}{2} : 2\frac{1}{2}$

    e $1\frac{1}{3} : \frac{2}{3}$ **f** $\frac{3}{4} : 1\frac{1}{2}$ **g** $6 : 1\frac{1}{2}$ **h** $\frac{1}{2} : \frac{1}{3} : \frac{1}{4}$

USING A CALCULATOR TO SIMPLIFY RATIOS

You can sometimes use your calculator to simplify ratios, but remember that you must still be able to perform the process by hand.

Instructions can be found in the **General Calculator Instructions** section on page **11**.

4 Use your calculator to simplify the ratios:

    a $\frac{1}{3} : \frac{1}{2}$ **b** $1\frac{1}{3} : 2\frac{1}{2}$ **c** $\frac{2}{3} : 3\frac{1}{4}$ **d** $1\frac{3}{10} : 1\frac{2}{3}$

5 Write the following comparisons as ratios in simplest form. Compare the first quantity mentioned with the second quantity mentioned.

    a a shirt costing €64 to another shirt costing €32

    b a rockmelon of mass 3 kg to a watermelon of mass 9 kg c   the height of a 1.5 m shrub to the height of a 6 m tree

d   a wetsuit costing \$175 to a wetsuit costing \$250

e   the top speed of a car which is 150 km h^{-1} to the top speed of a formula one car which is 350 km h^{-1}

f   a log of length 4 m to a stick of length 10 cm

g   the height of an insect which is 2 mm to the height of a rat which is 10 cm.

6   Rectangle A is 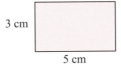 Rectangle B is

3 cm

5 cm

6 cm

10 cm

Find the ratio of:

a   shorter side of A : shorter side of B

b   longer side of A : longer side of B

c   area of A : area of B   d   area of B : area of A

Extension

7   A gardener spends 16 hours on a job. He spends $\frac{1}{4}$ of the time mowing lawns, $\frac{3}{8}$ of the time weeding, $\frac{1}{4}$ of the time edging, and $\frac{1}{8}$ of the time sweeping up.

a   Find the ratio of the time spent mowing to the time spent weeding.

b   Find the ratio of the time spent mowing to the time spent sweeping up.

c   Find the ratio of the time spent edging to the time spent weeding.

d   What time was spent on each activity?

C   EQUAL RATIOS

Ratios are **equal** if they can be expressed in the same simplest form.

Sometimes we need to find one quantity given the ratio and the other quantity. To do this we use equal ratios.

Example 6   ◀)) Self Tutor

The masses of two house bricks are in the ratio of $3 : 4$. If the smaller brick has mass 6 kg, what is the mass of the larger brick?

If the larger brick has mass x kg, then we can write $3 : 4 = 6 : x$

To go from 3 to 6 we multiply by 2

$$\therefore \quad 4 \times 2 = x \quad \text{also}$$
$$\therefore \quad x = 8$$

$3 : 4 = 6 : x$

×2
×2

So the larger brick has mass 8 kg.

EXERCISE 12C

1 Find x if:

    a $2 : 3 = 8 : x$ **b** $1 : 4 = x : 12$ **c** $3 : 2 = 15 : x$

    d $4 : 3 = x : 21$ **e** $5 : 7 = 25 : x$ **f** $6 : 11 = x : 77$

    g $5 : 12 = 40 : x$ **h** $7 : 10 = x : 80$ **i** $4 : 5 = x : 45$

Example 7   🔊 Self Tutor

Find $\square$ if: **a** $3 : 5 = 6 : \square$ **b** $15 : 20 = \square : 16$

a $\overset{\times 2}{3 : 5 = 6 : \square}$

    $\therefore \quad \square = 5 \times 2$

    $\therefore \quad \square = 10$

b $15 : 20 = 15 \div 5 : 20 \div 5$

              $= 3 : 4$

    $\therefore \quad \overset{\times 4}{3 : 4 = \square : 16}$

    $\therefore \quad \square = 3 \times 4 = 12$

---

2 Find $\square$ if:

    a $4 : 5 = 12 : \square$ **b** $3 : 9 = \square : 18$ **c** $2 : 3 = 10 : \square$

    d $5 : 10 = \square : 18$ **e** $16 : 4 = 12 : \square$ **f** $21 : 28 = 12 : \square$

Example 8   🔊 Self Tutor

The ratio of walkers to guides on the Milford Track walk was $9 : 2$. How many guides were needed if there were 27 walkers?

Let the number of guides be x.

    walkers : guides $= 27 : x$

    $\therefore \quad \overset{\times 3}{9 : 2 = 27 : x}$

    $\therefore \quad x = 2 \times 3$

    $\therefore \quad x = 6$

    $\therefore$ 6 guides were needed.

---

3 A recipe for tomato soup uses tomatoes and onions in the ratio $7 : 2$. If 21 kg of tomatoes are used, how many kilograms of onions are needed?

4 An orchard has apple trees and pear trees in the ratio $5 : 3$. If there are 180 pear trees, how many apple trees are there?

5 A car cleaning service increases the cost of a \$15 'standard clean' to \$18. The \$25 'deluxe clean' is increased in the same ratio as the 'standard'. How much does a 'deluxe clean' cost now?

6 Concrete is mixed in a ratio of premix to cement of $6 : 1$. If I have 540 kg of premix, how much cement do I need?

7 The mass of two bags is in the ratio $7 : 12$. The bigger bag has a mass of 48 kg.

    a Find the mass of the smaller bag.

    b Find the combined mass of the bags.

8 The ratio of the masses of Fido to Sammy is $6 : 17$. Fido has a mass of 12 kg. What is the mass of Sammy?

9 The ratio of the volume of a small suitcase to that of a larger suitcase is $4 : 7$. The volume of the smaller case is $120\,000$ cm^3. The aeroplane will not take luggage whose volume is greater than $250\,000$ cm^3. Will the larger piece of luggage be accepted?

D   THE UNITARY METHOD FOR RATIOS

Some ratio problems are easily handled using the **unitary method**.

Consider **Example 8** where   walkers : guides $= 27 : x$

               i.e., $9 : 2 = 27 : x$

The unitary method is: 9 parts is   27

         $\therefore$ 1 part is $27 \div 9 = 3$

         $\therefore$ 2 parts is $3 \times 2 = 6$

     $\therefore$ 6 guides were needed.

> The unitary method works well with harder ratio problems.

Example 9   🔊 **Self Tutor**

The ratio of Pam's height to Sam's height is $7 : 6$. If Pam is 1.63 m tall, how tall is Sam?

Let Sam's height be x m.	Let Sam's height be x m.
Pam : Sam $= 7 : 6$	Pam : Sam $= 7 : 6$
$\therefore$ $1.63 : x = 7 : 6$	$\therefore$ $1.63 : x = 7 : 6$
So, 7 parts is 1.63 m	$\therefore$ $\dfrac{x}{1.63} = \dfrac{6}{7}$
$\therefore$ 1 part is $1.63 \div 7$ m	$\therefore$ $x = \frac{6}{7} \times 1.63$
$\therefore$ 6 parts is $1.63 \div 7 \times 6$ m	$\therefore$ $x \approx 1.40$
$\therefore$ Sam's height is ≈ 1.40 m.	$\therefore$ Sam's height is ≈ 1.40 m.

or

EXERCISE 12D

Use the *unitary method* to solve these problems.

1 The ratio of Bob's weight to Colin's weight is 6 : 7. If Bob weighs 83.7 kg, how much does Colin weigh?

2 If Kayo and Sally split their profits in the ratio of 5 : 4 respectively and Kayo gets $23 672, how much does Sally get, to the nearest dollar?

3  Jack's lawn is on average 8.3 cm high. The ratio of height of Jack's lawn to Henri's lawn is 1 : 1.13. Find the average height of Henri's lawn (to 2 dec. places).

4 The ratio of water to alcohol in a bottle of wine is 15 : 2. If there are 662 mL of water in the bottle, what is the quantity of alcohol in the bottle?

5 The masses of two strawberries are in the ratio 7 : 9. If the smaller one weighs 9.3 grams, what is the mass of the larger one?

6 A block of land is divided in the ratio 6 : 11 and the larger portion is 875 m². Find, to the nearest whole number, the area of the smaller block.

LINKS
click here

ALL THAT GLITTERS IS NOT GOLD

Areas of interaction:
Human ingenuity

E   USING RATIOS TO DIVIDE QUANTITIES

Quantities can be divided in a particular ratio by considering the **number of parts** the whole is to be divided into.

Example 10   ◀◎ **Self Tutor**

An inheritance of $60 000 is to be divided between Donny and Marie in the ratio 2 : 3. How much does each receive?

There are $2 + 3 = 5$ parts.

$\therefore$ Donny gets $\frac{2}{5}$ of $60 000   and Marie gets $\frac{3}{5}$ of $60 000

$\phantom{\therefore \text{Donny gets }} = \frac{2}{5} \times 60\,000 \phantom{\text{and Marie gets }} = \frac{3}{5} \times 60\,000$

$\phantom{\therefore \text{Donny gets }} = \$24\,000 \phantom{\text{and Marie gets xxxx}} = \$36\,000$

You could also use the *unitary method* to solve the following problems.

EXERCISE 12E

1 What is the total number of parts represented by the following ratios?

    a   2 : 3   **b**   4 : 1   **c**   7 : 9   **d**   12 : 5

    e   10 : 3   **f**   3 : 16   **g**   7 : 4   **h**   9 : 10

2 Divide a 50 cm piece of string in the following ratios:

    a   1 : 1   **b**   4 : 1   **c**   3 : 2   **d**   7 : 13

3 Divide: **a** $50 in the ratio 1 : 4   **b**   €35 in the ratio 3 : 4

           c   90 kg in the ratio 4 : 5

4 Lottery winnings of $400 000 are to be divided in the ratio 5 : 3. Find the larger share.

5 The ratio of girls to boys in a school is 5 : 4. If there are 918 students at the school, how many are girls?

6 My block of land is 1500 m². It is divided into house and garden in the ratio 7 : 8. How many m² is my garden?

7  When planting early lettuces, the ratio of success to failure (due to frosts and bugs) is 5 : 2. If I plant 56 early lettuces, how many will succeed and how many will fail?

8 A man leaves 200 000 euros to his sons Aleksi and Kristo in the ratio of their ages when he dies. Aleksi is 4 years older than Kristo. When the father dies, Aleksi is 62.

    a   How old is Kristo?

    b   How much does Aleksi inherit (to the nearest euro)?

    c   How much does Kristo inherit (to the nearest euro)?

9 Divide an inheritance of £36 000 in the ratio 3 : 5 : 10.

10 The ratio of flour : sugar : cocoa in a cake recipe is 2 : 1.5 : 0.5.
If 10 kg of flour is used, how much:

    a   sugar   **b**   cocoa is used?

11 At the moorings on a river, there are yachts, motorboats, houseboats and row-boats. The ratio of yachts : motorboats : houseboats is 4 : 5 : 3. If there are 50 watercraft on the river and two of them are rowboats, how many are:

    a   yachts   **b**   motorboats

    c   houseboats?

F SCALE DIAGRAMS

Scale diagrams are used to accurately display objects such as buildings when it is impossible to draw the object to its actual size. Architects frequently draw house and building plans 'to scale' so all of the lengths are shown *in proportion* to their real sizes.

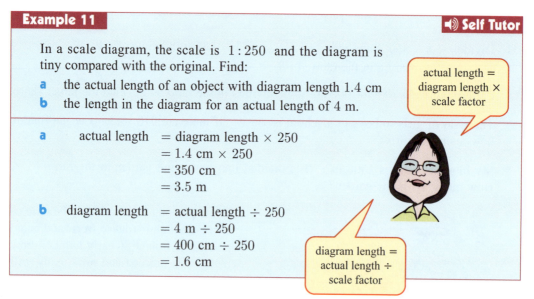

Example 11 ◀)) **Self Tutor**

In a scale diagram, the scale is $1 : 250$ and the diagram is tiny compared with the original. Find:

a the actual length of an object with diagram length 1.4 cm

b the length in the diagram for an actual length of 4 m.

> actual length = diagram length × scale factor

a actual length = diagram length × 250
                  = 1.4 cm × 250
                  = 350 cm
                  = 3.5 m

b diagram length = actual length ÷ 250
                  = 4 m ÷ 250
                  = 400 cm ÷ 250
                  = 1.6 cm

> diagram length = actual length ÷ scale factor

EXERCISE 12F

1 Find the actual length of a large object given:

  a a scale of $1 : 200$ and a diagram representation of 3.1 cm

  b a scale of $1 : 150$ and a diagram representation of 4.6 cm

  c a scale of $1 : 750$ and a diagram representation of 13 mm.

2 Find the scale diagram length of a large object given:

  a a scale of $1 : 500$ and an actual length of 46 m

  b a scale of $1 : 250$ and an actual length of 7.2 m

  c a scale of $1 : 125$ and an actual length of 14 m.

3 Draw a scale diagram of:

  a a 24 m by 16 m rectangle using a scale of $1 : 400$

  b a 115 m by 87 m rectangle using a scale of $1 : 1600$.

4 The scale of a map is $1 : 250\,000$.

  a Find the actual distance between two towns which are 11 cm apart on the map.

  b Find the distance on the map between two villages which are 9 km apart.

5 Two cities are 300 km apart, from centre to centre. On a map they are 15 cm apart. Find the map's scale in the form $1 : n$.

6 The scale on a map is $1 : 500\,000$. An area on the map is 12 cm². Find the actual area in km².

G RATES

We use rates nearly every day.

Here are some examples:

- Jack works in a car wash at a service station. He earns £7.50 per hour.

- Jack's mother drives him to work, being careful not to go over the speed limit of 50 kilometres per hour.

- While she is at the service station, Jack's mother fills the car with petrol which costs 124.4 cents per litre.

Each of these statements uses a **rate**.
Notice that each quantity is measured with two different units, separated by '*per*'.

- Jack's **rate of pay** is 7.50 pounds *per* hour.
- His mother's **rate of travel** or **speed** is below 50 kilometres *per* hour.
- The petrol's **price** or **unit cost** is 124.4 cents *per* litre.

> A **rate** is a comparison of two quantities of different kinds (and units).

Other examples are:

- An infection rate for an illness is five people per 1000 people in the population.
- A mobile telephone call costs 5 yen per 30 seconds.

Example 12   ◄)) Self Tutor

a Complete: Pumpkins cost $5 for 10 kg. This is a rate of $...... per kg.

b What measurements are connected by the following rate?
  Fertiliser should be used at a rate of 60 grams per m².

---

a This is a rate of 50 cents per kg or $0.50 per kg.

b Grams are used to measure *mass*.
  m² are used to measure *area*   ∴   the rate measures *mass* per *area*.

EXERCISE 12G

1 Complete the following rate statements.

a 20 metres of pipe costing $40 is a rate of ...... per metre.

b A waiter who works six hours and earns $90 is being paid at a rate of ...... per hour.

c A two litre bottle of soft drink costing $3.60 is a rate of ...... per litre.

d A tanker pumping 1000 litres of water in five minutes is working at a rate of ...... per minute.

2 Name the two measurements which are connected in the following rates, e.g., cost, time, mass, volume, length, etc.

- **a** Walnuts are \$12 per kilogram.
- **b** A medicine dosage is five millilitres per day.
- **c** The rainfall is measured in millimetres per year.
- **d** A paint formula is in millilitres per litre.
- **e** A hire car company charges \$2.50 per kilometre.

Example 13 — Self Tutor

John walks at 4 km h^{-1}.

- **a** How far will he walk in 5 hours?
- **b** How long will it take him to walk 12 km?

a 4 km h^{-1} means that in 1 hour John will walk 4 km.
$\therefore$ in 5 hours John will walk $4 \text{ km} \times 5 = 20 \text{ km}$.

b It will take him $12 \div 4 = 3$ hours.

3 A plumber charges \$30 per hour to do a job. How much will the plumber charge to do a job which lasts:

- **a** 6 hours
- **b** 18 hours?

4 My car uses 8.5 L of petrol per 100 km travelled.

- **a** If I travel 400 km, how many litres of petrol will my car use?
- **b** If petrol costs 93.9 pence per litre, how much will the petrol cost for my trip?
- **c** If I took another trip and used 25.5 L of petrol, how much would the petrol for this trip cost?

5 The local postal centre is able to handle 245 parcels every hour.

- **a** How many parcels could it handle in:
  - **i** 4 hours
  - **ii** 2.5 hours
  - **iii** an 8 hour day?
- **b** If a major consignment of 2536 parcels came, how long would it take the postal centre to handle them?

6 Our best cricket batsman has a strike rate of 4.8 runs per over.

- **a** How many runs would she expect to make in a game where she batted for:
  - **i** 6 overs
  - **ii** 15 overs
  - **iii** 4.5 overs?
- **b** If she scored a century (100 runs) at the rate of 4.8 runs per over, how many overs would she have faced?

7 Tracy is to paint her house walls with two coats. The total area of the walls is 120 m^2.

- **a** If she can paint at a rate of 18 m^2 per hour, how long would it take her to finish painting with no stops?
- **b** If paint covers 14 m^2 per litre, how many litres of paint are needed?
- **c** The paint costs \$85 per 4 L can. What will be the total cost of paint needed?

8 Paquita's Video Rental hires "new release" DVDs at a rate of $7 per night, while "old" DVDs are hired at $4 per week.

   a If Georgio hires a "new release" DVD for three nights, how much does it cost him?

   b Ian hires two "old" DVDs for four nights. What does this cost him?

   c How much will it cost Gabriella to hire one "new release" and four "old" DVDs for three nights?

   d If Paquita offers a special deal of $30 for *any* five DVDs for a week, should Gabriella take this special deal instead of her original plan? Explain your answer.

SPEED

A common rate we use is **speed**, which indicates how fast something is travelling.

> **Average speed** is distance travelled compared with time taken.

So,   **average speed** $= \dfrac{\textbf{distance travelled}}{\textbf{time taken}}$ *or*   in symbols, $S = \dfrac{D}{T}$.

Example 14   🔊 **Self Tutor**

A car travels 450 km in 5 hours. Express this as a rate.

$$\text{Rate} = \frac{450 \text{ km}}{5 \text{ h}}$$
$$= 90 \text{ km per hour}$$

Notice that rates have units. In the above example $\dfrac{\text{km}}{\text{h}} = \text{km h}^{-1}$ which is km per hour.

Example 15   🔊 **Self Tutor**

Convert 60 km h^{-1} into m s^{-1}.

$$60 \text{ km h}^{-1}$$
$$= \frac{60 \text{ km}}{1 \text{ hour}}$$
$$= \frac{60 \times 1000 \text{ m}}{1 \times 60 \times 60 \text{ sec}}$$
$$\approx 16.7 \text{ m s}^{-1}$$

It is useful to remember the conversion $1 \text{ m s}^{-1} = 3.6 \text{ km h}^{-1}$

9 Use the conversion $1 \text{ m s}^{-1} = 3.6 \text{ km h}^{-1}$ to convert:

   a 100 km h^{-1} into m s^{-1} **b** 20 m s^{-1} into km h^{-1}

10 **a**   A cyclist travels 75 km in 5 hours. Express this as a rate.

      b   A snail crawls 4.2 m in 2 hours. Express this as a rate.

By rearranging the formula for average speed, we can calculate distances travelled or times taken.

If we wish to find D, we use

$$D = S \times T$$

If we wish to find T, we use

$$T = \dfrac{D}{S}$$

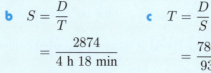

Example 16   ◀)) **Self Tutor**

a   A car travels at 60 km h^{-1} for 2 hours and 23 minutes. How far does it travel?

b   An aeroplane travels 2874 km in 4 hours and 18 minutes. Calculate its speed.

c   A train travelled a distance of 780 km at a speed of 93 km h^{-1}.
   How long did the journey take?

---

a $D = S \times T$
   $= 60 \times 2$ h 23 min
   $= 143$ km

b $S = \dfrac{D}{T}$
   $= \dfrac{2874}{4 \text{ h } 18 \text{ min}}$
   ≈ 668 km h^{-1}

c $T = \dfrac{D}{S}$
   $= \dfrac{780}{93}$
   ≈ 8 h 23 min

Calculator:

TI-83

a   60 ⊠ 2 [2nd] [MATRX]
   (ANGLE) 1:° 23 [2nd] [MATRX]
   (ANGLE) 2:′ [ENTER] .

b   2874 ÷ 4 [2nd] [MATRX]
   (ANGLE) 1:° 18 [2nd] [MATRX]
   (ANGLE) 2:′ [ENTER] .

c   780 ÷ 93 [2nd] [MATRX]
   (ANGLE) 4:▶DMS [ENTER] .

Casio

a   60 ⊠ 2 [OPTN] [F6] (▷) [F5]
   (ANGL) [F4] (o///) 23 [F4]
   (o///) [EXE] .

b   2874 ÷ 4 [OPTN] [F6] (▷)
   [F5] (ANGL) [F4] (o///) 18 [F4]
   (o///) [EXE] .

c   780 ÷ 93 [OPTN] [F6] (▷)
   [F5] (ANGL) [F6] (▷) [F3]
   (▶DMS) [EXE] .

```
60*2°23'
              143
2874/4°18'
         668.372093
780/93▶DMS
      8°23'13.548"
```

```
60×2° 23°
              143
2874÷4° 18°
         668.372093
780÷93▶DMS
      8°23'13.55"
Pol( Rec( ▶DMS      ▷
```

---

11   **a**   If I walk at 5 km h^{-1}, how far will I walk in 3 hours?

   b   How far will a car travelling at 80 km h^{-1} travel in $1\frac{3}{4}$ hours?

   c   A train travels at 80 km h^{-1}. How far will it travel in 30 minutes?

   d   A cyclist cycled at 20 km h^{-1} for $2\frac{1}{2}$ hours. How far did the cyclist travel?

   e   A spacecraft travels 9000 km in 45 minutes.
      Calculate the average speed of the spacecraft in km h^{-1}.

f A train travels at a speed of 120 km h^{-1} for 3 hours and 25 minutes. Calculate the distance travelled by the train.

g A marathon runner runs 42.2 km in 2 hours and 10 minutes. Calculate her average speed to the nearest km h^{-1}.

h A rocket travels 1768 km at a speed of 340 km h^{-1}.
How long does it take the rocket to travel this distance?

 # RATE GRAPHS

If we have measurements of two related quantities we can plot them on a graph. The rate at which one measurement changes with respect to the other can be found from the slope of the graph.

Example 17   ◀) **Self Tutor**

A tank is being filled with water. The table following shows the number of litres in the tank as time increases.

Number of minutes	0	1	2	3	4	5	6	7	8
Number of litres	0	50	100	150	200	250	300	350	400

a Graph the data with *Number of minutes* on the horizontal axis.

b Complete: The rate of change is ...... litres per minute.

a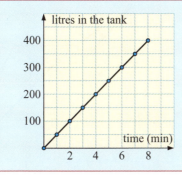

b 50 litres enter the tank each minute.

So, the rate of change is 50 L per min.

Note: • The plotted points should be joined with line segments in this case.
For example, after $1\frac{1}{2}$ minutes 75 L of water has been added.

• The rate of filling is **constant** and this is shown by the straight line.

• The slope of the graph is $\frac{400-0}{8-0} = 50$ L per min.

EXERCISE 12H

1 A pool is being filled with water at a constant rate. The following table shows the number of litres of water in the pool as time increases.

Number of minutes	0	1	2	3	4	5
Number of litres	0	200	400	600	800	1000

a Graph the data with *Number of minutes* on the horizontal axis.

b Complete: The rate of change is ...... litres per minute.

2 Construct a table and draw a rate graph for the statement:

"The rate at which the pool is filling (from empty) is 40 L per minute."

3 The earnings in dollars of three workers is plotted on the graph shown.

    a Who is earning at the:

      i highest rate

      ii lowest rate?

    b Explain how you can use the dotted line on the graph to answer **a**.

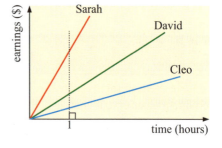

4

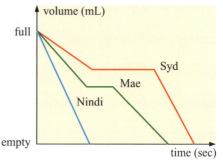

The water levels in the Cannon and Lawrence reservoirs this summer are decreasing due to the continuing drought.

    a In which reservoir is the water level falling faster? Explain.

    b Which reservoir had more water in it at the start of the summer? Explain.

5 Nindi, Syd and Mae were drinking large glasses of water.

    a Who finished first?

    b Who finished last?

    c Who drank their glass of water without stopping? How can you tell?

    d Who had the longest rest in the middle? How can you tell?

6 The graph shows the change in temperature in Darwin between 8 am and midnight.

Use the graph to answer the following questions:

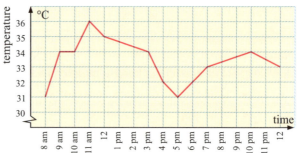

    a At what rate (degrees per hour) did the temperature rise from 8 am to 9 am?

    b What happened from 9 am to 10 am?

    c When did the temperature rise the fastest?

    d What was the maximum temperature?

    e For how many hours was the temperature rising?

    f Between what times was the temperature dropping the quickest?

TRAVEL GRAPHS

Suppose a car travels 150 kilometres in 1.5 hours.

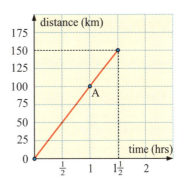

$$\text{Average speed} = \frac{\text{distance}}{\text{time}}$$

$$= \frac{150}{1.5}$$

$$= 100 \text{ km h}^{-1}$$

Notice that the point A on the graph indicates we have travelled 100 km in one hour.

Example 18	◀)) **Self Tutor**

The graph alongside indicates the distance a homing pigeon travelled from its point of release until it reached its home.
Use the graph to determine:

a   the total length of the flight

b   the time taken for the pigeon to reach home

c   the time taken to fly the first 200 km

d   the time taken to fly from the 240 km mark to the 400 km mark

e   the average speed for the first 4 hours

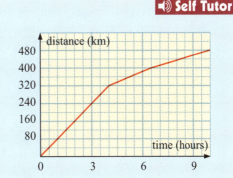

a   Length of flight is 480 km.   **b**   Time to reach home is 10 hours.

c   Time for first 200 km is $2\frac{1}{2}$ hours.

d   It takes 3 hours to fly 240 km. It takes $6\frac{1}{2}$ hours to fly 400 km.
∴   it takes $3\frac{1}{2}$ hours to fly from 240 km to 400 km.

e   In the first 4 hours it flies 320 km   ∴   average speed $= \dfrac{320}{4} = 80 \text{ km h}^{-1}$.

EXERCISE 12I

1   The graph alongside shows the distance Frances walks to work.
Use the graph to determine:

   a   the distance to work

   b   the time taken to get to work

   c   the distance walked after

     i   12 minutes   **ii**   20 minutes

   d   the time taken to walk

     i   0.4 km   **ii**   1.3 km

   e   the average speed for the whole distance.

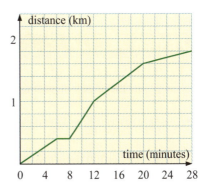

2 Two cyclists took part in a handicap time trial. The distance-time graph indicates how far each has travelled.

Use the graph to find:

  a the handicap time given to cyclist B

  b the distance travelled by each cyclist

  c how far both cyclists had travelled when A caught B

  d how long it took each cyclist to travel 80 km

  e how much faster A completed the time trial than B

  f the average speed of each cyclist.

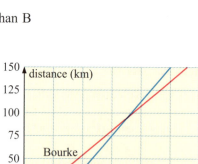

3 The Adams and Bourke families live next door to each other in Melbourne. They are going to their favourite beach along the Great Ocean Road, 150 km from where they live.

  a Who left first?

  b Who arrived first?

  c Who travelled fastest?

  d How long after the first family left did they pass each other on the road?

  e How long had the second family been driving when they passed the first family?

  f Approximately how far from Melbourne is this "passing point"?

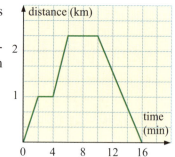

4 Amy drives from home to the supermarket. She draws a graph which can be used to explain her journey.

The vertical axis shows her distance from home in kilometres. The horizontal axis measures the time from when she left home in minutes.

  a When did she stop for the red traffic light?

  b How long did the light take to change?

  c How long did she spend at the supermarket?

  d How far away is the supermarket from her home?

  e When was her rate of travel (speed) greatest?

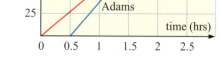

REVIEW SET 12A

1   **a** Find the ratio of the   coloured area : total area in the given diagram.

  b Write 750 mL is to 2 litres as a ratio in simplest form.

2 **a** Express 96 : 72 as a ratio in simplest form.

  b Express 0.4 : 0.9 as a ratio in simplest form.

  c Express the ratio $3 : 2\frac{1}{2}$ in simplest form.

3 A farm has 6000 animals. 2500 are sheep and the rest are cattle. Find the ratio of the number of: **a** sheep : total number of animals   **b** sheep : cattle.

4 $3 : 8 = \square : 40$.   Find the missing number.

5 The ratio of girls to boys in a sports club is 4 : 5. If there are 20 girls, how many boys are there?

6 If two families share the cost of buying 75 kg of meat in the ratio 7 : 8, how much meat should each family receive?

7 If €3200 is divided in the ratio 3 : 5, what is the smaller share?

8 **a** Find the real length of a large object given a scale of 1 : 500 and a diagram representation of 5.2 cm.

  b Find the scale diagram length of an object given a scale of 1 : 200 and an actual length of 23 m.

9 Avril is paid at the rate of $18.60 per hour.

  a How much is she paid if she works 8 hours?

  b How much is she paid if she works $2\frac{1}{2}$ hours?

10 Ben drives at a steady speed for 8 hours and covers a distance of 760 km. His car uses 65 L of petrol. Find:

  a   his average speed (in $km\,h^{-1}$)   **b**   the petrol consumption (in $km\,L^{-1}$)

11 Convert 210 metres per minute into kilometres per hour, using $1\,m\,s^{-1} = 3.6\,km\,h^{-1}$.

12 Water is leaking out of a water tank. The graph shows how much water remains in the tank at the end of every day for five days:

  a How much water is in the tank to start with?

  b Copy and complete the following statements:

    i In two days, the water remaining in the tank is ...... kilolitres.

      This is a loss of ...... kilolitres.

      The rate at which the water is leaking is .... kilolitres per day.

    ii In five days the water remaining in the tank is ...... kilolitres.

      This is a loss of ...... kilolitres.

      The rate at which the water is leaking is .... kilolitres per day.

  c Is the water leaking at a constant rate? Explain your answer.

  d If no water is added to the tank, when will the tank be empty?

REVIEW SET 12B

1 Write as a ratio in simplest form:

    a 25 g is to 60 g   **b** 45 seconds is to 1.5 minutes.

2 Express as a ratio in simplest form:

    a $6 : 9 : 15$ **b** $0.2 : 0.5$ **c** $\frac{1}{2} : \frac{1}{3}$

3 Cube A has sides 3 cm in length and cube B has sides 5 cm in length. Find the ratio of:

    a length of side of B : length of side of A

    b area of one face of A : area of one face of B

    c volume of A : volume of B

4 Ming-na has a box of chocolates. 15 have soft centres and the rest have hard centres. If the ratio of soft centres : hard centres is $5 : 3$, how many have hard centres?

5 The ratio of cordial to water in a glass is $3 : 20$. If there are 250 mL of water in the glass, how many mL of cordial are there?

6 A fruit grower plants apricot trees and peach trees in the ratio $4 : 5$. If he plants a total of 3600 trees, how many of each type did he plant?

7 If 21 000 Yen is divided in the ratio $1 : 2 : 4$, what is the largest share?

8 The scale on a map of England is $1 : 400\,000$.

    a Find the actual distance between Liverpool and Manchester, which are 12.5 cm apart on the map.

    b Find the distance on the map between Birmingham and Coventry, which are 27.6 km apart.

9 Water from a hose will fill a 2 L bucket in 10 seconds. How long will it take to fill a 12 L tank?

10 Construct a table and draw a rate graph for the statement: 'A tank contains 800 L of water and it empties at a rate of 25 L per minute.'

11 An Olympic runner takes 10.2 seconds to run 100 metres. Use the conversion $1 \text{ m s}^{-1} = 3.6 \text{ km h}^{-1}$ to calculate his speed in km h^{-1}.

12 The graph shows the distance travelled by two families between Vienna and Salzburg.

Use the graph to find:

    a the distance from Vienna to Salzburg

    b how much quicker the Mahler family completed the trip than the Schumann family

    c the average speed for each family over the first two hours

    d the average speed for the Schumanns over the whole trip.

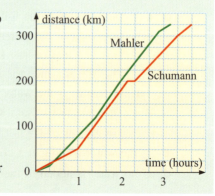

Chapter 13

Algebraic factorisation

Contents:

A Common factors

B Factorising with common factors

C Factorising expressions with four terms

D Factorising quadratic trinomials

E Factorisation of $ax^2 + bx + c$ $(a \neq 1)$

F Difference of two squares factorising

OPENING PROBLEM

Problem 1:   What is the highest common factor of:

a 18 and 63   **b** x^2 and x **c** $2x^2y$ and $4xy^2$?

Problem 2: $12x^2 + x - 6 = (4x + a)(3x - b)$
Can you find the values of a and b?

When an expression is written as a **product** of its **factors**, it is said to have been **factorised**.
For example, $3x + 15 = 3 \times (x + 5)$ where the factors are 3 and $(x + 5)$.

Notice that $3(x + 5) = 3x + 15$ using the **distributive law**, and so **factorisation** is really the **reverse** process to **expansion**.

A   COMMON FACTORS

Numbers can be expressed as products of **factors**. A **prime number** has only two different factors, the number itself and 1. Some prime numbers are 2, 3, 5, 7, 11, ...

1 is not a prime number.

Factors that are prime numbers are called **prime factors**. Prime factors of any number can be found by repeated division.

For example:

2	24
2	12
2	6
3	3
	1

$\therefore 24 = 2 \times 2 \times 2 \times 3$

2	42
3	21
7	7
	1

$\therefore 42 = 2 \times 3 \times 7$

COMMON FACTORS AND HCF

Notice that 2 and 3 are factors of both 24 and 42. They are called **common factors**.
Obviously 6, which is 2×3, would be a common factor as well.

> A **common factor** is a number that is a factor of two or more other numbers.
>
> The **highest common factor (HCF)** is the largest factor that is common to two or more numbers.

To find the highest common factor of a group of numbers it is often best to express the numbers as products of prime factors. Then the common prime factors can be found and multiplied to give the HCF.

Example 1   ◀) Self Tutor

Find the highest common factor of 36 and 81.

So,

2	36
2	18
3	9
3	3
	1

$36 = 2 \times 2 \times 3 \times 3$ and

3	81
3	27
3	9
3	3
	1

$81 = 3 \times 3 \times 3 \times 3$

$\therefore$ HCF $= 3 \times 3 = 9$

We can use the same technique to find the **highest common factor** of a group of algebraic products.

Example 2
🔊 **Self Tutor**

Find the highest common factor of:

a $8a$ and $12b$

b $4x^2$ and $6xy$

a $8a = 2 \times 2 \times 2 \times a$
     $12b = 2 \times 2 \times 3 \times b$
   ∴   HCF $= 2 \times 2$
          $= 4$

b $4x^2 = 2 \times 2 \times x \times x$
     $6xy = 2 \times 3 \times x \times y$
   ∴   HCF $= 2 \times x$
          $= 2x$

> Write each term as a product of its **factors**!

EXERCISE 13A

1 Find the highest common factor of:

  a 45 and 63
  b 25 and 45
  c 36 and 48

  d 80 and 120
  e 49 and 91
  f 81 and 108

2 Find the missing factor:

  a $3 \times \square = 6a$
  b $3 \times \square = 15b$
  c $2 \times \square = 8xy$

  d $2x \times \square = 8x^2$
  e $\square \times 2x = 2x^2$
  f $\square \times 5x = -10x^2$

  g $-a \times \square = ab$
  h $\square \times a^2 = 4a^3$
  i $3x \times \square = -9x^2y$

3 Find the highest common factor of the following:

  a $2a$ and 6
  b $5c$ and $8c$
  c $8r$ and 27

  d $12k$ and $7k$
  e $3a$ and $12a$
  f $5x$ and $15x$

  g $25x$ and $10x$
  h $24y$ and $32y$
  i $36b$ and $54d$

4 Find the HCF of the following:

  a $23ab$ and $7ab$
  b abc and $6abc$
  c $36a$ and $12ab$

  d a^2 and a
  e $9r$ and r^3
  f $3q$ and qr

  g $3b^2$ and $9b$
  h dp^2 and pd
  i $4r$ and $8r^2$

  j $3pq$ and $6pq^2$
  k $2a^2b$ and $6ab$
  l $6xy$ and $18x^2y^2$

  m $15a$, $20ab$ and $30b$
  n $12wxz$, $12wz$, $24wxyz$
  o $24p^2qr$, $36pqr^2$

ACTIVITY

ALGEBRAIC COMMON FACTOR MAZE

To find your way through this maze, follow the given instructions. After you have completed the maze you may like to construct your own maze for a friend to follow.

Instructions:

1 You are permitted to move horizontally or vertically but **not** diagonally.

2 Start at the starting term, 12. A move to the next cell is only possible if that cell has a factor in common with the one you are presently on.

3 Try to get to the exit following the rules above.

$6m$	$2a$	3	$9c^2$	$3c$	c^2	8	$2p^2$
$4m$	mn	$6n$	$5c$	25	$5m$	12	$4p$
$8y$	xy	2	$6a$	$5a$	mn	$6n^2$	7
$7y$	21	$3z$	$5x$	$3y$	y^2	$3p$	p
ab	$7a$	yz	xy	$15x$	xy	p^2	7
17	pq	$3q$	q^2	63	$7b$	b^2	6
12	5	10	$10b$	12	y^2	$9b$	$3b$
$6a$	a^2	$5a$	$3a$	$4x$	xy	$2x$	x^2

start $\longrightarrow$ (to 12 in bottom-left area)

$p \longrightarrow$ exit

Example 3   ◆) **Self Tutor**

Find the HCF of $3(x+3)$ and $(x+3)(x+1)$.

$$3(x+3) = 3 \times (x+3) \qquad (x+3)(x+1) = (x+3) \times (x+1)$$

$$\therefore \quad \text{HCF} = (x+3)$$

---

5 Find the HCF of:

a $5(x+2)$ and $(x+8)(x+2)$ **b** $2(x+5)^2$ and $6(x+9)(x+5)$

c $3x(x+4)$ and $x^2(x+2)$ **d** $6(x+1)^2$ and $2(x+1)(x-2)$

e $2(x+3)^2$ and $4(x+3)(x-7)$ **f** $4x(x-3)$ and $6x(x-3)^2$

B | FACTORISING WITH COMMON FACTORS

Factorisation is the process of writing an expression as a **product** of its **factors**.

Factorisation is the reverse process of expansion.

In **expansions** we have to *remove brackets*, whereas in **factorisation** we have to *insert brackets*.

Notice that $3(x+2)$ is the *product of two factors*, 3 and $x+2$.

The brackets are essential as:

$3(x+2)$ multiplies 3 by the whole of $x+2$,

whereas in $3x+2$ only the x is multiplied by 3.

is **expansion**

$$3(x+2) = 3x+6$$

is **factorisation**

To factorise an algebraic expression involving a number of terms we look for the HCF of the terms and write it down in front of a set of brackets. We then find the contents of the brackets.

For example, $5x^2$ and $10xy$ have HCF of $5x$.

So, $5x^2 + 10xy = 5x \times x + 5x \times 2y$
$$= 5x(x + 2y)$$

FACTORISE FULLY

Notice that $4a + 12 = 2(2a + 6)$ is not fully factorised as $(2a + 6)$ still has a common factor of 2 which could be removed. Although 2 is a common factor it is not the HCF. The HCF is 4 and so
$$4a + 12 = 4(a + 3)   \text{ is fully factorised.}$$

Note: All factorisations can be checked by expansion.

With practice the middle line is not necessary.

Example 4		◀ **Self Tutor**

Fully factorise: **a** $3a + 6$ **b** $ab - 2bc$

a $3a + 6$
$= 3 \times a + 3 \times 2$
$= 3(a + 2)$ {HCF is 3}

b $ab - 2bc$
$= a \times b - 2 \times b \times c$
$= b(a - 2c)$ {HCF is b}

EXERCISE 13B

1 Copy and complete:

a $2x + 4 = 2(x + ...)$
b $3a - 12 = 3(a - ...)$
c $15 - 5p = 5(... - p)$
d $18x + 12 = 6(... + 2)$
e $4x^2 - 8x = 4x(x - ...)$
f $2m + 8m^2 = 2m(... + 4m)$

2 Copy and complete:

a $4x + 16 = 4(... + ...)$
b $10 + 5d = 5(... + ...)$
c $5c - 5 = 5(... - ...)$
d $cd + de = d(... + ...)$
e $6a + 8ab = ...(3 + 4b)$
f $6x - 2x^2 = ...(3 - x)$
g $7ab - 7a = ...(b - 1)$
h $4ab - 6bc = ...(2a - 3c)$

Remember to check your factorisations by expanding back out!

3 Fully factorise:

a $3a + 3b$	**b** $8x - 16$	**c** $3p + 18$	**d** $28 - 14x$
e $7x - 14$	**f** $12 + 6x$	**g** $ac + bc$	**h** $12y - 6a$
i $5a + ab$	**j** $bc - 6cd$	**k** $7x - xy$	**l** $xy + y$
m $a + ab$	**n** $xy - yz$	**o** $3pq + pr$	**p** $cd - c$

Example 5
◀) **Self Tutor**

Fully factorise: **a** $8x^2 + 12x$ **b** $3y^2 - 6xy$

a $8x^2 + 12x$
$= 2 \times 4 \times x \times x + 3 \times 4 \times x$
$= 4x(2x + 3)$ {HCF is $4x$}

b $3y^2 - 6xy$
$= 3 \times y \times y - 2 \times 3 \times x \times y$
$= 3y(y - 2x)$ {HCF is $3y$}

4 Fully factorise:

a $x^2 + 2x$	**b** $5x - 2x^2$	**c** $4x^2 + 8x$
d $14x - 7x^2$	**e** $6x^2 + 12x$	**f** $x^3 + 9x^2$
g $x^2y + xy^2$	**h** $4x^3 - 6x^2$	**i** $9x^3 - 18xy$
j $a^3 + a^2 + a$	**k** $2a^2 + 4a + 8$	**l** $3a^3 - 6a^2 + 9a$

Example 6
◀) **Self Tutor**

Fully factorise: $-2a + 6ab$

$-2a + 6ab$
$= 6ab - 2a$ {Rewrite with $6ab$ first. Why?}
$= 2 \times 3 \times a \times b - 2 \times a$
$= 2a(3b - 1)$ {as $2a$ is the HCF}

5 Fully factorise:

a $-9a + 9b$	**b** $-3 + 6b$	**c** $-8a + 4b$
d $-7c + cd$	**e** $-a + ab$	**f** $-6x^2 + 12x$
g $-5x + 15x^2$	**h** $-2b^2 + 4ab$	**i** $-a + a^2$

Example 7
◀) **Self Tutor**

Fully factorise: $-2x^2 - 4x$

$-2x^2 - 4x$
$= -2 \times x \times x + -2 \times 2 \times x$
$= -2x(x + 2)$ {as HCF is $-2x$}

6 Fully factorise:

a $-6a - 6b$	**b** $-4 - 8x$	**c** $-3y - 6z$
d $-9c - cd$	**e** $-x - xy$	**f** $-5x^2 - 20x$
g $-12y - 3y^2$	**h** $-18a^2 - 9ab$	**i** $-16x^2 - 24x$

Example 8
🔊 **Self Tutor**

Fully factorise:

a $2(x+3) + x(x+3)$ **b** $x(x+4) - (x+4)$

a $2(x+3) + x(x+3)$ has HCF of $(x+3)$
$= (x+3)(2+x)$

b $x(x+4) - (x+4)$
$= x(x+4) - 1(x+4)$ has HCF of $(x+4)$
$= (x+4)(x-1)$

7 Fully factorise:

a $2(x-7) + x(x-7)$ **b** $a(x+3) + b(x+3)$

c $4(x+2) - x(x+2)$ **d** $x(x+9) + (x+9)$

e $a(b+4) - (b+4)$ **f** $a(b+c) + d(b+c)$

g $a(m+n) - b(m+n)$ **h** $x(x+3) - x - 3$

Example 9
🔊 **Self Tutor**

Fully factorise $(x-1)(x+2) + 3(x-1)$

$(x-1)(x+2) + 3(x-1)$ has HCF of $(x-1)$
$= (x-1)[(x+2) + 3]$
$= (x-1)(x+5)$

Notice the use of square brackets in the second line.

8 Fully factorise:

a $(x+3)(x-5) + 4(x+3)$ **b** $5(x-7) + (x-7)(x+2)$

c $(x+6)(x+4) - 8(x+6)$ **d** $(x-2)^2 - 6(x-2)$

e $(x+2)^2 - (x+2)(x+1)$ **f** $5(a+b) - (a+b)(a+1)$

g $3(a-2)^2 - 6(a-2)$ **h** $(x+4)^2 + 3(x+4)(x-1)$

i $x(x-1) - 6(x-1)(x-5)$ **j** $3(x+5) - 4(x+5)^2$

C

FACTORISING EXPRESSIONS WITH FOUR TERMS

Some four-termed expressions do not have an overall common factor, but can be factorised by *pairing* the four terms.

For example, $\underbrace{ab + ac}_{} + \underbrace{bd + dc}_{}$

$= a(b + c) + d(b + c)$ {factorising each pair separately}

$= (b + c)(a + d)$ {removing common factor $(b + c)$}

Note:
- Many 4-termed expressions cannot be factorised using the method above.
- Sometimes it is necessary to reorder the terms before using the method above.

Example 10   ◀) Self Tutor

Factorise: **a** $3ab + d + 3ad + b$ **b** $x^2 + 2x + 5x + 10$

a $3ab + d + 3ad + b$

$= \underbrace{3ab + b}_{} + \underbrace{3ad + d}_{}$ {reorder}

$= b(3a + 1) + d(3a + 1)$

$= (3a + 1)(b + d)$

b $\underbrace{x^2 + 2x}_{} + \underbrace{5x + 10}_{}$

$= x(x + 2) + 5(x + 2)$

$= (x + 2)(x + 5)$

EXERCISE 13C

1 Factorise:

a $3a + 3 + ab + b$ **b** $6d + ac + ad + 6c$ **c** $ab + 6 + 2b + 3a$

d $mn + 3p + np + 3m$ **e** $x^2 + 3x + 6x + 18$ **f** $x^2 + 8x + 3x + 24$

g $3x^2 + 3x + x + 1$ **h** $3x^2 + 6x + 4x + 8$ **i** $10x^2 + 5x + 6x + 3$

Example 11   ◀) Self Tutor

Factorise: **a** $x^2 + 3x - 4x - 12$ **b** $x^2 + 3x - x - 3$

a $\underbrace{x^2 + 3x}_{} \underbrace{- 4x - 12}_{}$

$= x(x + 3) - 4(x + 3)$

$= (x + 3)(x - 4)$

b $\underbrace{x^2 + 3x}_{} \underbrace{- x - 3}_{}$

$= x(x + 3) - (x + 3)$

$= x(x + 3) - 1(x + 3)$

$= (x + 3)(x - 1)$

2 Factorise:

a $x^2 + 4x - 5x - 20$ **b** $x^2 - 7x + 3x - 21$ **c** $x^2 - 3x + 2x - 6$

d $x^2 - 6x - 3x + 18$ **e** $x^2 + 7x - 9x - 63$ **f** $2x^2 + x - 6x - 3$

g $3x^2 + 2x - 12x - 8$ **h** $4x^2 - 3x - 8x + 6$ **i** $9x^2 + 4x - 9x - 4$

D FACTORISING QUADRATIC TRINOMIALS

A **quadratic trinomial** is an algebraic expression of the form $ax^2 + bx + c$ where x is a variable and a, b, c are constants where $a \neq 0$.

In this exercise we will consider $a = 1$ only.

Recall that: $(x + 2)(x + 5)$ $=$ x^2 $+$ $\underbrace{5x + 2x}$ $+$ 10 {using FOIL}

the **product**   the **sum** of   the **product**
of the 'firsts'   the 'outers'   of the 'lasts'
and 'inners'

So, $(x + 2)(x + 5) = x^2 + [2 + 5]x + [2 \times 5]$
$= x^2 + [\textbf{sum of 2 and 5}]x + [\textbf{product of 2 and 5}]$
$= x^2 + 7x + 10$

This shows that, if we want to factorise a quadratic trinomial such as $x^2 + 7x + 10$ into $(x + ...)(x + ...)$ we must find two numbers (to go into the vacant places) which have a *sum* of 7 and a *product* of 10.

In the general case, x^2 $+$ $(a + b)x$ $+$ ab $=$ $(x + a)(x + b)$

the coefficient   the constant term
of x is the **sum**   is the **product** of
of a and b a and b

EXERCISE 13D

1 Find two numbers which have:

a	product 10 and sum 7	**b**	product 12 and sum 8
c	product 16 and sum 10	**d**	product 30 and sum 11
e	product -14 and sum 5	**f**	product -21 and sum -4
g	product -18 and sum -3	**h**	product -30 and sum 7

Example 12   ◀ッ **Self Tutor**

Factorise: $x^2 + 11x + 24$

We need to find two numbers with sum 11 and product 24.
Pairs of factors of 24:

Factor product	1×24	2×12	3×8	4×6
Factor sum	25	14	11	10

this one

The numbers we want are 3 and 8.

So, $x^2 + 11x + 24$
$= (x + 3)(x + 8)$

Most of the time we can find these two numbers mentally.

Note: Only the last two lines of the previous example need to be shown in your working.

2 Factorise:

    a $x^2 + 5x + 4$ **b** $x^2 + 7x + 10$ **c** $x^2 + 10x + 21$

    d $x^2 + 15x + 54$ **e** $x^2 + 12x + 20$ **f** $x^2 + 9x + 18$

    g $x^2 + 14x + 24$ **h** $x^2 + 15x + 36$ **i** $x^2 + 19x + 48$

Example 13   ◀) **Self Tutor**

Factorise: $x^2 - 7x + 12$

sum $= -7$ and   product $= 12$

$\therefore$ numbers are -3 and -4

So, $x^2 - 7x + 12$

      $= (x - 3)(x - 4)$

> The sum is negative but the product is positive, so both numbers must be negative.

---

3 Factorise:

    a $x^2 - 5x + 4$ **b** $x^2 - 4x + 3$ **c** $x^2 - 5x + 6$

    d $x^2 - 13x + 22$ **e** $x^2 - 15x + 56$ **f** $x^2 - 16x + 48$

    g $x^2 - 16x + 28$ **h** $x^2 - 25x + 24$ **i** $x^2 - 15x + 36$

Example 14   ◀) **Self Tutor**

Factorise: **a** $x^2 - 2x - 15$ **b** $x^2 + x - 6$

    a   sum $= -2$ and product $= -15$

        $\therefore$ numbers are -5 and $+3$

       So, $x^2 - 2x - 15$

          $= (x - 5)(x + 3)$

    b   sum $= 1$ and   product $= -6$

        $\therefore$ numbers are -2 and $+3$

       So, $x^2 + x - 6$

          $= (x - 2)(x + 3)$

> The product is negative, so the numbers are opposite in sign.

---

4 Factorise:

    a $x^2 - 8x - 9$ **b** $x^2 + 4x - 21$ **c** $x^2 - x - 6$

    d $x^2 - 3x - 18$ **e** $x^2 + 5x - 24$ **f** $x^2 - 11x - 12$

    g $x^2 + 3x - 54$ **h** $x^2 + x - 56$ **i** $x^2 - 3x - 28$

    j $x^2 - x - 20$ **k** $x^2 - 2x - 63$ **l** $x^2 + 7x - 60$

5 Factorise:

a	$a^2 - 7a + 12$	**b**	$b^2 - b - 6$	**c**	$c^2 - 7c + 6$
d	$d^2 + 4d + 4$	**e**	$e^2 - e - 20$	**f**	$f^2 + 13f + 36$
g	$g^2 - 6g + 9$	**h**	$h^2 - 10h + 9$	**i**	$i^2 - 9$
j	$j^2 - 25$	**k**	$k^2 - 100$	**l**	$l^2 - 625$
m	$2x^2 - 8$	**n**	$3x^2 - 27$	**o**	$4x^2 - 1$

E   FACTORISATION OF $ax^2 + bx + c$ $(a \neq 1)$

In the previous section we revised techniques for factorising quadratic expressions in the form $ax^2 + bx + c$ where $a = 1$.

For example: $x^2 + 5x + 6 = (x + 3)(x + 2)$

Factorising a quadratic expression such as $3x^2 + 11x + 6$ is more complicated because the coefficient of x^2 is not 'one' and is not a common factor.

We need to develop a method for factorising this type of quadratic expression.

Two methods for factorising $ax^2 + bx + c$ where $a \neq 1$ are commonly used.

These are:
- trial and error
- 'splitting' the x-term

TRIAL AND ERROR

For example,   consider the quadratic $3x^2 + 13x + 4$.

Since 3 is a prime number, $3x^2 + 13x + 4 = (3x \quad)(x \quad)$

with labels "outers" and "inners" indicating the outer and inner products.

To fill the gaps we seek two numbers with a product of 4 and the sum of the inners and outers being $13x$.

As the product is 4 we will try   2 and 2,   4 and 1,   and   1 and 4.

$$(3x + 2)(x + 2) = 3x^2 + 6x + 2x + 4 \quad \text{fails}$$
$$(3x + 4)(x + 1) = 3x^2 + 3x + 4x + 4 \quad \text{fails}$$
$$(3x + 1)(x + 4) = 3x^2 + 12x + x + 4 \quad \text{is successful}$$
$$\text{So,} \quad 3x^2 + 13x + 4 = (3x + 1)(x + 4)$$

Now, if a and c are not prime in $ax^2 + bx + c$ there can be many possibilities.

For example,   consider $8x^2 + 22x + 15$.

By simply using trial and error the possible factorisations are:

$(8x + 5)(x + 3)$	✗	$(4x + 5)(2x + 3)$	✓	this is correct
$(8x + 3)(x + 5)$	✗	$(4x + 3)(2x + 5)$	✗	
$(8x + 1)(x + 15)$	✗	$(4x + 15)(2x + 1)$	✗	
$(8x + 15)(x + 1)$	✗	$(4x + 1)(2x + 15)$	✗	

As you can see, this process can be very tedious and time consuming.

FACTORISATION BY 'SPLITTING' THE x-TERM

Using the distributive law to expand we see that

$$(2x + 3)(4x + 5)$$
$$= 8x^2 + 10x + 12x + 15$$
$$= 8x^2 + 22x + 15$$

We will now *reverse* the process to factorise the quadratic expression $8x^2 + 22x + 15$.

Notice that: $8x^2 + 22x + 15$

$$= 8x^2 + 10x + 12x + 15 \qquad \{\text{'splitting' the middle term}\}$$
$$= (8x^2 + 10x) + (12x + 15) \qquad \{\text{grouping in pairs}\}$$
$$= 2x(4x + 5) + 3(4x + 5) \qquad \{\text{factorising each pair separately}\}$$
$$= (4x + 5)(2x + 3) \qquad \{\text{completing the factorisation}\}$$

But how do we correctly 'split' the middle term? That is, how do we determine that $22x$ must be written as $+10x + 12x$?

When looking at $8x^2 + 10x + 12x + 15$ we notice that $8 \times 15 = 120$ and $10 \times 12 = 120$
and also $10 + 12 = 22$.

So, in $8x^2 + 22x + 15$, we are looking for two numbers such that their *sum* is 22 and their *product* is $8 \times 15 = 120$. These numbers are 10 and 12.

Likewise in $6x^2 + 19x + 15$ we seek two numbers with sum 19 and product $6 \times 15 = 90$.

These numbers are 10 and 9.   So, $6x^2 + 19x + 15$

$$= 6x^2 + 10x + 9x + 15$$
$$= (6x^2 + 10x) + (9x + 15)$$
$$= 2x(3x + 5) + 3(3x + 5)$$
$$= (3x + 5)(2x + 3)$$

Rules for **splitting the x-term**:

> The following procedure is recommended for factorising $ax^2 + bx + c$:
>
> *Step 1:*   Find ac and then the factors of ac which add to b.
> *Step 2:*   If these factors are p and q, replace bx by $px + qx$.
> *Step 3:*   Complete the factorisation.

Example 15   🔊 Self Tutor

Show how to split the middle term of the following so that factorisation can occur:

a $3x^2 + 7x + 2$ **b** $10x^2 - 23x - 5$

a   In $3x^2 + 7x + 2$, $ac = 6$ and $b = 7$. We are looking for two numbers with a product of 6 and a sum of 7. These are 1 and 6.
So, the split is $7x = x + 6x$.

b   In $10x^2 - 23x - 5$, $ac = -50$ and $b = -23$. We are looking for two numbers with a product of -50 and a sum of -23. These are -25 and 2.
So, the split is $-23x = -25x + 2x$.

Example 16   🔊 **Self Tutor**

Factorise, using the 'splitting method':

a $6x^2 + 19x + 10$ **b** $3x^2 - x - 10$

a $6x^2 + 19x + 10$ has $ac = 60$ and $b = 19$.   We are looking for two numbers with product 60 and sum 19.

Searching amongst the factors of 60, only 4 and 15 have a sum of 19.

$\therefore \quad 6x^2 + 19x + 10$
$= 6x^2 + 4x + 15x + 10$ {splitting the x-term}
$= 2x(3x + 2) \ + \ 5(3x + 2)$ {factorising in pairs}
$= (3x + 2)(2x + 5)$ {taking out the common factor}

b $3x^2 - x - 10$ has $ac = -30$ and $b = -1$.   We are looking for two numbers with product -30 and sum -1.

Searching amongst the factors of -30, only 5 and -6 have a sum of -1.

$\therefore \quad 3x^2 - x - 10$
$= 3x^2 + 5x - 6x - 10$ {splitting the x-term}
$= x(3x + 5) \ - \ 2(3x + 5)$ {factorising in pairs}
$= (3x + 5)(x - 2)$ {taking out the common factor}

Remember to check your factorisations by expansion!

EXERCISE 13E

1   Fully factorise:

a $2x^2 + 7x + 3$ **b** $2x^2 + 11x + 5$ **c** $7x^2 + 9x + 2$
d $3x^2 + 8x + 4$ **e** $3x^2 + 11x + 6$ **f** $3x^2 + 7x + 4$
g $8x^2 + 10x + 3$ **h** $21x^2 + 17x + 2$ **i** $6x^2 + 7x + 1$
j $6x^2 + 19x + 3$ **k** $10x^2 + 11x + 3$ **l** $14x^2 + 17x + 5$

2   Fully factorise:

a $2x^2 - 3x - 5$ **b** $3x^2 + x - 2$ **c** $3x^2 - 5x - 2$
d $2x^2 + 3x - 2$ **e** $2x^2 + 13x - 7$ **f** $5x^2 - 9x - 2$
g $5x^2 - 16x + 3$ **h** $11x^2 - 8x - 3$ **i** $3x^2 - 7x - 6$
j $2x^2 - 9x + 9$ **k** $3x^2 - 11x + 10$ **l** $5x^2 + 13x - 6$
m $3x^2 + 10x - 8$ **n** $2x^2 + 17x - 9$ **o** $2x^2 + 9x - 18$
p $2x^2 + x - 21$ **q** $15x^2 + x - 2$ **r** $15x^2 - 44x - 3$
s $9x^2 - 15x + 4$ **t** $12x^2 + 31x - 30$ **u** $8x^2 + 19x - 15$

F   DIFFERENCE OF TWO SQUARES FACTORISING

We can factorise expressions such as $x^2 - 9$ using the sum and product method. For example:

$x^2 - 9 = (x + 3)(x - 3)$ as $+3$ and -3 have sum of 0 and product of -9.

However, if we notice that:

$$(a + b)(a - b) = a^2 - ab + ab - b^2 = a^2 - b^2 \quad \{\text{using FOIL}\}$$

then in general: $$a^2 - b^2 = (a + b)(a - b)$$

Note: $a^2 - b^2$, where one squared term is subtracted from another, is known as **"the difference of two squares"**.

Example 17   ◄) Self Tutor

Write each term as a perfect square.

Fully factorise:

a $x^2 - 4$ **b** $1 - 25y^2$

a $x^2 - 4$	**b** $1 - 25y^2$
$= x^2 - 2^2$	$= 1^2 - (5y)^2$
$= (x + 2)(x - 2)$	$= (1 + 5y)(1 - 5y)$

EXERCISE 13F

1   Fully factorise:

a $a^2 - b^2$	**b** $p^2 - q^2$	**c** $q^2 - p^2$	**d** $m^2 - x^2$
e $x^2 - 25$	**f** $x^2 - 81$	**g** $a^2 - 9$	**h** $4x^2 - 1$
i $4x^2 - 9$	**j** $9y^2 - 16$	**k** $64 - x^2$	**l** $16 - 9a^2$
m $x^2 - 100$	**n** $x^2 - 169$	**o** $9x^2 - 4y^2$	**p** $1 - t^2$
q $9 - y^2$	**r** $121u^2 - 4v^2$	**s** $x^2 - 1$	**t** $49a^2 - 400$

REVIEW SET 13A

1   Find the highest common factor of:

a $3x$ and 6 **b** $10a$ and $15a$ **c** cd and cd^2

2   Find the HCF of:

a $3(x + 1)$ and $(x + 1)(x - 4)$ **b** $(x - 2)^2$ and $2(x - 2)(x - 5)$

3   Fully factorise:

a $ab + b$ **b** $3x^2 - 6x$ **c** $-4c - 12c^2$

4 Fully factorise:

    a $3(x - y) - 2x(x - y)$ **b** $(x - 3)(x + 2) + 5(x + 2)$

5 Factorise:

    a $x^2 - 4x - 7x + 28$ **b** $6x^2 + 9x - 4x - 6$

6 Factorise:

    a $x^2 + 10x + 16$ **b** $x^2 - x - 6$ **c** $x^2 - 16$

7 Fully factorise:

    a $2x^2 + 9x + 7$ **b** $6x^2 - 19x + 15$ **c** $25x^2 - 1$

REVIEW SET 13B

1 Find the highest common factor of:

    a $12y$ and $16y$ **b** $2d$ and d^3 **c** ab^2 and a^2b

2 Find the HCF of:

    a $2x(5 - x)$ and $x^2(5 - x)$ **b** $(x + 2)^2$ and $5(x - 4)(x + 2)$

3 Fully factorise:

    a $14 - 7b$ **b** $8a^2 - 6a$ **c** $xy^2 - xy$

4 Fully factorise:

    a $a(2 - x) - 3(2 - x)$ **b** $(x + y)(x - y) - 3(x + y)$

5 Factorise:

    a $x^2 - 7x + 6x - 42$ **b** $2x^2 - 8x - x + 4$

6 Factorise:

    a $x^2 - 2x - 24$ **b** $x^2 - 11x + 24$ **c** $x^2 - 49$

7 Fully factorise:

    a $2x^2 + 3x + 1$ **b** $3x^2 - 7x - 6$ **c** $9x^2 - 4$

PUZZLE   FACTORISING SKILLS

 Fully factorise the following expressions, and place the letter in the boxes corresponding to the correct solution, to reveal the message.

A $x^2 - 7x + 10$ **L** $x^2 + 8x - 48$ **T** $12x^2 - 5x - 2$

C $x(x+2) - (x+2)^2$ **N** $x + x^2 + x^4$ **U** $(x+2)(x+3) - 2(x+2)$

E $6x^2 + 7x - 3$ **O** $16x^2 - 25$ **W** $x^2 - 121$

F $x^2 - 13x + 22$ **P** $12x^2 + 2x - 2$ **X** $6x^2 - 7x - 3$

G $-6x^3 + 4x$ **R** $7x - 21$ **Y** $x^2 + 3x - 18$

I $36x^2 - 49y^2$ **S** $2xy + 6y$

$-2(x+2)$ ☐	$(x+6)(x-3)$ ☐	$(3x-1)(2x+3)$ ☐
$(4x+5)(4x-5)$ ☐	$(4x+5)(4x-5)$ ☐	$(3x+1)(2x-3)$ ☐
$x(1+x+x^3)$ ☐	$(x+1)(x+2)$ ☐	$2(3x-1)(2x+1)$ ☐
$2x(2-3x^2)$ ☐	$-2(x+2)$ ☐	$7(x-3)$ ☐
$7(x-3)$ ☐	$(x-2)(x-5)$ ☐	$(3x-1)(2x+3)$ ☐
$(x-2)(x-5)$ ☐	$x(1+x+x^3)$ ☐	$2y(x+3)$ ☐
$(3x-2)(4x+1)$ ☐	$(x-2)(x-11)$ ☐	$2y(x+3)$ ☐
$(x+1)(x+2)$ ☐	$(x-2)(x-5)$ ☐	$(6x+7y)(6x-7y)$ ☐
$(x+12)(x-4)$ ☐	$-2(x+2)$ ☐	$(4x+5)(4x-5)$ ☐
$(x-2)(x-5)$ ☐	$(3x-2)(4x+1)$ ☐	$x(1+x+x^3)$ ☐
$(3x-2)(4x+1)$ ☐	$(4x+5)(4x-5)$ ☐	$2y(x+3)$ ☐
$(6x+7y)(6x-7y)$ ☐	$7(x-3)$ ☐	$x(1+x+x^3)$ ☐
$(4x+5)(4x-5)$ ☐	$(6x+7y)(6x-7y)$ ☐	$(4x+5)(4x-5)$ ☐
$x(1+x+x^3)$ ☐	$2y(x+3)$ ☐	$(x+11)(x-11)$ ☐
$2y(x+3)$ ☐	$(3x-1)(2x+3)$ ☐	

Chapter 14

Congruence and similarity

Contents:

A Congruence of figures
B Congruent triangles
C Similarity
D Similar triangles
E Problem solving with similar triangles

CONGRUENCE AND SIMILARITY

We are similar.

Two figures are **congruent** if they are identical in every respect, apart from position.

Two figures are **similar** if one figure is an enlargement of the other.

We are congruent.

OPENING PROBLEM

If a group of people were each asked to draw triangle ABC in which $\hat{ABC} = 40°$, $\hat{BCA} = 65°$ and $\hat{CAB} = 75°$, would every person draw an identical triangle? In other words, if each triangle was cut out with a pair of scissors, would they match perfectly when placed on top of each other?

The question arises: "What information is sufficient to draw a **unique** triangle?"

You should find that: • knowing the lengths of its three sides is sufficient
   • knowing the size of its three angles is not sufficient.

A   CONGRUENCE OF FIGURES

In mathematics we use the term **congruent** to describe things which have the same shape and size. The closest we get to congruence in humans is identical twins.

EXERCISE 14A

1 Which of the following figures are congruent?

a   b   c   d   e

2 Which of the following geometric figures are congruent?

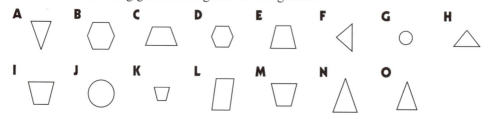

3 Here are some pairs of congruent geometric figures.

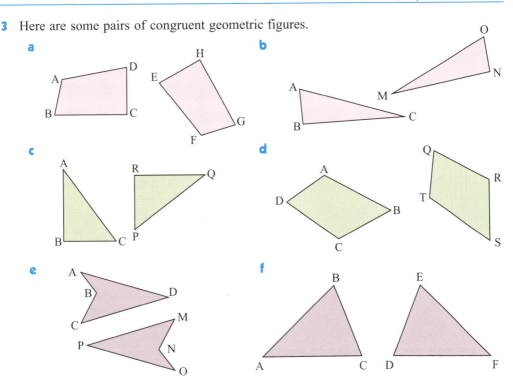

For each pair:

i Identify the side in the second figure corresponding to the side AB in the first figure.

ii Identify the angle in the second figure corresponding to $\stackrel{\frown}{ABC}$ in the first figure.

B   CONGRUENT TRIANGLES

Two triangles are **congruent** if they are identical in every respect except for position.

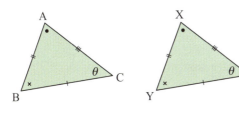

The above triangles are congruent.

We write $\triangle ABC \cong \triangle XYZ$,   where $\cong$ reads   *"is congruent to"*.

Note: When writing the congruence statement above, we label the vertices that are in corresponding positions in the same order, i.e., we write $\triangle ABC \cong \triangle XYZ$ but **not** $\triangle YXZ$ **or** $\triangle ZYX$, etc.

If one triangle was cut out with scissors and placed on the top of the other, they would match each other perfectly.

We have already seen how triangles being equiangular (having all three angles equal) is *not* a test for congruence.

For example, these triangles are equiangular but clearly triangle **B** is much larger than triangle **A**.

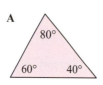

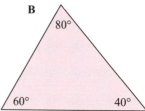

If we are given two sides and a non-included angle, more than one triangle can be drawn.

For example, triangles **C** and **D** have two equal sides and the same non-included angle, but they are *not* the same triangle.

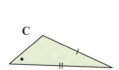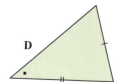

One and only one triangle can be drawn if we are given:

- two sides and the *included* angle between them
- one angle is a right angle, the hypotenuse, and one other side
- two angles and a side.

DEMO

There are, however, four acceptable tests for the **congruence** of two triangles.

TESTS FOR TRIANGLE CONGRUENCE

Two triangles are congruent if one of the following is true:

- All corresponding sides are equal in length. **(SSS)**

- Two sides and the **included** angle are equal. **(SAS)**

- Two angles and a pair of **corresponding sides** are equal. **(AAcorS)**

- For right angled triangles, the hypotenuses and one pair of sides are equal. **(RHS)**

The information we are given will help us decide which test to use to prove two triangles are congruent. The diagrams in the following exercise are sketches only and **are not** drawn to scale. However, the information on them is **correct**.

Example 1

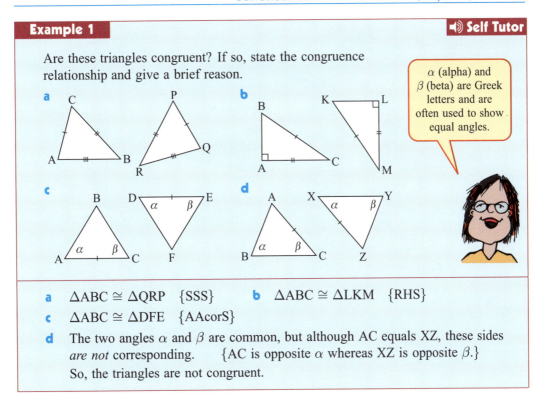

Are these triangles congruent? If so, state the congruence relationship and give a brief reason.

α (alpha) and β (beta) are Greek letters and are often used to show equal angles.

a $\triangle ABC \cong \triangle QRP$ {SSS}   **b** $\triangle ABC \cong \triangle LKM$ {RHS}

c $\triangle ABC \cong \triangle DFE$ {AAcorS}

d The two angles α and β are common, but although AC equals XZ, these sides *are not* corresponding.   {AC is opposite α whereas XZ is opposite β.}

So, the triangles are not congruent.

EXERCISE 14B

1 In each set of three triangles, two are congruent. The diagrams are *not* drawn to scale. State which pair is congruent, together with a reason (SSS, SAS, AAcorS or RHS).

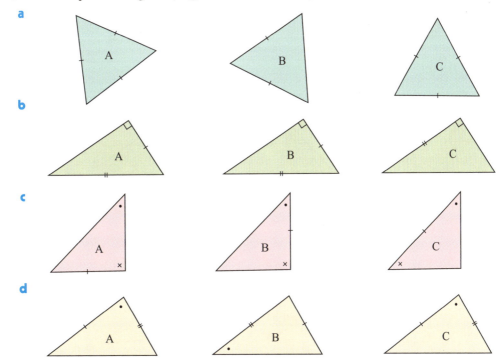

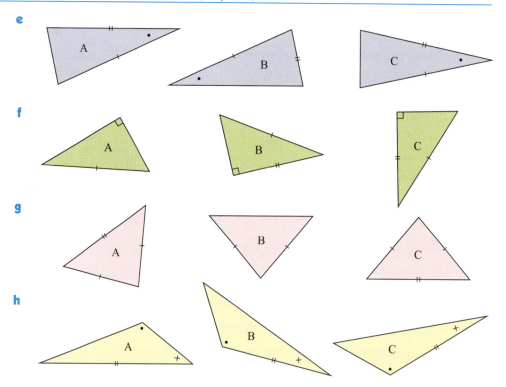

2 Are the following pairs of triangles congruent? If so, state the congruence relationship and give a brief reason.

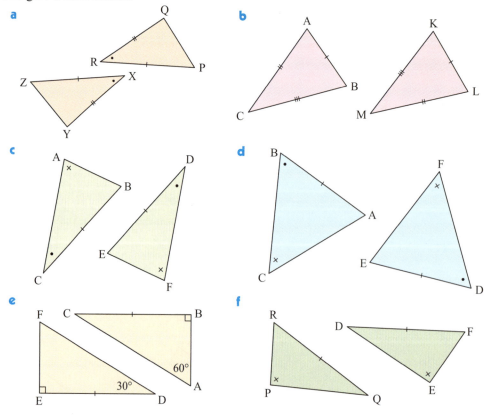

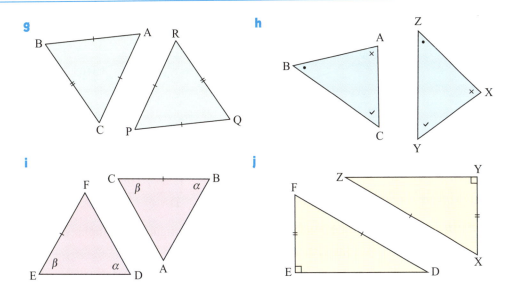

C SIMILARITY

Two figures are **similar** if one is an enlargement of the other (regardless of orientation).

DISCUSSION

- Discuss whether the following pairs of figures are similar:

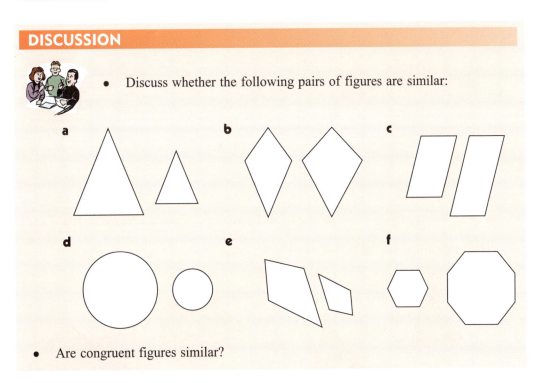

- Are congruent figures similar?

If two figures are similar then their corresponding sides are *in proportion*. This means that the lengths of sides will be increased (or decreased) by the same ratio from one figure to the next. This ratio is called the **enlargement factor**.

Consider the enlargement below for which the enlargement factor k is 1.5.

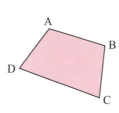

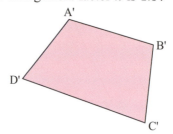

Since $k = 1.5$,   notice that $\dfrac{A'B'}{AB} = \dfrac{B'C'}{BC} = \dfrac{C'D'}{CD} = \dfrac{D'A'}{DA} = \dfrac{B'D'}{BD} = ... = 1.5$

Angle sizes do not change under enlargements. So, if two figures are **similar** then:

- the figures are equiangular, and
- the corresponding sides are *in proportion*.

Example 2   ◀)) Self Tutor

These figures are similar.
Find x to 2 d.p.

Since the figures are similar, their corresponding sides are in the same ratio.

$$\therefore \quad \frac{x}{4} = \frac{5}{3}$$

$$\therefore \quad x = \frac{5}{3} \times 4$$

$$\therefore \quad x = \frac{20}{3}$$

$$\therefore \quad x \approx 6.67$$

EXERCISE 14C

1 Solve for x:

   a $x : 6 = 2 : 15$ **b** $x : 5 = 7 : 31$ **c** $x : 8 = 9 : 102$

2 Find x given that the figures are similar:

   a

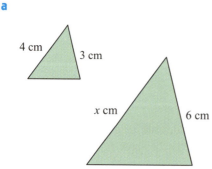

   b

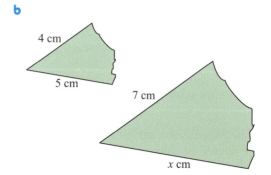

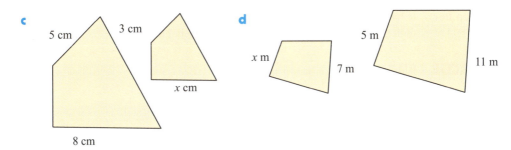

D   SIMILAR TRIANGLES

If two triangles are equiangular then they are **similar**.

Similar triangles have corresponding sides in the same ratio.

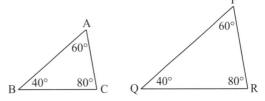

If two triangles are equiangular then one of them must be an enlargement of the other.

For example, $\triangle ABC$ is *similar* to $\triangle PQR$.

To establish that two triangles are similar, we need to show that they are equiangular or that their sides are in proportion.

In the above example, $\dfrac{QR}{BC} = \dfrac{RP}{CA} = \dfrac{PQ}{AB}$ where each fraction equals the enlargement factor.

Example 3   ◀)) Self Tutor

Show that the following figures possess similar triangles:

a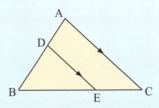

b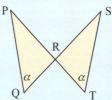

a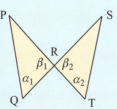

$\triangle$'s ABC and DBE are equiangular as:

- $\alpha_1 = \alpha_2$ {equal corresponding angles}
- angle B is common to both triangles
- $\therefore$ the triangles are similar.

b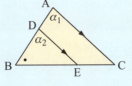

$\triangle$'s PQR and STR are equiangular as:

- $\alpha_1 = \alpha_2$ {given}
- $\beta_1 = \beta_2$ {vertically opposite angles}
- $\therefore$ the triangles are similar.

Remember: If two angles of one triangle are equal in size to two angles of the other triangle
then the remaining angle of each triangle is equal.

EXERCISE 14D

1 Show that the following figures possess similar triangles:

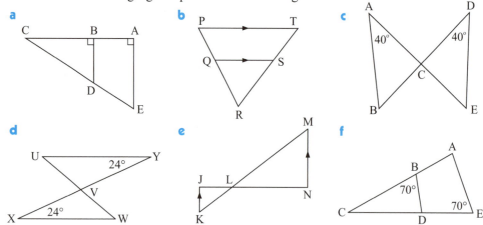

FINDING SIDE LENGTHS

Once we have established that two triangles are similar, we may use the fact that corresponding
sides are in the same ratio to find unknown lengths.

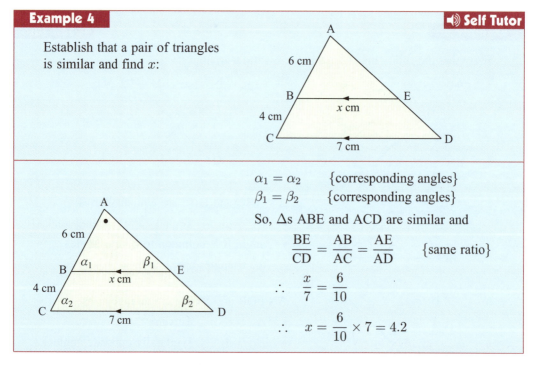

Example 4   ◀) **Self Tutor**

Establish that a pair of triangles
is similar and find x:

$\alpha_1 = \alpha_2$ {corresponding angles}
$\beta_1 = \beta_2$ {corresponding angles}

So, Δs ABE and ACD are similar and

$$\frac{BE}{CD} = \frac{AB}{AC} = \frac{AE}{AD}   \text{\{same ratio\}}$$

$$\therefore \quad \frac{x}{7} = \frac{6}{10}$$

$$\therefore \quad x = \frac{6}{10} \times 7 = 4.2$$

When solving similar triangle problems, it may be useful to use the following method, written
in the context of the example above:

Step 1: Label equal angles.

Step 2: Put the information in table form, showing the equal angles and the sides opposite these angles.

Step 3: Since the triangles are equiangular, they are similar.

Step 4: Use the columns to write down the equation for the ratio of the corresponding sides.

Step 5: Solve the equation.

α	β	$\bullet$	
-	6	x	small Δ
-	10	7	large Δ

from which $\dfrac{6}{10} = \dfrac{x}{7}$

$\therefore \quad x = 4.2$

Example 5
🔊 **Self Tutor**

Establish that a pair of triangles is similar, then find x if $BD = 20$ cm:

	α	β	$\bullet$	
	-	$x + 2$	x	small Δ
	-	20	12	large Δ

The triangles are equiangular and hence similar.

$\therefore \quad \dfrac{x+2}{20} = \dfrac{x}{12}$ {same ratio}

$\therefore \quad 12(x+2) = 20x$

$\therefore \quad 12x + 24 = 20x$

$\therefore \quad 24 = 8x$

$\therefore \quad x = 3$

---

2 In the following, establish that a pair of triangles is similar, then find x:

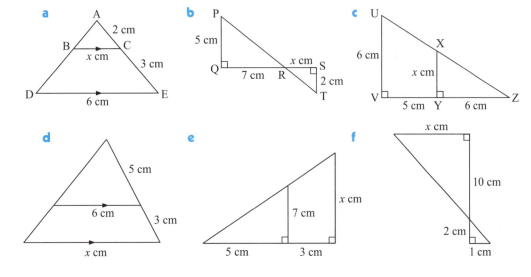

g
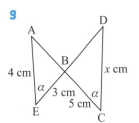

h
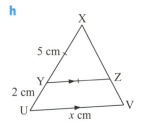

i
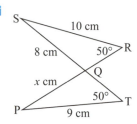

E   PROBLEM SOLVING WITH SIMILAR TRIANGLES

The properties of similar triangles have been known since ancient times. But even with the technologically advanced measuring instruments available today, similar triangles are important for finding heights and distances which would otherwise be difficult to measure.

Step 1:   Read the question carefully and draw a sketch showing all the given information.

Step 2:   Introduce a pronumeral (unknown) such as x, to represent the quantity to be found.

Step 3:   Set up an equation involving the unknown and then solve for the unknown.

Step 4:   Answer the question in a sentence.

Diagrams are very important. They often help you to solve the problem. Make sure your diagrams are large enough.

Example 6   ◀) Self Tutor

Find the height of the pine tree:

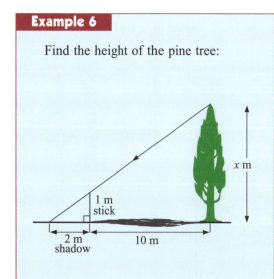

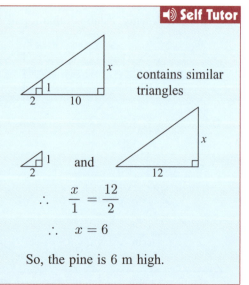

contains similar triangles

$$\therefore \quad \frac{x}{1} = \frac{12}{2}$$

$$\therefore \quad x = 6$$

So, the pine is 6 m high.

EXERCISE 14E

1 Find the height of the pine tree:

a

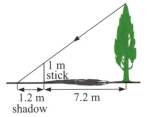

1.2 m
shadow   7.2 m

b

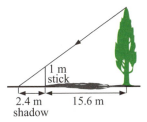

2.4 m
shadow   15.6 m

2 A ramp is built to enable wheel-chair access to a building that is 24 cm above ground level. The ramp has a constant slope of 2 in 15, which means that for every 15 cm horizontally it rises 2 cm. Calculate the length of the base of the ramp.

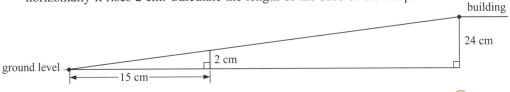

3 A boy who is 1.6 m tall casts a 2.4 m shadow when he stands 8.1 m from the base of an electric light pole. How high above the ground is the light globe?

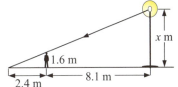

4

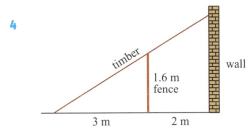

A piece of timber leaning against a wall, just touches the top of a fence, as shown. Find how far up the wall the timber reaches.

5 At the same time as the shadow cast by a 30 cm long ruler is 45 cm long, Rafael's shadow is 264 cm long.

    a Draw a fully labelled sketch of the situation.   **b** Find Rafael's height.

6 There is an electric light post E on one side of a straight road, and a mail box M directly opposite on the other side of the road.

Taj walks 30 metres along the road away from E to point T.

Kanvar is 8 metres away from M at point S, so that E, M, and S are in a straight line. Kanvar walks 6 m parallel to the road in the opposite direction to Taj, to K. Now T, M and K are in a straight line.

    a Explain why triangles TEM and KSM are similar.

    b Find the width of the road.

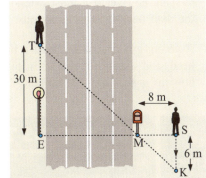

Example 7   ◀)) **Self Tutor**

When a 30 cm ruler is stood vertically on the ground it casts a 24 cm shadow.
At the same time a man casts a shadow of length 152 cm. How tall is the man?

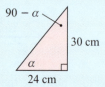

The triangles are equiangular and ∴ similar.

∴ $\dfrac{h}{30} = \dfrac{152}{24}$ {same ratio}

∴ $h = \dfrac{152}{24} \times 30$

∴ $h = 190$ i.e., the man is 190 cm tall.

	α	$90 - \alpha$	90	
	30 cm	24 cm	-	small △
	h cm	152 cm	-	large △

7 A father and son are standing side-by-side. How tall is the son if the father is 1.8 m tall
and casts a shadow 3.2 m long, while his son's shadow is 2.4 m long?

8

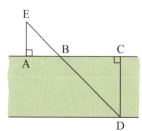

A, B, C and D are pegs on the bank of a canal
which has parallel straight sides. C and D are
directly opposite each other. AB = 30 m and
BC = 140 m.

When I walk from A directly away from the
bank, I reach a point E, 25 m from A, where
E, B and D line up. How wide is the canal?

9 An engineer was asked to construct a bridge
across a river. He noticed that if he started at
C and walked 70 m away from the river to D
and 30 m parallel to the river to E, then C and
E formed a straight line with a statue at B.

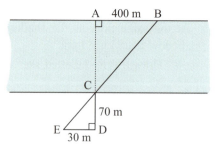

Determine the length of the bridge to be built
to span the river if it must extend 40 m from
the river bank in both directions.

10 A young girl is standing near a building. The end of her 3.5 m shadow, the top of her
head, and the top of the 28 m tall building are in a straight line. If she is 1.5 m tall,
how far is she from the building?

LINKS
click here

HOW WIDE IS THE CANAL?

Areas of interaction:
Human ingenuity

REVIEW SET 14A

1 Which of the following figures are congruent?

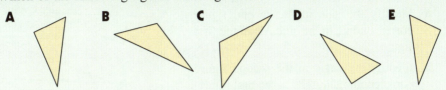

2 In each set of three triangles, two are congruent. The diagrams are not drawn to scale. State which pair is congruent, together with a reason (SSS, SAS, AAcorS or RHS).

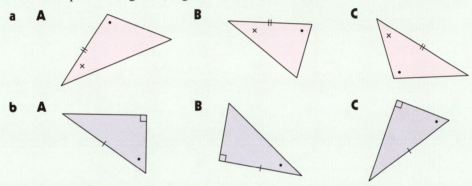

3 Find x, given that the figures are similar:

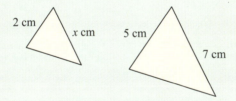

4 Show that the following figures possess similar triangles.

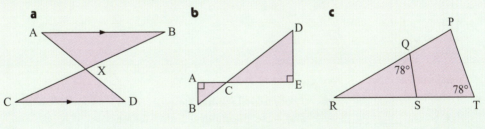

5

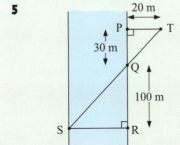

P and Q are markers on the banks of a canal which has parallel sides. R and S are telegraph poles which are directly opposite each other. PQ = 30 m and QR = 100 m.

When I walked 20 m from P directly away from the bank, I reached a point T such that T, Q and S lined up. How wide is the canal?

REVIEW SET 14B

1 In this pair of congruent figures:

    a Identify the side in the second figure corresponding to the side AB in the first figure.

    b Identify the angle in the second figure corresponding to $\hat{ABC}$ in the first figure.

2 Are these triangles congruent? If so, state the congruence relationship and give a brief reason.

  a
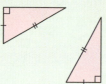
  b

  c

3 Solve for x: **a** $x : 6 = 7 : 18$ **b** $x : 7 = 11 : 20$

4 In the following figures, establish that a pair of triangles is similar, then find x:

  a
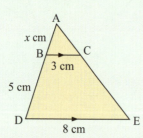
  b
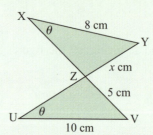

  c
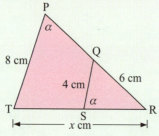

5
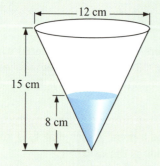

A conical flask has height 15 cm and base diameter 12 cm. Water is poured into the flask to a depth of 8 cm.

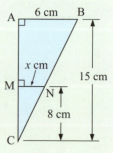

  a Show that triangles ABC and MNC are similar.

  b Hence, show that $x = 3.2$.

  c Find the diameter of the surface of the water.

Chapter **15**

Volume and capacity

Contents:
   A   Volume
   B   Capacity
   C   Problem solving

OPENING PROBLEM

23 mm of rain falls on a relatively flat roof of a house. The roof is rectangular and measures 18 m by 15 m. 95% of the water runs into a tank.

a How much water (in m^3) is collected by the roof?

b How much water runs into the tank?

c The tank has a radius of 3 m, and before the rain fell the water level was 1.2 m above the base. What will be the new water level after the rain?

A   VOLUME

The **volume** of a solid is the amount of space it occupies.

VOLUME FORMULAE

RECTANGULAR PRISM (BOX)

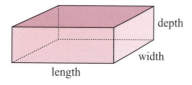

$$\text{Volume} = \text{length} \times \text{width} \times \text{depth}$$

SOLIDS OF UNIFORM CROSS-SECTION

Notice in the triangular prism alongside, that vertical slices parallel to the front triangular face will all be the same size and shape as that face. We say that solids like this are solids of *uniform cross-section*. The cross-section in this case is a triangle.

solid   cross-section

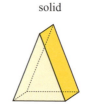

Another example is the hexagonal prism shown opposite.

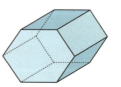

For any solid of uniform cross-section:

$$\text{Volume} = \text{area of cross-section} \times \text{length}$$

In particular, for a **cylinder**, the cross-section is a circle and so:

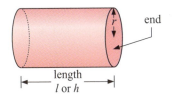

Volume = area of circle × length
$$= \pi r^2 \times l$$

i.e., $V = \pi r^2 l$ or $V = \pi r^2 h$

Find, correct to 3 significant figures, the volume of the following prisms:

a

4.5 cm

6 cm

7.5 cm

b

10 cm

10 cm

a   Volume
= length × width × depth
= 7.5 cm × 6 cm × 4.5 cm
≈ 203 cm³

b   Volume
= area of cross-section × height
= $\pi r^2 \times h$
= $\pi \times 5^2 \times 10$
≈ 785 cm³

EXERCISE 15A

1 Find the volume of the following:

a

5 m

7 m

11 m

b

12 cm

6 cm

c

5 cm

8 cm

16 cm

d

area 15 cm²

3 cm

e

10 cm

8 cm

12 cm

8 cm

f

8 cm

9 cm

g

18 cm

6 cm

h

12 cm

8 cm

3 cm

i

9 cm

20 cm

PYRAMIDS AND CONES

These **tapered solids** have a flat base and come to a point called the **apex**. They **do not** have identical cross-sections. The cross-sections always have the same shape, but not the same size.

For example,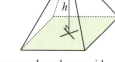

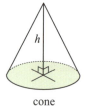

| square-based pyramid | triangular-based pyramid | cone |

$$\text{Volume} = \tfrac{1}{3} \text{ (area of base} \times \text{height)}$$

Note: This formula may be demonstrated using water displacement. Compare tapered solids with solids of uniform cross-section with identical bases and the same heights.

For example: • a cone and a cylinder
• a square-based pyramid and a square-based prism.

Example 2   ◄)) **Self Tutor**

Find the volumes of these solids:

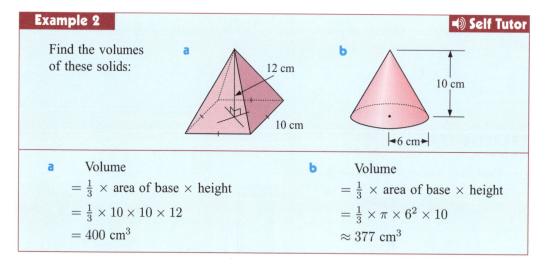

a   Volume
$= \tfrac{1}{3} \times$ area of base $\times$ height
$= \tfrac{1}{3} \times 10 \times 10 \times 12$
$= 400$ cm^3

b   Volume
$= \tfrac{1}{3} \times$ area of base $\times$ height
$= \tfrac{1}{3} \times \pi \times 6^2 \times 10$
≈ 377 cm^3

---

2   Find the volume of the following:

a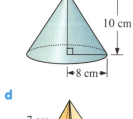

b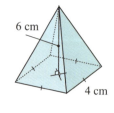

c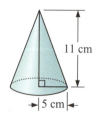

d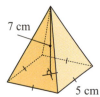

e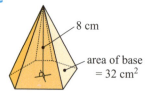

f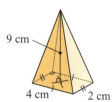

SPHERES

The Greek philosopher **Archimedes** was born in Syracuse in 287 BC. Amongst many other important discoveries, he found that the volume of a sphere is equal to two thirds of the volume of the smallest cylinder which encloses it.

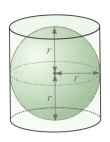

$$\text{Volume of cylinder} = \pi r^2 \times h$$
$$= \pi r^2 \times 2r$$
$$= 2\pi r^3$$

$$\therefore \quad \text{volume of sphere} = \tfrac{2}{3} \times \text{volume of cylinder}$$
$$= \tfrac{2}{3} \times 2\pi r^3$$
$$= \tfrac{4}{3}\pi r^3$$

Archimedes' tomb was marked by a sphere inscribed in a cylinder!

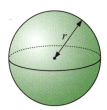

Thus,

$$V = \tfrac{4}{3}\pi r^3$$

Example 3	◀ɴ **Self Tutor**

Find the volume of the sphere in cubic centimetres, to the nearest whole number:

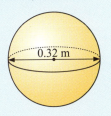

First, convert 0.32 m to cm.

$$0.32 \text{ m} = 32 \text{ cm}$$

$$V = \tfrac{4}{3}\pi r^3$$

$$\therefore \quad V = \tfrac{4}{3}\pi \times 16^3$$

$$\therefore \quad V \approx 17\,157 \text{ cm}^3$$

Change the units to centimetres before calculating the volume.

3 Find the volume of the following:

a

6.2 m

b

7 cm

c

5 cm

4 Find the formula for the volume V of:

  a a cone of base radius r and height $2r$
  b a hemispherical bowl of radius r
  c a cylinder of radius r and height $3r$.

PROBLEM SOLVING

5 In the town square, there is a fountain in the middle of a circular pond. The pond is 6 metres in diameter. A concrete wall 30 cm wide and 60 cm high is built around the edge of the pond.

    a Draw a plan view of the situation.

    b Find the area of the top of the wall.

    c Find the volume of concrete required for the wall.

6 A swimming pool has dimensions shown alongside.

    a Find the area of a trapezium-shaped side.

    b Determine the volume of water required to fill the pool.

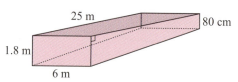

7

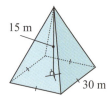

The conservatory for tropical plants at the Botanic gardens is a square-based pyramid with sides 30 metres long and height 15 metres. Calculate the volume of air in this building.

8 A concrete tank has an external diameter of 14 m and an internal height of 4 m. The walls and base of the tank are 20 cm thick.

    a Find the volume of concrete in the base.

    b Find the volume of concrete in the walls.

    c Find the total volume of concrete required.

    d Find the cost of the concrete at \$145 per m^3.

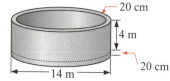

9

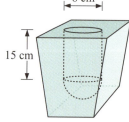

If each person in a classroom must have at least 5 cubic metres of air, how many people could occupy a classroom 8 m by 6 m by 3.2 m?

10 How many spherical fishing sinkers with diameter 1 cm could be made by melting a rectangular block of lead 20 cm by 5 cm by 6 cm and casting the molten product?

11 The inner part of a glass vase is shaped as a cylinder with diameter 8 cm and depth 15 cm, and with a hemi-spherical base.

Find the volume of water that the vase can hold.

12 A garden ornament is shaped like a mushroom. The base is a cylinder 8 cm high and 6 cm in diameter. The top of the mushroom is 20 cm in diameter.

What volume of concrete is needed to make 50 mushrooms?

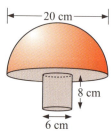

13 5 upright cylindrical steel posts protect the plate glass window of a store that sells computers. The posts are 90 cm high and 12 cm in diameter. If the steel weighs 7.8 grams cm^{-3}, find the weight of the posts in kg.

14 Spherical hollow glass baubles for a Christmas tree have internal diameter 4.9 cm and external diameter 5.0 cm. Find the volume of glass in each bauble.

15 A conical heap of garden soil is dumped on a flat surface. If the diameter of the heap equals its height, and its volume is 1.5 m^3, how high is the heap?

INVESTIGATION 1   THE SURFACE AREA AND VOLUME OF A SPHERE

What effect does doubling the radius of a sphere have on its surface area and volume? We can investigate this effect using a spreadsheet.

SPREADSHEET

What to do:

1 Click on the icon to load the spreadsheet.

We begin with *Sphere 1* which has a radius of 2 cm. In cells C2 and D2 are the surface area and volume of this sphere. Click on these cells and check that the formulae are correct:

$$\text{Surface area} = 4\pi r^2 \qquad \text{Volume} = \tfrac{4}{3}\pi r^3$$

2 For *Sphere 2*, we will *double* the radius, so in B3,   enter   =B2*2.

For C3,   **fill** the formula from C2 **down**.

For D3,   **fill** the formula from D2 **down**.

3 We now check the ratios of surface areas and volumes for *Spheres 1* and *2*.

In E3,   enter   =C3/C2.   In F3,   enter   =D3/D2.

By what factor is the *surface area* increased when the radius of the sphere is *doubled*?

By what factor is the *volume* increased when the radius of the sphere is *doubled*?

4 Confirm your observations by doubling the radius another three times. Highlight the formulae in Row 3 and **fill down** to Row 6. Were your suspicions correct?

5 What do you think the effect on surface area and volume would be if the radius was *tripled* each time?

Change the formula in B3 to   =B2*3   and **fill down** to Row 6.

By what factor is the *surface area* increased when the radius of the sphere is *trebled*?

By what factor is the *volume* increased when the radius of the sphere is *trebled*?

6 If the radius of a sphere is increased by a factor of 'k', by what factor will the:

    a   surface area be increased   **b**   volume be increased?

7 Ask your teacher to help you **prove** your assertions in **6 algebraically**.

INVESTIGATION 2 MAXIMUM VOLUME BY GRAPHICS CALCULATOR

 The Post Office decides that it will not handle any rectangular boxes for which the sum length + width + depth exceeds 120 cm.

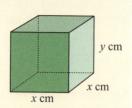

A distributor of packaged goods uses rectangular boxes with square bases. He wants to know which shaped box to use that will satisfy the restriction on dimensions and give him the greatest possible volume.

Suppose we let the base be x cm by x cm and the depth be y cm.

What to do:

1 Write down a formula for y in terms of x.

2 Write down a formula for the volume of the box in terms of x.

3 From **2** you should have found that $V = 120x^2 - 2x^3$. Enter the **function** $Y_1 = 120X^2 - 2X^3$ into a graphics calculator.

4 Set up a **table** that calculates the volume of the box for values of x from 0, 1, 2, ... 60.

5 Scroll through the **table** and find the greatest volume of the box. Hence find the dimensions of the box of greatest volume.

6 Check your maximum volume by drawing a **graph** of $Y_1 = 120X^2 - 2X^3$. Remember to change the **window** settings as necessary.

7 If the Post Office increased the total maximum length from 120 cm to 130 cm, use your graphics calculator to find the new shape for maximum volume.

8 A box must have base x cm by $2x$ cm. What are the dimensions of the box of maximum volume if its length + width + depth $\leqslant 140$ cm?

B   CAPACITY

The **capacity** of a container is the amount of a material (solid or fluid) that it can contain.

Reminder:

1 L = 1000 mL	1 mL $\equiv$ 1 cm^3
1 kL = 1000 L = 1 000 000 mL	1 L $\equiv$ 1000 cm^3
1 ML = 1000 kL = 1 000 000 L	1 kL $\equiv$ 1 m^3

Example 4   ◀)) Self Tutor

How many kL of water would a 3 m by 2.4 m by 1.8 m tank hold when full?

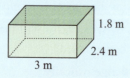

$$V = \text{area of cross-section} \times \text{height}$$
$$= (3 \times 2.4) \times 1.8 \text{ m}^3$$
$$= 12.96 \text{ m}^3$$

$\therefore$ capacity is 12.96 kL

EXERCISE 15B

1 Find the capacity (in kL) of the following tanks:

a
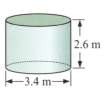
2.1 m
2.5 m
4.2 m

b
2.6 m
◄—3.4 m—►

c
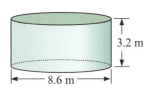
3.2 m
◄——8.6 m——►

2 A new perfume in a 36 mm (internal) diameter spherical bottle comes on to the market.

  a Calculate the capacity of the bottle in mL.

  b If the bottle costs $25 and the bottle and its contents cost $105, how much does the perfume cost per mL?

36 mm

3 Which container of orange juice would give the better value:

  A a cylindrical bottle of diameter 16 cm and height 19.9 cm costing $5.75   *or*

  B a rectangular cask measuring 20 cm by 15 cm by 10 cm costing $4.50?

4 A roof has surface area of 110 m² and one night 12 mm of rain falls on the roof. All the water goes into a tank of base diameter 4 m.

  a Find the volume of water which falls on the roof.

  b How many kL of water enter the tank?

  c By how much will the water level rise in the tank?

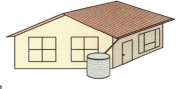

5

A motor car has a rectangular prism petrol tank 48 cm by 56 cm by 20 cm. If the car consumes petrol at an average rate of 8.7 litres per 100 km, how far could it travel on a full tank of petrol?

6 Water is pumped into a cylindrical tank at 80 L per minute. The base diameter of the tank is 2.4 m and the height is 4 m.

  a Find the volume of the full tank.

  b Convert 80 L min^{-1} into m³ min^{-1}.

  c How long will it take to fill the tank?

7 A hemispherical bowl has internal diameter 18 cm. How many litres of water could it contain?

8 A cone has diameter 8 cm and height 6 cm. How many litres of water could it contain?

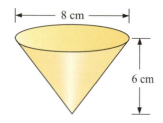

9 How many cylindrical bottles 12 cm high and with 6 cm diameter could be filled from a tank containing 125 L of detergent?

10 An elliptical swimming pool with dimensions as shown is filled to a depth of 1.2 metres. Find the number of kilolitres of water needed.

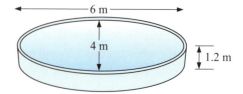

11 An industrial funnel is a cone with radius 20 cm and height 50 cm. Fuel is pumped into the funnel at a rate of 3 L min^{-1}, and it then passes through a pipe to a tank 40 cm by 50 cm by 80 cm.

   a Find the capacity of the funnel in kL.

   b If the pipe becomes blocked, how long will the attendant have to realise and shut off the pump before the funnel overflows?

   c How long will it take to fill the tank?

Example 5   ◀) Self Tutor

Water pours into a cylindrical tank of diameter 4 m at a constant rate of 1 kL per hour. By how much does the water level rise in 5 hours (to the nearest mm)?

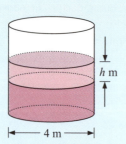

In 5 hours the capacity of water that flows in

$$= 1 \text{ kL per hour} \times 5 \text{ hours}$$
$$= 5 \text{ kL}$$

Since $1 \text{ kL} \equiv 1 \text{ m}^3$, the volume of water that flows in is 5 m^3.

If h metres is the height increase, then the volume of water that must have entered the tank is:

$$V = \pi r^2 h$$
$$\therefore \quad V = \pi \times 2^2 \times h$$
$$\therefore \quad V = 4\pi h$$
$$\therefore \quad 4\pi h = 5 \qquad \text{\{equating volumes\}}$$
$$\therefore \quad h = \frac{5}{4\pi} \approx 0.398 \qquad \text{\{dividing both sides by } 4\pi\text{\}}$$

$\therefore$ the water level rises 0.398 m.

12 2 litres of tomato soup is poured into a rectangular plastic box which has a 20 cm by 12 cm base. To what height does the soup rise?

13 38 mm of rain fell overnight onto a flat roof 30 m by 20 m. If 90% of the water went into an empty cylindrical tank of base diameter 6 m, by how much did the water level rise?

C   PROBLEM SOLVING

In this section you will need to select and apply the appropriate formula from any of the previous sections to solve problems.

There are simple **steps** to follow when **solving problems**:
- Read the question carefully.
- Draw a diagram with the information clearly marked on it.
- Label the unknowns.
- Choose the correct formula or formulae.
- Work step by step through the problem, making sure the units are correct.
- Answer the original question in words.

Example 6   ◀ Self Tutor

Sand from a quarry pours out from a giant hose and forms a conical heap on the ground. The heap has a base diameter of 25 m and a height of 8.9 m.

a Find the volume of sand in the heap to the nearest m^3.

b Find the total mass (to the nearest 10 tonne) of the sand given that 1 m^3 of it weighs 2.35 tonnes.

The diameter is 25 m, so $r = 12.5$.
The height is 8.9 m, so $h = 8.9$.

Notice in **b** that we used the *unrounded* volume from **a**.

a   Volume
$= \frac{1}{3}\pi r^2 h$
$= \frac{1}{3} \times \pi \times 12.5^2 \times 8.9$
≈ 1456.259
≈ 1456 m^3

b   Total mass
= number of m^3
        $\times$ weight per m^3
$\approx 1456.259 \times 2.35$
≈ 3422.209
≈ 3420 tonne

EXERCISE 15C

1 A conical heap of salt is 3.5 metres in diameter and 4.2 metres high. Find:

a the volume of the heap of salt

b the total mass of salt given that 1 m^3 weighs 769 kg

c the total value of the salt given that 1 kg is worth €0.85 retail price.

2   A cylindrical tank contains oil to a depth of 1.5 m. If it has a diameter of 2 m, how many 1.2 L bottles could be filled from the tank?

3   A rectangular house 15 m by 6 m is surrounded by a concrete path which is 2 m wide. Find:

 a   the area of the path

 b   the cost of paving the path with concrete to a depth of 10 cm if the concrete costs $165 per cubic metre.

4   Reinforced rubber tubing has dimensions as shown:

 a   Find the area of one end of the tube.

 b   Hence find the volume of rubber needed to make 25 m of tube.

 c   If the reinforced rubber weighs 140 kg per m^3, find the weight of a 25 m roll of tubing.

25 m · 3 cm · 2.4 cm

Example 7 ◀) Self Tutor

A sphere has a volume of 200 cm^3. Find its radius.

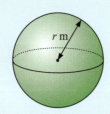

r m

Volume of sphere $= \frac{4}{3}\pi r^3$

$\therefore \quad \frac{4}{3}\pi r^3 = 200$

$\therefore \quad \frac{3}{4} \times \frac{4}{3}\pi r^3 = \frac{3}{4} \times 200$ {× both sides by $\frac{3}{4}$}

$\therefore \quad \pi r^3 = 150$

$\therefore \quad r^3 = \dfrac{150}{\pi} \approx 47.746$

$\therefore \quad r = \sqrt[3]{47.746} \approx 3.628$

$\therefore$ the radius is 3.63 cm

---

5   A spherical ball has a volume of 350 cm^3. Find its radius.

6   A cylindrical tin can has base radius 6 cm and a volume of 905 cm^3. Find its height.

7   A conical heap of sand has diameter twice its height. How high is the heap if its volume is 3 m^3?

8   A grain silo is made up of a cylinder with a hemi-spherical top as shown.

 a   Find the capacity of the silo if the diameter is 12 m and the height is 15 m.

 b   Find the height if the diameter is 12 m and the capacity is 2500 kL.

 c   Find the diameter if the height is 15 m and the capacity is 1800 kL.

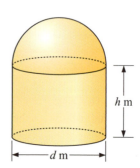

h m

d m

REVIEW SET 15A

1 Find the volume of the following, correct to 2 decimal places:

a

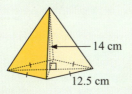

14 cm

12.5 cm

b

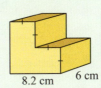

8.2 cm   6 cm

2 Calculate the volume of a sphere with diameter 5 cm.

3 Find the formula for the volume V of a cone with base radius $2x$ cm and height $5x$ cm.

4 The diagram shows the cross-section of a railway cutting that is to be excavated. Find how much soil, in m³, needs to be removed for each metre length of the cutting.

8.5 m

7 m

6 m

5 Water enters the tank shown at the rate of 60 L per minute.

a Find the volume of the tank when full.

b Convert the volume of the tank to capacity in litres.

c Find out how long, in hours and minutes, it would take to fill the tank.

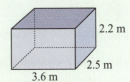

2.2 m

2.5 m

3.6 m

6

5.6 m

2.5 m

Find the capacity of the tank shown in kL.

7 **a** Find the capacity of a swimming pool with dimensions shown:

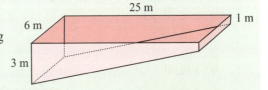

25 m

1 m

6 m

3 m

b If the pool was filled to a depth 10 cm from the top, how many kilolitres of water would it contain?

8 The Pyramid of Khufu in Egypt has a square base with sides 230.4 m and a height of 146.5 m.

a Find the total volume of the pyramid.

b If each cubic metre of stone weighs 2.67 tonnes, find the total mass of stone used. Give your answer in standard form, correct to 2 significant figures.

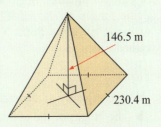

146.5 m

230.4 m

c The King's Chamber in the pyramid is rectangular and measures 5.23 m by 5.76 m by 6.25 m. Find the capacity of the chamber, correct to 3 significant figures.

REVIEW SET 15B

1 Find the volume of the following, correct to 2 decimal places:

a

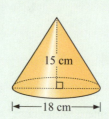

12 cm

3 cm

b

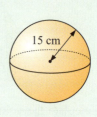

15 cm

18 cm

c

15 cm

2 Calculate the volume of a square based pyramid with base 8 cm long and height 12 cm.

3 Find the formula for the volume V of the triangular prism shown:

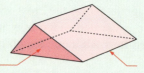

area $2x^2$ cm^2

length $5x$ cm

4 After a heavy rain it was found that the water level in a cylindrical tank had risen by 45 cm. If the radius of the tank was 1.2 m, find the volume of water collected.

5 A semi-circular tunnel with dimensions shown is made of concrete.

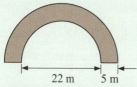

22 m   5 m

a What is the cross-sectional area of the tunnel?

b If the tunnel is 200 m long and concrete costs $120 per cubic metre, find the cost of constructing the tunnel.

6 A cylindrical tank made of concrete has an *external* diameter of 6 m and an *internal* height of 4 m. The walls and base of the tank are 20 cm thick.

a Find the volume of concrete in the base.

b Find the volume of concrete in the walls.

c Find the total volume of concrete required.

d Find the *capacity* of the tank.

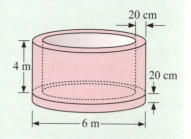

20 cm

4 m

20 cm

6 m

7 St Paul's Cathedral in London is cross-shaped with a cylinder and a hemi-spherical dome on top as shown. The cylinder has a diameter of 38 m and the dome has a diameter of 32 m. Point X is 85 m above the floor. Some other dimensions of the cathedral are shown.

Find:

a the capacity of the cross-shape

b the height of the cylinder

c the capacity of the cylinder

d the capacity of the dome

e the total capacity of the cathedral.

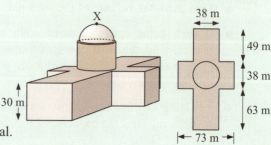

X

30 m

38 m

49 m

38 m

63 m

73 m

Chapter 16

Trigonometry

Contents:

A Labelling sides of a right angled triangle

B Trigonometric ratios

C Using the sine ratio

D Using the cosine ratio

E Using the tangent ratio

F Problem solving with trigonometry

G Bearings

OPENING PROBLEM

Candice is sitting on a park bench and looking up to the top of a tall building on the other side of the road.

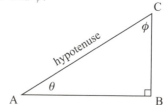

roadway

She wonders what the building's height would be. She is not allowed to go to the top of the building for safety reasons.

Things to think about and discuss:

- How can she find with reasonable accuracy the height of the building?
- What measurements need to be made so that a calculation can be done?
- What instruments might she use to get accurate measurements?
- What accuracy can she expect from the calculations she makes?
- What assumptions would she be making?

Notice that in the **Opening Problem** we are dealing with a right angled triangle. There is a convention for labelling the sides of a right angled triangle.

A   LABELLING SIDES OF A RIGHT ANGLED TRIANGLE

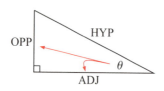

For the right angled triangle with angle θ:
- the **hypotenuse (HYP)** is the longest side
- the **opposite (OPP)** side is opposite θ
- the **adjacent (ADJ)** side is adjacent to θ.

Given a right angled triangle ABC with angles of θ and ϕ:

For angle θ, BC is the **opposite side**
AB is the **adjacent side**.

For angle ϕ, AB is the **opposite side**
BC is the **adjacent side**.

In any right angled triangle, locate the hypotenuse first. Then locate the opposite side for the angle you are working with.

θ is theta
ϕ is phi
α is alpha
β is beta

Example 1

For the triangle following, name:
- **a** the hypotenuse
- **b** the side opposite θ
- **c** the side adjacent to θ.

- **a** The hypotenuse is QR.
  (the longest side, opposite the right angle)
- **b** PQ
- **c** PR

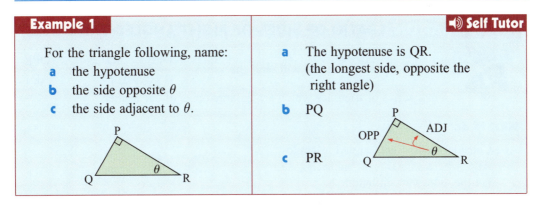

EXERCISE 16A

1 For the triangles given, name:
- **i**   the hypotenuse
- **ii** the side opposite angle θ
- **iii** the side adjacent to θ

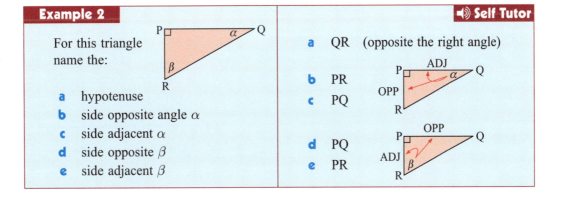

Example 2

For this triangle name the:
- **a** hypotenuse
- **b** side opposite angle α
- **c** side adjacent α
- **d** side opposite β
- **e** side adjacent β

- **a** QR   (opposite the right angle)
- **b** PR
- **c** PQ
- **d** PQ
- **e** PR

2 For the triangle given, name the:
- **i**   hypotenuse
- **ii** side opposite α
- **iii** side adjacent to α
- **iv** side opposite β
- **v**   side adjacent to β

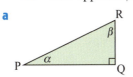
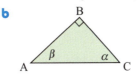

INVESTIGATION   RATIO OF SIDES OF RIGHT ANGLED TRIANGLES

In this investigation we will find the ratios $\dfrac{\text{OPP}}{\text{HYP}}$, $\dfrac{\text{ADJ}}{\text{HYP}}$ and $\dfrac{\text{OPP}}{\text{ADJ}}$

in a series of triangles which are enlargements of each other.

What to do:

1 Consider four right angled triangles ABC where $\angle CAB$ is 30° in each case but the sides vary in length.

By accurately measuring to the nearest millimetre, complete a table like the one following:

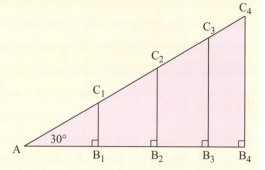

Triangle	AB	BC	AC	$\dfrac{AB}{AC}$	$\dfrac{BC}{AC}$	$\dfrac{BC}{AB}$
1						
2						
3						
4						

Convert all fractions to 2 decimal places.

PRINTABLE WORKSHEET

2 Repeat **1** for the set of triangles alongside.

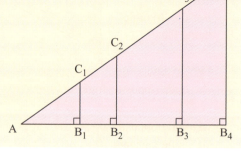

3 What have you discovered from **1** and **2**?

Notice that $\dfrac{AB}{AC} = \dfrac{\text{ADJ}}{\text{HYP}}$, $\dfrac{BC}{AC} = \dfrac{\text{OPP}}{\text{HYP}}$ and $\dfrac{BC}{AB} = \dfrac{\text{OPP}}{\text{ADJ}}$.

From the **Investigation** you should have discovered that:

For a fixed angled right angled triangle, the ratios $\dfrac{\text{OPP}}{\text{HYP}}$, $\dfrac{\text{ADJ}}{\text{HYP}}$ and $\dfrac{\text{OPP}}{\text{ADJ}}$ are constant no matter how much the triangle is enlarged.

B   TRIGONOMETRIC RATIOS

Trigonometry is the study of the connection between the lengths of sides and the sizes of angles of triangles.

In this course we consider only right angled triangles.

Some uses of trigonometry are in:

- navigation
- finding heights and distances for inaccessible objects
- building and construction (architecture)
- defence.

TRIGONOMETRIC RATIOS

For a particular angle of a right angled triangle the ratios $\dfrac{\text{OPP}}{\text{HYP}}$, $\dfrac{\text{ADJ}}{\text{HYP}}$ and $\dfrac{\text{OPP}}{\text{ADJ}}$ are fixed.

These ratios have the traditional names **sine**, **cosine** and **tangent** respectively.

We abbreviate them to **sin**, **cos** and **tan**.

So, in any right angled triangle with one angle θ we have:

$$\textbf{sin } \theta = \frac{\text{OPP}}{\text{HYP}}, \quad \textbf{cos } \theta = \frac{\text{ADJ}}{\text{HYP}}, \quad \textbf{tan } \theta = \frac{\text{OPP}}{\text{ADJ}}$$

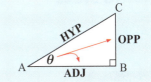

We can use these ratios to find unknown sides and angles of right angled triangles.

Example 3   ◀) **Self Tutor**

For the given triangle find $\sin\theta$, $\cos\theta$ and $\tan\theta$.

5 cm   3 cm   4 cm θ

$$\sin\theta = \frac{\text{OPP}}{\text{HYP}} \qquad \cos\theta = \frac{\text{ADJ}}{\text{HYP}} \qquad \tan\theta = \frac{\text{OPP}}{\text{ADJ}}$$

$$= \tfrac{4}{5} \qquad\qquad\quad = \tfrac{3}{5} \qquad\qquad\quad = \tfrac{4}{3}$$

EXERCISE 16B

1   Find in the right angled triangles, *not drawn to scale*, **i** $\sin\theta$ **ii** $\cos\theta$ **iii** $\tan\theta$:

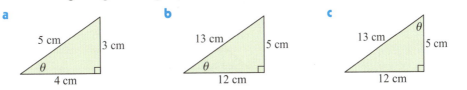

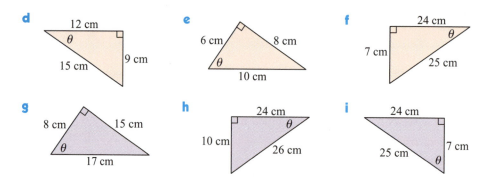

C   USING THE SINE RATIO

Trigonometry can be used to find either unknown sides or unknown angles in a triangle.

Warning!

Always check that your calculator is set to **degrees**. Press MODE and scroll down to Degree in the display.

FINDING SIDES

Recall that: $\sin \theta = \dfrac{\text{OPP}}{\text{HYP}}$

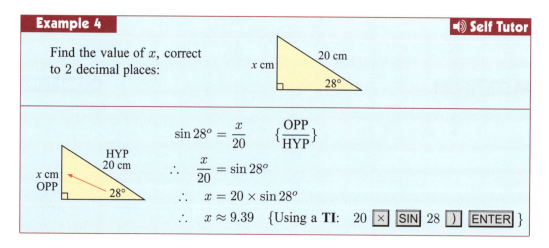

Example 4   ◆) **Self Tutor**

Find the value of x, correct to 2 decimal places:

$\sin 28^o = \dfrac{x}{20}$ $\{\dfrac{\text{OPP}}{\text{HYP}}\}$

$\therefore \quad \dfrac{x}{20} = \sin 28^o$

$\therefore \quad x = 20 \times \sin 28^o$

$\therefore \quad x \approx 9.39$ {Using a **TI**: 20 ✕ SIN 28) ENTER }

EXERCISE 16C

1 Find the value of x, giving your answer correct to 2 decimal places:

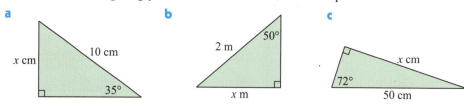

Example 5

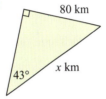

Find the value of x, correct to 3 significant figures:

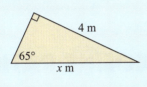

$$\sin 65^o = \frac{4}{x}$$

$$\therefore \quad \frac{4}{x} = \frac{\sin 65^o}{1}$$

$$\therefore \quad \frac{x}{4} = \frac{1}{\sin 65^o} \quad \{\text{using reciprocals}\}$$

$$\therefore \quad x = \frac{4}{\sin 65^o}$$

$$\therefore \quad x \approx 4.41$$

2 Find the value of x, giving your answer correct to 3 significant figures:

a

b
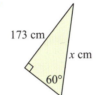

c
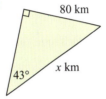

FINDING ANGLES

Angles can be found using **inverse functions**.

For example, if $\sin x = \frac{7}{11}$, then $x = \sin^{-1}\left(\frac{7}{11}\right)$

$x = \sin^{-1}\left(\frac{7}{11}\right)$ is read as: x is the angle whose sine is $\frac{7}{11}$.

The inverse function may be $\boxed{\text{2nd F}}$, $\boxed{\text{INV}}$, $\boxed{\text{2nd}}$ or $\boxed{\text{SHIFT}}$, depending on your calculator. calculator

To find $\sin^{-1}\left(\frac{7}{11}\right)$ we may need to press $\boxed{\text{2nd}}$ $\boxed{\text{SIN}}$ (**SIN^{-1}**) 7 $\boxed{\div}$ 11 $\boxed{)}$ $\boxed{\text{ENTER}}$.

Instructions for graphics calculators can be found on page **14**.

Example 6

Find, to 3 significant figures, the measure of the angle marked θ:

$$\sin \theta = \frac{28}{40} \quad \left\{\frac{\text{OPP}}{\text{HYP}}\right\}$$

$$\therefore \quad \theta = \sin^{-1}\left(\frac{28}{40}\right)$$

$$\therefore \quad \theta \approx 44.4$$

> sin^{-1} (....) reads the angle with a sine of .....

{Using a **TI**: $\boxed{\text{2nd}}$ $\boxed{\text{SIN}}$ (**SIN^{-1}**) 28 $\boxed{\div}$ 40 $\boxed{)}$ $\boxed{\text{ENTER}}$ }

3 Find, correct to 3 significant figures, the value of θ:

a

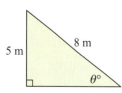

b

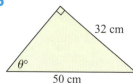

c

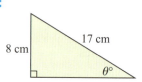

D   USING THE COSINE RATIO

Recall that:

$$\cos \theta = \frac{\text{ADJ}}{\text{HYP}}$$

Example 7   ◄)) Self Tutor

Find, to 3 significant figures, the value of x in:

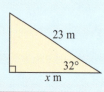

$\cos 32^o = \dfrac{x}{23} \quad \{\dfrac{\text{ADJ}}{\text{HYP}}\}$

$\therefore \quad \dfrac{x}{23} = \cos 32^o$

$\therefore \quad x = 23 \times \cos 32^o$

$\therefore \quad x \approx 19.5$

{Using a **TI**: 23 $\times$ $\boxed{\text{COS}}$ 32 $\boxed{)}$ $\boxed{\text{ENTER}}$ }

EXERCISE 16D

1 Find, correct to 3 significant figures, the value of x in:

a

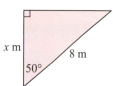

b

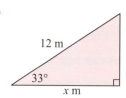

c

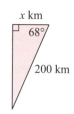

Example 8   ◄)) Self Tutor

Find, to 3 significant figures, the value of x in:

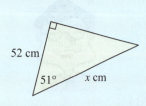

$\cos 51^o = \dfrac{52}{x} \quad \{\dfrac{\text{ADJ}}{\text{HYP}}\}$

$\therefore \quad \dfrac{52}{x} = \cos 51^o$

$\therefore \quad \dfrac{x}{52} = \dfrac{1}{\cos 51^o}$

$\therefore \quad x = \dfrac{52}{\cos 51^o}$

$\therefore \quad x \approx 82.6$

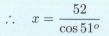

2 Find, correct to 3 significant figures, the value of x in:

a

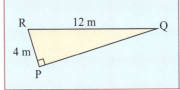
43 cm
40°
x cm

b

15 m
15°
x m

c

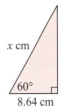
x cm
60°
8.64 cm

Example 9   🔊 **Self Tutor**

Find the measure of the angle at R correct to 3 significant figures:

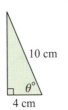
R   12 m   Q
4 m
P

$\cos R = \frac{4}{12}$ $\{\frac{ADJ}{HYP}\}$

$\therefore \quad R = \cos^{-1}\left(\frac{4}{12}\right)$

$\therefore \quad R \approx 70.5°$

$\therefore$ the angle at R is approximately $70.5°$

{Using a **TI**: [2nd] [COS] 4 [÷] 12 [)] [ENTER] }

HYP 12 m
R   Q
4 m
ADJ
P

---

3 Find, correct to 3 significant figures, the unknown angle in:

a

10 cm
$\theta°$
4 cm

b

9 m
$a°$
12 m

c

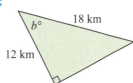
$b°$ 18 km
12 km

E   USING THE TANGENT RATIO

The tangent ratio, $\tan\theta = \dfrac{OPP}{ADJ}$,   can also be used to find unknown lengths of sides and unknown angles.

Example 10   🔊 **Self Tutor**

Find the value of x correct to 2 decimal places:

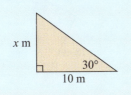
x m
30°
10 m

$\tan 30° = \dfrac{x}{10}$ $\{\dfrac{OPP}{ADJ}\}$

$\therefore \quad \dfrac{x}{10} = \tan 30°$

$\therefore \quad x = 10 \times \tan 30°$

$\therefore \quad x \approx 5.77$

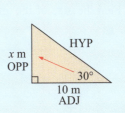
HYP
x m
OPP
30°
10 m
ADJ

EXERCISE 16E

1 Find the value of x, giving your answer correct to 2 decimal places:

a
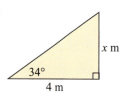

b
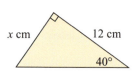

c
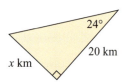

Example 11   🔊 **Self Tutor**

Find x, correct to 3 significant figures:

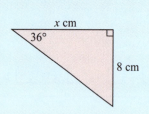

$\tan 36^o = \dfrac{8}{x} \quad \{\dfrac{\text{OPP}}{\text{ADJ}}\}$

$\therefore \quad \dfrac{8}{x} = \dfrac{\tan 36^o}{1}$

$\therefore \quad \dfrac{x}{8} = \dfrac{1}{\tan 36^o}$

$\therefore \quad x = \dfrac{8}{\tan 36^o}$

$\therefore \quad x \approx 11.0$

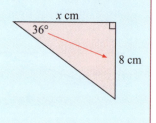

---

2 Find the value of x, correct to 3 significant figures:

a
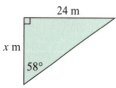

b

c
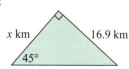

Example 12   🔊 **Self Tutor**

Find the size of angle ϕ, correct to 2 decimal places:

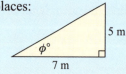

$\tan \phi = \dfrac{5}{7} \quad \{\dfrac{\text{OPP}}{\text{ADJ}}\}$

$\therefore \quad \phi = \tan^{-1}\left(\dfrac{5}{7}\right)$

$\therefore \quad \phi \approx 35.54$

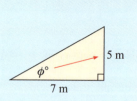

---

3 Find the size of the angle marked ϕ, correct to 2 decimal places:

a
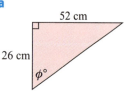

b
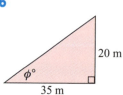

c
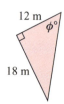

F PROBLEM SOLVING WITH TRIGONOMETRY

In the previous exercises we have practised using trigonometry to find unknown sides and angles in right angled triangles. We can now use these skills to solve problems.

PRELIMINARIES

Problem solving with trigonometry often involves the use of **angles of elevation** or **depression**.

When an object is **higher** than an observer, the **angle of elevation** is the angle from the horizontal **up** to the object.

When an object is **lower** than an observer, the **angle of depression** is the angle from the horizontal **down** to the object.

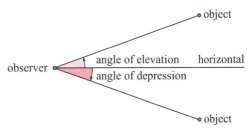

THE PROBLEM SOLVING STEPS

To **solve problems** involving trigonometry, follow these **steps**:

- If a diagram is not given, draw a diagram to illustrate the situation.
- Mark on the diagram the unknown angle or side that needs to be calculated. Often x is used for a length and θ for an angle.
- Check any assumptions about horizontal lines, vertical lines or right angles.
- Write an equation between an angle and two sides of the triangle using the correct trigonometric ratio.
- Solve for the unknown.
- Write your answer in sentence form.

Example 13   ◀)) **Self Tutor**

A kite is flying at a height of 45 m above the ground at the end of a string of length 70 m. Find the angle of elevation, to the nearest degree, between the string and the ground.

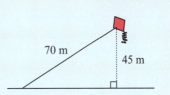

$\therefore \quad \sin \theta = \frac{45}{70} \qquad \left\{ \dfrac{\text{OPP}}{\text{HYP}} \right\}$

$\therefore \quad \theta = \sin^{-1}\left(\frac{45}{70}\right)$

$\therefore \quad \theta \approx 40$

$\therefore$ angle of elevation is approximately 40°.

EXERCISE 16F

1   A kite is flying at a height of 52 m above ground at the end of a string which is 82 m long. Find the angle of elevation between the string and the ground.

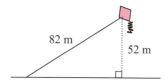

2

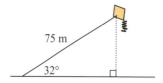

A kite is flying on the end of a 75 m long string. If the string makes an angle of $32°$ with the ground, how far horizontally is the kite from the end of the string?

3   A kite string is pinned to the ground. The string makes an angle of $55°$ with the ground and is 80 m long. How high is the kite above the ground?

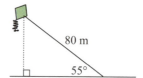

Example 14   ◄◎ **Self Tutor**

A ladder leans against a vertical wall. It reaches 3.5 m up the wall and makes an angle of $55°$ with the ground. Find the length of the ladder.

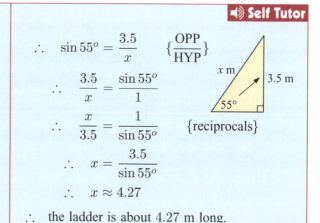

$$\therefore \quad \sin 55° = \frac{3.5}{x} \quad \left\{ \frac{\text{OPP}}{\text{HYP}} \right\}$$

$$\therefore \quad \frac{3.5}{x} = \frac{\sin 55°}{1}$$

$$\therefore \quad \frac{x}{3.5} = \frac{1}{\sin 55°} \quad \{\text{reciprocals}\}$$

$$\therefore \quad x = \frac{3.5}{\sin 55°}$$

$$\therefore \quad x \approx 4.27$$

$\therefore$ the ladder is about 4.27 m long.

---

4   A ladder leans against a vertical wall. It reaches 5.4 m up the wall and makes an angle of $68°$ with the ground. Find the length of the ladder.

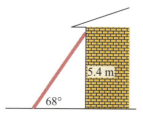

5

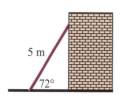

A ladder is 5 m long and makes an angle of $72°$ with the ground. How far up the wall does it reach (to the nearest cm)?

6 A 5 m ladder leaning against a wall has its base 2.7 m from the foot of the wall. Find the angle between the ladder and the ground.

5 m

2.7 m

7

A window cleaner has a 6 m long ladder.

For safety reasons the greatest angle the ladder is allowed to make with the ground is 70°.

What distance up the wall can the ladder reach?

8 A highway climbs at a constant rate up a mountain pass.

After travelling 23.8 km, a car has ascended 1371 metres. What is the angle of incline (θ^o)?

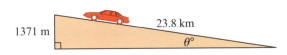

1371 m   23.8 km

θ^o

9

A driver travels 1.5 km up a long steady incline which is angled at 12° to the horizontal.

How far has the driver climbed vertically?

10 When the sun is at an angle of elevation of 63°, a tree casts a shadow of length 6.2 m.

Find the height of the tree.

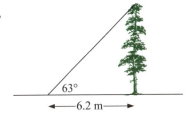

$63°$

←—6.2 m—→

11

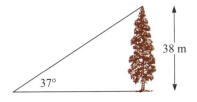

38 m

$37°$

A tree 38 m high casts a shadow. The angle of elevation from the end of the shadow to the top of the tree is 37°.

Find the length of the shadow to the nearest 10 cm.

12 A surveyor needs to measure the width of a river.

He finds a point B directly opposite a tree T, on the bank on the other side of the river. He then moves 32 m along the bank at right angles to BT to a point A.

With a theodolite he measures angle BAT as 55°.

Calculate the width of the river to the nearest metre.

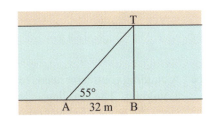

T

$55°$

A   32 m   B

Example 15   ◀) **Self Tutor**

A fisherman is 650 m out to sea. He
looks up at an angle of elevation of
$15°$ to the top of a cliff. Find, to the
nearest metre, the height of the cliff.

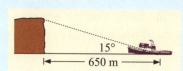

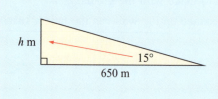

$$\therefore \quad \tan 15° = \frac{h}{650} \quad \{\frac{\text{OPP}}{\text{ADJ}}\}$$

$$\therefore \quad \frac{h}{650} = \tan 15°$$

$$\therefore \quad h = 650 \times \tan 15°$$

$$\therefore \quad h \approx 174.2$$

The cliff is about 174 m high.

13

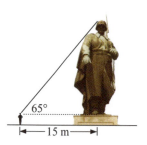

Tim, whose eyes are 1.4 metres above ground
level, stands 15 m from the base of a statue. If
he looks up to the top of the statue, the angle of
elevation is $65°$. Find the height of the statue.

14 The top of a vertical cliff is 50 m
above sea level. From the clifftop,
the angle of depression of a boat
straight out to sea is $15°$. How far
is the boat from the foot of the cliff
(to the nearest metre)?

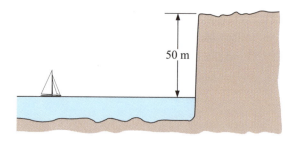

15 If an 11.8 m high tree casts a shadow of length 18.4 m, find the angle of elevation of
the sun.

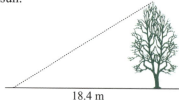

16 A building contractor needs to know the height of
a building. The building casts a 26.2 m shadow
when the angle of elevation of the sun is $64°$.

How high is the building?

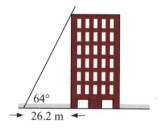

G   BEARINGS

THREE FIGURE BEARINGS

A **bearing** is a direction from one map point to another.

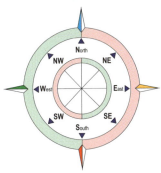

Bearings are measured using **clockwise** rotations from the **true north** direction and so angles between $0°$ and $360°$ are used.

Examples:

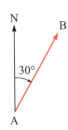   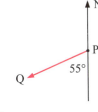   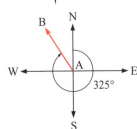

This bearing is represented by $030°$.

This bearing is represented by $240°$.

This bearing is represented by $325°$.

EXERCISE 16G

1   Write the bearing of Q from P in these diagrams which are **not drawn to scale**.

a

b

c

d

e

f

2   This diagram is *not drawn to scale*. Find the bearing of:

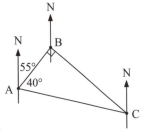

   a   B from A   **b**   A from B

   c   C from A   **d**   A from C

   e   C from B   **f**   B from C

3   For the diagrams in question **1**, find the bearing of P from Q.

Example 16   🔊 **Self Tutor**

A rally driver travels in a direction $145°$ for 28.5 km.
How far east of the starting position is the rally driver?

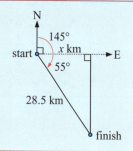

$$\cos 55° = \frac{x}{28.5} \qquad \left\{ \frac{ADJ}{HYP} \right\}$$

$$\therefore \quad \frac{x}{28.5} = \cos 55°$$

$$\therefore \quad x = 28.5 \times \cos 55°$$

$$\therefore \quad x \approx 16.35$$

i.e., the driver is about 16.35 km east.

4 An athlete ran for $2\frac{1}{2}$ hours in a direction $064°$ at
a speed of 14 km h^{-1}.

   a Draw a fully labelled diagram of the situation.

   b Find the distance travelled by the athlete.

   c Find how far east of the starting point the athlete is.

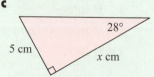

5 A is 40 km due north of B and C is 100 km due east of B.

   a Draw a diagram of the situation.

   b Find the distance between A and C.

   c Find the bearing of C from A.

6 A canoeist paddles due west for 1.5 km. He then
turns due south and covers a further 800 m.

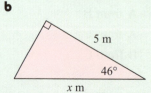

   a Draw a diagram of the situation.

   b How far is he from his starting point?

   c In what direction must he travel to return to his starting point?

LINKS
click here

HOW FAR AWAY IS THE MOON AND HOW LARGE IS IT?

Areas of interaction:
Human ingenuity

REVIEW SET 16A

1 Find the value of x, giving your answer correct to 2 decimal places:

  a 6 cm, 32°, x cm

  b 5 m, 46°, x m

  c 5 cm, 28°, x cm

2 Find, to 2 significant figures, the value of θ:

a

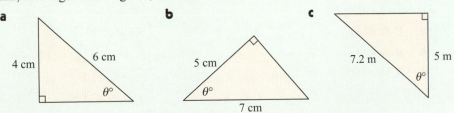

6 cm

4 cm

$\theta°$

b

5 cm

$\theta°$

7 cm

c

7.2 m

5 m

$\theta°$

3 A rectangular gate is 3 m long. The angle between the diagonal support and the bottom of the gate is $18°$.

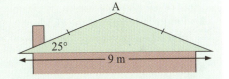

3 m

18°

a How high is the gate?

b How long is the diagonal?

4

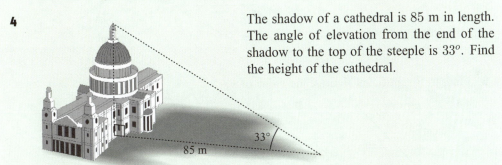

The shadow of a cathedral is 85 m in length. The angle of elevation from the end of the shadow to the top of the steeple is $33°$. Find the height of the cathedral.

33°

85 m

5 The pitch of the roof of a house is the angle between the ceiling and the roof. The pitch of the roof alongside is $25°$. How high is the highest point, A, above the ceiling?

A

25°

9 m

6 For safety reasons, the angle of the loading ramp at the back of a truck must be no greater than $25°$. If the tray of the truck is 1.13 m above the ground, what is the shortest length that the ramp may be?

7 Two cyclists depart from A at the same time. X cycles in a direction $145°$ for two hours at a speed of 42 km per hour. Y cycles due East and at the end of the two hours is directly North of X.

N

145°

A

Y

X

a How far did X travel in 2 hours?

b How far did Y travel in 2 hours?

c Determine the average speed at which Y has travelled.

8 A tree-feller notices that the shadow cast by a tree is 13.2 m when the angle of elevation of the sun is $42°$.

The tree is 12 m from the house. If the tree is cut at ground level and it falls directly towards the house, will it miss the house?

9 This diagram is *not* drawn to scale.

Find the bearing of:

   a P from Q

   b R from Q

   c R from P

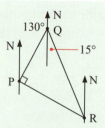

REVIEW SET 16B

1 Find the value of x, giving your answer correct to 2 decimal places:

   a

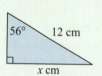

   b

   c

2 Find, to 2 significant figures, the value of θ:

   a

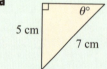

   b

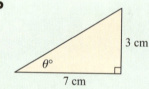

3 Find the length of the shadow cast by a 1.8 m tall boy when the sun is 72° above the horizon.

4 An aeroplane takes off at a constant angle of 22°. When it has flown 500 m, what is its altitude to the nearest metre?

5 A farmer has an isosceles triangle shaped paddock which has equal angles of 62° and a base of 360 m. He decides to divide the paddock in two, with a fence from the apex to the midpoint of the base. Find the length of the new fence.

6 A boat has an anchor rope of length 48 m. Due to the ocean current the boat drifts so that the rope makes an angle of 52° with the surface of the water. Find the depth of the water at the position where the anchor lies on the bottom.

7 Two cars leave point S at the same time. Car X travels due east at 72 km h^{-1}, and car Y travels due north. After an hour the cars are 84.9 km apart.

   a Calculate the average speed of car Y.

   b Find the bearing of Y from X.

8 Three towns P, Q and R are such that Q lies 10.8 km southeast of P and R lies 15.4 km southwest of P.

   a Draw a labelled diagram of the situation.

   b Find the distance from R to Q.

   c Find the bearing of Q from R.

Chapter 17

Coordinates and lines

Contents:

A Plotting points on the Cartesian Plane

B Distance between two points

C Midpoints

D Gradient (or slope)

E Linear relationships

F Linear functions

G Finding equations of straight lines

H Graphing lines

I Points on lines

J Other line forms

K Parallel and perpendicular lines

L Using gradients

OPENING PROBLEM

Joachim and Stefanie live in two towns which are 60 km apart. They decide to meet somewhere between the towns. Stefanie leaves Balen and rides her bike at a constant speed of 18 km h^{-1} towards Herstal. Joachim leaves 30 minutes later from Herstal and rides at a constant speed of 24 km h^{-1} towards Balen.

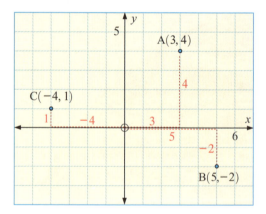

Things to think about:

- Can you write an equation for the distance travelled by each rider in terms of the time variable t hours?
- Can you graph each equation?
- Would each graph be linear?
- What would be the interpretation of the vertical axis intercept in each case?
- If the graphs are linear, what would be your interpretation of their gradients?
- What can be found from the point of intersection of the graphs?
- Can you use the graphs to find how far apart Joachim and Stefanie will be 30 minutes after Joachim has left Herstal?

A   PLOTTING POINTS ON THE CARTESIAN PLANE

To plot the point A(3, 4):
- start at the origin O
- move right along the x-axis 3 units
- then move upwards 4 units.

To plot the point B(5, −2):
- start at the origin O
- move right along the x-axis 5 units
- then move downwards 2 units.

To plot the point C(−4, 1):
- start at the origin O
- move left along the x-axis 4 units
- then move upwards 1 unit.

Note: For A(3, 4) we say that:
3 is the **x-coordinate** of A
4 is the **y-coordinate** of A.

DEMO

The x-coordinate is always given first. It indicates the movement away from the origin in the horizontal direction.

QUADRANTS

The x and y-axes divide the Cartesian plane into four regions referred to as **quadrants**. These quadrants are numbered in an **anti-clockwise direction** as shown alongside.

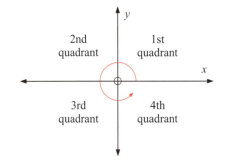

| **Example 1** | ◀》 **Self Tutor** |

Plot the points A(3, 5), B(−1, 4), C(0, −3), D(−3, −2) and E(4, −2) on the same set of axes.

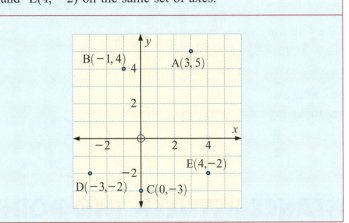

Start at O and move horizontally first, then vertically.
→ is positive
← is negative
↑ is positive
↓ is negative.

EXERCISE 17A

1 State the coordinates of the points J, K, L, M and N:

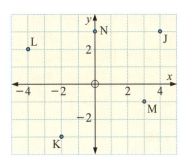

2 On the same set of axes plot the following points:

a P(2, 1)	**b** Q(2, −3)	**c** R(−3, −1)	**d** S(−2, 3)
e T(−4, 0)	**f** U(0, −1)	**g** V(−5, −3)	**h** W(4, −2)

3 State the quadrant in which each of the points in question **2** lies.

Example 2

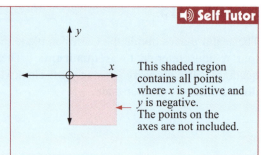

On a Cartesian plane, show all the points with positive x-coordinate and negative y-coordinate.

This shaded region contains all points where x is positive and y is negative. The points on the axes are not included.

4 On different sets of axes show all points with:

a x-coordinate equal to -2 **b** y-coordinate equal to -3

c x-coordinate equal to 0 **d** y-coordinate equal to 0

e negative x-coordinate   **f** positive y-coordinate

g negative x and y-coordinates **h** positive x and negative y-coordinates

5 On separate axes plot the following sets of points:

a $\{(0, 0), (1, -1), (2, -2), (3, -3), (4, -4)\}$

b $\{(-2, 3), (-1, 1), (0, -1), (1, -3), (2, -5)\}$

    i Are the points collinear?

    ii Do any of the following rules fit the set of points?

    A $y = 2x + 1$ **B** $y = 2x - 1$ **C** $y = x$

    D $y = -2x - 1$ **E** $x + y = 0$

B   DISTANCE BETWEEN TWO POINTS

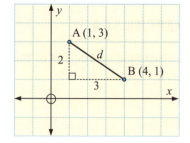

Consider the points A(1, 3) and B(4, 1). We can join the points by a straight line segment of length d units. Suppose we draw a right angled triangle with hypotenuse AB and with sides parallel to the axes.

It is clear that $d^2 = 3^2 + 2^2$ {Pythagoras' Rule}

$\quad\quad \therefore \quad d^2 = 13$

$\quad\quad \therefore \quad d = \sqrt{13}$ {as $d > 0$}

$\therefore$ the distance from A to B is $\sqrt{13}$ units.

EXERCISE 17B

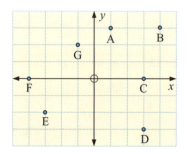

1 If necessary, use Pythagoras' Rule to find the distance between:

a A and B   **b** C and D

c F and C   **d** F and A

e G and F   **f** A and D

g E and G   **h** E and D

2 By plotting points and using Pythagoras' Rule, find the distance between:

    a P(3, 4) and Q(1, 2)   **b** R(0, −3) and S(−2, 0)   **c** T(−2, 6) and U(3, −3)

THE DISTANCE FORMULA

To avoid drawing a diagram each time we wish to find a distance, a **distance formula** can be developed.

Consider the points A(x_1, y_1) and B(x_2, y_2).

In going from A to B, the x-step $= x_2 - x_1$, and

$$y\text{-step} = y_2 - y_1.$$

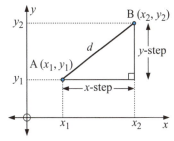

Now, using Pythagoras' Rule,

$$(AB)^2 = (x\text{-step})^2 + (y\text{-step})^2$$

$$\therefore \quad AB = \sqrt{(x\text{-step})^2 + (y\text{-step})^2}$$

$$\therefore \quad d = \sqrt{(x_2 - x_1)^2 + (y_2 - y_1)^2}.$$

If A(x_1, y_1) and B(x_2, y_2) are two points in a plane, then the distance between these points is given by $AB = \sqrt{(x_2 - x_1)^2 + (y_2 - y_1)^2}$

or $d = \sqrt{(x\text{-step})^2 + (y\text{-step})^2}$

Example 3   🔊 **Self Tutor**

Find the distance between A(−2, 1) and B(3, 4).

A(−2, 1) B(3, 4)
   x_1 y_1 x_2 y_2

$$AB = \sqrt{(3 - -2)^2 + (4 - 1)^2}$$
$$= \sqrt{5^2 + 3^2}$$
$$= \sqrt{25 + 9}$$
$$= \sqrt{34} \text{ units}$$

The distance formula saves us having to graph the points each time we want to find a distance.

3 Find the distance between the following pairs of points:

    a A(8, 1) and B(5, 3)   **b** C(−2, 5) and D(6, 5)

    c O(0, 0) and K(−2, 4)   **d** E(8, 0) and F(2, 0)

    e G(0, −3) and H(0, 5)   **f** I(−3, 0) and J(0, −1)

    g R(4, −1) and S(−2, 3)   **h** W(−5, −2) and Z(−3, −3)

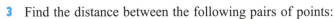

C   MIDPOINTS

If point M is halfway between points A and B
then M is the **midpoint** of AB.

Consider the points A(1, 2) and B(5, 4).

It is clear from the diagram alongside that the midpoint
M of AB is (3, 3).

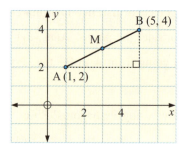

We notice that: $\dfrac{1+5}{2} = 3$ and $\dfrac{2+4}{2} = 3.$

So,   the x-coordinate of M is the *average* of the
       x-coordinates of A and B,

and   the y-coordinate of M is the *average* of the
       y-coordinates of A and B.

In general,   if $A(x_1, y_1)$ and $B(x_2, y_2)$ are two points then the **midpoint** M of
               AB has coordinates

$$\left(\frac{x_1 + x_2}{2}, \ \frac{y_1 + y_2}{2} \right).$$

EXERCISE 17C

1

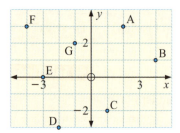

Use this diagram only to find the coordinates
of the midpoint of the line segment:

a	AB	**b**	AF
c	AC	**d**	BC
e	CD	**f**	GF
g	EG	**h**	CB

Example 4   ◀)) **Self Tutor**

Find the coordinates of the midpoint of AB for   A(−1, 3)   and   B(4, 7).

x-coordinate of midpoint	y-coordinate of midpoint
$= \dfrac{-1+4}{2}$	$= \dfrac{3+7}{2}$
$= \dfrac{3}{2}$	$= 5$
$= 1\frac{1}{2}$	

∴   the midpoint of AB is $(1\frac{1}{2}, 5)$

---

2 Find the coordinates of the midpoint of the line segment joining the pairs of points:

   a   (6, 3) and (4, 1)   **b**   (0, −1) and (4, 1)
   c   (−2, 0) and (0, 4)   **d**   (−3, −2) and (−3, 5)
   e   (−1, 4) and (5, 1)   **f**   (6, −2) and (−2, 3)
   g   (1, −4) and (−2, 1)   **h**   (−5, −3) and (−1, 4)

Example 5　　　🔊 **Self Tutor**

M is the midpoint of AB. Find the coordinates of B if A is (1, 3) and M is (4, −2).

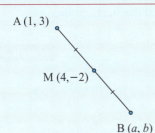

Let B be (a, b)

$\therefore \quad \dfrac{a + 1}{2} = 4 \quad$ and $\quad \dfrac{b + 3}{2} = -2$

$\therefore \quad a + 1 = 8 \quad$ and $\quad b + 3 = -4$

$\therefore \quad a = 7 \quad$ and $\quad b = -7$

i.e., B is $(7, -7)$

3 M is the midpoint of AB. Find the coordinates of B for:

a A(2, 3) and M(−1, 1)
b A(−3, 2) and M(0, 0)
c A(−4, 2) and M(−1, 3)
d A(4, 0) and M(2, −1)
e A(2, −3) and M($\frac{1}{2}$, 0)
f A(5, 1) and M(2, −2)

D　　GRADIENT (OR SLOPE)

When looking at line segments drawn on a set of axes, it is clear that different line segments are inclined to the horizontal at different angles. Some appear to be *steeper* than others.

> The **gradient** or **slope** of a line is a measure of its steepness.

If we choose any two distinct (different) points on the line, the **horizontal step** and **vertical step** between them may be determined.

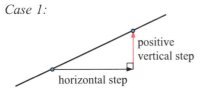

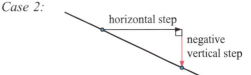

> The **gradient** of a line may be determined by the fraction $\dfrac{\textbf{vertical step}}{\textbf{horizontal step}}$ or $\dfrac{y\textbf{-step}}{x\textbf{-step}}$.

Note: • In *Case 1*, both steps are positive and so the gradient is positive.

• In *Case 2*, the steps are opposite in sign and so the gradient is negative.

Lines like  are forward sloping and have **positive gradients**.

Lines like  are backward sloping and have **negative gradients**.

Have you ever wondered why gradient is measured by y-step divided by x-step rather than x-step divided by y-step?

Perhaps it is because horizontal lines have no gradient and zero (0) should represent this. Also, as lines become steeper we would want their numerical gradients to increase.

Example 6   ◀)) **Self Tutor**

Find the gradient of each line segment:

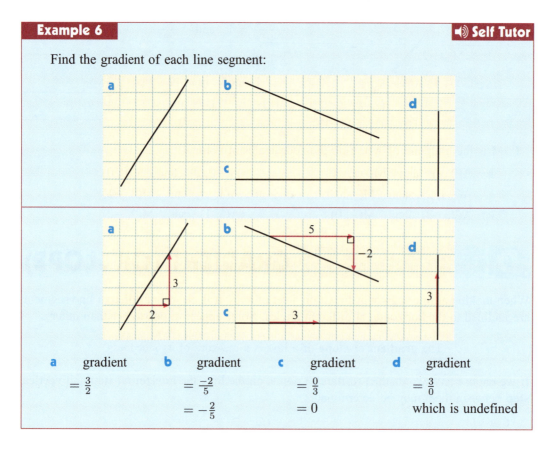

a gradient	**b** gradient	**c** gradient	**d** gradient
$= \frac{3}{2}$	$= \frac{-2}{5}$	$= \frac{0}{3}$	$= \frac{3}{0}$
	$= -\frac{2}{5}$	$= 0$	which is undefined

Note:

- The gradient of a **horizontal** line is **0**, since the vertical step (i.e., the numerator) is 0.
- The gradient of a **vertical** line is **undefined**, since the horizontal step (i.e., the denominator) is 0.

EXERCISE 17D

1 Find the gradient of each line segment:

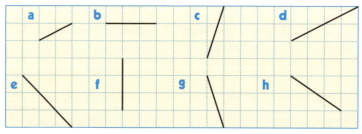

2 On grid paper draw a line segment with gradient:

   a $\frac{2}{3}$ **b** $-\frac{1}{3}$ **c** 3   **d** -2 **e** 0   **f** $-\frac{3}{4}$

THE GRADIENT FORMULA

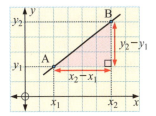

If A is (x_1, y_1) and B is (x_2, y_2) then

the **gradient** of AB is $\dfrac{y_2 - y_1}{x_2 - x_1}$.

Example 7 ◀)) Self Tutor

Find the gradient of the line through $(3, -2)$ and $(6, 4)$.

$(3, -2)$ $(6, 4)$
$\quad x_1 \ y_1 \quad x_2 \ y_2$

$$\text{gradient} = \frac{y_2 - y_1}{x_2 - x_1}$$

$$= \frac{4 - -2}{6 - 3}$$

$$= \frac{6}{3}$$

$$= 2$$

---

3 Find the gradient of the line segment joining the following pairs of points:

    a $(2, 1)$ and $(5, 2)$ **b** $(5, 3)$ and $(2, 2)$

    c $(2, -2)$ and $(4, 1)$ **d** $(7, 2)$ and $(-3, 2)$

    e $(-6, -2)$ and $(-6, -4)$ **f** $(5, -1)$ and $(-3, -3)$

    g $(-5, 4)$ and $(4, 0)$ **h** $(0, -5)$ and $(-2, -3)$

Example 8 ◀)) Self Tutor

Through $(2, 4)$ draw a line with gradient $-\frac{2}{3}$.

Plot the point $(2, 4)$.

$$\text{gradient} = \frac{y\text{-step}}{x\text{-step}} = \frac{-2}{3}$$

$\therefore$ let y-step $= -2$, x-step $= 3$.

Use these steps to find another point and draw the line through these points.

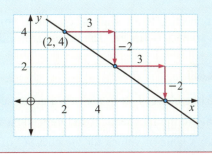

> It is a good idea to use a positive x-step.

---

4 On the same set of axes draw lines through $(1, 3)$ with gradients of $\frac{3}{4}$, $\frac{1}{2}$, 1, 2 and 3.

5 On the same set of axes draw lines through $(-1, 2)$ with gradients of 0, $-\frac{1}{2}$, -1 and -3.

E   LINEAR RELATIONSHIPS

Consider the pattern:

1st	2nd	3rd	4th	etc.

A table of values can be created connecting the diagram number n to the number of points P.

n	1	2	3	4
P	1	3	5	7

It is clear that each new diagram contains *two more* points than the previous one.

The **rule** or **equation** which connects n and P in this example is $P = 2n - 1$.

You can easily check this by **substituting** $n = 1, 2, 3, 4, ...$ etc to find P.

For example, if $n = 4$, $P = 2 \times 4 - 1 = 8 - 1 = 7$ ✓

We say that:
- n is the **independent variable**
- P is the **dependent variable** as its values depend on n.

When we graph relationships like this one:

the *independent variable* is placed on the *horizontal axis* and

the *dependent variable* is placed on the *vertical axis*.

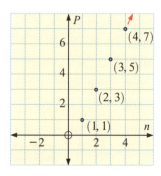

Note:
- If $n = -1$, $P = 2 \times -1 - 1$
$$= -3$$
but $(-1, -3)$ is meaningless for this example. Why?

- If $n = 1\frac{1}{2}$, $P = 2 \times \frac{3}{2} - 1$
$$= 3 - 1$$
$$= 2$$
but $(1\frac{1}{2}, 2)$ is also meaningless. Why?

Can you see why this set of points *should not* be connected by a straight line?

If the graph connecting two variables consists of points on a straight line, then the relationship between the variables is **linear**. The points are said to be **collinear**.

Example 9   ◀) Self Tutor

A taxi driver charges \$3 to pick up a customer and then \$2 per km travelled.

a   What are the independent and dependent variables?

b   Make a table of values for the cost \$$C$ of travelling d km, where $d = 0, 1, 2, ..., 8$.   Plot the graph of C against d.

c   Is the relationship between C and d linear?

d   Is it sensible to join the points graphed with a straight line?

e   For every increase of 1 km for d, what is the change in C?

f   In hiring the taxi, what is   **i**   the fixed cost   **ii**   the variable cost?

g Find the cost of a $6\frac{1}{2}$ km taxi ride.

a The *charge* depends on the *distance travelled*

∴ *distance travelled* is the independent variable and *charge* is the dependent variable.

b Each extra km travelled adds \$2 extra to the charge.

d (km)	0	1	2	3	4	5	6	7	8
C (\$)	3	5	7	9	11	13	15	17	19

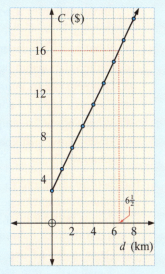

c The points lie in a straight line so the relationship is linear.

d Yes, as costs for distances such as $d = 5.3$ km could be found.

e \$2

f **i**   fixed cost = \$3   (regardless of distance)
    ii variable cost = \$2 per km

g From the table or from the graph, when $d = 6\frac{1}{2}$, $C = 16$, so the cost is \$16.

EXERCISE 17E

1 For a one-day tour, a tour company charges \$200 for the use of a bus, plus \$25 for each passenger.

    a What are the independent and dependent variables?

    b Construct a table and draw a graph of the charge \C against the number of passengers p, where $p = 0, 1, 2, 3, ..., 10$.

    c Is the relationship linear?

    d Is it sensible to join the points with a straight line?

    e For each extra passenger, what will be the increase in charge?

    f **i**   What is the fixed charge?   **ii**   What is the variable charge?

2 150 g blocks of chocolate can be bought for €2.30 each.

    a Copy and complete the table:

Number of blocks n	0	1	2	3	4	5	6	7	8
Cost in euros C									

    b Plot the graph of C against n.

    c What are the independent and dependent variables?

    d Is the relationship between C and n linear?

    e Is it sensible to join the points graphed with a straight line?

    f For each extra block of chocolate bought, what is the change in C?

    g Find the cost of 5 blocks of chocolate.

    h How many blocks of chocolate could be bought for €20.70?

3 Leopold has 25 litres of soup. The customers in his restaurant receive 400 mL of soup in each serve.

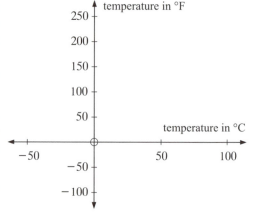

  a Make a table of values for the volume of soup (V litres) remaining after Leopold has served n bowls of soup ($n = 0, 1, 2, ..., 8$), and plot the graph of V against n.

  b What are the independent and dependent variables?

  c Is the relationship between V and n linear?

  d Is it sensible to join the points graphed with a straight line?

  e For each serve of soup, what is the change in V?

  f What volume of soup remains after Leopold has served 7 customers?

  g How many customers have been served soup if there are 21.4 litres of soup remaining?

4 Elizabeth is travelling from London to New York to visit her cousins. She looks at the international weather report and sees that the temperatures are given in degrees Fahrenheit (^{o}F). She is only familiar with degrees Celsius (^{o}C), however, so she needs to know how to convert degrees Fahrenheit into degrees Celsius.

  a Draw a set of axes as shown, using a scale of 1 cm represents 10°C on the horizontal axis and 1 cm represents 20°F on the vertical axis.

  b What are the independent and dependent variables?

  c There is a linear relationship between ^{o}F and ^{o}C. The boiling point of water is 100°C or 212°F. The freezing point of water is 0°C or 32°F.

Mark these points on your graph and join them with a straight line.

  d Extend your graph if necessary to find the point where the number of degrees Celsius equals the same number of degrees Fahrenheit. What is the temperature?

  e Elizabeth saw that the maximum temperatures were:

    i 35°F on Monday   **ii** 25°F on Tuesday.

Convert these temperatures to ^{o}C.

  f Use your graph to copy and complete the following chart:

Temperature ^{o}F					20	10	0
Temperature ^{o}C	10	20	30	40			

F   LINEAR FUNCTIONS

Consider the equation $y = 2x + 1$.

We can choose any value we like for x and use our equation to find the corresponding value for y. The y values depend on the x values, so x is the independent variable and y is the dependent variable.

Table of values:

x	-3	-2	-1	0	1	2	3
y	-5	-3	-1	1	3	5	7

For example, $y = 2 \times -3 + 1$
$= -6 + 1$
$= -5$

For example, $y = 2 \times 2 + 1$
$= 4 + 1$
$= 5$

From this table we plot the points
$(-3, -5)$, $(-2, -3)$, $(-1, -1)$, $(0, 1)$, etc.

The tabled points are collinear and we can connect them with a straight line.

When $x = 1\frac{1}{2}$, $y = 2 \times 1\frac{1}{2} + 1$
$= 3 + 1$
$= 4$

This shows that $(1\frac{1}{2}, 4)$ also lies on the line.

In fact there are infinitely many points which make up the continuous straight line with equation $y = 2x + 1$.

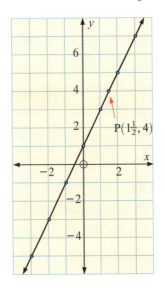

DEMO

Example 10
◀) **Self Tutor**

Consider the equation $y = x - 2$.
a What are the independent and dependent variables?
b Construct a table of values using $x = -3, -2, -1, 0, 1, 2$ and 3.
c Draw the graph of $y = x - 2$.

a x is the independent variable.
y is the dependent variable.

b

x	-3	-2	-1	0	1	2	3
y	-5	-4	-3	-2	-1	0	1

c
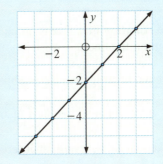

EXERCISE 17F

1 For the following equations:
   i State the independent and dependent variables.
   ii Construct a table of values where the independent variable values are from -3 to 3.
   iii Plot the graph.

a $y = x$	**b** $y = 3x$	**c** $y = \frac{1}{3}x$	**d** $y = -3x$
e $y = 2x + 1$	**f** $y = -2x + 1$	**g** $y = \frac{1}{2}x + 3$	**h** $y = -\frac{1}{2}x + 3$

2 Arrange the graphs **1a**, **1b** and **1c** in order of steepness. What part of the equation controls the degree of steepness of a line?

3 Compare the graphs of **1b** and **1d**. What part of the equation controls whether the graph is forward sloping or backward sloping?

4 Compare the graphs of **1b**, **1e** and **1g**. What part of the equation controls where the graph cuts the y-axis?

INVESTIGATION 1   **GRAPHS OF THE FORM** $y = mx + c$

The use of a graphics calculator or suitable graphing package is recommended for this investigation.

GRAPHING PACKAGE

What to do:

1 On the same set of axes graph the family of lines of the form $y = mx$:

    a where $m = 1, 2, 4, \frac{1}{2}, \frac{1}{5}$ **b** where $m = -1, -2, -4, -\frac{1}{2}, -\frac{1}{5}$

2 What are the slopes of the lines in question **1**?

3 What is your interpretation of m in the equation $y = mx$?

4 On the same set of axes, graph the family of lines of the form $y = 2x + c$ where $c = 0, 2, 4, -1, -3$.

5 What is your interpretation of c for the equation $y = 2x + c$?

G   FINDING EQUATIONS OF STRAIGHT LINES

> The **equation of a line** is an equation which connects the x and y values for every point on the line.

In the above investigation we established that:

> $y = mx + c$ is the equation of a line with gradient m and y-intercept c.

This is known as the **gradient-intercept form**.

For example:

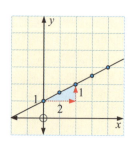

The illustrated line has

$$\text{gradient} = \frac{y\text{-step}}{x\text{-step}} = \frac{1}{2}$$

and the y-intercept is 1

$\therefore$ its equation is $y = \frac{1}{2}x + 1$.

EXERCISE 17G

1 Find the equations of the lines with:

    a gradient 4 and y-intercept -1 **b** gradient 2 and y-intercept 3

    c gradient -3 and y-intercept 0   **d** gradient -5 and y-intercept $\frac{1}{2}$.

2 Find the gradient and y-intercept of each of the following:

    a $y = 2x - 3$ **b** $y = -x$ **c** $y = 6 - x$ **d** $y = \frac{1}{2}x + 1$

    e $2y = 3x$ **f** $x = 2y + 1$ **g** $2x - 3y = 9$ **h** $3x + 4y = 12$

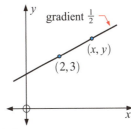

We are not always given both the gradient and y-intercept of a line.

For example, consider the illustrated line which has

gradient $\frac{1}{2}$ and passes through the point $(2, 3)$.

Suppose (x, y) is any point on the line.

The gradient between $(2, 3)$ and (x, y) is $\dfrac{y - 3}{x - 2}$.

Equating gradients gives us $\dfrac{y - 3}{x - 2} = \frac{1}{2}$ {gradient formula}

$$\therefore \quad y - 3 = \tfrac{1}{2}(x - 2) \quad \text{\{multiplying both sides by } (x - 2)\text{\}}$$

$$\therefore \quad y - 3 = \tfrac{1}{2}x - 1 \quad \text{\{expanding the brackets\}}$$

$$\therefore \quad y = \tfrac{1}{2}x + 2 \quad \text{\{adding 3 to both sides\}}$$

Another way of finding the equation is to use the gradient-intercept form $y = mx + c$.

Since $m = \frac{1}{2}$, $y = \frac{1}{2}x + c$

But $(2, 3)$ lies on this line, so $3 = \frac{1}{2}(2) + c$

$$\therefore \quad c = 2 \qquad \text{and we hence find} \quad y = \tfrac{1}{2}x + 2.$$

So,   to find the equation of a line we need to know:

- the **gradient**
- the coordinates of any **point** on the line.

Example 11

🔊 **Self Tutor**

Find the equation of the line with slope $\frac{3}{5}$ which passes through $(-2, 4)$.

Method 1:

Equating gradients,

$$\dfrac{y - 4}{x - (-2)} = \tfrac{3}{5}$$

$$\therefore \quad y - 4 = \tfrac{3}{5}(x + 2)$$

$$\therefore \quad y - 4 = \tfrac{3}{5}x + \tfrac{6}{5}$$

$$\therefore \quad y = \tfrac{3}{5}x + \tfrac{6}{5} + 4$$

$$\therefore \quad y = \tfrac{3}{5}x + 5\tfrac{1}{5}$$

Method 2:

Let the equation be $y = mx + c$

$$\therefore \quad y = \tfrac{3}{5}x + c$$

But $(-2, 4)$ lies on the line

$$\therefore \quad 4 = \tfrac{3}{5}(-2) + c$$

$$\therefore \quad 4 + \tfrac{6}{5} = c$$

$$\therefore \quad c = 5\tfrac{1}{5}$$

$$\therefore \quad \text{the equation is} \quad y = \tfrac{3}{5}x + 5\tfrac{1}{5}$$

3 Find the equation of the line through:

   a $(1, -2)$ having a gradient of 3 **b** $(-4, -1)$ having a gradient of -2

   c $(5, -2)$ having a gradient of -3 **d** $(5, 2)$ having a gradient of $\frac{1}{3}$

   e $(-2, 8)$ having a gradient of $-\frac{1}{4}$ **f** $(7, -3)$ having a gradient of 0

   g $(1, 6)$ with gradient $\frac{2}{3}$ **h** $(-5, 4)$ with gradient $\frac{3}{5}$

   i $(8, 0)$ with gradient $-\frac{1}{4}$ **j** $(8, -2)$ with gradient $-\frac{3}{4}$

   k $(-2, -4)$ with gradient 3 **l** $(5, -1)$ with gradient -5

Example 12   ◀)) Self Tutor

Find the equation of the line which passes through the points A$(-1, 5)$ and B$(2, 3)$.

The gradient of the line is $\dfrac{3-5}{2-(-1)} = \dfrac{-2}{3}$

$\therefore$ using point A the equation is $\dfrac{y-5}{x-(-1)} = -\dfrac{2}{3}$ {or $\dfrac{y-3}{x-2} = -\dfrac{2}{3}$

$\therefore$ $y - 5 = -\dfrac{2}{3}(x+1)$ using point B}

$\therefore$ $y - 5 = -\dfrac{2}{3}x - \dfrac{2}{3}$

$\therefore$ $y = -\dfrac{2}{3}x + 5 - \dfrac{2}{3}$

$\therefore$ $y = -\dfrac{2}{3}x + 4\dfrac{1}{3}$

> Check that you get the same final answer using point B instead of A.

---

4 Find the equation of the line which passes through the points:

   a   A$(1, 5)$ and   B$(3, 7)$ **b**   C$(0, 4)$ and   D$(-2, 3)$

   c   E$(-3, -2)$ and   F$(5, -2)$ **d**   G$(-3, 3)$ and   H$(6, 0)$

   e   P$(4, -1)$ and   Q$(-1, -2)$ **f**   R$(-2, -3)$ and   S$(-5, -6)$

5 Find the equation of the line:

   a   which has gradient $\frac{1}{2}$ and cuts the y-axis at 3

   b   which is parallel to a line with gradient 2, and passes through the point $(-1, 4)$

   c   which cuts the x-axis at 5 and the y-axis at -2

   d   which cuts the x axis at -1, and passes through $(-3, 4)$

FINDING THE GRADIENT FROM THE EQUATION OF THE LINE

From equations of lines such as $y = \frac{1}{3}x + \frac{2}{3}$ and $y = 5 - 2x$,   we can easily find the gradient by looking at the coefficient of x.

However, some lines may be given in the form $Ax + By = C$,   called **general form**. We can rearrange equations in general form to find the gradient.

Example 13   ◀») **Self Tutor**

Find the gradient of the line $2x + 5y = 17$.

$2x + 5y = 17$

$\therefore \quad 5y = 17 - 2x$ {subtracting $2x$ from both sides}

$\therefore \quad y = \dfrac{17}{5} - \dfrac{2x}{5}$ {dividing both sides by 5}

$\therefore \quad y = -\tfrac{2}{5}x + \tfrac{17}{5}$ and so the gradient is $-\tfrac{2}{5}$.

6 Find the gradient of the line with equation:

   a $y = 4x + 5$
   b $y = 1 - 3x$
   c $y = 0$

   d $x = 2$
   e $y = \dfrac{4x - 5}{3}$
   f $6x + y = 4$

   g $4x - 5y = 3$
   h $4x + 5y = 4$
   i $6x - 2y = 1$

   j $3x + 4y = 7$
   k $Ax - By = C$
   l $Ax + By = C$

EQUATIONS FROM GRAPHS

If a graph contains sufficient information then we can determine its equation.

Remember that we must have at least one point and we must be able to determine its gradient.

Example 14   ◀») **Self Tutor**

Find the equation (in gradient-intercept form) of the line with graph:

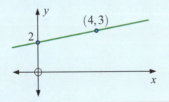

Two points on the line are $(0, 2)$ and $(4, 3)$.

$\therefore$ gradient $m = \dfrac{3 - 2}{4 - 0} = \tfrac{1}{4}$

and the y-intercept $c = 2$

$\therefore$ the equation is $y = \tfrac{1}{4}x + 2$.

Example 15   ◀») **Self Tutor**

Find the equation of the line with graph:

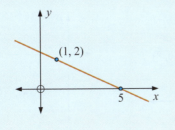

Two points on the line are $(1, 2)$ and $(5, 0)$.

$\therefore$ gradient $m = \dfrac{0 - 2}{5 - 1} = \dfrac{-2}{4} = \dfrac{-1}{2}$

As we do not know the y-intercept we equate

gradients: $\dfrac{y - 2}{x - 1} = -\tfrac{1}{2}$

$\therefore \quad y - 2 = -\tfrac{1}{2}(x - 1)$

$\therefore \quad y = -\tfrac{1}{2}x + \tfrac{1}{2} + 2$

$\therefore \quad y = -\tfrac{1}{2}x + 2\tfrac{1}{2}$

7 Find the equations of the illustrated lines:

a
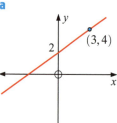

b
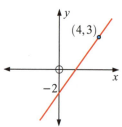

c
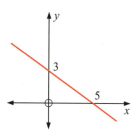

d
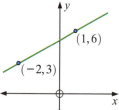

e
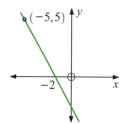

f
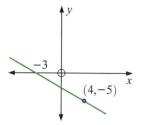

Example 16   ◄)) **Self Tutor**

Find the equation connecting the variables in:

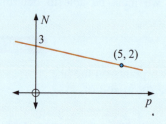

(0, 3) and (5, 2) lie on the straight line.

∴   gradient $m = \dfrac{2-3}{5-0} = -\dfrac{1}{5}$

and the Y-intercept is $c = 3$.

The equation is of the form $Y = mX + c$
where N is on the Y-axis and p is on the
X-axis.

The equation is $N = -\dfrac{1}{5}p + 3$.

---

8 Find the equation connecting the variables given:

a
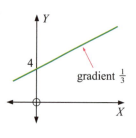

b
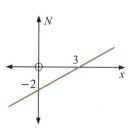

c
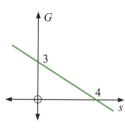

d
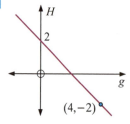

e
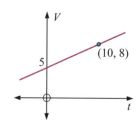

f
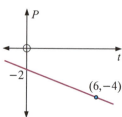

GRAPHING LINES

It is useful to be able to accurately graph straight lines from their equations.

GRAPHING FROM THE GRADIENT-INTERCEPT FORM

Lines with equations given in the gradient-intercept form are easily graphed by finding two points on the graph, one of which is the y-intercept.

The other can be found by substitution or using the gradient.

Example 17   ◀)) **Self Tutor**

Graph the line with equation $y = \frac{1}{3}x + 2$.

Method 1:

The y-intercept is 2.

When $x = 3$, $y = 1 + 2 = 3$.

$\therefore$ (0, 2) and (3, 3) lie on the line.

Method 2:

The y-intercept is 2 and the gradient $= \frac{1}{3}$ ◀— y-step / ◀— x-step

So, we start at (0, 2) and move to another point by moving across 3, then up 1.

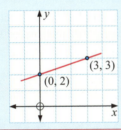

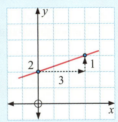

EXERCISE 17H

1 Draw the graph of the line with equation:

  a $y = 2x + 3$ **b** $y = \frac{1}{2}x - 3$ **c** $y = -x + 5$

  d $y = -4x - 2$ **e** $y = -\frac{1}{3}x$ **f** $y = -3x + 4$

  g $y = \frac{3}{4}x$ **h** $y = \frac{1}{3}x - 1$ **i** $y = -\frac{3}{2}x + 2$

2   **a**   The line with equation $y = 2x - 1$ is reflected in the x-axis. Graph the line and draw its image. Find the equation of the reflected line.

    b   The line with equation $y = \frac{1}{2}x + 2$ is reflected in the y-axis. Graph the line and draw its image. Find the equation of the reflected line.

GRAPHING FROM THE GENERAL FORM

Remember that the form $Ax + By = C$ is called the **general form** of a line.

The easiest way to graph lines in general form is to use axes intercepts.

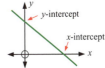

> The x-intercept is found by letting $y = 0$.
> The y-intercept is found by letting $x = 0$.

Example 18   ◀)) **Self Tutor**

Graph the line with equation $2x - 3y = 12$ using axes intercepts.

For $2x - 3y = 12$:

when $x = 0$, $-3y = 12$

                  $\therefore \quad y = -4$

when $y = 0$, $2x = 12$

                  $\therefore \quad x = 6$

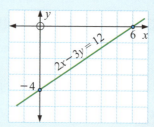

3 Use axes intercepts to draw sketch graphs of:

a	$2x + y = 4$	**b**	$3x + y = 6$	**c**	$3x - 2y = 12$
d	$3x + 4y = 12$	**e**	$x - y = 2$	**f**	$x + y = -2$
g	$2x - 3y = -9$	**h**	$4x + 5y = 20$	**i**	$5x - 2y = -10$

4 a i Graph the line with equation $3x + 2y = 1$ and show that $(-1, 2)$ lies on it.

  ii If the line with equation $3x + 2y = 1$ is rotated clockwise about the point $(-1, 2)$ through an angle of $90°$, find the equation of the rotated line.

  b Graph the line with equation $3x - 5y = 15$. If the line is rotated anticlockwise about the origin through an angle of $180°$, find the equation of this new line.

I   POINTS ON LINES

A point lies on a line if its coordinates satisfy the equation of the line.

This is a very basic and important concept, but is often overlooked or forgotten.

For example: $(2, 3)$ lies on the line $3x + 4y = 18$ as $3 \times 2 + 4 \times 3 = 6 + 12 = 18$ ✓

                $(4, 1)$ does not lie on the line as $3 \times 4 + 4 \times 1 = 12 + 4 = 16$.

EXERCISE 17I

> To satisfy an equation is to make the equation true for a given substitution.

1 a Does $(3, 4)$ lie on the line with equation $5x + 2y = 23$?

  b Does $(-1, 4)$ lie on the line with equation $3x - 2y = 11$?

  c Does $(5, -\frac{1}{2})$ lie on the line with equation $3x + 8y = 11$?

2 Find k if:

  a $(2, 5)$ lies on the line with equation $3x - 2y = k$

  b $(-1, 3)$ lies on the line with equation $5x + 2y = k$.

3 Find a given that:

    a $(a, 3)$ lies on the line with equation $\quad y = 2x - 11$

    b $(a, -5)$ lies on the line with equation $\quad y = 4 - x$

    c $(4, a)$ lies on the line with equation $\quad y = \frac{1}{2}x + 3$

    d $(-2, a)$ lies on the line with equation $\quad y = 4 - 2x$.

J | OTHER LINE FORMS

TWO SPECIAL CASES (HORIZONTAL AND VERTICAL LINES)

Lines parallel to the x-axis and lines parallel to the y-axis are special cases. If their equations are written in general form, then the coefficient of either x or y is zero.

INVESTIGATION 2   **SPECIAL LINES**

What to do:

1 Using graph paper, plot the following sets of points on the Cartesian plane. Rule a line through each set of points.

    a $(3, 4)$, $(3, 2)$, $(3, 0)$, $(3, -2)$, $(3, -4)$

    b $(6, -1)$, $(6, -3)$, $(6, 1)$, $(6, 5)$, $(6, 3)$

    c $(0, -5)$, $(0, -2)$, $(0, 1)$, $(0, 4)$, $(0, -3)$

    d $(-3, -1)$, $(5, -1)$, $(-1, -1)$, $(4, -1)$, $(0, -1)$

    e $(-2, 6)$, $(-2, -3)$, $(-2, 0)$, $(-2, -2)$, $(-2, 2)$

    f $(4, 0)$, $(0, 0)$, $(7, 0)$, $(-1, 0)$, $(-3, 0)$

2 Can you state the gradient of each line? If so, what is it?

3 Can you state the y-intercept of each line? If so, what is it?

4 How are these lines different from other lines previously studied?

5 Can you state the equation of each line?

VERTICAL LINES

The vertical line $\quad x = a \quad$ (where a is a constant) is one such special line.

A sketch of the vertical lines $x = -2$ and $x = 1$ is shown alongside.

For all points on a vertical line, regardless of the value of the y-coordinate, the value of the x-coordinate is always the same.

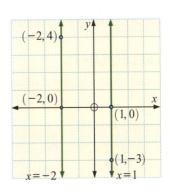

All **vertical** lines have equations of the form $x = a$.

The gradient of a vertical line is **undefined**.

HORIZONTAL LINES

The horizontal line $y = b$ (where b is a constant) is the other special line.

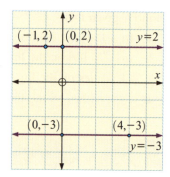

A sketch of the horizontal lines $y = -3$ and $y = 2$ is shown alongside.

For all points on a horizontal line, regardless of the value of the x-coordinate, the value of the y-coordinate is always the same.

All **horizontal** lines have equations of the form $y = b$.
The gradient of a horizontal line is **zero**.

EXERCISE 17J

1 Identify as either a vertical or horizontal line and hence plot the graph of:

   a $y = 6$ **b** $x = -3$ **c** $x = 2$ **d** $y = -4$

2 Identify as either a vertical or horizontal line:

   a a line with zero gradient   **b** a line with undefined gradient

3 Find the equation of:

   a the x-axis   **b** the y-axis

   c a line parallel to the x-axis and three units below it

   d a line parallel to the y-axis and 4 units to the right of it

4 Find the equation of:

   a the line with zero gradient that passes through $(-1, 3)$

   b the line with undefined gradient that passes through $(4, -2)$.

K PARALLEL AND PERPENDICULAR LINES

PARALLEL LINES

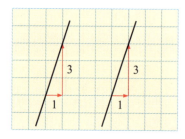

Notice that the given lines are parallel and both of them have a gradient or slope of 3.

In fact:

- if two lines are **parallel**, then they have **equal gradient**, and

- if two lines have **equal gradient**, then they are **parallel**.

PERPENDICULAR LINES

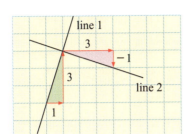

Notice that *line 1* and *line 2* are perpendicular.

Line 1 has gradient $\frac{3}{1} = 3$

Line 2 has gradient $\frac{-1}{3} = -\frac{1}{3}$

We see that the gradients are *negative reciprocals* of each other and their product is $3 \times -\frac{1}{3} = -1$.

For lines which are not horizontal or vertical:

- if the lines are **perpendicular** then their gradients are **negative reciprocals**
- if the gradients are **negative reciprocals** then the lines are **perpendicular**.

The negative reciprocal of $\frac{b}{a}$ is $-\frac{a}{b}$

Example 19   ◀ Self Tutor

If a line has gradient $\frac{2}{3}$, find the gradient of:

a all lines parallel to the given line

b all lines perpendicular to the given line.

a Since the original line has gradient $\frac{2}{3}$, the gradient of all parallel lines is also $\frac{2}{3}$.

b The gradient of all perpendicular lines is $-\frac{3}{2}$.   {the negative reciprocal}

EXERCISE 17K

1 Find the gradient of all lines perpendicular to a line with a gradient of:

a $\frac{1}{2}$ **b** $\frac{2}{5}$ **c** 3 **d** 7

e $-\frac{2}{5}$ **f** $-2\frac{1}{3}$ **g** -5 **h** -1

2 The gradients of two lines are listed below. Which of the line pairs are perpendicular?

a $\frac{1}{3},\ 3$ **b** $5,\ -5$ **c** $\frac{3}{7},\ -2\frac{1}{3}$ **d** $4,\ -\frac{1}{4}$

e $6,\ -\frac{5}{6}$ **f** $\frac{2}{3},\ -\frac{3}{2}$ **g** $\frac{p}{q},\ \frac{q}{p}$ **h** $\frac{a}{b},\ -\frac{b}{a}$

Example 20   ◄◎ Self Tutor

Find a given that the line joining A(2, 3) to B(a, −1) is parallel to a line
with gradient −2.

$$\text{gradient of AB} = -2 \qquad \{\text{parallel lines have equal gradient}\}$$

$$\therefore \quad \frac{-1-3}{a-2} = -2 \qquad \{\text{gradient formula}\}$$

$$\therefore \quad \frac{-4}{a-2} = \frac{-2}{1}$$

$$\therefore \quad \frac{-4}{a-2} = \frac{-2}{1}\left(\frac{a-2}{a-2}\right) \qquad \{\text{achieving a common denominator}\}$$

$$\therefore \quad -4 = -2(a-2) \qquad \{\text{equating numerators}\}$$

$$\therefore \quad -4 = -2a + 4$$

$$\therefore \quad 2a = 8$$

$$\therefore \quad a = 4$$

3 Find a given that the line joining:

   a A(−1, 5)   to   B(3, a)   is parallel to a line with gradient 2

   b C(a, −4)   to   D(5, −1)   is parallel to a line with gradient $\frac{1}{3}$

   c E(2, a)   to   F(a, 1)   is parallel to a line with gradient $\frac{2}{5}$.

Example 21   ◄◎ Self Tutor

Find t given that the line joining D(−1, −3) to C(1, t) is perpendicular to a line
with gradient 2.

$$\text{gradient of DC} = -\tfrac{1}{2} \qquad \{\text{perpendicular to line of gradient 2}\}$$

$$\therefore \quad \frac{t--3}{1--1} = -\tfrac{1}{2} \qquad \{\text{equating gradients}\}$$

$$\therefore \quad \frac{t+3}{2} = \frac{-1}{2} \qquad \{\text{simplifying}\}$$

$$\therefore \quad t+3 = -1 \qquad \{\text{equating numerators}\}$$

$$\therefore \quad t = -4$$

4 Find t given that the line joining:

   a A(2, −4)   to   B(−3, t)   is perpendicular to a line with gradient $1\frac{1}{4}$

   b C(t, −2)   to   D(1, 4)   is perpendicular to a line with gradient $\frac{2}{3}$

   c P(t, −2)   to   Q(1, t)   is perpendicular to a line with gradient $-\frac{1}{4}$.

5 Given the points   A(1, 4),   B(−1, 0),   C(6, 3)   and   D(t, −1),   find t if:

   a   AB is parallel to CD   **b**   AC is parallel to DB

   c   AB is perpendicular to CD   **d**   AD is perpendicular to BC

L   USING GRADIENTS

In real life gradients occur in many situations, and can be interpreted in a variety of ways.

For example, the sign alongside would indicate to motor vehicle drivers that there is an uphill climb ahead.

Consider the situation in the graph alongside where a motor vehicle travels at a constant speed for a distance of 600 km in 8 hours.

Clearly, the gradient of the line $= \dfrac{\text{vertical step}}{\text{horizontal step}}$

$$= \frac{600}{8}$$

$$= 75$$

However,   speed $= \dfrac{\text{distance}}{\text{time}} = \dfrac{600 \text{ km}}{8 \text{ hours}} = 75 \text{ km h}^{-1}.$

So, in a graph of distance against time, the *gradient* can be interpreted as the *speed*.

In the following exercise we will consider a number of problems where gradient can be interpreted as a rate.

EXERCISE 17L

1

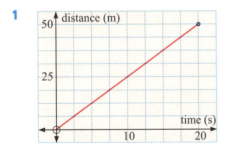

The graph alongside indicates the distances and corresponding times as Inge swims freestyle over 50 metres.

   a   Find the gradient of the line.

   b   Interpret the gradient found in **a**.

   c   Is the speed of the swimmer constant or variable? What evidence do you have for your answer?

2 The graph alongside indicates the distances travelled by a train. Determine:

   a   the average speed for the whole trip

   b   the average speed from

       i A to B   **ii** B to C

   c   the time interval over which the speed was greatest.

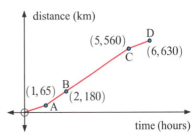

3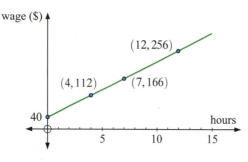

The graph alongside indicates the wages paid to taxi drivers.

a What does the intercept on the vertical axis mean?

b Find the gradient of the line. What does this gradient mean?

c Determine the wage for working:
  i 6 hours   **ii** 15 hours.

d If no payment is made for not working, but the same payment shown in the graph is made for 8 hours' work, what is the new rate of pay?

4 The graphs alongside indicate the fuel consumption and distance travelled at speeds of 60 km h^{-1} (graph A) and 90 km h^{-1} (graph B).

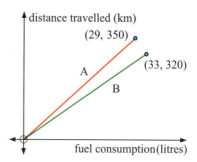

a Find the gradient of each line.

b What do these slopes mean?

c If fuel costs $1.24 per litre, how much more would it cost to travel 1000 km at 90 km h^{-1} compared with 60 km h^{-1}?

5 The graph alongside indicates the courier charge for different distances travelled.

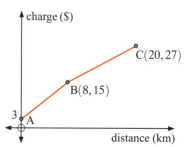

a What does the value at A indicate?

b Find the gradients of the line segments AB and BC. What do these gradients indicate?

c If a straight line segment was drawn from A to C, find its gradient. What would this gradient mean?

REVIEW SET 17A

1 Plot the following points on the number plane:
  A(1, 3)   B(−2, 0)   C(−2, −3)   D(2, −1)

2 Find the distance between the following sets of points:
  a   P(4, 0) and Q(0, −3)   **b**   R(2, −5) and S(−1, −3)

3 Find the coordinates of the midpoint of the line segment joining A(8, −3) and B(2, 1).

4 Find the gradients of the lines in the following graphs:

  a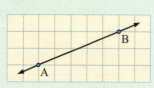

  b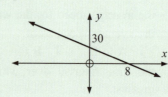

5 A company manufactures saws. The set-up costs for the plant and machinery are $2000. The total cost $C to produce x saws is given by $C = 2000 + 4x$ dollars.

    a What are the independent and dependent variables?

    b Make a table of values for the cost $C of producing x saws, where $x = 0$, 100, 200, 300, 400, and plot the graph of C against x.

    c Is the relationship linear?

    d What does the value of C when $x = 0$ represent?

    e What will it cost to make 650 saws?

6 For the rule $y = 3x + 2$:

x	0	1	2	3	4
y					

    a copy and complete the table

    b plot the points on the table and draw a straight line through them.

7 Find the equation of the line with gradient -2 and y-intercept 3.

8 Find the gradient and y-intercept of the line $x = 1 - 3y$.

9 Find the equation of the line with gradient $\frac{2}{3}$ which passes through $(-3, 4)$.

10 Use axes intercepts to draw a sketch graph of $3x - 2y = 6$.

11 Find k if $(-3, -1)$ lies on the line $4x - y = k$.

12 Find the equation of the line with zero gradient that passes through $(5, -4)$.

13 Find t given that the line joining A(3, 4) and B(1, t) is parallel to a line with gradient $\frac{3}{5}$.

14 The graph alongside shows the distance travelled by a train over a 2 hour journey between two cities.

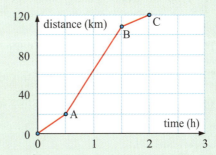

    a Find the average speed from:

        i O to A   **ii** A to B

        iii B to C

    b Compare your answers to **a** with the gradients of the line segments:

        i OA   **ii** AB   **iii** BC

    c Find the average speed for the whole journey.

REVIEW SET 17B

1 On different sets of axes, show all points with:

    a x-coordinates equal to -3 **b** y-coordinates equal to 5

    c positive x-coordinates and negative y-coordinates

2 Find the distance between V$(-5, -3)$ and W$(-2, 6)$.

3 If M(1, -1) is the midpoint of AB, and A is $(-3, 2)$, find the coordinates of B.

4 Find the gradient of the line segment joining:

    a $(5, -1)$ and $(-2, 6)$ **b** $(5, 0)$ and $(5, -2)$

5 Jacques sells vacuum cleaners. Each week he is paid a basic salary of €150 plus €25 for each vacuum cleaner that he sells.

    a What are the independent and dependent variables?

    b Construct a table and draw a graph of income I against vacuum cleaners sold v, where $v = 0, 1, 2, 3, \ ..... \ 8$.

    c Is the relationship linear?

    d Is it sensible to join the points with a straight line?

    e For each vacuum sold, what will be the increase in income?

    f **i** What is the fixed income?   **ii** What is the variable income?

    g Find Jacques' income in a week when he sells 5 vacuum cleaners.

6 From a table of values, plot the graph of the line with equation $y = \frac{1}{2}x - 1$.

7 Find the equations of the following graphs:

    a 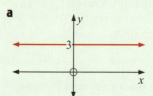   **b**    **c**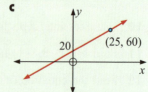

8 Find the equation of the line with gradient 4 and y-intercept -2.

9 Find the gradient and y-intercept of the line with equation:

    a $y = 5x - 7$ **b** $y = 6 - \frac{3}{2}x$ **c** $y = 10x$

10 Find the gradient of the line with equation $4x + 3y = 5$.

11 Find the equation of the line through $(1, -5)$ with gradient $\frac{1}{3}$.

12 **a** Find the gradient of the line with equation $y = 2x - 3$.

    b Find the equation of the line perpendicular to $y = 2x - 3$ which passes through $(4, 1)$.

13 The graph alongside shows the amount charged by a plumber according to the time he takes to do a job.

    a What does the value at A indicate?

    b Find the gradients of the line segments AB and BC. What do these gradients indicate?

    c If a straight line segment was drawn from A to C, what would be its gradient? What would this gradient mean?

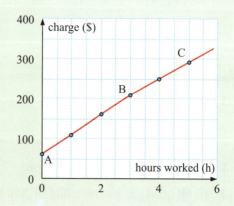

Chapter 18

Simultaneous linear equations

Contents:

A The point of intersection of linear graphs

B Simultaneous equations

C Algebraic methods for solving simultaneous equations

D Problem solving

E Using a graphics calculator to solve simultaneous equations

OPENING PROBLEM

A farmer has only hens and pigs in an enclosure. He said to his daughter Susan, "You know we have only hens and pigs. I counted 48 heads altogether and 122 legs. Can you tell me how many of each animal type we have?"

It was too dark for Susan to go out and count them, but she thought for a while and gave the correct answer. What answer did she obtain, and how did she do it?

Doing the work in this chapter should make it easier for you to solve this and other similar problems.

Let us consider the graphs of two straight lines which are not parallel. These lines will meet somewhere. The point where they meet is called the **point of intersection**.

Notice that the point of intersection is the only point common to both lines.

If (a, b) is the point of intersection then (a, b) satisfies the equations of both lines.

point of intersection

At the point of intersection we have the **simultaneous solution** of **both equations**, since this point *satisfies both equations at the same time*.

Note that not all line pairs meet at one point. Two other situations can occur:

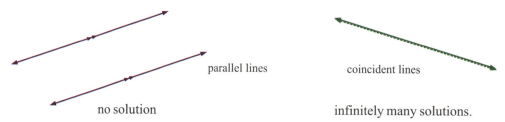

parallel lines   coincident lines

no solution   infinitely many solutions.

A   THE POINT OF INTERSECTION OF LINEAR GRAPHS

Example 1

 Self Tutor

Find the point of intersection of the lines with equations $y = 2x + 5$ and $y = -x - 1$.

For $y = 2x + 5$:

when $x = 0$, $y = 5$

when $y = 0$, $2x + 5 = 0$

$\therefore$ $2x = -5$

$\therefore$ $x = -\frac{5}{2}$

$\therefore$ $(0, 5)$ and $(-\frac{5}{2}, 0)$ lie on the graph.

For $y = -x - 1$:

when $x = 0$, $y = -1$

when $y = 0$, $-x - 1 = 0$

$\therefore$ $x = -1$

$\therefore$ $(0, -1)$ and $(-1, 0)$ lie on the graph.

$\therefore$ the graphs meet at the point $(-2, 1)$.

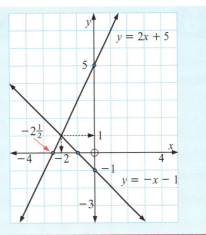

EXERCISE 18A

1 Find the point of intersection of the following pairs of lines by drawing the graphs of the two lines on the same set of axes:

a $y = x$
$y = 4 - x$

b $y = x - 4$
$y = -3x$

c $y = 2x + 3$
$y = x + 3$

d $y = -3x + 1$
$y = -x - 1$

e $y = 5 - 2x$
$y = x - 1$

f $y = -5x - 3$
$y = -2x + 3$

2 Find the simultaneous solution of the following pairs of equations using graphical methods:

a $y = x - 2$
$y = 3x + 6$

b $y = x + 1$
$y = 7 - x$

c $y = 5 - x$
$y = x + 4$

d $y = -x - 2$
$y = 6x - 9$

e $y = 3x + 2$
$y = 2x + 3$

f $y = 5x + 1$
$y = 2x - 5$

B   SIMULTANEOUS EQUATIONS

If we have two equations and we wish to make both equations true at the same time, we require values for the variables which satisfy both equations. These values are the **simultaneous solution** to the pair of equations.

In this course we will consider linear simultaneous equations containing two unknowns. There are infinitely many points (x, y) which satisfy the first equation. Likewise, there are infinitely many points which satisfy the second equation. In general, however, only one point satisfies both equations at the same time.

For example, consider the simultaneous equations $\begin{cases} x + y = 9 \\ 2x + 3y = 21 \end{cases}$.

If $x = 6$ and $y = 3$ then:

- $x + y = (6) + (3) = 9$ ✓   i.e., the first equation is satisfied
- $2x + 3y = 2(6) + 3(3) = 12 + 9 = 21$ ✓   i.e., the second equation is satisfied.

So, $x = 6$ and $y = 3$ is the **solution** to the simultaneous equations $\begin{cases} x + y = 9 \\ 2x + 3y = 21 \end{cases}$.

The solutions to **linear simultaneous equations** can be found by **trial and error**, but this can be quite tedious. They may also be found **graphically** as in **Section A**, but this can be slow and also inaccurate if the solutions are not integers.

We thus consider an **algebraic** method for finding the simultaneous solution.

Example 2   ◀) **Self Tutor**

Find the simultaneous solution to the following pair of equations:
$$y = 2x - 1, \quad y = x + 3$$

If $y = 2x - 1$ and $y = x + 3$, then

$$2x - 1 = x + 3 \qquad \{\text{equating } y\text{'s}\}$$
$$\therefore \quad 2x - 1 - x = x + 3 - x \qquad \{\text{subtract } x \text{ from both sides}\}$$
$$\therefore \quad x - 1 = 3 \qquad \{\text{simplify}\}$$
$$\therefore \quad x = 4 \qquad \{\text{add 1 to both sides}\}$$
$$\text{and so} \quad y = 4 + 3 \qquad \{\text{using } y = x + 3\}$$
$$\therefore \quad y = 7$$

So, the simultaneous solution is $x = 4$ and $y = 7$.

Check: In $y = 2x - 1$, $y = 2 \times 4 - 1 = 8 - 1 = 7$ ✓

In $y = x + 3$, $y = 4 + 3 = 7$ ✓

Always check your solution in both equations.

EXERCISE 18B

1 Find the simultaneous solution to the following pairs of equations using an algebraic method:

a $y = x - 2$
$y = 3x + 6$

b $y = x + 2$
$y = 2x - 3$

c $y = 6x - 6$
$y = x + 4$

d $y = 2x + 1$
$y = x - 3$

e $y = 5x + 2$
$y = 3x - 2$

f $y = 3x - 7$
$y = 3x - 2$

g $y = 3x + 2$
$y = 2x + 3$

h $y = 3x + 1$
$y = 3x + 5$

i $y = 5x - 2$
$y = 10x - 4$

Example 3
◀)) **Self Tutor**

Find the point of intersection of the two lines $y = 2x + 5$ and $y = -x - 1$.

The lines meet when

$2x + 5 = -x - 1$ {equating y's}

∴ $2x + 5 + x = -x - 1 + x$ {add x}

∴ $3x + 5 - 5 = -1 - 5$ {subtract 5 from both sides}

∴ $3x = -6$ {collect like terms}

∴ $x = -2$ {divide both sides by 3}

Thus, $y = 2 \times (-2) + 5$ {using $y = 2x + 5$}

∴ $y = -4 + 5$

∴ $y = 1$ So, the lines meet at $(-2, 1)$.

2 Use an algebraic method to find the point of intersection of:

a $y = x + 4$
$y = 5 - x$

b $y = x + 1$
$y = 7 - x$

c $y = 2x - 5$
$y = 3 - 2x$

d $y = x - 4$
$y = -2x - 4$

e $y = 3x + 2$
$y = -2x - 3$

f $y = 4x + 6$
$y = 6 - 2x$

INVESTIGATION 2   THE COINS PROBLEM

In my pocket I have 8 coins. They are $1 and $2 coins, and their total value is $11.

How many of each type of coin do I have?

What to do:

1 Copy and complete the following table:

Number of $1 coins	0	1	2	3	4	5	6	7	8
Value of $1 coins									
Number of $2 coins	8	7							
Value of $2 coins									
Total value of coins									

2   Use the table to find the solution to the problem.

3   Suppose I have x \$1 coins and y \$2 coins in my pocket.

    a   By considering the total number of coins, explain why $x + y = 8$.

    b   By considering the total value of the coins, explain why $x + 2y = 11$.

4   You should have found that there were five \$1 coins and three \$2 coins.

    a   Substitute $x = 5$ and $y = 3$ into $x + y = 8$.   What do you notice?

    b   Substitute $x = 5$ and $y = 3$ into $x + 2y = 11$.   What do you notice?

5   My friend has 12 coins in her pocket. They are all either £1 or £2. If the total value of her coins is £17, how many of each type does she have? Can you find the solution by algebraic means?

C   ALGEBRAIC METHODS FOR SOLVING SIMULTANEOUS EQUATIONS

SOLUTION BY SUBSTITUTION

The method of **solution by substitution** is used when at least one equation is given with either x or y as the **subject** of the formula, or if it is easy to make x or y the subject.

Example 4   ◀))) **Self Tutor**

Solve simultaneously, by substitution: $y = 9 - x$

                                        $2x + 3y = 21$

> We substitute $9 - x$ for y in the other equation.

$$y = 9 - x \quad \text{...... (1)}$$
$$2x + 3y = 21 \quad \text{...... (2)}$$

Since $y = 9 - x$,   then $2x + 3(9 - x) = 21$

$$\therefore \quad 2x + 27 - 3x = 21$$
$$\therefore \quad 27 - x = 21$$
$$\therefore \quad x = 6$$

When $x = 6$, $y = 9 - 6$ {substituting $x = 6$ into (1)}

$$\therefore \quad y = 3$$

Solution is: $x = 6$, $y = 3$.

Check: (1) $3 = 9 - 6$ ✓   (2) $2(6) + 3(3) = 12 + 9 = 21$ ✓

Example 5   ◀))) **Self Tutor**

Solve simultaneously, by substitution: $2y - x = 2$

                                         $x = 1 + 8y$

$2y - x = 2$ ...... (1) $x = 1 + 8y$ ...... (2)

Substituting (2) into (1) gives

$$2y - (1 + 8y) = 2$$
$$\therefore \quad 2y - 1 - 8y = 2$$
$$\therefore \quad -6y = 3$$
$$\therefore \quad y = -\tfrac{1}{2}$$

Substituting $y = -\frac{1}{2}$ into (2) gives
$$x = 1 + 8 \times -\tfrac{1}{2} = -3$$

The solution is $x = -3, \quad y = -\frac{1}{2}$

Check: (1) $2(-\frac{1}{2}) - (-3) = -1 + 3 = 2$ ✓

(2) $1 + 8(-\frac{1}{2}) = 1 - 4 = -3$ ✓

x is the subject of the second equation, so we substitute $1+8y$ for x in the first equation.

EXERCISE 18C

1 Solve simultaneously, using substitution:

a $y = 3 + x$, $5x - 2y = 0$
b $y = x - 2$, $x + 3y = 6$
c $y = 5 - x$, $4x + y = 5$
d $y = 2x - 1$, $3x - y = 6$
e $y = 3x + 4$, $2x + 3y = 12$
f $y = 5 - 2x$, $5x - 2y = 8$

2 Use the substitution method to solve simultaneously:

a $x = y + 2$, $3x - 2y = 9$
b $x = -1 + 5y$, $x = 3 - 5y$
c $x = 6 - 3y$, $3x - 3y = 2$
d $x = 1 - 2y$, $2x + 3y = 4$
e $x = -4 - 2y$, $2y - 3x = 8$
f $x = -y - 8$, $2x - 4y = 5$

3 **a** Try to solve by substitution: $y = 2x + 5$ and $y = 2x + 7$.
b What is the simultaneous solution for the equations in **a**? Explain your answer.

4 **a** Try to solve by substitution: $y = 4x + 3$ and $2y = 8x + 6$.
b How many simultaneous solutions do the equations in **a** have? Explain your answer.

SOLUTION BY ELIMINATION

In many problems which require the simultaneous solution of linear equations, each equation will be of the form $ax + by = c$. Solution by substitution is often tedious in such situations and the method of **elimination** of one of the variables is preferred.

One method is to make the coefficients of x (or y) the **same size** but **opposite in sign** and then **add** the equations. This has the effect of **eliminating** one of the variables.

Example 6 **Self Tutor**

Solve simultaneously, by elimination: $4x + 3y = 2$ ......(1)
$x - 3y = 8$ ......(2)

Notice that coefficients of y are the same size but opposite in sign.
We **add** the LHS's and the RHS's to get an equation which contains x only.

$$4x + 3y = 2$$
$$+ \quad x - 3y = 8$$
$$\overline{\quad\quad 5x \quad\quad = 10} \qquad \text{\{adding the equations\}}$$
$$\therefore \quad x = 2 \qquad \text{\{dividing both sides by 5\}}$$

Substituting $x = 2$ into (1) gives $4(2) + 3y = 2$
$$\therefore \quad 8 + 3y = 2$$
$$\therefore \quad 3y = -6$$
$$\therefore \quad y = -2$$

The solution is $x = 2$ and $y = -2$.

Check: in (2): $(2) - 3(-2) = 2 + 6 = 8$ ✓

5 What equation results when the following are added vertically?

a $3x + 4y = 6$
$8x - 4y = 5$

b $2x - y = 7$
$-2x + 5y = 5$

c $7x - 3y = 2$
$2x + 3y = 7$

d $6x - 11y = 12$
$3x + 11y = -6$

e $-7x + 2y = 5$
$7x - 3y = 6$

f $2x - 3y = -7$
$-2x - 8y = -4$

6 Solve the following using the method of elimination:

a $5x - y = 4$
$2x + y = 10$

b $3x - 2y = 7$
$3x + 2y = -1$

c $-5x - 3y = 14$
$5x + 8y = -29$

d $4x + 3y = -11$
$-4x - 2y = 6$

e $2x - 5y = 14$
$4x + 5y = -2$

f $-6x - y = 17$
$6x + 5y = -13$

In problems where the coefficients of x (or y) are **not** the **same size** or **opposite in sign**, we may first have to **multiply** each equation by a number.

Example 7 ◀) Self Tutor

Solve simultaneously, by elimination: $3x + 2y = 7$
$2x - 5y = 11$

$3x + 2y = 7$ ...... (1) $2x - 5y = 11$ ...... (2)

We can eliminate y by multiplying (1) by 5 and (2) by 2.

$$\therefore \quad 15x + 10y = 35$$
$$+ \quad 4x - 10y = 22$$
$$\overline{\therefore \quad 19x \quad\quad = 57} \qquad \text{\{adding the equations\}}$$
$$\therefore \quad x = 3 \qquad \text{\{dividing both sides by 19\}}$$

Substituting $x = 3$ into equation (1) gives
$$3(3) + 2y = 7$$
$$\therefore \quad 9 + 2y = 7$$
$$\therefore \quad 2y = -2$$
$$\therefore \quad y = -1$$

So, the solution is: $x = 3$, $y = -1$.

Check: $3(3) + 2(-1) = 9 - 2 = 7$ ✓ $2(3) - 5(-1) = 6 + 5 = 11$ ✓

7 Give the equation that results when both sides of the equation:

    a $2x + 5y = 1$ are multiplied by 5   **b** $3x - y = 4$ are multiplied by -1

    c $x - 7y = 8$ are multiplied by 3   **d** $5x + 4y = 9$ are multiplied by -2

    e $-3x - 2y = 2$ are multiplied by 6   **f** $4x - 2y = 3$ are multiplied by -4

Example 8   ◀)) Self Tutor

Solve by elimination: $3x + 4y = 14$
                               $4x + 5y = 17$

$$3x + 4y = 14 \quad \text{...... (1)}$$
$$4x + 5y = 17 \quad \text{...... (2)}$$

To eliminate x, multiply both sides of

    (1) by 4: $12x + 16y = 56$ ...... (3)
    (2) by -3: $-12x - 15y = -51$ ...... (4)
                                 $y = 5$ {adding (3) and (4)}

Substituting $y = 5$ into (2) gives

               $4x + 5(5) = 17$
      $\therefore$ $4x + 25 = 17$
      $\therefore$ $4x = -8$
      $\therefore$ $x = -2$ *Check:*

Thus $x = -2$ and $y = 5$.   (1) $3(-2) + 4(5) = (-6) + 20 = 14$ ✓
                                        (2) $4(-2) + 5(5) = (-8) + 25 = 17$ ✓

WHICH VARIABLE TO ELIMINATE

There is always a choice whether to eliminate x or y, so our choice depends on which variable is easier to eliminate.

In **Example 8**, try to solve by multiplying (1) by 5 and (2) by -4. This eliminates y rather than x. The final solution should be the same.

8 Solve the following using the method of elimination:

    a $2x + y = 8$ **b** $3x + 2y = 7$ **c** $5x - 2y = 17$
        $x - 3y = 11$ $x + 3y = 7$ $3x - y = 9$

    d $2x + 3y = 13$ **e** $4x - 3y = 1$ **f** $2x + 5y = 14$
        $3x + 2y = 17$ $2x + 5y = 7$ $5x - 3y + 27 = 0$

    g $7x - 2y = 20$ **h** $3x - 2y = 5$ **i** $2x - 7y - 18 = 0$
        $4x + 3y = -1$ $5x - 3y = 8$ $3x - 5y - 5 = 0$

9 Use the method of elimination to attempt to solve:

    a $2x - y = 3$ **b** $3x + 4y = 6$
        $4x - 2y = 6$ $6x + 8y = 7$ Comment on your results.

D ## PROBLEM SOLVING

Many problems can be described mathematically by a **pair of linear equations**, or two equations of the form $ax + by = c$, where x and y are the two variables (unknowns).

We have already seen an example of this in **Investigation 2** on page **361**.

Once the equations are formed, they can then be solved simultaneously and thus the original problem solved. The following method is recommended:

Step 1:   Decide on the two unknowns; call them x and y, say. Do not forget the units.

Step 2:   Write down **two** equations connecting x and y.

Step 3:   Solve the equations simultaneously.

Step 4:   Check your solutions with the original data given.

Step 5:   Give your answer in sentence form.

Note: The form of the original equations will help you decide whether to use the substitution method, or the elimination method.

Example 9   ◀) **Self Tutor**

Two numbers have a sum of 45 and a difference of 13. Find the numbers.

Let x and y be the unknown numbers, where $x > y$.

Then $x + y = 45$ ...... (1)   {'sum' means add}
and $\underline{x - y = 13}$ ...... (2)   {'difference' means subtract}

$\therefore \ 2x \quad = 58$ {adding (1) and (2)}
$\therefore \quad x = 29$ {dividing both sides by 2}

Substituting into (1) gives   *Check:*

$29 + y = 45$ (1) $29 + 16 = 45$ ✓

$\therefore \quad y = 16$ (2) $29 - 16 = 13$ ✓

The numbers are 29 and 16.

> When solving problems with simultaneous equations we must find two equations containing two unknowns.

EXERCISE 18D

1   The sum of two numbers is 72 and their difference is 40. Find the numbers.

2   Find two numbers whose sum is 30 and half their difference is 7.

3   The larger of two numbers is three times the smaller number, and their difference is 34. Find the two numbers.

Example 10   ◀)) **Self Tutor**

When shopping in Jamaica, 5 coconuts and 14 bananas cost me $8.70, and 8 coconuts and 9 bananas cost $9.90.
Find the cost of each coconut and each banana.

Let each coconut cost x cents and each banana cost y cents.

$$\therefore \quad 5x + 14y = 870 \quad ...... \text{ (1)}$$
$$8x + 9y = 990 \quad ...... \text{ (2)}$$

Note: The units must be the same on both sides of each equation, i.e., cents.

To eliminate x, we multiply (1) by 8 and (2) by -5.

$$\therefore \quad 40x + 112y = 6960 \quad ..... \text{ (3)}$$
$$-40x - 45y = -4950 \quad ..... \text{ (4)}$$
$$\overline{\hspace{4cm}}$$
$$67y = 2010 \quad \{\text{adding (3) and (4)}\}$$
$$\therefore \quad y = 30 \quad \{\text{dividing both sides by 67}\}$$

Substituting in (2) gives

$$8x + 9 \times 30 = 990$$
$$\therefore \quad 8x = 990 - 270$$
$$\therefore \quad 8x = 720$$
$$\therefore \quad x = 90 \quad \{\text{dividing both sides by 8}\}$$

Check: $5 \times 90 + 14 \times 30 = 450 + 420 = 870$ ✓
$8 \times 90 + 9 \times 30 = 720 + 270 = 990$ ✓

Thus coconuts cost 90 cents each and bananas cost 30 cents each.

4   Three pieces of fish and two serves of chips cost a total of £8.10, whereas five pieces of fish and three serves of chips cost a total of £13.25. Find the cost of each piece of fish and each serve of chips.

5   Seven cups of coffee and four muffins cost a total of €25.30, whereas two cups of coffee and three muffins cost a total of €9.55. Find the cost of each item.

Example 11   ◀)) **Self Tutor**

In my pocket I have only 5-cent and 10-cent coins. How many of each type of coin do I have if I have 24 coins altogether and their total value is $1.55?

Let x be the number of 5-cent coins and y be the number of 10-cent coins.

$$\therefore \quad x + y = 24 \quad ...... \text{ (1)} \quad \{\text{the total number of coins}\}$$
$$\text{and} \quad 5x + 10y = 155 \quad ...... \text{ (2)} \quad \{\text{the total value of coins}\}$$

Multiplying (1) by -5 gives

$$-5x - 5y = -120 \quad \text{...... (3)}$$
$$\underline{5x + 10y = 155} \quad \text{...... (2)}$$
$$\therefore \quad 5y = 35 \qquad \text{\{adding (3) and (2)\}}$$
$$\therefore \quad y = 7 \qquad \text{\{dividing both sides by 5\}}$$

Substituting into (1) gives $\quad x + 7 = 24$
$$\therefore \quad x = 17$$

Check: $\quad 17 + 7 = 24 \quad \checkmark$

$$5 \times 17 + 10 \times 7 = 85 + 70 = 155 \quad \checkmark$$

Thus I have 17 five cent coins and 7 ten cent coins.

6 Margaret saves 50-cent and 10-cent coins. She has 56 of these coins and their total value is $17.60. How many of each coin type does she have?

7 André and Michelle have €65.25 between them. André's money is two thirds of Michelle's amount. How much money does each have?

8 Milk is sold in either 600 mL or 1 L cartons. A supermarket manager ordered 79.8 litres of milk and received 93 cartons. How many of each size carton did the manager receive?

9 Given that the triangle alongside is equilateral, find a and b.

$(b + 6)$ cm $(2a + b)$ cm

$(4a - 1)$ cm

10 A rectangle has perimeter 56 cm. If 4 cm is taken from the length and added to the width, the rectangle becomes a square. Find the dimensions of the original rectangle.

E   USING A GRAPHICS CALCULATOR TO SOLVE SIMULTANEOUS EQUATIONS

Simultaneous equations can be solved using a graphics calculator. This is done by drawing graphs of the equations, and then finding their point of intersection.

When using a graphics calculator it is often necessary to rearrange linear equations of the form $Ax + By = C$ so that y is the **subject** of the formula.

For example, if $2x + 5y = 11$, we need to rearrange it into the form $y = \text{......}$

Example 12   ◄)) Self Tutor

Rearrange $2x + 5y = 11$ to make y the subject.

$$2x + 5y = 11$$
$$\therefore \quad 2x + 5y - 2x = 11 - 2x \qquad \text{\{taking } 2x \text{ from both sides\}}$$
$$\therefore \quad 5y = 11 - 2x$$
$$\therefore \quad y = \frac{11 - 2x}{5} \qquad \text{\{dividing both sides by 5\}}$$

EXERCISE 18E

1   Rearrange to make y the subject of the formula:

    a $5x + y = 10$ **b** $4x + y = 8$ **c** $2x + y = 12$

    d $2x + 3y = 6$ **e** $4x + 3y = 12$ **f** $7x + 3y = 10$

    g $2x + 9y = -7$ **h** $11x + 8y = 88$ **i** $16x + 5y = 40$

Example 13　　　　　　　　　　　　　　　　　　　　　　**◆》 Self Tutor**

Rearrange $3x - 5y = 13$ to make y the subject.

$$3x - 5y = 13$$
$$\therefore \quad 3x - 5y - 3x = 13 - 3x \quad \text{\{taking } 3x \text{ from both sides\}}$$
$$\therefore \quad -5y = 13 - 3x$$
$$\therefore \quad y = \frac{13 - 3x}{-5} \quad \text{\{dividing both sides by } -5\text{\}}$$

Note: This could also be written as $y = \dfrac{3x - 13}{5}$.   Why?

---

2   Rearrange to make y the subject of the formula:

    a $5x - y = 5$ **b** $2x - y = 3$ **c** $9x - y = 18$

    d $2x - 3y = 7$ **e** $4x - 3y = 5$ **f** $6x - 5y = 20$

    g $3x - 7y = 14$ **h** $8x - 11y = 3$ **i** $11x - 9y = 33$

Suppose we wish to solve $3x + y = 11$ and $x + 2y = 12$ simultaneously. We first rearrange them so that y is the subject. This gives us $y = 11 - 3x$ and $y = \dfrac{12 - x}{2}$.

We are now ready to graph the lines and find where they intersect. Instructions for doing this on a graphics calculator can be found on page **22**.

You should find the solution is $x = 2, \ y = 5$.

If you are using a **Casio fx-9860G** you can also solve these equations using the **simultaneous equation solver**.

3   Use a graphics calculator to find the point of intersection of:

    a $2x + y = 30$ **b** $x - y = -19$ **c** $x + 2y = 39$
        $x - 3y = 22$ $2x + 3y = -13$ $3x - 2y = 45$

    d $2x + 3y = 35$ **e** $3x - 2y = 59$ **f** $4x + 5y = 23$
        $3x - y = -30$ $3x + 5y = 10$ $3x - 7y = 157$

4   Use a graphics calculator to solve these problems:

    a   When he went on safari, Morgan saw giraffes and ostriches. He counted 39 heads and 114 legs. How many giraffes and how many ostriches did he see?

    b   A carpenter is making chairs with 4 legs, and stools with 3 legs. He has 23 seats and 86 legs which can be used for stools and chairs. If he uses all of the legs and seats, how many of each item does he make?

    c   3 apples and 5 oranges cost a total of $6.20 whereas 7 apples and 4 oranges cost a total of $7.95. What is the cost of one apple and one orange?

d Jorg had 23 pieces of timber that were either 1.5 metres or 4 metres long. In total he had 64.5 metres of timber. How many of each length did he have?

e Kim bought 4 CDs and 3 DVDs for a total cost of RM109.85. Li paid the same prices for her CDs and DVDs as Kim. She bought 3 CDs and 2 DVDs for a total cost of RM77.40. Find the cost of each of these items.

f 17 small bags of potatoes and 13 large bags weigh a total of 99 kg, whereas 15 small bags and 21 large bags weigh a total of 135 kg. Find the weight of each size of bag.

REVIEW SET 18A

1 Find the point of intersection of the following pairs of lines by drawing graphs of the two lines on the same set of axes:

a $y = 2x$
$y = x - 2$

b $y = 2x - 4$
$y = 1 - 3x$

2 Find the simultaneous solution of $y = 6x - 5$ and $y = 2x + 3$ using an algebraic method.

3 Solve simultaneously, by substitution: $y - 5x = 8$ and $y = 3x + 6$.

4 Try to solve $2x + 4y = 2$ and $x = 1 - 2y$ simultaneously. Interpret your result.

5 Solve the following using the method of elimination: $3x + 2y = 4$ and $2x - y = 5$.

6 6 adult tickets and 5 student tickets for the theatre cost $168, whilst 2 adult tickets and 3 student tickets cost $72. Find the cost of each type of ticket.

7 Carmel has 21 coins in total. There are 50 pence coins and 20 pence coins and their total value is £8.40. How many of each type of coin does Carmel have?

REVIEW SET 18B

1 Find the point of intersection of the following pairs of lines by drawing graphs of the two lines on the same set of axes:

a $y = -x + 5$
$y = 3x + 1$

b $y = -2x + 1$
$y = 2x - 5$

2 Find the simultaneous solution of $y = 3x + 4$ and $y = -2x - 6$ using an algebraic method.

3 Solve simultaneously, by substitution: $y = 3x - 4$ and $2x - y = 8$.

4 Try to solve $x - 2y = 5$ and $x - 2y = 7$ simultaneously. Interpret your result.

5 Solve the following using the method of elimination: $3x - 2y = 3$ and $4x + 3y = 4$.

6 The larger of two numbers is 2 more than three times the smaller number. If their difference is 12, find the numbers.

7 3 sausages and 4 chops cost $12.40, and 5 sausages and 3 chops cost $11.50. Find the cost of each item.

Chapter 19

Probability

Contents:

A Probability by experiment
B Theoretical probability
C Expectation
D Probabilities from tabled data
E Representing combined events
F Probabilities from lists and diagrams
G Multiplying probabilities
H Using tree diagrams
I Sampling with and without replacement
J Mutually exclusive and non-mutually exclusive events
K Independent events

INTRODUCTION

Consider these statements:

- "The Wildcats will probably win over the Lions on Friday."
- "It is unlikely that lightning will prevent play in the golf tournament."
- "I have a 50-50 chance of arriving tomorrow."

Each of these statements indicates a **likelihood** or **chance** of a particular event happening.

We can indicate the likelihood of an event happening in the future by using a percentage.

> 0%   indicates we believe the event **will not occur**.
> 100%   indicates we believe the event **is certain to occur**.

All events can therefore be assigned a percentage between 0% and 100% (inclusive).

A number close to 0% indicates the event is **unlikely** to occur, whereas a number close to 100% means that it is **highly likely** to occur.

In mathematics, we usually write probabilities as either decimals or fractions rather than percentages. However, as $100\% = 1$, comparisons or conversions from percentages to fractions or decimals are very simple.

> An impossible event which has 0% chance of happening is assigned a probability of 0.
> A certain event which has 100% chance of happening is assigned a probability of 1.
> All other events can be assigned a probability between 0 and 1.

The number line below shows how we could interpret different probabilities:

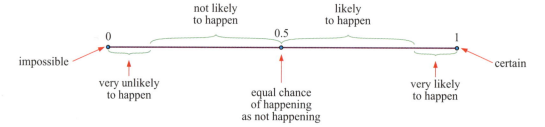

The assigning of probabilities is usually based on either:

- observing the results of an experiment (experimental probability),   or
- using arguments of symmetry (theoretical probability).

PROBABILITY

To find the probability that an event will happen we use:

$$P(\text{event happens}) = \frac{\text{number of ways the event can happen}}{\text{total number of possible outcomes}}$$

For example:

- a **coin** has two sides ("heads", H and "tails", T) on which it could land. It is equally likely to land on either side when flipped into the air.

$$\therefore \quad P(\text{"heads"}) = \tfrac{1}{2} \quad \begin{matrix} \longleftarrow \text{ one way of getting an H} \\ \longleftarrow \text{ two possible outcomes H or T} \end{matrix}$$

Note: We could also use a decimal (0.5) or a percentage (50%), but a fraction is the usual representation.

- A bag contains 4 red and 2 blue balls. One ball is selected at random.

$$\therefore \quad P(\text{red ball}) = \tfrac{4}{6} \quad \begin{matrix} \longleftarrow \text{ any one of 4 red balls could be selected} \\ \longleftarrow \text{ there are 6 balls which could be selected} \end{matrix}$$

Note: We could reduce this fraction to $\tfrac{2}{3}$, but we often leave it as $\tfrac{4}{6}$ to relate to the context of 4 balls out of 6.

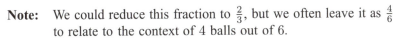
A   PROBABILITY BY EXPERIMENT

TERMINOLOGY

We should use suitable language to help us describe what we are doing and the results we expect and get.

- The **number of trials** is the total number of times the experiment is repeated.
- The **outcomes** are the different results possible for one trial of the experiment.
- The **frequency** of a particular outcome is the number of times that this outcome is observed.
- The **relative frequency** of an outcome is the frequency of that outcome divided by the total number of trials.

For example, when tossing a tin can in the air we notice that in 150 tosses it comes to rest on an end 29 times. We say:

- the number of trials is 150 and the outcomes are *ends* and *sides*
- the frequency of *ends* is 29 and the frequency of *sides* is 121
- the relative frequency of *ends* $= \tfrac{29}{150} \approx 0.193$ and

  the relative frequency of *sides* $= \tfrac{121}{150} \approx 0.807$

EXPERIMENTAL PROBABILITY

Sometimes the only way of finding the probability of a particular event occurring is by experiment.

Tossing a tin can is one such example. The probability of a can of this shape coming to rest on its end is the relative frequency found by experimentation.

We say that: | The **estimated experimental probability** is the relative frequency of the outcome.

We write: Experimental $P(\text{end}) \approx 0.193$

The larger the number of trials, the more confident we are that the experimental probability obtained is accurate.

Example 1   ◀)) **Self Tutor**

Find the experimental probability of:

a tossing a head with one toss of a coin if it falls heads 96 times in 200 tosses

b rolling a *six* with a die given that when it was rolled 300 times, a *six* occurred 54 times.

a   Experimental P(getting a head)
= relative frequency of getting
a head
$= \frac{96}{200}$
$= 0.48$

b   Experimental P(rolling a *six*)
= relative frequency of rolling a *six*
$= \frac{54}{300}$
$= 0.18$

EXERCISE 19A

1 Find the experimental probability of rolling *an odd number* with a die if *an odd number* occurred 33 times when the die was rolled 60 times.

2 Clem fired 200 arrows at a target and hit the target 168 times. Find the experimental probability of Clem hitting the target.

3 Ivy has free-range hens. Out of the first 123 eggs that they laid she found that 11 had double-yolks. Calculate the experimental probability of getting a double-yolk egg from her hens.

4 Jackson leaves for work at the same time each day. Over a period of 227 working days, on his way to work he had to wait for a train at the railway crossing on 58 days. Calculate the experimental probability that Jackson has to wait for a train on his way to work.

5 Ravi has a circular spinner marked P, Q and R on 3 equal sectors. Find the experimental probability of getting a Q if the spinner was twirled 417 times and finished on Q on 138 occasions.

6 Each time Claude shuffled a pack of cards before a game, he recorded the suit of the top card of the pack.

His results for 140 games were 34 Hearts, 36 Diamonds, 38 Spades and 32 Clubs.

Find the experimental probability that the top card of a shuffled pack is:

a a Heart   **b** a Club or Diamond.

B   THEORETICAL PROBABILITY

The **theoretical probability** of an event happening is based on what we expect to occur.

Remember that: $\text{P(event happens)} = \dfrac{\text{number of ways the event can happen}}{\text{total number of possible outcomes}}$

Example 2   ◀ Self Tutor

A die is rolled. What is the theoretical probability of getting:
  a   a 'six'   **b**   a 'prime number'?

  a   The possible outcomes are: 1, 2, 3, 4, 5 and 6

$$\therefore \ \ \text{P(a 'six')} = \tfrac{1}{6} \ \longleftarrow \ \text{only one 6}$$
$$\longleftarrow \ \text{6 possible outcomes}$$

  b   The possible 'prime' number outcomes are: 2, 3 and 5.

$$\therefore \ \ \text{P(a 'prime')} = \tfrac{3}{6} \ \text{or} \ \tfrac{1}{2}.$$

Example 3   ◀ Self Tutor

A bag contains 1 yellow, 2 green and 5 blue beads. One
bead is chosen at random. Find the probability that it is:
  a   yellow   **b**   not yellow.

  a $\text{P(yellow)} = \dfrac{1}{1+2+5}$

$$= \tfrac{1}{8} \quad \{\text{1 in 8 beads are yellow}\}$$

  b $\text{P(not yellow)} = \dfrac{2+5}{8} = \dfrac{7}{8} \quad \{\text{7 in 8 are not yellow}\}$

Note: "not yellow" is the **complementary** event to "yellow" and so their probabilities must
add to 1. Either "yellow" or "not yellow" *must* occur.

> For any event E with **complementary** event E',
> $$\text{P}(E) + \text{P}(E') = 1 \quad \text{or} \quad \text{P}(E') = 1 - \text{P}(E).$$

In some situations it is easier to find $\text{P}(E')$ than to find $\text{P}(E)$. Once we have found $\text{P}(E')$
we can then easily find $\text{P}(E)$.

EXERCISE 19B

1   A die numbered 1 to 6 is rolled once. Find:
  a   P(3)
  b   P(even number)
  c   P(a number at least 1)
  d   P(5)
  e   P(not a 5)
  f   P(a number greater than 6)

2   A die has the numbers   0, 0, 1, 1, 4, 5   on its faces. Find:
  a   P(1)
  b   P(a number less than 5)
  c   P(1 or 4 or 5)
  d   P(not 0)
  e   P(a prime number)
  f   P(a non-prime number)

3   The five illustrated cards are well
shuffled and placed face down on a
table. One of the cards is randomly
chosen. Find:
  a   P(A)
  b   P(C)
  c   P(not C)
  d   P(A or B)

$$\boxed{A} \ \boxed{A} \ \boxed{B} \ \boxed{B} \ \boxed{C}$$

4 A bag contains 10 beads. 5 are white, 2 are red, 1 is blue, 1 is green and 1 is black. A bead is taken at random from the bag. Find:

    a   P(white)   **b**   P(blue)   **c**   P(not black).

5 A letter is randomly chosen from GENEVA.

    a Find the probability that it is: **i**   an E   **ii**   a Z.

    b Given that the letter chosen first is a G and it is removed, what is the probability that a second randomly chosen letter is a vowel?

6 A dart board has 30 sectors, numbered 1 to 30. A dart is thrown towards the bulls-eye and misses in a random direction. Determine the probability that the dart hits:

    a a multiple of 5

    b a number between 7 and 13 inclusive

    c a number greater than 18

    d 15

    e a multiple of 7

    f an even number that is a multiple of 3.

7 What is the probability that a randomly chosen person has his or her next birthday:

    a   on a Tuesday   **b**   on a weekend   **c**   in July   **d**   in January or February?

8 A square game board is divided into sixteen smaller squares. Fourteen of the squares are painted as shown.

    a What colour(s) should the remaining squares be painted so that the probability of landing on red is $\frac{3}{8}$ and it is impossible to land on black?

    b What colour(s) should the remaining squares be painted so that the probability of landing on red is $\frac{5}{16}$ and the probability of landing on yellow is $\frac{1}{8}$?

red	yellow	red	blue
white	red	white	blue
red	blue	white	red
white	yellow	?	?

C   EXPECTATION

The probability of an event can be used to predict the number of times the event will occur in a number of trials.

For example, when rolling an ordinary die, the probability of rolling a '4' is $\frac{1}{6}$.

If we roll the die 120 times, we expect $120 \times \frac{1}{6} = 20$ of the outcomes to be '4's.

> Suppose the probability of an event occurring is p. If the trial is repeated n times, the **expectation** of the event, or the number of times we expect it to occur, is np.

> ### Example 4
> ◀) **Self Tutor**
>
> Each time a footballer kicks for goal he has a $\frac{4}{5}$ chance of being successful. If, in a series of games, he has 62 kicks for goal, how many goals would you expect him to kick?
>
> $p = P(\text{goal}) = \frac{4}{5}$
>
> For a sample space of $n = 62$, the expected number of goals is $\quad n \times p$
>
> $\qquad\qquad = 62 \times \frac{4}{5}$
>
> $\qquad\qquad \approx 50$
>
>

EXERCISE 19C

1 In a particular region in Africa, the probability that it will rain on any one day is 0.177. On how many days of the year would you expect it to rain?

2 **a** If 2 coins are tossed, what is the chance that they both fall heads?

  b If the 2 coins are tossed 300 times, on how many occasions would you expect them to both fall heads?

3 A certain type of drawing pin, when tossed 400 times, landed on its back 144 times.

  a Estimate the probability that it will land on its back if it is tossed once.

  b If the drawing pin is tossed 72 times, how many "backs" would you expect?

4 A bag contains 5 red and 3 blue discs. A disc is chosen at random and then replaced. This is repeated 200 times. How many times would you expect a red disc to be chosen?

5 A die has the numbers 0, 1, 2, 2, 3 and 4 on its faces. The die is rolled 600 times. How many times might we expect a result of:

  a 0   **b** 2   **c** 1, 2 or 3   **d** not a 4?

6 A charity fundraiser gets a licence to run the following gambling game: A die is rolled and the returns to the player are given in the 'pay table' alongside. To play the game $4 is needed. A result of '6' wins $10, so in fact you are ahead by $6 if you get a '6' on the first roll.

Result	Wins
6	$10
4, 5	$4
1, 2, 3	$1

  a What are your chances of playing one game and winning:

   i $10   **ii** $4   **iii** $1?

  b Your *expected* return from throwing a 6 is $\frac{1}{6} \times \$10$. What is your expected return from throwing:

   i a 4 or 5   **ii** a 1, 2 or 3   **iii** a 1, 2, 3, 4, 5 or 6?

  c What is your expected *result* at the end of one game? Remember to include the cost of playing the game.

  d What is your expected result at the end of 100 games?

PROBABILITIES FROM TABLED DATA

If we are given a table of frequencies then we use **relative frequencies** to estimate the probabilities of the events.

Remember that $\text{relative frequency} = \dfrac{\text{frequency}}{\text{number of trials}}$.

Example 5 🔊 Self Tutor

A marketing company surveys 80 randomly selected people to discover what brand of shoe cleaner they use. The results are shown in the table alongside:

a   Based on these results, what is the experimental probability of a community member using:
   i Brite   **ii** Cleano?

b   Would you classify the estimate of **a** to be very good, good, or poor? Why?

Brand	Frequency
Shine	27
Brite	22
Cleano	20
No scuff	11

a   We start by calculating the relative frequency for each brand.

   i Experimental P(Brite)
      $= 0.275$
   ii Experimental P(Cleano)
      $= 0.250$

b   Poor, as the sample size is very small.

Brand	Frequency	Relative Frequency
Shine	27	0.3375
Brite	22	0.2750
Cleano	20	0.2500
No scuff	11	0.1375

EXERCISE 19D

1 A marketing company was commissioned to investigate brands of products usually found in the bathroom. The results of a soap survey are given below:

   a   How many people were randomly selected in this survey?

   b   Calculate the relative frequency of use of each brand of soap.

   c   Using the results obtained by the marketing company, what is the experimental probability that the soap used by a randomly selected person is:

   i Just Soap   **ii** Indulgence   **iii** Silktouch?

Brand	Freq	Relative Frequency
Silktouch	125	
Super	107	
Just Soap	93	
Indulgence	82	
Total		

2 Two coins were tossed 489 times and the *number of heads* occurring at each toss was recorded. The results are shown opposite:

   a   Copy and complete the table given.

   b   Estimate the chance of the following events occurring:

   i 0 heads   **ii** 1 head   **iii** 2 heads.

Outcome	Freq	Rel Freq
0 heads	121	
1 head		
2 heads	109	
Total		

3 At the Annual Show the toffee apple vendor estimated that three times as many people preferred red toffee apples to green toffee apples.

a If 361 people wanted green toffee apples, estimate how many wanted red.

b Copy and complete the table given.

c Estimate the probability that the next customer will ask for:

    i a green toffee apple   **ii** a red toffee apple.

Colour	Freq	Rel Freq
Green	361	
Red		
Total		

4 The tickets sold for a tennis match were recorded as people entered the stadium. The results are shown:

a How many tickets were sold in total?

b Copy and complete the table given.

c If a person in the stadium is selected at random, what is the probability that the person bought a Concession ticket?

Ticket Type	Freq	Rel Freq
Adult	3762	
Concession	1084	
Child	389	
Total		

5 The results of a local Council election are shown in the table. It is known that 6000 people voted in the election.

a Copy and complete the table given.

b What is the chance that a randomly selected person from this electorate voted for a female councillor?

Councillor	Freq	Rel Freq
Mr Tony Trimboli	2167	
Mrs Andrea Sims	724	
Mrs Sara Chong	2389	
Mr John Henry		
Total		

E   REPRESENTING COMBINED EVENTS

The possible outcomes for tossing two coins are listed below:

    two heads   head and tail   tail and head   two tails

These results are the combination of two events: tossing coin 1 and tossing coin 2. If H represents a 'head' and T a 'tail', the sample space of possible outcomes is   HH, HT, TH and TT.

> A **sample space** is the set of all possible outcomes of an experiment.

Possible ways of representing sample spaces are:

- listing them
- using a 2-dimensional grid
- using a tree diagram
- using a Venn diagram

Example 6

⏺)) **Self Tutor**

Represent the sample space for tossing two coins using:

a a list   **b** a 2-D grid   **c** a tree diagram

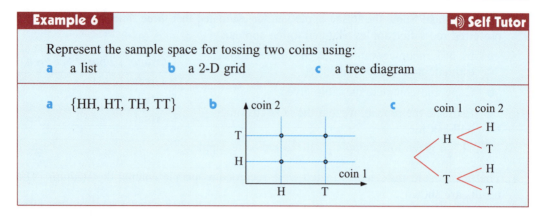

Example 7

⏺)) **Self Tutor**

Illustrate, using a tree diagram, the possible outcomes when drawing two marbles from a bag containing several marbles of each of the colours red, green and yellow.

Let

R be the event of getting a red
G be the event of getting a green
Y be the event of getting a yellow

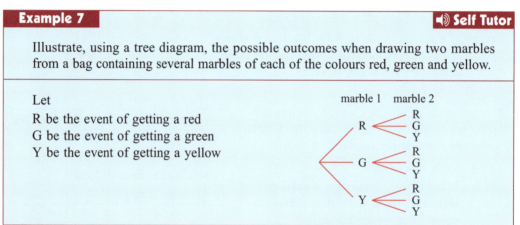

EXERCISE 19E

1 List the sample space for the following:

  a twirling a square spinner labelled A, B, C, D
  b the sexes of a 2-child family
  c the order in which 4 blocks A, B, C and D can be lined up
  d the 8 different 3-child families.
  e spinning a coin **i** twice **ii** three times **iii** four times.

2 Illustrate on a 2-dimensional grid the sample space for:

  a rolling a die and tossing a coin simultaneously
  b rolling two dice
  c rolling a die and spinning a spinner with sides A, B, C, D
  d twirling two square spinners: one labelled A, B, C, D and the other 1, 2, 3, 4.

3 Illustrate on a tree diagram the sample space for:

  a tossing a 5-cent and 10-cent coin simultaneously
  b tossing a coin and twirling an equilateral triangular spinner labelled A, B and C
  c twirling two equilateral triangular spinners labelled 1, 2 and 3 and X, Y and Z
  d drawing two tickets from a hat containing a number of pink, blue and white tickets.
  e drawing two beads from a bag containing 3 red and 4 blue beads.

4   Draw a Venn diagram to show a class of 20 students where 7 study History and Geography, 10 study History, 15 study Geography, and 2 study neither subject.

F   PROBABILITIES FROM LISTS AND DIAGRAMS

From the methods of showing sample spaces in the previous section, we can find the probabilities of combined events.

Example 8   ◀) Self Tutor

Three coins are tossed. Write down a list of all possible outcomes. Find the probability of getting:

a   3 heads   b   at least one head

c   3 heads if it is known that there is at least one head.

Notice how we list the outcomes in a systematic way.

The sample space is: HHH   HHT   TTH   TTT
                       HTH   THT
a   P(3 heads) $= \frac{1}{8}$ THH   HTT

b   P(at least one H) $= \frac{7}{8}$ {all except TTT}

c   P(HHH knowing at least one H) $= \frac{1}{7}$

{The sample space now excludes TTT}

Example 9   ◀) Self Tutor

A die has the numbers 0, 0, 1, 1, 4 and 5. It is rolled *twice*. Illustrate the sample space using a 2-D grid. Hence find the probability of getting:

a   a total of 5   b   two numbers which are the same.

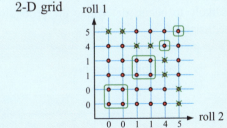

There are $6 \times 6 = 36$ possible outcomes.

a   P(total of 5)
    $= \frac{8}{36}$ {those with a ×}

b   P(same numbers)
    $= \frac{10}{36}$ {those circled}

EXERCISE 19F

1   a   List all possible orderings of the letters O, D and G.

    b   If these three letters are placed at random in a row, what is the probability of:

        i   spelling DOG   ii   O appearing first   iii   O not appearing first

        iv   spelling DOG or GOD?

2 The Venn diagram shows the sports played by boys at the local high school.

A student is chosen at random. Find the probability that he:

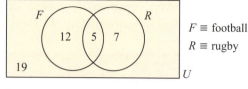

$F \equiv$ football
$R \equiv$ rugby

   a   plays football
   b   plays both codes
   c   plays football or rugby
   d   plays exactly one of these sports
   e   plays neither of these sports
   f   plays football, given that he is in at least one team
   g   plays rugby, given that he plays football.

3 Draw the grid of the sample space when a 10-cent and a 50-cent coin are tossed simultaneously. Hence determine the probability of getting:

   a   two heads
   b   two tails
   c   exactly one head
   d   at least one head

4 A coin and a pentagonal spinner with sectors 1, 2, 3, 4 and 5 are tossed and spun respectively.

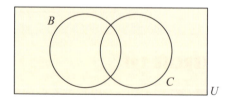

   a   Draw a grid to illustrate the sample space of possible outcomes.
   b   How many outcomes are possible?
   c   Use your grid to determine the chance of getting:

     i   a head and a 4
     ii   a tail and an odd number
     iii   an even number
     iv   a tail or a 3

5 List the six different orders in which Alex, Bodi and Kek may sit in a row. If the three of them sit randomly in a row, determine the probability that:

   a   Alex sits in the middle
   b   Alex sits at the left end
   c   Alex sits at the right end
   d   Bodi and Kek are seated together

6 **a**   List the 8 possible 3-child families, according to the gender of the children. For example, BGB means *"the first is a boy, the second is a girl, and the third is a boy"*.

   b   Assuming that each of these is equally likely to occur, determine the probability that a randomly selected 3-child family consists of:

     i   all boys
     ii   all girls
     iii   boy, then girl, then girl
     iv   two girls and a boy
     v   a girl for the eldest
     vi   at least one boy

7 In a class of 24 students, 10 take Biology, 12 take Chemistry, and 5 take neither Biology nor Chemistry. Find the probability that a student picked at random from the class takes:

   a   Chemistry but not Biology
   b   Chemistry or Biology.

8 **a**   List, in systematic order, the 24 different orders in which four people P, Q, R and S may sit in a row.

b Hence, determine the probability that when the four people sit at random in a row:

   i P sits on one end

   ii Q sits on one of the two middle seats

   iii P and Q are seated together

   iv P, Q and R are seated together, not necessarily in that order.

9 A pair of dice is rolled.

  a Show that there are 36 members in the sample space of possible outcomes by displaying them on a grid.

  b Hence, determine the probability of a result with:

   i one die showing a 4 and the other a 5

   ii both dice showing the same result

   iii at least one of the dice showing a result of 3

   iv either a 4 or 6 being displayed

   v both dice showing even numbers

   vi the sum of the values being 7.

10 60 married men were asked whether they gave their wife flowers or chocolates for their last birthday. The results were: 26 gave chocolates, 21 gave flowers, and 5 gave both chocolates and flowers. If one of the married men was chosen at random, determine the probability that he gave his wife:

  a flowers but not chocolates   **b** neither chocolates nor flowers

  c chocolates or flowers

11 List the possible outcomes when four coins are tossed simultaneously. Hence determine the probability of getting:

  a all heads   **b** two heads and two tails   **c** more tails than heads

  d at least one tail   **e** exactly one head

12 **a** Copy and complete the grid alongside for the sample space of drawing one card from an ordinary pack.

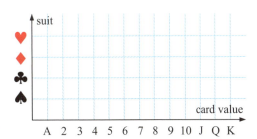

  b Use your grid to determine the probability of getting:

   i a Queen   **ii** the Jack of hearts

   iii a spade   **iv** a picture card

   v a red 7   **vi** a diamond or a club

   vii a King or a heart   **viii** a Queen and a 3

13 The medical records for a class of 28 children show whether they had previously had measles or mumps. The records show 22 have had measles, 13 have had measles and mumps, and 27 have had measles or mumps. If one child from the class is selected at random, determine the probability that he or she has had:

  a measles   **b** measles but not mumps   **c** neither mumps nor measles.

G   MULTIPLYING PROBABILITIES

Consider tossing a coin and rolling a die simultaneously.

We have already seen how to display the possible outcomes on a grid:

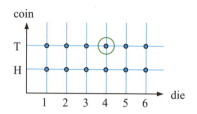

When asked "What is the probability of getting a tail and a 4?" we get an answer of $\frac{1}{12}$, since there are 12 possible outcomes but only one with the property that we want.

$$\text{But} \quad P(\text{tail}) = \tfrac{1}{2} \quad \text{and} \quad P(\text{a '4'}) = \tfrac{1}{6} \quad \text{and} \quad \tfrac{1}{2} \times \tfrac{1}{6} = \tfrac{1}{12}$$

This suggests that $\quad P(\text{tail and a '4'}) = P(\text{tail}) \times P(\text{'4'})$,

i.e., we **multiply** the separate probabilities.

In general:

> If A and B are two events then $\quad P(A \text{ and } B) = P(A) \times P(B)$.

Example 10   ◀) Self Tutor

Sunil has probability $\frac{4}{5}$ of hitting a target and Monika has probability $\frac{5}{6}$.
If they both fire simultaneously at the target, determine the probability that:

a they both hit it   **b** they both miss it.

a   P(both hit)
= P(Sunil hits and Monika hits)
= P(Sunil hits) $\times$ P(Monika hits)
= $\frac{4}{5} \times \frac{5}{6}$
= $\frac{2}{3}$

b   P(both miss)
= P(Sunil misses and Monika misses)
= P(Sunil misses) $\times$ P(Monika misses)
= $\frac{1}{5} \times \frac{1}{6}$
= $\frac{1}{30}$

EXERCISE 19G

1 Janice and Lee take set shots at a netball goal from 3 m. From past experience, Janice throws a goal on average 2 times in every 3 shots, whereas Lee throws a goal 4 times in every 7. If they both shoot for goals, determine the probability that:

    a both score a goal   **b** both miss

    c Janice goals but Lee misses

2 When a nut was tossed 400 times it finished on its edge 84 times and on its side for the rest. Use this information to estimate the probability that when two identical nuts are tossed:

edge   side

    a they both fall on their edges   **b** they both fall on their sides.

3 Tei has probability $\frac{1}{3}$ of hitting a target with an arrow, while See has probability $\frac{2}{5}$. If they both fire at the target, determine the probability that:

    a   both hit the target   **b**   both miss the target

    c   Tei hits the target and See misses   **d**   Tei misses the target and See hits

4 A certain brand of drawing pin was tossed into the air 600 times. It landed on its back ⊥ 243 times and on its side ⟋ for the remainder. Use this information to estimate the probability that:

    a   one drawing pin, when tossed, will fall on its **i** back   **ii** side

    b   two drawing pins, when tossed, will both fall on their backs

    c   two drawing pins, when tossed, will both fall on their sides.

H | USING TREE DIAGRAMS

Tree diagrams can be used to illustrate sample spaces, provided that the alternatives are not too numerous.

Once the sample space is illustrated, the tree diagram can be used for determining probabilities.

Consider **Example 10** again. The tree diagram for this information is:

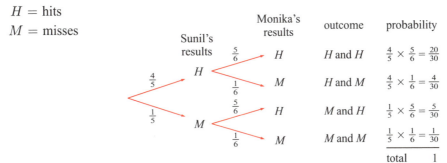

H = hits
M = misses

Notice that:

- The probabilities for hitting and missing are marked on the branches.
- There are *four* alternative paths and each path shows a particular outcome.
- All outcomes are represented and the probabilities of each outcome are obtained by **multiplying** the probabilities along that path.

Example 11   ◀)) **Self Tutor**

Stephano is not having much luck lately. His car will only start 90% of the time and his motorbike will only start 70% of the time.

    a   Draw a tree diagram to illustrate this situation.

    b   Use the tree diagram to determine the chance that:

       i both will start   **ii** Stephano has no choice but to use his car.

a C = car starts M = motorbike starts

			outcome	probability
			C and M	$0.9 \times 0.7 = 0.63$
			C and M'	$0.9 \times 0.3 = 0.27$
			C' and M	$0.1 \times 0.7 = 0.07$
			C' and M'	$0.1 \times 0.3 = 0.03$
			total	1.00

car $0.7 \rightarrow M$
C
0.9 $0.3 \rightarrow M'$
0.1 $0.7 \rightarrow M$
C'
$0.3 \rightarrow M'$

motorbike

b i   P(both start)
$= P(C \text{ and } M)$
$= 0.9 \times 0.7$
$= 0.63$

ii   P(car starts, but motorbike does not)
$= P(C \text{ and } M')$
$= 0.9 \times 0.3$
$= 0.27$

EXERCISE 19H

1 Suppose this spinner is spun twice:

a Copy and complete the branches on the tree diagram shown.

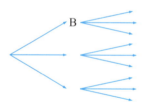

b What is the probability that blue appears on both spins?

c What is the probability that yellow appears on both spins?

d What is the probability that different colours appear on both spins?

e What is the probability that blue appears on *either* spin?

2 In a particular board game there are nine tiles: five are green and the remainder are brown. The tiles start face down on the table so they all look the same.

a If a player is required to pick a tile at random, determine the probability that it is:

   i green   **ii** brown.

b Suppose a player has to pick two tiles in a row, replacing the first and shuffling them before the second is selected. Copy and complete the tree diagram illustrating the possible outcomes.

c Using **b**, determine the probability that:

   i   both tiles are green

   ii both tiles are brown

   iii tile 1 is brown and tile 2 is green

   iv one tile is brown and the other is green.

tile 2

tile 1

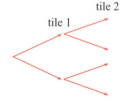

3 The probability of rain tomorrow is estimated to be $\frac{1}{4}$. If it does rain, Rising Tide will start favourite with probability $\frac{2}{5}$ of winning. If it is fine he has a 1 in 20 chance of winning.

   a Display the sample space of possible results on a tree diagram.

   b Determine the probability that Rising Tide will win tomorrow.

4 Machine A makes 60% of the bottles produced at a factory. Machine B makes the rest. Machine A spoils 3% of its product, while Machine B spoils 4%. Determine the probability that the next bottle inspected at this factory will be spoiled.

Example 12 ◄») **Self Tutor**

Bag A contains 4 green and 1 yellow ticket. Bag B contains 2 green and 3 yellow tickets. A bag is randomly selected by tossing a coin and one ticket is removed from it. Determine the probability that it is yellow.

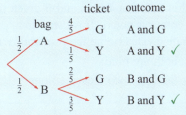

$P(\text{yellow}) = P(A \text{ and } Y) + P(B \text{ and } Y)$

$\qquad\qquad = \frac{1}{2} \times \frac{1}{5} + \frac{1}{2} \times \frac{3}{5}$ {branches marked with a ✓}

$\qquad\qquad = \frac{4}{10}$

$\qquad\qquad = \frac{2}{5}$

> To get a yellow we take either the first branch ticked **or** the second one ticked. We **add** the probabilities for these outcomes.

---

5 Bag A contains 2 blue and 3 red discs and Bag B contains 5 blue and 1 red disc. A bag is chosen at random (by the flip of a coin) and one disc is taken at random from it. Determine the probability that the disc is red.

6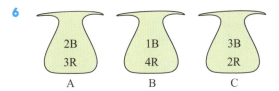

Three bags contain different numbers of blue and red marbles. A bag is selected using a die which has three A faces, two B faces, and one C face.

One marble is selected randomly from the chosen bag. Determine the probability that it is: **a** blue   **b** red.

SAMPLING WITH AND WITHOUT REPLACEMENT

Sampling is the process of selecting an object from a large group of objects and inspecting it for some particular feature. The object is then either **put back** (sampling **with replacement**) or **put to one side** (sampling **without replacement**).

Sometimes the inspection process makes it impossible to return the object to the large group. Such processes include:

- Is the chocolate hard- or soft-centred? Bite it or squeeze it to see.
- Does the egg contain one or two yolks? Break it open and see.
- Is the object correctly made? Pull it apart to see.

The sampling process is used for Quality Control in industrial processes.

Example 13 ◀》 **Self Tutor**

A bin contains 4 blue and 5 green marbles. A marble is selected from this bin and its colour is noted. It is then *replaced*. A second marble is then drawn and its colour is noted. Determine the probability that:

a both are blue
b the first is blue and the second is green
c there is one of each colour.

Tree diagram:

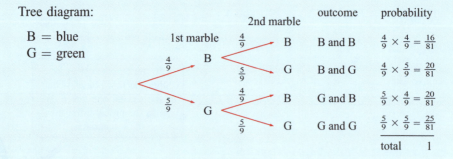

a   P(both blue)

$= \frac{4}{9} \times \frac{4}{9}$

$= \frac{16}{81}$

b   P(first is B and second is G)

$= \frac{4}{9} \times \frac{5}{9}$

$= \frac{20}{81}$

c   P(one of each colour)

$=$ P(B then G or G then B)

$=$ P(B then G) $+$ P(G then B)

$= \frac{4}{9} \times \frac{5}{9} + \frac{5}{9} \times \frac{4}{9}$

$= \frac{40}{81}$

Example 14   ◀) **Self Tutor**

Consider **Example 13** again, but on this occasion the first marble is not replaced before the second is drawn. What are the probabilities now?

Tree diagram:

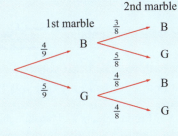

	outcome	probability
B	B and B	$\frac{4}{9} \times \frac{3}{8} = \frac{12}{72}$
G	B and G	$\frac{4}{9} \times \frac{5}{8} = \frac{20}{72}$
B	G and B	$\frac{5}{9} \times \frac{4}{8} = \frac{20}{72}$
G	G and G	$\frac{5}{9} \times \frac{4}{8} = \frac{20}{72}$
	total	1

a   P(both blue)

$= \frac{4}{9} \times \frac{3}{8}$

$= \frac{12}{72}$

b   P(first is B and second is G)

$= \frac{4}{9} \times \frac{5}{8}$

$= \frac{20}{72}$

c   P(one of each colour)

$=$ P(B then G or G then B)

$=$ P(B then G) $+$ P(G then B)

$= \frac{4}{9} \times \frac{5}{8} + \frac{5}{9} \times \frac{4}{8}$

$= \frac{40}{72}$

EXERCISE 19I

1 A box contains 6 red and 3 yellow tickets. Two tickets are drawn at random (the first being *replaced* before the second is drawn). Draw a tree diagram to represent the sample space and use it to determine the probability that:

    a   both are red
    b   both are yellow
    c   the first is red and the second is yellow
    d   one is red and the other is yellow

2 7 tickets numbered 1, 2, 3, 4, 5, 6 and 7 are placed in a hat. Two of the tickets are taken from the hat at random *without replacement*. Determine the probability that:

    a   both are odd
    b   both are even
    c   the first is even and the second is odd
    d   one is even and the other is odd

3 Sadi has a bag of 8 sweets which are all identical in shape. 5 have orange centres and 3 have lemon centres. She selects one sweet at random, eats it, and then takes another, also at random. Determine the probability that:

    a   both sweets had lemon centres
    b   both sweets had orange centres
    c   the first had an orange centre and the second had a lemon centre
    d   the first had a lemon centre and the second had an orange centre

Add your answers to **a**, **b**, **c** and **d**. Explain why the answer must be 1.

4 A cook selects an egg at random from a carton containing 7 ordinary eggs and 5 double-yolk eggs. She cracks the egg into a bowl and sees whether it has two yolks or not. She then selects another egg at random from the carton and checks it.

Let S represent "a single yolk egg" and D represent "a double yolk egg".

   a Draw a tree diagram to illustrate this sampling process.
   b What is the probability that both eggs had two yolks?
   c What is the probability that both eggs had only one yolk?

5

Freda selects a chocolate at random from a box containing 8 hard-centred and 11 soft-centred chocolates. She bites it to see whether it is hard-centred or not. She then selects another chocolate at random from the box and checks it.

Let H represent "a hard-centred chocolate" and S represent "a soft-centred chocolate".

   a Draw a tree diagram to illustrate this sampling process.
   b What is the probability that both chocolates have hard centres?
   c What is the probability that both chocolates have soft centres?

6 A sporting club runs a raffle in which 200 tickets are sold. There are two winning tickets which are drawn at random, in succession, without replacement. If Adam bought 8 tickets in the raffle, determine the probability that he:
   a wins first prize   **b** does not win first prize
   c wins second prize *given that* he did not win first prize.

J   MUTUALLY EXCLUSIVE AND NON-MUTUALLY EXCLUSIVE EVENTS

Suppose we select a card at random from a normal pack of 52 playing cards. Consider carefully these events:

Event X: the card is a heart   *Event Y:* the card is an ace   *Event Z:* the card is a 7

Notice that:
   • X and Y have a common outcome: the Ace of hearts
   • X and Z have a common outcome: the 7 of hearts
   • Y and Z do not have a common outcome.

When considering a situation like the one above:

   • if two events have no common outcomes we say they are **mutually exclusive** or **disjoint**

   • if two events have common outcomes they are **not mutually exclusive**.

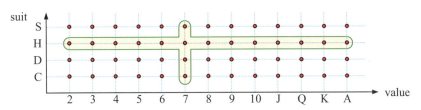

Notice: P (ace **or** seven) $= \frac{8}{52}$ and   P(ace) + P(seven) $= \frac{4}{52} + \frac{4}{52} = \frac{8}{52}$

So,

> if two events A and B are **mutually exclusive** then
> $$P(A \text{ or } B) = P(A) + P(B)$$

Notice: P(heart **or** seven) $= \frac{16}{52}$ and   P(heart) + P(seven) $= \frac{13}{52} + \frac{4}{52} = \frac{17}{52}$

Actually,   P(heart **or** seven) = P(heart) + P(seven) − P(heart **and** seven)

So,

> if two events A and B are **not mutually exclusive** then
> $$P(A \text{ or } B) = P(A) + P(B) - P(A \text{ and } B).$$

EXERCISE 19J

1   An ordinary die with faces 1, 2, 3, 4, 5 and 6 is rolled once. Consider these events:

  A: getting a 1 B: getting a 3
  C: getting an odd number D: getting an even number
  E: getting a prime number F: getting a result greater than 3.

  a   List all possible pairs of events which are mutually exclusive.

  b   Find:

      i   P(B or D)   **ii**   P(D or E)   **iii**   P(A or E)

      iv   P(B or E)   **v**   P(C or D)   **vi**   P(A or B or F)

2   A coin and an ordinary die are tossed simultaneously.

  a   Draw a grid showing the 12 possible outcomes.

  b   Find the probabilites of getting: **i**   a 'head' and a 5   **ii**   a 'head' or a 5

  c   Check that: P(H or 5) = P(H) + P(5) − P(H **and** 5).

3   Two ordinary dice are rolled.

  a   Draw a grid showing the 36 possible outcomes.

  b   Find the probability of getting: **i**   a 3 and a 4   **ii**   a 3 or a 4

  c   Check that: P(3 or 4) = P(3) + P(4) − P(3 **and** 4)

K   INDEPENDENT EVENTS

Two events are **independent** if one event does not affect the outcome of the other event.

Examples of independent events are:

- rolling a '6 with a die' and getting a 'head with a coin'
- choosing a 'red bead from a bag' and 'a blue bead from a second bag'
- choosing a '7 from a pack of cards' and 'it is raining'.

> If events A and B are independent then
>
> $$P(A \text{ and } B) = P(A) \times P(B).$$

EXERCISE 19K

1   A die is numbered 2, 3, 3, 3, 4, 5.   This die is rolled and an ordinary coin is tossed. Find the probabilities of getting:

   a   a 2 and a tail   **b**   a 3 and a head   **c**   at least 3, and a head

2   A die numbered 1 to 6 is rolled twice. Without using a 2-dimensional grid, find:

   a   P(a 6 and a 6)   **b**   P(at least 3 and a 4 in that order)

   c   P(at least 3 both times)   **d**   P(a 3 and a 4 in either order)

3   In Milford Sound in New Zealand it rains on average 328 days a year. Determine the probability of not getting rain on:

   a   two successive days   **b**   three successive days.

4   If a coin is tossed 4 times, what is the probability of getting the sequence:

   a   HTHT   **b**   THTH   **c**   HHTT?

5   A business has three photocopiers, and the probabilities of them malfunctioning on any one day are 5%, 10%, and 14% respectively. What is the probability that on any given day:

   a   all function   **b**   none function   **c**   at least one functions?

6   When two shooters fire at a target they hit it 90% and 80% of the time respectively. If they both fire simultaneously at a target, what is the chance that:

   a   both hit it   **b**   both miss it   **c**   only one hits it?

LINKS
click here

WHAT ARE YOUR SURVIVAL PROSPECTS?

Areas of interaction:
Environments/Health and social education

REVIEW SET 19A

1 A shuttlecock used in badminton was hit in the air 384 times and it finished on its feathers 47 times. What is the experimental probability that a shuttlecock will finish on:

    a its feathers   **b** its side?

2 A die has the numbers 0, 1, 1, 2, 2, 2 on its faces. If the die is rolled once, determine the probability that the result is:

    a a 1   **b** a 3   **c** a 0 or a 2   **d** a non-2   **e** a prime number.

3 A pair of dice has the same numbers on its faces as in question **2**. These dice are both rolled once.

    a Copy and complete the grid of possible results.

    b Hence determine the probability of getting:

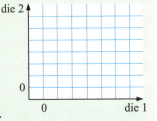

        i a pair of 1s   **ii** a pair

      iii a 0 **and** a 1   **iv** a sum of 3   **v** a 0 **or** a 1.

4 When Cassie hits a golf ball with a driver, the ball passes the 180 m marker with probability 0.72. If Cassie uses her driver on 14 tees during a golf round, how many times would she expect to drive more than 180 m?

5 The school student population is 827. The students all cast a vote for the 'head student'.

    a Copy and complete the given table and add to it a Relative Frequency column.

    b What is the probability that a randomly selected student:

        i is one of the candidates   **ii** voted for student McKay?

Student	Frequency
Chen	179
Hendry	213
Shustrai	168
McKay	
Total	

6 **a** List the sexes of a three child family.

    b What is the probability that a randomly selected three child family consists of:

        i all girls   **ii** at least one boy   **iii** exactly one boy?

7 Members of a youth club in Singapore were asked to indicate which of the sports table tennis (T) and badminton (B) they play. The numbers on the Venn diagram indicate how many are in each of the categories. If a member is selected at random, determine the probability that he or she plays:

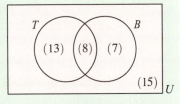

    a table tennis   **b** badminton   **c** both of these sports

    d table tennis but not badminton   **e** table tennis or badminton

8 Jude has probability 0.8 of kicking a field goal whereas Sam has probability 0.6.

    a Copy and complete the tree diagram:

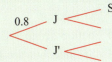

        J is the event 'Jude kicks a goal'

        S is the event 'Sam kicks a goal'.

b If they both have a kick for goal, what is the likelihood that:

    i they both fail to kick a goal   **ii** at least one of them kicks a goal?

REVIEW SET 19B

1 When spinning two coins, what is:

    a the probability of spinning two heads

    b the expectation of spinning two heads from 88 spins?

2 A die is numbered 1, 2, 2, 2, 3, 3. This die is rolled and a coin is tossed. Find the probability of getting:

    a a 3 and a 'tail'   **b** a 'head' and at least a 2?

3 If a pair of dice like the one in question **2** are rolled once only:

    a draw a 2-dimensional grid to display the possible outcomes

    b hence, find the chance of getting:

        i a pair of 3s   **ii** a 1 **and** a 2   **iii** a 1 **or** a 3

4 **a** What is meant by saying that 'two events are independent'?

    b Give an example of two events which are:

        i independent   **ii** not independent.

5 A biased coin falls heads 60% of the time. If the coin is tossed 3 times, what is the likelihood (probability) that it falls:

    a HHH   **b** TTT   **c** THT?

6 An ordinary die and a coin are tossed simultaneously.

    a Draw a grid which shows all possible outcomes.

    b Find the probability of getting:

        i a tail **and** a 2   **ii** a tail **or** a 2.

    c Check that: P(T or 2) = P(T) + P(2) − P(T and 2).

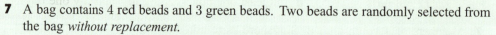

7 A bag contains 4 red beads and 3 green beads. Two beads are randomly selected from the bag *without replacement*.

    a Draw a fully labelled tree diagram showing possible outcomes and assign probabilities to its branches.

    b What is the probability of getting:

        i two green beads   **ii** one of each colour?

8 In a group of 42 students, 27 study Science and 28 study French. 3 study neither of these two subjects.

    a Display this information on a Venn diagram.

    b If a student is randomly selected from the group, determine the probability the student studies:

        i both Science and French   **ii** Science or French

        iii Science, but not French   **iv** exactly one of Science or French.

Chapter 20

Functions, graphs and notation

Contents:

A   Graphical interpretation
B   Interpreting line graphs
C   Conversion graphs
D   Time series data
E   Step graphs
F   Mappings
G   Functions
H   Function notation

OPENING PROBLEM

Graphs show information about what has happened in the past. They are sometimes useful in helping us predict what might happen in the future.

For example, the following graph shows the progress of two yachts in a 'round-the-world' challenge, starting and finishing in Plymouth, England. The total length of the race is 48 000 km.

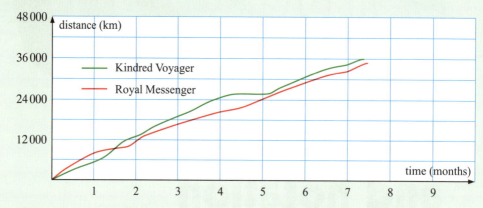

- How can you describe the progress of the two vessels from the graph?
- Can you suggest what it means when there are horizontal stretches on the graph?
- Can you predict how long it will take to finish the race? Can you predict who will win?

A   GRAPHICAL INTERPRETATION

Graphs are of little use to us if we are unable to interpret them. We need to understand how they are constructed and be able to identify any trends in the data.

Example 1   🔊 Self Tutor

The given graph shows the ages and work done by 5 employees.

a Which person is the oldest?

b Who has done the most work?

c Who has done the least work?

---

a E has the largest value on the age axis ∴ E is the oldest.

b B and E are the highest on the work done axis.
  ∴ B and E have done the most work.

c A is the lowest on the work done axis.
  ∴ A has done the least work.

EXERCISE 20A

1 The given graph shows productivity for various hours of training for five employees.

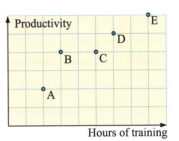

   a Who received the most hours of training?
   b Who is the most productive?
   c Are there employees with equal productivity?
   d Comment on the general trend of this graph.

2 The workers of five factories were surveyed on their average hours of sleep. The results were graphed with the number of industrial accidents.

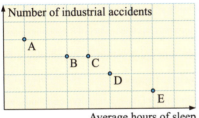

   a Which factory had the most accidents?
   b Which factory had employees with the least number of hours of sleep?
   c Did any factories have the same number of accidents?
   d Comment on the relationship between average hours of sleep and the number of industrial accidents.

Example 2   ◀)) **Self Tutor**

Josie delivers letters and parcels in her 'Pick up and deliver' business.

The graph shows a short time interval during her day.

Write a short story which could describe what has happened in this interval.

Josie is travelling at a constant speed.	{shown by AB}
She slows to a stop.	{shown by BC}
She delivers a parcel.	{shown by CD, no speed}
She then increases speed to her usual rate.	{shown by DE}
She resumes her normal constant speed.	{shown by E ...}

---

3 After examining **Example 2**, write a short story about one of Josie's delivery intervals for:

   a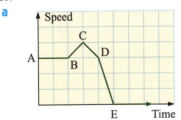

   b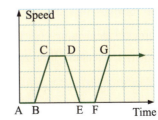

4 Make up a story of your own similar to **Example 2** and draw the corresponding graph.

Example 3   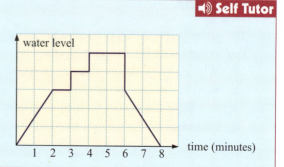 ◆》 **Self Tutor**

This graph shows the water level of a spa bath.

Write a story explaining the graph.

DEMO

The spa bath is filling for 2 minutes. After one minute a person gets in, and one minute later someone else gets in. After 2 minutes they both get out. The water is then let out of the spa bath.

5 Write a story for each of the following graphs showing the water level in a spa bath:

a

b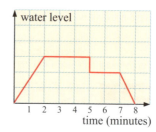

6 Draw graphs to illustrate the following stories:

a A spa bath is run for 3 minutes. A boy gets in and stays in for 2 minutes, then his brother gets in. They both get out after a further 3 minutes. The spa bath is emptied and this takes 2 minutes.

b A spa bath is run for 2 minutes. Two people get in and after 3 minutes one gets out. After 2 minutes the other person gets out and the spa bath is emptied, taking 2 minutes.

B   INTERPRETING LINE GRAPHS

LINE GRAPHS

Line graphs are used to show variations between two quantities.

- An upward sloping line (as we look from left to right) indicates an **increasing** quantity.
- A downward sloping line indicates a **decreasing** quantity.

The following two graphs display the same information.

The first is a **dot graph** or **dot plot** which shows the temperatures at hourly intervals during a 12 hour period, from 6 am to 6 pm.

The second is a **line graph** where the dots are connected by straight lines.

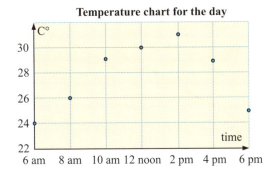

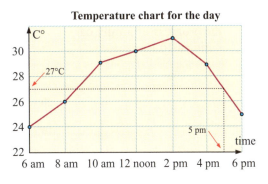

In reality, the lines between the dots would almost certainly not be straight, but because we do not have more accurate data, the straight lines give an **estimate** of what happened.

From both graphs we can read off information such as:
- The highest temperature recorded for the day was at 2 pm.
- The lowest temperature recorded was at 6 am.
- The temperature increased from 6 am to 2 pm and then decreased until 6 pm.
- The temperature at 8 am was 26^oC.

For this particular information, the line graph is more useful than the point graph because **in-between values** can be **estimated**.

For example, the temperature at 5 pm can be estimated as 27^oC (as shown by the dotted line on the line graph).

EXERCISE 20B

1   Managers of a retail store conduct a customer count to help them decide how to roster sales staff. The results are shown in the line graph:

   a   At what time was there the greatest number of people in the store?

   b   At what time was there the lowest number of people in the store?

   c   Describe what happened in the store between 3 pm and 4 pm.

   d   Use the graph to estimate the number of people in the store at 9.30 am.

   e   What is wrong with this graph?

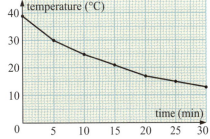

2   When a bottle of soft drink was placed in a refrigerator, its temperature was measured at 5-minute intervals and the results were graphed. From the graph:

   a   determine the temperature of the liquid when it was first placed in the refrigerator

   b   find how long it took for the temperature to drop to 20^oC

   c   find the temperature after 10 minutes in the refrigerator

   d   find the fall in temperature during   i   the first 15 minutes   ii   the next 15 minutes.

3 The given graph shows the progress of a rally car during a 10 lap race.

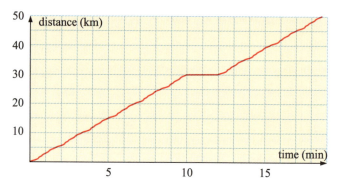

Use the graph to estimate:

   a the total length of   **i** the race   **ii** each lap

   b the time required for each lap

   c the number of laps completed before the car went into the pits for new tyres and more fuel

   d the time the car spent in the pits

   e the overall average speed of the car for the whole race.

C   CONVERSION GRAPHS

Conversion graphs are line graphs which enable us to convert from one quantity to another.

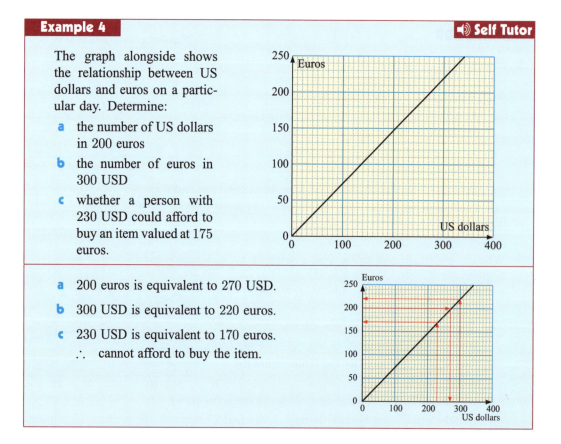

Example 4	◀)) **Self Tutor**

The graph alongside shows the relationship between US dollars and euros on a particular day. Determine:

   a the number of US dollars in 200 euros

   b the number of euros in 300 USD

   c whether a person with 230 USD could afford to buy an item valued at 175 euros.

   a 200 euros is equivalent to 270 USD.

   b 300 USD is equivalent to 220 euros.

   c 230 USD is equivalent to 170 euros.

      ∴ cannot afford to buy the item.

ACTIVITY   **CURRENCY TRENDS**

Over a period of a month, collect the currency conversions which compare the euro to the currency of another country. These are available from the daily newspaper or from the internet. If using the internet, search for 'currency conversion'.

Graph your results, updating your graph each day.

EXERCISE 20C

1 Use the currency conversion graph in **Example 4** to estimate:

   a the number of US dollars in   **i**   155 euros   **ii**   125 euros

   b the number of euros in   **i**   100 USD   **ii**   250 USD

2 The graph shows the relationship between distances measured in miles and kilometres. Convert:

   a **i**   45 km to miles

      ii   28 km to miles

   b **i**   48 miles to km

      ii   30 miles to km.

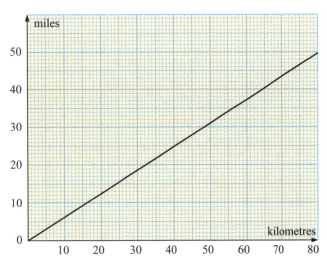

3 Fahrenheit and Celsius (Centigrade) are two different ways of measuring temperature. The graph below shows how to convert from one unit of measure to the other.

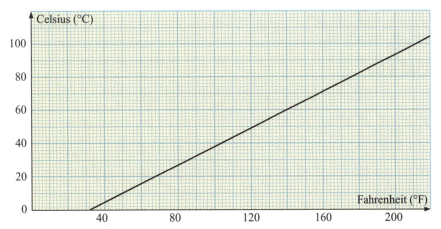

   a If pure water boils at 212°F, find the equivalent temperature in degrees Celsius.

   b Determine the degrees Fahrenheit equivalent to:

      i   40°C   **ii**   75°C   **iii**   0°C.

TIME SERIES DATA

Data that is collected over time and at regular intervals is often referred to as **time series data**.

This data is usually presented on a **line graph** with time intervals on the horizontal axis and the variable being measured on the vertical axis.

For example, the following graph shows the number of tourists at Hawkins Farmstay over a five year period from 2000 to 2005 recorded at 3 month intervals.

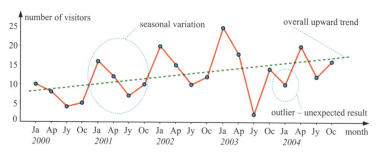

A time series is used to identify **trends** or patterns in the data over a period of time.

These trends fall into three main types:

- **short-term variations** where the graph changes over a short time span
- **long-term variations** such as seasonal fluctuations
- **overall trends** where the general shape of the graph may be increasing, decreasing or staying approximately the same over the whole time span.

From the Hawkins Farmstay graph we note that the total number of visitors is increasing overall.

However, there are clear seasonal variations as nearly every year there are more visitors in January and less in July.

There is a short term variation shown here with the data in January 2004. How could this be explained?

A time series graph may show **outliers**. They are data values that do not fit the identifying patterns. On the graph they are either above or below the expected pattern. In the graph above, January 2004 would be an outlier, because January usually has the greatest number of visitors for the year.

EXERCISE 20D

1 The time series graph alongside shows the number of kilograms of tomatoes produced from Sam's glasshouse each year over a 10-year period.

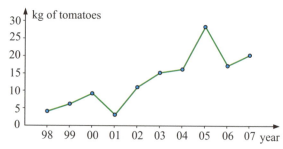

   a What is the overall trend for the number of kgs of tomatoes that Sam's glasshouse is producing?

   b Identify any outliers and give an explanation as to what may have caused them.

   c Predict how many kgs of tomatoes that Sam will have in 2008. How accurate do you think your prediction will be?

2 This data shows the percentage of students in a school who participated in sport on a regular basis over a ten year period.

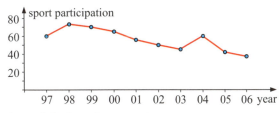

a What long-term trend does this graph show?

b Identify one outlier and explain what might have happened.

c What health concerns may arise in future as a result of the trend shown?

3 The data below shows the total rainfall per month in my backyard over a year:

Month	J	F	M	A	M	J	J	A	S	O	N	D
Rainfall (mm)	10	29	4	5	25	35	40	32	24	14	10	6

a Draw a line graph of this data.

b Describe any patterns you notice about the rainfall and explain each of them.

c Identify any outliers and attempt to explain them.

4 Heather's school bus was supposed to arrive at 7.30 am each day. It was always late so Heather decided to record the minutes it was late over a month. She wanted to see if there were any patterns in order to predict if she could sleep in on some days. Her results are as follows:

Day	M	T	W	T	F	M	T	W	T	F	M	T	W	T	F	M	T	W	T	F
Mins late	5	2	10	12	15	3	1	8	12	16	6	3	11	13	17	4	1	10	12	15

a Draw a line graph of this data.

b Identify any patterns that you see. Write a story that may explain one of these.

c On which days do you think Heather could sleep in, and for how long?

E STEP GRAPHS

A **step graph** is another form of a line graph. It shows distinct steps where the graph 'jumps'.

Example 5 ◀) **Self Tutor**

Frank and Shirley have a TV repair service and their charges are as shown in the given graph.

a Use the graph to find the cost of a repair service taking 38 minutes.

b Find the maximum length of a service costing $75.

c If the call out fee is $35, how much do they charge for each 15 minutes or part thereof?

d Without extending the graph, find the cost of a 65 minute service.

a For > 30 mins but $\leqslant 45$ mins it costs \$95.

∴ a 38 minute service costs \$95.

b For a \$75 service, the maximum period is 30 mins.

c The gap between each step is the same and is \$20

∴ each extra 15 mins (or part thereof) costs \$20.

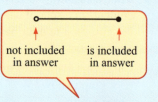

not included in answer   is included in answer

d

Time	Cost($)
0	35
$0 < t \leqslant 15$	55
$15 < t \leqslant 30$	75
$30 < t \leqslant 45$	95
$45 < t \leqslant 60$	115
$60 < t \leqslant 75$	135

∴ it costs \$135 for a 65 minute service.

EXERCISE 20E

1 The graph shows Car Parking Fees for Tom's Car Parking Service.

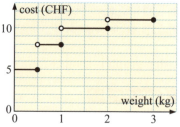

a Find the cost of parking for:

i $1\frac{1}{2}$ hours   **ii** 5 hours

iii 5 hours 3 mins.

b What is the most time a car can be parked for:

i \$4   **ii** \$16?

c What is the range of times a car can be parked for \$12?

2 A business in Switzerland frequently sends small parcels to the UK. The rates are given by the step graph alongside.

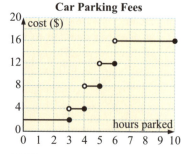

a Find the cost of sending a parcel weighing:

i 325 grams   **ii** 1.2 kg.

b What is the heaviest parcel that could be sent for CHF10?

c Write out the information given in the graph in table form.

3

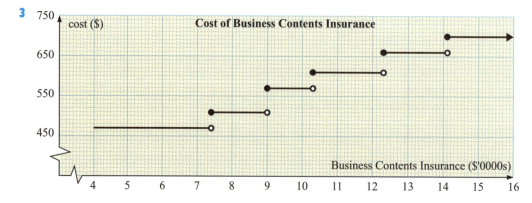

The graph gives the cost of insuring the assets of a business including furniture, photocopiers, computers, and so on.

a   Find the cost of insuring the assets for: **i** $65 000   **ii** $106 000.

b   What is the range in the value of assets which could be insured for a cost of $660?

MAPPINGS

A **mapping** is used to map the members or **elements** of one set called the **domain**, onto the members of another set called the **range**.

In particular we can define:

- The **domain** of a mapping is the set of elements which are to be mapped.
- The **range** of a mapping is the set of elements which are the result of mapping the elements of the domain.

Consider these two mappings:

For the mapping $y = x + 3$:

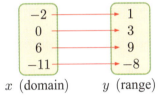

For the mapping $y = x^2 + 1$:

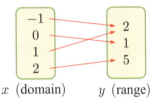

$y = x + 3$ or 'add 3 onto x' is called a **one-one** mapping because every element in the domain maps onto one and only one element in the range.

$y = x^2 + 1$ or 'square x and then add 1' is called a **many-one** mapping because more than one element in the domain maps onto the same element in the range.

EXERCISE 20F

1   Copy and complete the following 'sets and mappings' diagrams, and state whether the mapping is one-one, many-one, one-many or many-many.

a   mapping '$y = 2x - 5$'

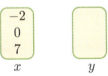

b   mapping 'is not equal to'

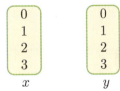

c   mapping '$x = y^2$'

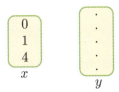

d   mapping 'is greater than'

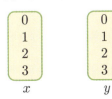

e   mapping 'add 1'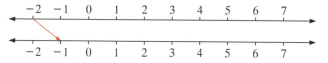

2   For these domains and mappings, describe the corresponding range:

    a   domain   {real numbers}   mapping: 'subtract 20'

    b   domain   {odd numbers}   mapping: 'double'

    c   domain   {positive real numbers}   mapping: 'find the square root'

    d   domain   {real numbers $\geqslant 0$}   mapping: 'add 10'

    e   domain   {even numbers}   mapping: 'divide by 2'

    f   domain   {angles θ where $0^o \leqslant \theta < 180^o$}   mapping: 'find $\sin\theta$'

G   FUNCTIONS

We can also use set notation to describe mappings.

For example, consider the set $\{0, 1, 2, 3\}$ under the mapping 'square the number'.

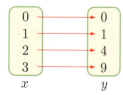

$\{0, 1, 2, 3\}$ maps onto $\{0, 1, 4, 9\}$

We say that: $\{0, 1, 2, 3\}$ is the domain and
              $\{0, 1, 4, 9\}$ is the range.

We could write this mapping as $x \mapsto x^2$

This is a one-one mapping, and is an example of a *function*.

> A **function** is a mapping in which each element of the domain maps onto *exactly one* element of the range.

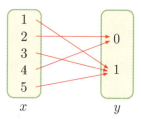

is an example of a **many-one** function

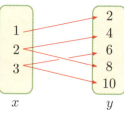

is an example of a **one-many** mapping. This is **not a function**

Note: • Functions can only be one-one or many-one mappings.

       • One-many and many-many mappings are *not* functions.

Example 6   ◀)) **Self Tutor**

For the domain $\{0, 1, 2, 3\}$ and the function 'subtract 2', find the range.

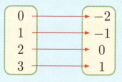

So, the range is $\{-2, -1, 0, 1\}$

EXERCISE 20G

1 Find the range for the functions with domain D:

    a $D = \{-1, 0, 2, 7, 9\}$, function: 'add 3'.

    b $D = \{-2, -1, 0, 1, 2\}$, function: 'square and then divide by 2'.

    c $D = \{x \mid -2 < x < 2\}$, function: 'multiply x by 2 then add 1'.

    d $D = \{x \mid -3 \leqslant x \leqslant 4\}$, function: 'cube x'.

Example 7 ◀⧸ **Self Tutor**

State the domain and range of:

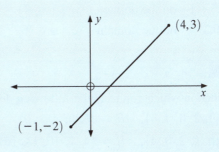

The domain is $\{x \mid -1 \leqslant x \leqslant 4\}$. The range is $\{y \mid -2 \leqslant y \leqslant 3\}$

---

2 Find the domain and range for the following functions:

a

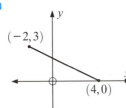

b

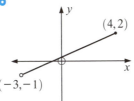

c

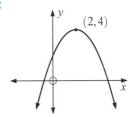

d

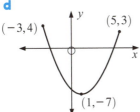

e

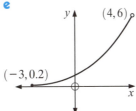

f

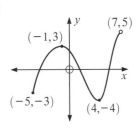

g

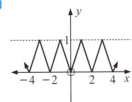

h

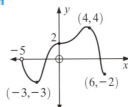

3 For each of these functions: **i** use a graphics calculator to help sketch the function
                                         ii find the range.

a $y = 3x + 1$ on the domain $\{x \mid -2 \leqslant x \leqslant 2\}$

b $y = x^2$ on the domain $\{x \mid -3 \leqslant x \leqslant 4\}$

c $y = 2^x$ on the domain $\{x \mid -2 \leqslant x \leqslant 3\}$

d $y = \dfrac{1}{x-1}$ on the domain $\{x \mid 0 \leqslant x \leqslant 3, \ x \neq 1\}$

$\mathbb{R}$ is the set of real numbers.

e $y = x + \dfrac{1}{x}$ on the domain $\{x \mid -4 \leqslant x \leqslant 4, \ x \neq 0\}$

f $y = x^2 + 1$ on the domain $\{x \mid x \in \mathbb{R}\}$

g $y = (0.5)^x$ on the domain $\{x \mid x \in \mathbb{R}\}$

Example 8   🔊 **Self Tutor**

Find the function which connects the following domains and ranges:

a $D = \{1, 2, 3, 4, 5\}$, $R = \{5, 6, 7, 8, 9\}$

b $D = \{0, 1, 2, 3, 4\}$, $R = \{4, 7, 10, 13, 16\}$

a

x	y
1 →	5
2 →	6
3 →	7
4 →	8
5 →	9

The function is $y = x + 4$
as 4 is added to each x value
to get the y-value,

i.e., $y = x + 4, \ x \in D$.

b

x	y
0 →	4
1 →	7
2 →	10
3 →	13
4 →	16

The y-values are increasing
by 3 as the x-values increase
by 1.

This suggests $y = 3x + k$

But, when $x = 0$, $y = 4$

$\therefore \quad 4 = 3(0) + k$

$\therefore \quad k = 4$

So, $y = 3x + 4, \ x \in D$.

---

4 Find the function which connects the following domains and ranges:

a $D = \{0, 1, 2, 3\}$, $R = \{5, 6, 7, 8\}$

b $D = \{2, 3, 4, 5\}$, $R = \{9, 10, 11, 12\}$

c $D = \{1, 2, 3, 4, 5\}$, $R = \{5, 4, 3, 2, 1\}$

d $D = \{1, 2, 3, 4, 5\}$, $R = \{1, 4, 9, 16, 25\}$

e $D = \{-4, -3, -2, -1, 0, 1, 2, 3, 4\}$, $R = \{0, 1, 4, 9, 16\}$

f $D = \{0, 1, 4, 9, 16, 25\}$, $R = \{0, 1, 2, 3, 4, 5\}$

g $D = \{1, 2, 3, 4, 5\}$, $R = \{3, 5, 7, 9, 11\}$

h $D = \{1, 2, 3, 4, 5\}$, $R = \{1, \frac{1}{2}, \frac{1}{3}, \frac{1}{4}, \frac{1}{5}\}$

i $D = \{2, 3, 4, 5, 6\}$, $R = \{-1, 2, 5, 8, 11\}$

j $D = \{3, 4, 5, 6, 7\}$, $R = \{-1, -3, -5, -7, -9\}$

k $D = \{-1, 0, 1, 2, 3, 4\}$, $R = \{\frac{1}{2}, 1, 2, 4, 8, 16\}$

l $D = \{0, 1, 2, 3, 4\}$, $R = \{1, 2, 5, 10, 17\}$

m $D = \{1, 2, 3, 4, 5\}$, $R = \{40, 37, 34, 31, 28\}$

| **H** | # FUNCTION NOTATION |

Consider the relationship between the distance travelled by a car, d km, and the time taken, t hours. The distance the car travelled was recorded each hour, and tabulated and graphed as shown:

t (hours)	0	1	2	3
d (km)	0	80	160	240

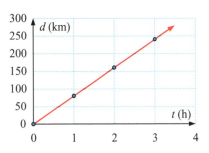

An equation connecting d and t is $d = 80t$ for $t \geqslant 0$.

We say the distance travelled is a **function** of the time taken.

We could write d as $f(t)$ or $d = f(t)$.

read as a   'function of t'
 or   'f of t'

As the graph of d against t is a straight line, we have an example of a **linear function**. In this case $f(t) = 80t$.

If we wish to find the distance travelled after 5 hours, we substitute $t = 5$ into this function.

We write $f(5) = 80 \times 5 = 400$,

and since $d = f(t)$, we find the distance $d = 400$ km.

Other letters such as g, h, F, etc. are also used to represent functions.

If we are considering two different functions we use two different letters to represent them.

Note: • $f(x) = x^2 + 1$ can also be represented by $f : x \mapsto x^2 + 1$.

• $f(2) = 2^2 + 1 = 4 + 1 = 5$

means that 2 in the domain is mapped onto 5 in the range and the graph of the function contains the point (2, 5).

Example 9   ◀ᴺ) **Self Tutor**

If $f(x) = 5x + 2$ and $g(x) = x^2 - 1$ find and interpret:

a $f(6)$ **b** $g(-3)$

a $f(6) = 5(6) + 2$ This means that 6 is mapped onto 32 and $(6, 32)$
       $= 30 + 2$ lies on the graph of the function f.
       $= 32$

b $g(-3) = (-3)^2 - 1$ This means that -3 is mapped onto 8 and $(-3, 8)$
       $= 9 - 1$ lies on the graph of the function g.
       $= 8$

EXERCISE 20H

1 **a** If $f(x) = 3x - 7$, find and interpret $f(5)$.

 b If $g(x) = x - x^2$, find and interpret $g(3)$.

 c If $H(x) = \dfrac{2x + 5}{x - 1}$, find and interpret $H(4)$.

2   **a**   If $f(x) = 5 - 4x$,   find: **i** $f(0)$ **ii** $f(3)$ **iii** $f(-4)$ **iv** $f(100)$

    b   If $E(x) = 2^x$,   find: **i** $E(0)$ **ii** $E(1)$ **iii** $E(5)$ **iv** $E(-2)$

    c   If $h(x) = \dfrac{x}{x-3}$,   find: **i** $h(2)$ **ii** $h(5)$ **iii** $h(10)$ **iv** $h(-7)$

3   **a**   If $f(x) = 5 - x^2$,   find: **i** $f(4)$ **ii** x when $f(x) = 1$.

    b   If $g(x) = 3^x$,   find: **i** $g(4)$ **ii** a when $g(a) = \frac{1}{9}$.

    c   If $m(x) = x^2 - 3$,   find: **i** x when $m(x) = 0$ **ii** x when $m(x) = 1$.

    d   If $f(x) = 3x + 5$ and $g(x) = x^2$,   find x when $f(x) = g(x)$.

4   The value of a car t years after purchase is given by $V(t) = 35\,000 - 3000t$ euros.

    a   Find $V(0)$ and interpret its meaning.

    b   Find $V(3)$ and interpret its meaning.

    c   Find t when $V(t) = 5000$ and explain what this represents.

5   Sketch the graph of $y = f(x)$ where $f(x) = 2x - 1$ on the domain $\{x \mid -3 \leqslant x \leqslant 1\}$.   State the range of this function.

6   Sketch the graph of $y = g(x)$ where $g(x) = 2^{-x}$ on the domain $\{x \mid -2 \leqslant x \leqslant 2\}$.   State the range of this function.

7   The graph of a function is given alongside. Use the graph to:

    a   find $f(2)$

    b   estimate x, to 1 decimal place, when $f(x) = -3$.

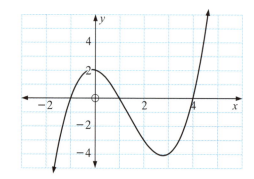

REVIEW SET 20A

1   Five hockey clubs were surveyed on their players' average hours of general fitness training and the number of injuries to players during matches.

    a   Which club had the lowest number of injuries?

    b   Which club's players had the lowest number of hours of fitness training?

    c   Write a sentence describing the general trend of the graph.

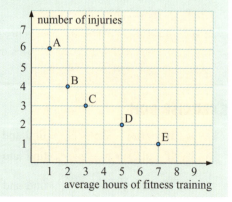

2 The graph alongside shows the price of a minerals exploration stock on the Australian share market during the course of a day.

   a At what time was the price highest?

   b **i** When was the price lowest?

   ii Estimate the day's lowest price.

   c During which time interval did the price rise by the greatest amount?

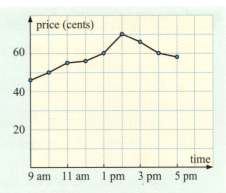

3

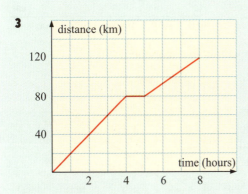

The graph shows a typical day's journey for Miguel on his long-distance cycling tour.

   a How far did Miguel cycle?

   b How long did he take to ride the:

   i first 40 km   **ii** last 40 km?

   c If Miguel set out at 9 am, what time did he stop for lunch?

   d Find Miguel's average speed for the:

   i whole trip   **ii** first 4 hours.

4 The graph shows the charges according to weight of a parcel delivery company.

   a What is the company's minimum charge?

   b What is the charge for a parcel weighing 10.2 kg?

   c Andrea used the company to send two parcels to the same address, two weeks apart. The parcels weighed 7.5 kg and 4 kg. How much would she have saved if she had combined the items in one parcel?

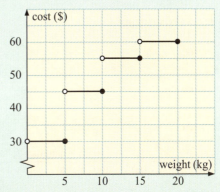

5 For these functions, find the domain and range:

   a

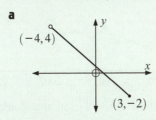

   b

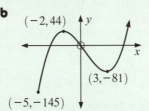

   c

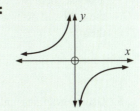

6 **a** If $f(x) = 5x + 2$, find and interpret $f(-3)$.

   b If $f(x) = 4 - x^2$, find: **i** $f(2)$ **ii** $f(-5)$.

   c If $f(x) = 2^x$, find: **i** $f(5)$ **ii** x when $f(x) = \frac{1}{8}$.

REVIEW SET 20B

1 The graph shows the population of a city over the period 1960-2000.

    a Use the graph to estimate the population in:

        i 1960   **ii** 1985

    b Estimate the year when the population passed 40 000.

    c During which decade did the population grow by the largest amount?

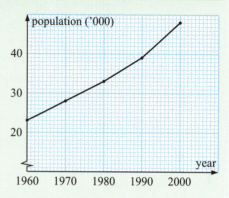

2 The graph shows the journeys of two competitors in a marathon.

    a Use the graph to estimate the length in kilometres of a marathon race.

    b Because there were so many runners in the event, not everyone was able to start at the same time. If Jacob started at 8.15 am, what time did Sandy start?

    c How long did each of the runners take to complete the course?

    d What was Jacob's average speed over the first 20 km?

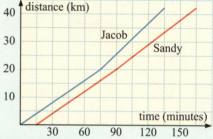

3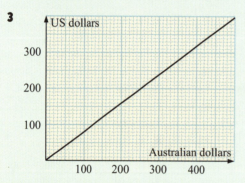

The graph alongside shows the relationship between Australian dollars and US dollars on a particular day. Determine:

    a the number of US dollars in 400 Australian dollars

    b the number of Australian dollars in 100 US dollars

    c whether a person with 150 Australian dollars could buy an item valued at 125 US dollars.

4 The graph shows the quarterly turnover of a department store. Identify *two* trends in the data and offer a possible explanation for them.

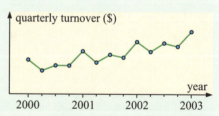

5 Use a graphics calculator to sketch the function $y = x^2 - 4$ on the domain $\{x \mid -2 \leqslant x \leqslant 3\}$ and find its range.

6 Find the function with domain $\{1, 2, 3, 4, 5\}$ and range $\{-1, 3, 7, 11, 15\}$.

7 If $G(x) = \dfrac{2x - 1}{x + 3}$, find and interpret $G(2)$.

Chapter 21

Geometry

Contents:

A Angle properties
B Triangles
C Isosceles triangles
D Angles of a quadrilateral
E Polygons
F The exterior angles of a polygon
G Nets of solids

OPENING PROBLEM

Jason and Hugo construct timber-framed panels for a new house.

For you to consider:

- If a frame is pentagonal in shape, what is the sum of the interior angles of the frame?

- If the pentagonal frame has two right angles for its base, and the remaining three angles are of equal size, what size must the remaining angles be?

- If two sides of a triangular frame are equal in length, and the angle between them is $110°$, what are the sizes of the other two angles of the frame?

VOCABULARY

It is assumed that you are familiar with these words used in geometry:

point	line	shape	vertex	edge	angle	parallel
triangle	quadrilateral	polygon	pentagon	hexagon	octagon	solid
prism	cube	cuboid	pyramid	cylinder	cone	sphere

If you have forgotten, **click** on any word and the meaning will appear.

NOTATION

You should remember that:

- Points or vertices are labelled by capital letters.

- Lines or edges are labelled by a small case letter.

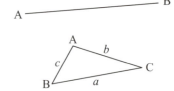

- An angle is often labelled using a small case letter or a letter of the Greek alphabet.

  Three point notation is also often used. For example, the illustrated angle is θ or $P\widehat{Q}R$ or $\angle PQR$.

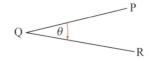

LINE TERMINOLOGY

- **Line AB** is the endless straight line passing through the points A and B.

- **Line segment AB** is the part of the straight line AB that connects A with B.

- **Concurrent lines** are three or more lines that all pass through a common point.

- **Collinear points** are points which lie in a straight line.

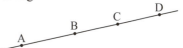

- **Perpendicular lines** intersect at right angles.

- **Parallel lines** are lines which never intersect. Arrow heads indicate parallelism.

- A **transversal** is a line which crosses over two other lines.

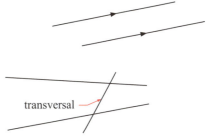

TYPES OF ANGLES

Revolution	Straight Angle	Right Angle
One complete turn. One revolution $= 360^o$.	$\frac{1}{2}$ turn. 1 straight angle $= 180^o$.	$\frac{1}{4}$ turn. 1 right angle $= 90^o$.
Acute Angle	**Obtuse Angle**	**Reflex Angle**
Less than a $\frac{1}{4}$ turn. An acute angle has size between 0° and 90°.	Between $\frac{1}{4}$ turn and $\frac{1}{2}$ turn. An obtuse angle has size between 90° and 180°.	Between $\frac{1}{2}$ turn and 1 turn. A reflex angle has size between 180° and 360°.

TYPES OF TRIANGLES

scalene

Three sides of different lengths.

right angled

One angle a right angle.

isosceles

Two sides are equal. (Notice the line of symmetry.)

equilateral

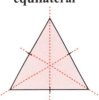

Three sides are equal. (Notice the 3 lines of symmetry.)

SOLIDS

> A **solid** is a body which occupies space. It has three dimensions.

The diagrams below show a collection of solids.
Each solid shape shown has the three dimensions: *length*, *width* and *height*.

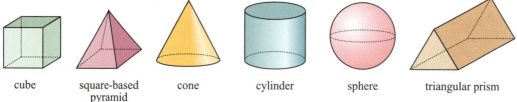

cube   square-based   cone   cylinder   sphere   triangular prism
          pyramid

The boundaries of a solid are called **surfaces**. These surfaces may be flat surfaces (or parts of planes), curved surfaces, or a mixture of both.

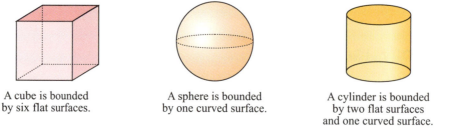

A cube is bounded
by six flat surfaces.

A sphere is bounded
by one curved surface.

A cylinder is bounded
by two flat surfaces
and one curved surface.

Dashed lines represent the boundaries that you would not really be able to see if you looked at the solid because they are hidden behind it. They remind us that the diagram is of a three-dimensional object.

Here are step-by-step drawings to help you to draw your own diagrams of some special solids:

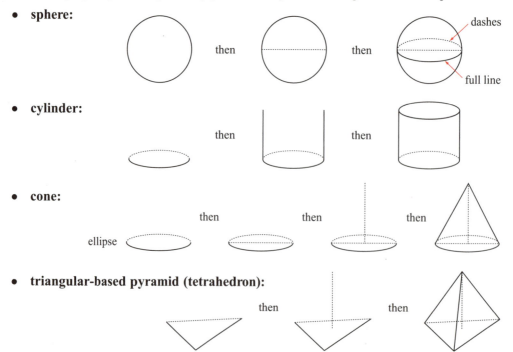

- **sphere:**

- **cylinder:**

- **cone:**

- **triangular-based pyramid (tetrahedron):**

- **square-based pyramid:**

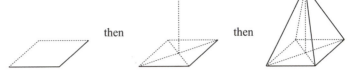

then   then

A solid with plane faces has vertices and edges.

For example, for this solid:

    C is a vertex

    AP is an edge

    BCRQ is a face.

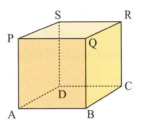

THEOREMS

Discoveries in geometry may be made by drawing accurate figures and then making precise measurements of sizes of angles and lengths of sides.

For example, if we draw a series of triangles of various sizes and shapes and on each occasion measure the interior angles we may discover an important fact about all triangles.

Consider these:

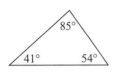
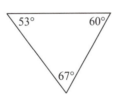
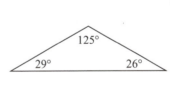

Using a protractor, check that all of the angles are correctly measured.

From an investigation like this, we may propose that:

    "The sum of the interior angles of any triangle is 180°."

FASCINATING GEOMETRY IN MOTION

Click on the icon to examine:

TANGENTS TO THREE CIRCLES   **ANGLE BISECTORS OF A TRIANGLE**   **MEDIANS OF A TRIANGLE**

 A   **ANGLE PROPERTIES**

ANGLE PAIRS

- Two angles with sizes which add to 90° are called **complementary angles**.
- Two angles with sizes which add to 180° are called **supplementary angles**.

- Two angles which have the same vertex and share a common arm are called **adjacent angles**.

  $P\hat{A}Q$ and $Q\hat{A}R$ are adjacent angles.

- For intersecting lines, angles which are directly opposite each other are called **vertically opposite angles**.

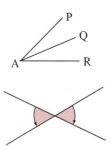

ANGLE PROPERTIES (Theorems)

Title	Theorem	Figure
Angles at a point	The sum of the sizes of the angles at a point is $360°$.	$a + b + c = 360$
Adjacent angles on a straight line	The sum of the sizes of the angles on a line is $180°$. The angles are supplementary.	$a + b = 180$
Adjacent angles in a right angle	The sum of the sizes of the angles in a right angle is $90°$. The angles are complementary.	$a + b = 90$
Vertically opposite angles	Vertically opposite angles are equal in size.	$a = b$
Corresponding angles	When two *parallel* lines are cut by a third line, then angles in corresponding positions are equal in size.	$a = b$
Alternate angles	When two *parallel* lines are cut by a third line, then angles in alternate positions are equal in size.	$a = b$

Title	Theorem	Figure
Co-interior angles (also called allied angles)	When two *parallel* lines are cut by a third line, then co-interior angles are supplementary.	$a + b = 180$
Angles of a triangle	The sum of the interior angles of a triangle is $180°$. **GEOMETRY PACKAGE**	$a + b + c = 180$
Exterior angle of a triangle	The size of the exterior angle of a triangle is equal to the sum of the interior opposite angles. **GEOMETRY PACKAGE**	$c = a + b$
Angles of a quadrilateral	The sum of the interior angles of a quadrilateral is $360°$. **GEOMETRY PACKAGE**	$a + b + c + d = 360$

EXERCISE 21A

1   Use the figure illustrated to answer the following questions:

AB is a fixed line and OP can rotate about O between OA and OB.

   a   If $x = 136$,   find y.
   b   If $y = 58$,   find x.
   c   What is x if y is 39?
   d   If x is 0, what is y?
   e   If $x = 81$,   find y.
   f   If $x = y$,   what is the value of each?

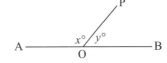

2   Find the complement of:

   a $25°$ **b** $63°$ **c** $x°$ **d** $(90 - y)°$

3   Find the supplement of:

   a $89°$ **b** $117°$ **c** $x°$ **d** $(180 - x)°$ **e** $(90 + a)°$

4 Find the values of the unknowns, giving brief reasons. You should **not** need to set up an equation.

a
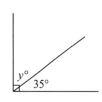

b
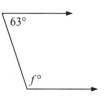

c
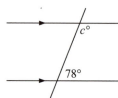

d
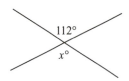

e
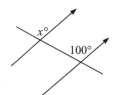

f
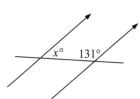

g
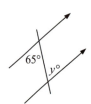

h

i

j
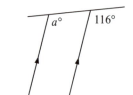

k
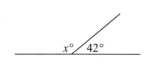

l
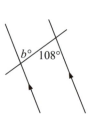

m
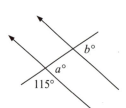

n
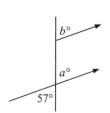

o
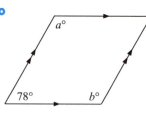

p
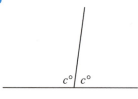

q
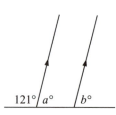

r
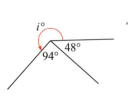

s
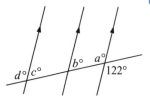

t
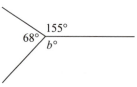

u
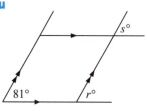

Some angle finding problems are neatly done by setting up and solving equations.

Example 1 ◀) **Self Tutor**

Find, giving brief reasons, the value of the unknown in:

a

b

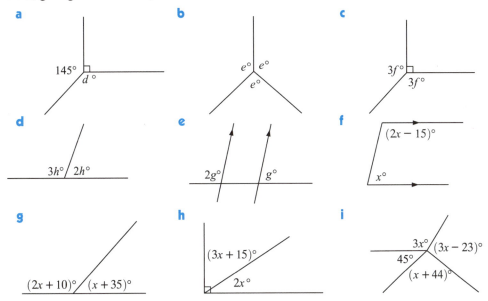

a $90 + a + 40 = 180$ {angles on a line}
$\therefore \quad a + 130 = 180$
$\therefore \quad a = 50$

b $2x - 100 = x$ {equal corresponding angles}
$\therefore \quad 2x - 100 - x = x - x$ {subtracting x from both sides}
$\therefore \quad x - 100 = 0$ {simplifying}
$\therefore \quad x = 100$

5 Find, giving brief reasons, the value of the unknown in:

a

b

c

d

e

f

g

h

i

6 State whether KL is parallel to MN, giving a brief reason for your answer. Note that these diagrams are sketches only and have not been drawn accurately.

a

b

c

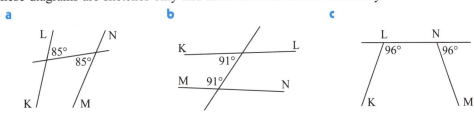

B TRIANGLES

A **triangle** is a polygon which has three sides.

All triangles have the following properties:

- The sum of the interior angles of a triangle is 180°.
- Any exterior angle is equal to the sum of the interior opposite angles.
- The longest side is opposite the largest angle.
- The triangle is the only **rigid** polygon.

DISCUSSION

Bridges and other specialised structures often have triangular supports rather than rectangular ones. The reason for this is that "*the triangle is the only rigid polygon*". What is meant by "rigid polygon"? Is the statement true?

Example 2   ◀)) Self Tutor

Find the unknown in the following, giving brief reasons:

a   **b**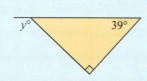

a $x = 180 - 38 - 19$ {angle sum of a triangle}
   ∴ $x = 123$

b $y = 39 + 90$ {exterior angle of a triangle}
   ∴ $y = 129$

EXERCISE 21B

1 Find the unknown in the following, giving brief reasons:

a 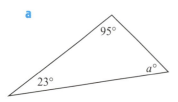   **b** 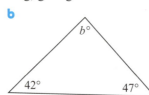   **c**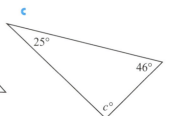

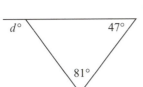 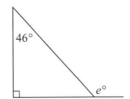 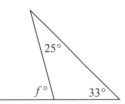

2 To try to trick you, the following triangles are *not* drawn to scale. State the longest side of each triangle.

a 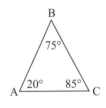   **b** 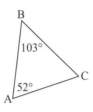   **c**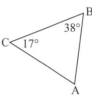

> The longest side is opposite the largest angle.

d   **e**   **f**

g 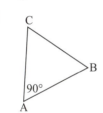   **h** 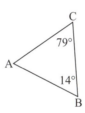   **i**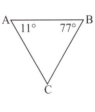

3 State whether the following statements are *true* or *false*:

  a The sum of the angles of a triangle is equal to two right angles.

  b A right angled triangle can contain an obtuse angle.

  c The sum of two angles of a triangle is always greater than the third angle.

  d The two smaller angles of a right angled triangle are supplementary.

  e A concave triangle is impossible.

Example 3 ◀») **Self Tutor**

Find the value of the unknown(s) in each triangle, giving a brief reason:

a   **b**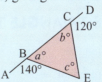

a $2x + x + (x + 20) = 180$ {angles of a triangle}

$\therefore \quad 4x + 20 = 180$

$\therefore \quad \quad 4x = 160$

$\therefore \quad \quad \ x = 40$

b $a = 180 - 140 = 40$ {angles on a line}

Likewise $b = 180 - 120 = 60$

But $a + b + c = 180$ {angles of a triangle}

$\therefore$ $40 + 60 + c = 180$

$\therefore$ $100 + c = 180$

$\therefore$ $c = 80$

4 Find the values of the unknowns in each triangle, giving a brief reason for each answer:

a

b

c

d

e

f

5 The three angles of a scalene triangle are x°, $(x - 12)^\circ$ and $(2x + 6)^\circ$. What are the sizes of these angles?

C   ISOSCELES TRIANGLES

An **isosceles triangle** is a triangle in which two sides are equal in length.

The angles opposite the two equal sides are called the **base angles**.

The vertex where the two equal sides meet is called the **apex**.

GEOMETRY PACKAGE

THE ISOSCELES TRIANGLE THEOREM

In an isosceles triangle:

- base angles are equal
- the line joining the apex to the midpoint of the base bisects the vertical angle and meets the base at right angles.

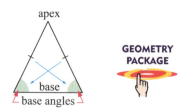

We can prove that the line joining the apex to the midpoint of the base bisects the vertical angle and meets the base at right angles, using congruent triangles.

CONVERSES

With many theorems there are converses which we often use in problem solving.

> *Converse 1:*   If a triangle has two equal angles then it is isosceles.
>
> *Converse 2:*   The angle bisector of the apex of an isosceles triangle bisects the base at right angles.
>
> *Converse 3:*   The perpendicular bisector of the base of an isosceles triangle passes through its apex.

- To prove *Converse 1*, Sam tries to use Figure 1 and triangle congruence.

  Will he be successful?

  Why or why not? Could Sam be successful using Figure 2?

- Can you prove *Converse 2* using triangle congruence?

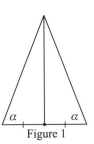

Figure 1

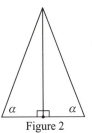

Figure 2

GEOMETRY PACKAGE

DISCUSSION

What does the word *converse* mean?

Can you find any other converses to the isosceles triangle theorem?

Example 4   ◀》 **Self Tutor**

Find x, giving brief reasons:

a

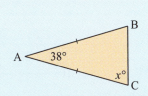

b

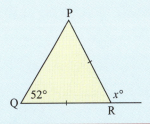

---

a

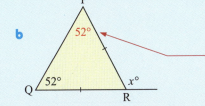

b

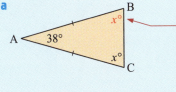

As AB = AC, the triangle is isosceles

∴ $A\widehat{B}C = x°$ also.

Now $x + x + 38 = 180$ {angles of a $\triangle$}

∴ $2x = 180 - 38$

∴ $2x = 142$

∴ $x = 71$

As PR = QR, the triangle is isosceles

∴ $Q\widehat{P}R = 52°$ {isosceles $\triangle$ theorem}

∴ $x = 52 + 52$ {exterior angle theorem}

∴ $x = 104$

EXERCISE 21C

1 Find x, giving reasons:

a
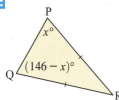

b
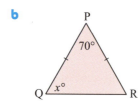

c
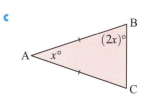

d

e
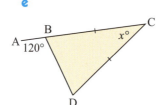

f
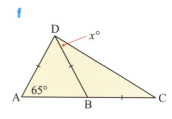

2 Find x, giving brief reasons:

a
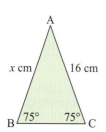

b
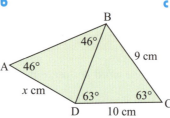

c
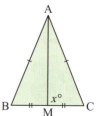

3 Classify the following inaccurately drawn triangles as equilateral, isosceles or scalene. The information marked on them is correct.

a
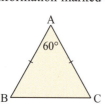

b
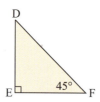

c
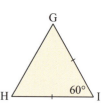

d
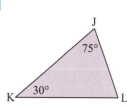

e
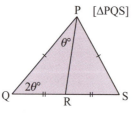

f
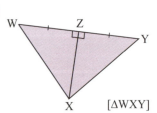

4 The figure alongside has not been drawn accurately:

a Find x.

b What can be deduced about the triangle?

5 Because of its symmetry, a regular pentagon can be made up of five isosceles triangles.

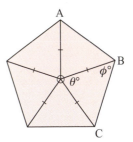

  a Find the size of angle θ at the centre O.

  b Hence, find ϕ.

  c Hence, find the measure of one interior angle such as $A\hat{B}C$.

6 Repeat question **5** but use a regular decagon. Remember that a decagon has 10 sides.

D   ANGLES OF A QUADRILATERAL

A **quadrilateral** is a plane figure with four straight sides.

Suppose a quadrilateral is drawn on a piece of paper.

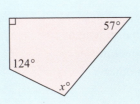

If the four angles are torn off and reassembled at a point, we notice that the angle sum must be $360°$.

DEMO

The above demonstration shows us that:

The sum of the angles of a quadrilateral is $360°$,

i.e.,   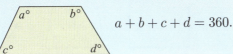 $a + b + c + d = 360$.

GEOMETRY PACKAGE

Example 5		◀) Self Tutor

Find the value of x in the quadrilateral, giving a brief reason:

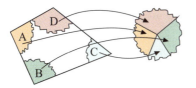

Using the angles of a quadrilateral theorem,

$$x + 57 + 90 + 124 = 360$$
$$\therefore \quad x + 271 = 360$$
$$\therefore \quad x = 89$$

EXERCISE 21D

1 Find, with reasons, the value of x in:

a
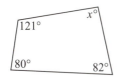

b

c
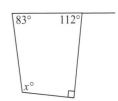

d 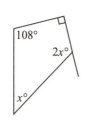   **e** 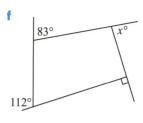   **f**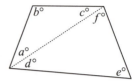

2 **a** Find $a + b + c$ and $d + e + f$.
  b What is $b + (c + f) + e + (a + d)$?
  c What does **b** enable us to deduce?

SPECIAL QUADRILATERALS

We will consider six special quadrilaterals:

> - A **parallelogram** is a quadrilateral which has opposite sides parallel.
> - A **rectangle** is a parallelogram with four equal angles of $90°$.
> - A **rhombus** is a quadrilateral in which all sides are equal
>   i.e., an equilateral quadrilateral.
> - A **square** is a rhombus with four equal angles of $90°$.
> - A **trapezium** is a quadrilateral which has a pair of parallel opposite sides.
> - A **kite** is a quadrilateral which has two pairs of equal adjacent sides.

parallelogram   rectangle   rhombus   square   trapezium   kite

The following properties of quadrilaterals are useful:

PARALLELOGRAM

In any
parallelogram:
  - opposite sides are equal in length
  - opposite angles are equal in size
  - diagonals bisect each other.

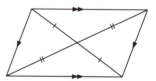

RHOMBUS

In any rhombus:
  - opposite sides are parallel
  - opposite angles are equal in size
  - diagonals bisect each other at right angles
  - diagonals bisect the angles at each vertex.

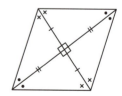

RECTANGLE

In any rectangle:
  - opposite sides are equal in length
  - diagonals are equal in length
  - diagonals bisect each other.

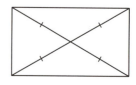

KITE

In any kite:
- two pairs of adjacent sides are equal
- the diagonals are perpendicular
- one diagonal splits the kite into two isosceles triangles.

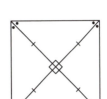

SQUARE

In any square:
- opposite sides are parallel
- all sides are equal in length
- all angles are right angles
- diagonals bisect each other at right angles
- diagonals bisect the angles at each vertex.

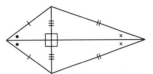

Example 6
🔊 **Self Tutor**

Classify the quadrilateral, and find the values of the variables.

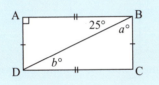

Since opposite sides are equal we have a parallelogram.

Also, one angle is a right angle,

∴   the quadrilateral is a rectangle.

Thus $a + 25 = 90$ {as $A\hat{B}C$ also measures $90°$}

∴ $a = 65$

and $b = 25$ {$A\hat{B}D$ and $C\hat{D}B$ are equal angles as AB ∥ DC}

---

3 Find the value of the unknowns in:

a
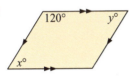

b
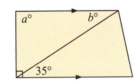

c
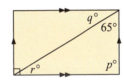

d
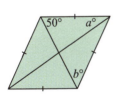

e
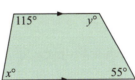

f

4 Using the information given in the diagrams, name the following quadrilaterals, giving brief reasons for your answer.

a
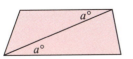

b

c

d
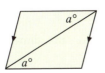

e
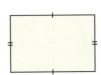

f

DISCUSSION   PROPERTIES OF QUADRILATERALS

What to do:

1   Copy and complete the following by answering "yes", "sometimes", or "at least 1 pair".

Property	Square	Rhombus	Rectangle	Parallelogram
opposite sides parallel				
opposite sides equal				
opposite angles equal				
all sides equal				
all angles equal				
diagonals equal				
diagonals bisect each other				
diagonals meet at right angles				
diagonals bisect the angles at the vertices				

2   Discuss the following questions in a group.   You may find the completed table in question **1** helpful in justifying your answer.

   a   Is a rectangle a quadrilateral?   **b**   Is a rectangle a square?

   c   Is a rhombus a parallelogram?   **d**   Is a rhombus a square?

   e   Is a square a rectangle?   **f**   Is a square a rhombus?

   g   Is a parallelogram a rectangle?

E   POLYGONS

A **polygon** is any plane figure with straight sides.

Triangles and quadrilaterals are the simplest types of polygons.

INVESTIGATION 1   ANGLES OF AN n-SIDED POLYGON

What to do:

1   Draw any pentagon (5-sided polygon) and label one of its vertices A. Draw in all the diagonals from A.

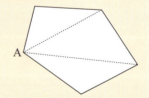

2   Repeat **1** for a hexagon, a heptagon (7-gon), an octagon, ..., etc., drawing diagonals from one vertex only.

3 Copy and complete the following table:

Polygon	Number of sides	Number of diagonals from A	Number of triangles	Angle sum of polygon
quadrilateral	4	1	2	$2 \times 180^o = 360^o$
pentagon				
hexagon				
octagon				
20-gon				

Note:

- The sum of the angles of a pentagon is 3×180°, since we formed 3 triangles.
- The sum of the angles of a hexagon is 4×180°, since we formed 4 triangles.
- The sum of the angles of any polygon can be found by dividing the polygon into triangles.

4 Copy and complete the following statement:

"The sum of the sizes of the interior angles of any n-sided polygon is ...... $\times 180^o$."

You should have discovered the following fact about polygons:

The sum of the sizes of the interior angles of any n-sided polygon is $(n - 2) \times 180^o$.

Example 7   ◀》 **Self Tutor**

Find x, giving a brief reason:

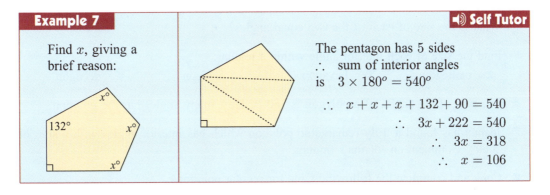

The pentagon has 5 sides
∴   sum of interior angles
is $3 \times 180^o = 540^o$

∴ $x + x + x + 132 + 90 = 540$
∴ $3x + 222 = 540$
∴ $3x = 318$
∴ $x = 106$

EXERCISE 21E

1 What is the sum of the interior angles of a:

  a   quadrilateral   **b**   pentagon   **c**   hexagon   **d**   octagon?

2 Find the value of the unknown in:

  a   **b**   **c**

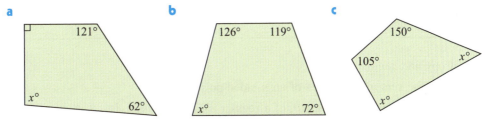

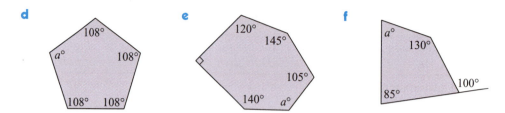

3 Find the value of x in each of the following, giving a reason:

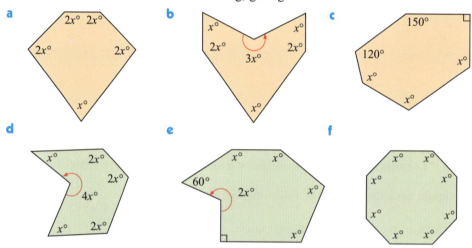

4 A pentagon has three right angles and two other equal angles.
What is the size of each of the two equal angles?

5 Find the size of each interior angle within a regular:

    a pentagon   **b** hexagon   **c** octagon   **d** decagon

6 The sum of the angles of a polygon is $1800°$. How many angles has the polygon?

7 Joanna has found a truly remarkable polygon which has interior angles with a sum of $2060°$. Comment on Joanna's finding.

8 Copy and complete the following table for regular polygons:

Regular polygon	Number of sides	Number of angles	Size of each angle
equilateral triangle			
square			
pentagon			
hexagon			
octagon			
decagon			

9 Copy and complete:

- the sum of the angles of an n-sided polygon is ......
- the size of each angle θ, of a regular n-sided polygon, is $\theta = $ ......

F   THE EXTERIOR ANGLES OF A POLYGON

INVESTIGATION 2   EXTERIOR ANGLES OF A POLYGON

The shaded angle is said to be an exterior angle of quadrilateral ABCD at vertex B.

The purpose of this investigation is to find the sum of all exterior angles of a polygon.

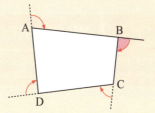

What to do:

1 In the school grounds, place four objects on the ground no more than 10 m apart, forming the vertices of an imaginary quadrilateral. Start at one vertex, and looking towards the next vertex, walk directly to it and turn to face the next vertex. Measure the angle that you have turned through.

2 Repeat this process until you are back to where you started from, and turn in the same way to face your original direction of sight, measuring each angle that you turn through.

3 Through how many degrees have you turned from start to finish?

4 Would your answer in **3** change if an extra object was included to form a pentagon?

5 Write a statement indicating what you have learnt about the sum of the exterior angles of any polygon.

From the investigation, you should have discovered that:

> *"the sum of the exterior angles of any polygon is always $360°$".*

This fact is useful for finding the size of an interior angle of a regular polygon.

Example 8	◄)) Self Tutor

A regular polygon has 15 sides. Calculate the size of each interior angle.

For a 15-sided polygon, each exterior angle is $360° \div 15 = 24°$

$\therefore$ each interior angle is $180° - 24° = 156°$

EXERCISE 21F

1 Calculate the size of each interior angle of these regular polygons:

    a   with 5 sides   **b**   with 8 sides   **c**   with 10 sides

    d   with 20 sides   **e**   with 100 sides   **f**   with n sides

2 Calculate the number of sides of a regular polygon given that an exterior angle is:

   a $45°$ **b** $15°$ **c** $2°$ **d** $\frac{1}{2}°$

3 Calculate the number of sides of a regular polygon with an interior angle of:

   a $120°$ **b** $150°$ **c** $175°$ **d** $179°$

LINKS
click here

WHAT REGION CAN BE EATEN BY A GOAT?

Areas of interaction:
Approaches to learning/Environments

G   NETS OF SOLIDS

A **net** is a two-dimensional shape which may be folded or shaped to form a solid.

A **cube** is formed when the "net" shown is cut out and folded along the dotted lines.

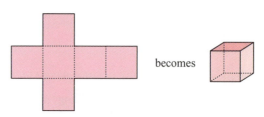

becomes

A **triangular-based pyramid** is formed when this "net" is cut out and folded along the dotted lines.

becomes

EXERCISE 21G

1 Draw a net, with lengths clearly marked, of the following 3-dimensional solids:

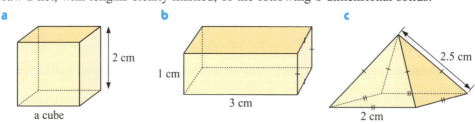

   a   2 cm   a cube   **b**   1 cm   3 cm   **c**   2.5 cm   2 cm

2 Draw and name the solids which would be formed from the following nets:

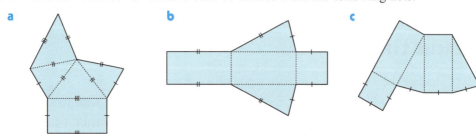

   a   **b**   **c**

d 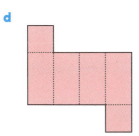 **e** 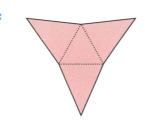 **f**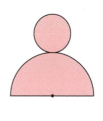

3 One of the cubes cannot be made from this net. Which one is it?

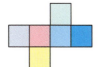 **P**   **Q**   **R**   **S**   **T**

4 a Sketch a net of a cube with sides 1.2 cm.

   b What is the surface area of the cube?

5 a Sketch a cuboid with sides 10 cm, 8 cm and 5 cm.

   b What is the surface area of the cuboid?

6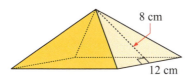

This pyramid has a square base 12 cm by 12 cm.

   a Sketch the net of the solid.

   b Find the surface area of the solid.

7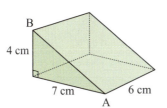

This triangular prism has a 6 cm by 7 cm base, and a height of 4 cm.

   a Find the length of AB to 2 decimal places.

   b Draw the net of the solid.

   c Find the surface area of the solid.

REVIEW SET 21A

1 Draw a freehand sketch of:

   a a reflex angle PQR   **b** an acute angle ABC

2 Find the value of the unknown, giving reasons for your answer:

   a 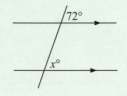   **b**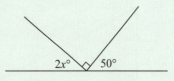

c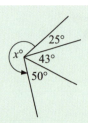

d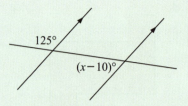

3 Decide if the figure contains parallel lines,
giving a brief reason for your answer:

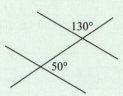

4 Find the value of x in:

a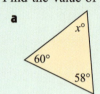

b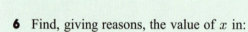

c

5 What can be deduced about triangle ABC
shown? Give reasons for your answer.

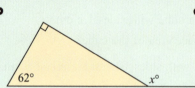

6 Find, giving reasons, the value of x in:

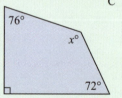

7 Find, giving reasons, the value of the unknowns in:

a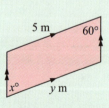

b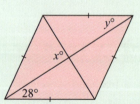

8 Using the information given in the diagrams, name the following quadrilaterals, giving
brief reasons for your answer.

a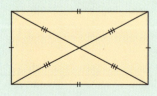

b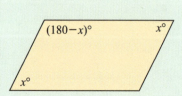

9 Find the value of x in each of the following, giving reasons:

a

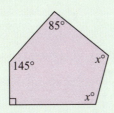

b

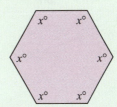

10 Draw a net with lengths clearly marked for the 3-dimensional solid shown:

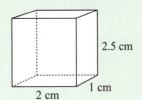

REVIEW SET 21B

1 **a** Find the complement of: **i** $35°$ **ii** $x°$
  b Find the supplement of: **i** $72°$ **ii** $(90 - x)°$

2 State the values of the unknowns in each figure, giving a brief reason for each answer:

a

b

c

d

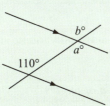

e

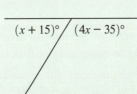

3 Find the value of the unknown in each figure, giving a brief reason for your answer:

a

b

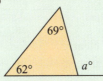

c

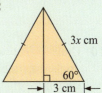

4 Find the values of x and y, giving brief reasons for your answers:

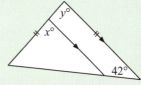

5 Classify each triangle, in as much detail as possible:

a

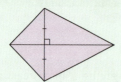

b

c

6 Find, giving reasons, the value of x in:

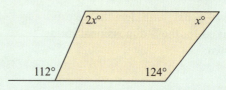

7 Classify each quadrilateral given below. The diagrams are not drawn accurately but the information on them is correct.

a   **b**   **c**

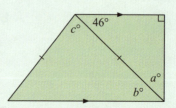

8 Find the values of the unknowns in:

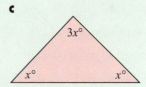

9 The sum of the sizes of the interior angles of any n-sided polygon is $(n-2) \times 180°$. Use this formula to complete the following table:

Polygon	Number of sides	Sum of angles
pentagon		
hexagon		
octagon		

10 Draw a net with lengths clearly marked for the 3-dimensional solid shown:

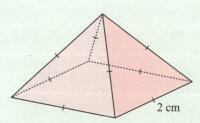

Chapter 22

Quadratic and other equations

Contents:

A Quadratic equations
B Problem solving with quadratics
C Exponential equations
D Solving harder equations with technology

OPENING PROBLEM

During a golf tournament, Sergio needs to hit his tee shot on a par 4 hole over a lake as shown.

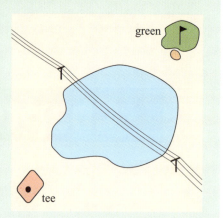

His caddy tells him that he must hit the ball 205 m to clear the lake, and he knows the hole is 240 m 'as the crow flies' from the tee.

Sergio hits his shot and watches it sail directly towards the hole over the lake. However, the ball hits a power line and falls into the water. Sergio is entitled to play another ball from the tee without being penalised any strokes, but unfortunately his next shot is nowhere near as good.

The commentators view a video tape of the first shot and are able to obtain these measurements:

Horizontal distance (x m) from the tee	25	50	75	100	125
Height (h m) of the ball above the ground	17.5	30	37.5	40	37.5

A relationship is found connecting the *horizontal distance* the ball travels and the *height* of the golf ball above the ground. The relationship is $h = 0.8x - 0.004x^2$.

Consider the following questions:

* Can the commentators use this relationship to determine where Sergio's ball would have landed?

* Would his ball have cleared the lake if it had not hit the power line?

A   QUADRATIC EQUATIONS

Equations of the form $ax + b = 0$ are called **linear equations** and usually have *one* solution.

For example, $3x - 2 = 0$ is a linear equation ($a = 3$, $b = -2$) and has the solution $x = \frac{2}{3}$.

> Equations of the form $ax^2 + bx + c = 0$ are called **quadratic equations** and may have *two*, *one* or *zero* solutions.

Here are some simple quadratic equations which clearly show the truth of this statement:

Equation	$ax^2 + bx + c = 0$ form	a	b	c	Solutions	No. of solutions
$x^2 - 4 = 0$	$x^2 + 0x - 4 = 0$	1	0	-4	$x = 2$ or $x = -2$	**two**
$(x - 2)^2 = 0$	$x^2 - 4x + 4 = 0$	1	-4	4	$x = 2$	**one**
$x^2 + 4 = 0$	$x^2 + 0x + 4 = 0$	1	0	4	none as x^2 is always $\geqslant 0$	**zero**

Now consider the example $x^2 + 3x - 10 = 0$.

If $x = 2$,

$$\begin{aligned} x^2 + 3x - 10 &= 2^2 + 3 \times 2 - 10 \\ &= 4 + 6 - 10 \\ &= 0 \end{aligned}$$

and if $x = -5$,

$$\begin{aligned} x^2 + 3x - 10 &= (-5)^2 + 3 \times (-5) - 10 \\ &= 25 - 15 - 10 \\ &= 0 \end{aligned}$$

$x = 2$ and $x = -5$ both satisfy the equation $x^2 + 3x - 10 = 0$, so we say that they are both **solutions**.

But, how do we find these solutions without using trial and error?

One method is to use **factorisation** and the **Null Factor** law.

THE NULL FACTOR LAW

When the product of two (or more) numbers is zero, then at least one of them must be zero. So, if $ab = 0$ then $a = 0$ or $b = 0$.

EXERCISE 22A

1   Discuss solutions to the following equations:

  a $5x = 0$
  b $3y = 0$
  c $p \times 7 = 0$
  d $q \times -3 = 0$

  e $-4r = 0$
  f $pq = 0$
  g $7xy = 0$
  h $pqr = 0$

  i $x^2 = 0$
  j $a^2 = 0$
  k $wxyz = 0$
  l $x^2 y = 0$

To use the **Null Factor** law when solving equations, we must have one side of the equation *equal to zero*.

STEPS FOR SOLVING QUADRATIC EQUATIONS

Step 1:   If necessary, rearrange the equation so one side is **zero**.
Step 2:   **Fully factorise** the other side (usually the LHS).
Step 3:   Use the **Null Factor** law.
Step 4:   **Solve** the resulting simple equations.
Step 5:   **Check** at least one of your solutions.

Example 1	◀ Self Tutor

Solve for x: **a** $5x(x + 2) = 0$ **b** $(x + 4)(x - 1) = 0$

a
$$5x(x + 2) = 0$$
$$\therefore \quad 5x = 0 \quad \text{or} \quad x + 2 = 0 \qquad \{\text{Null Factor law}\}$$
$$\therefore \quad x = 0 \quad \text{or} \quad x = -2 \qquad \{\text{solving linear equations}\}$$
$$\therefore \quad x = 0 \text{ or } -2$$

b
$$(x + 4)(x - 1) = 0$$
$$\therefore \quad x + 4 = 0 \quad \text{or} \quad x - 1 = 0 \qquad \{\text{Null Factor law}\}$$
$$\therefore \quad x = -4 \quad \text{or} \quad x = 1 \qquad \{\text{solving linear equations}\}$$
$$\therefore \quad x = -4 \text{ or } 1$$

2 Solve for x:

    a $x(x+2) = 0$ **b** $5x(x-3) = 0$ **c** $(x-4)(x-7) = 0$

    d $6x(2-x) = 0$ **e** $-2x(3x+2) = 0$ **f** $(3x+2)(2x-5) = 0$

    g $6(x-2)(3x+1) = 0$ **h** $4(x-3)^2 = 0$ **i** $-2(3x-2)^2 = 0$

Example 2   ◀)) Self Tutor

Solve for x: $x^2 = 3x$

$$x^2 = 3x$$
$$\therefore \quad x^2 - 3x = 0 \qquad \text{\{rearranging equation so RHS} = 0\}$$
$$\therefore \quad x(x-3) = 0 \qquad \text{\{factorising the LHS\}}$$
$$\therefore \quad x = 0 \quad \text{or} \quad x - 3 = 0 \qquad \text{\{Null Factor law\}}$$
$$\therefore \quad x = 0 \quad \text{or} \quad x = 3$$
$$\therefore \quad x = 0 \text{ or } 3$$

ILLEGAL CANCELLING

Let us reconsider the equation $x^2 = 3x$ from **Example 2**.

We notice that there is a common factor of x on both sides.

However, if we cancel x from both sides, we will have $\dfrac{x^{2\;1}}{x^{\;1}} = \dfrac{3x^{\;1}}{x^{\;1}}$ and thus finish with $x = 3$.

Consequently, we will 'lose' the solution $x = 0$.

From this example we conclude that:

> We must never cancel a variable that is a common factor from both sides of an equation unless we know that the factor cannot be zero.

3 Solve for x:

    a $x^2 - x = 0$ **b** $x^2 - 6x = 0$ **c** $x^2 = 4x$

    d $x^2 = 2x$ **e** $2x^2 + 8x = 0$ **f** $9x^2 + 2x = 0$

    g $4x^2 - 9x = 0$ **h** $3x^2 = 7x$ **i** $4x^2 = 8x$

Example 3   ◀)) Self Tutor

Solve for x: $x^2 + 3x = 28$

$$x^2 + 3x = 28$$
$$\therefore \quad x^2 + 3x - 28 = 0 \qquad \text{\{rearranging so RHS} = 0\}$$
$$\therefore \quad (x+7)(x-4) = 0 \qquad \text{\{sum} = +3 \text{ and product} = -28$$
$$\text{gives } +7 \text{ and } -4\}$$
$$\therefore \quad x + 7 = 0 \quad \text{or} \quad x - 4 = 0 \qquad \text{\{Null Factor law\}}$$
$$\therefore \quad x = -7 \text{ or } 4 \qquad \text{\{solving linear equations\}}$$

4 Solve for x:

  a $x^2 - 1 = 0$ **b** $x^2 - 4 = 0$ **c** $9x^2 - 1 = 0$

  d $4x^2 - 9 = 0$ **e** $(x - 3)^2 = 0$ **f** $(x + 7)^2 = 0$

  g $(3x + 1)^2 = 0$ **h** $(4x - 5)^2 = 0$ **i** $(7x + 3)^2 = 0$

5 Solve for x:

  a $x^2 + 4x + 3 = 0$ **b** $x^2 - 4x + 3 = 0$ **c** $x^2 + 5x + 4 = 0$

  d $x^2 - 5x + 4 = 0$ **e** $x^2 + 9x + 8 = 0$ **f** $x^2 + 7x + 10 = 0$

  g $x^2 + 2x + 1 = 0$ **h** $x^2 - 2x + 1 = 0$ **i** $x^2 + 6x + 9 = 0$

  j $x^2 - 4x + 4 = 0$ **k** $x^2 - 6x + 9 = 0$ **l** $x^2 + 10x + 25 = 0$

  m $x^2 + 11x = -28$ **n** $x^2 - 2x = 15$ **o** $x^2 - 4x = 12$

  p $x^2 - 24 = 10x$ **q** $x^2 + 16 = 8x$ **r** $x^2 + x = 30$

  s $x^2 = 2x + 24$ **t** $x^2 = -4x + 21$ **u** $x^2 = 2x + 35$

B | PROBLEM SOLVING WITH QUADRATICS

Many problems when converted to algebraic form result in a **quadratic equation**.

We use **factorisation** and the **Null Factor** law to solve these equations.

PROBLEM SOLVING METHOD

- Carefully **read the question** until you **understand** it. A **rough sketch** may be useful.
- Decide on the **unknown** quantity, calling it x, say.
- Find an **equation** which connects x and the information you are given.
- **Solve** the equation using factorisation and the **Null Factor** law.
- **Check** that any solutions satisfy the original problem.
- Write your answer to the question in **sentence form**.

Example 4   ◀️ **Self Tutor**

The sum of a number and its square is 30.   Find the number.

Let the number be x.

$$\text{So, } x + x^2 = 30 \qquad \text{\{the number plus its square is 30\}}$$

$$\therefore \quad x^2 + x = 30 \qquad \text{\{rearranging\}}$$

$$\therefore \quad x^2 + x - 30 = 0 \qquad \text{\{rearranging so } \text{RHS} = 0\text{\}}$$

$$\therefore \quad (x + 6)(x - 5) = 0 \qquad \text{\{factorising\}}$$

$$\therefore \quad x = -6 \quad \text{or} \quad x = 5$$

$\therefore$ the numbers are -6 and 5.

Check: If $x = -6$, we have $-6 + (-6)^2 = -6 + 36 = 30$ ✓

  If $x = 5$, we have $5 + 5^2 = 5 + 25 = 30$ ✓

EXERCISE 22B

1 The sum of a number and its square is 12. Find the number.

2 The sum of a number and its square is 72. Find the number.

3 If a number is subtracted from its square, the result is 56. What is the number?

4 If a number is subtracted from its square, the result is 110. What is the number?

5 **a** Two numbers have a sum of 9. If one of them is x, what is the other number?
   b If the sum of the squares of the numbers in **a** is 45, find the numbers.

6 **a** Two numbers have a sum of 16. If one of them is x, what is the other number?
   b If the sum of the squares of the numbers in **a** is 130, find the numbers.

Example 5   ◀⬥ **Self Tutor**

A rectangle has length 3 cm greater than its width. If it has an area of 28 cm^2, find the dimensions of the rectangle.

If x cm is the width, then $(x + 3)$ cm is the length

$$\therefore \quad x(x + 3) = 28 \qquad \{\text{width} \times \text{length} = \text{area}\}$$
$$\therefore \quad x^2 + 3x = 28 \qquad \{\text{expanding}\}$$
$$\therefore \quad x^2 + 3x - 28 = 0 \qquad \{\text{RHS} = 0\}$$
$$\therefore \quad (x + 7)(x - 4) = 0 \qquad \{\text{factorising LHS}\}$$
$$\therefore \quad x + 7 = 0 \quad \text{or} \quad x - 4 = 0 \qquad \{\text{Null Factor law}\}$$
$$\therefore \quad x = -7 \text{ or } 4$$
$$\therefore \quad x = 4 \qquad \{\text{lengths must be positive}\}$$

$\therefore$ the rectangle is 4 cm $\times$ 7 cm.

---

7 A rectangle has length 3 cm greater than its width.
   a If its width is x cm, what is its length?
   b If it has an area of 130 cm^2, find the dimensions of the rectangle.

8 A rectangle has length 6 cm greater than its width. If it has an area of 112 cm^2, find the dimensions of the rectangle.

9 A rectangular enclosure is made from 48 m of fencing.
   a If the width is x m, what is the length?
   b The area enclosed is 128 m^2. Find the dimensions of the enclosure.

10 A rectangular enclosure is made from 38 m of fencing. The area enclosed is 70 m^2. Find the dimensions of the enclosure.

11 A triangle has a base which is 3 cm longer than its altitude.
   a Find its altitude if its area is 44 cm^2.
   b Find its altitude if its area is 90 cm^2.

Example 6

A baker making cakes finds that his profit per hour, P, is given by the relationship $P = 20x - x^2$ where x is the number of cakes made per hour.
How many cakes must the company make per hour in order to make:

a $0 per hour profit   **b** $84 per hour profit?

a
$$\text{Let} \quad P = 0$$
$$\therefore \quad 20x - x^2 = 0$$
$$\therefore \quad x(20 - x) = 0 \qquad \{\text{factorising}\}$$
$$\therefore \quad x = 0 \ \text{ or } 20 - x = 0 \qquad \{\text{Null Factor law}\}$$
$$\therefore \quad x = 0 \ \text{ or } \ 20$$

i.e.,   when 0 or 20 cakes per hour are made.

b
$$\text{Let} \quad P = 84$$
$$\therefore \quad 20x - x^2 = 84$$
$$\therefore \quad -x^2 + 20x - 84 = 0 \qquad \{\text{RHS} = 0\}$$
$$\therefore \quad x^2 - 20x + 84 = 0 \qquad \{\text{multiplying both sides by } -1\}$$
$$\therefore \quad (x - 6)(x - 14) = 0 \qquad \{\text{factorising}\}$$
$$\therefore \quad x - 6 = 0 \ \text{ or } \ x - 14 = 0 \qquad \{\text{Null Factor law}\}$$
$$\therefore \quad x = 6 \ \text{ or } 14$$

i.e.,   when 6 or 14 cakes per hour are made.

Does it seem strange to you that there could be two answers to **Example 6**, part **b**?

To discover why this is so, we need to draw the graph of the profit equation $P = 20x - x^2$.

We could use a **graphing package** or **graphics calculator** to do this.

Many real life profit equations do have quadratic form as in the above example. The profits increase as the number of items made increases, but after a while, more items are made than can be sold. This is why their profit starts decreasing until ultimately they make a loss.

GRAPHING PACKAGE

12   A small business makes surfboards and finds that its profit, P per hour, is given by the formula $P = 75x - 5x^2$ where x is the number of surfboards made per hour.
When does the business make: **a** $0 profit per hour   **b** $250 profit per hour?

13   A manufacturer makes high quality ice-skates. The profit P per day is given by the formula $P = 72x - 3x^2$ where x is the number of pairs of skates made per day.
When does the manufacturer make: **a** $420 profit per day   **b**   no profit per day?

14   When a cricket ball is hit directly upwards, its height h above the ground is given by $h = 30t - 5t^2$ metres, where t is the time in seconds after the ball is hit.
When is the ball at a height of: **a**   0 m   **b**   25 m above the ground?

15   When a tennis ball is hit directly upwards, its height h above the ground is given by $h = 1 + 16t - 2t^2$ metres, where t is the time in seconds after the ball is hit.
When is the ball at a height of: **a**   15 m   **b**   33 m above the ground?

C   # EXPONENTIAL EQUATIONS

An **exponential equation** is an equation in which the unknown occurs as part of the index or exponent.

For example: $2^x = 8$ and $30 \times 3^x = 7$ are both exponential equations.

Note that if $2^x = 8$,   then $2^x = 2^3$.

Thus $x = 3$ is a solution, and is in fact the only solution to this equation.

In general: If $a^x = a^k$ then $x = k$.

So, if the base numbers are the same, we can **equate indices**.

Example 7   🔊 **Self Tutor**

Solve for x: **a** $2^x = 16$ **b** $3^{x+2} = \frac{1}{27}$

a $2^x = 16$

∴ $2^x = 2^4$

∴ $x = 4$

b $3^{x+2} = \frac{1}{27}$

∴ $3^{x+2} = \frac{1}{3^3}$

∴ $3^{x+2} = 3^{-3}$

∴ $x + 2 = -3$

∴ $x = -5$

Once we have the same base we can then equate the indices.

EXERCISE 22C

1 Write as powers of 2:

   a 4   **b** 8   **c** 1   **d** 16   **e** $\frac{1}{2}$ **f** 32   **g** $\frac{1}{4}$

2 Write as powers of 3:

   a 3   **b** 9   **c** 27   **d** 1   **e** $\frac{1}{3}$ **f** $\frac{1}{9}$ **g** $\sqrt{3}$

3 Write as powers of 5:

   a 25   **b** 5   **c** 1   **d** 125   **e** $\frac{1}{25}$ **f** 0.2

4 Solve for x:

   a $3^x = 3$ **b** $3^x = 9$ **c** $2^x = 16$ **d** $3^x = 1$

   e $2^x = \frac{1}{2}$ **f** $3^x = \frac{1}{3}$ **g** $2^x = \frac{1}{4}$ **h** $3^{x+1} = 9$

   i $2^{x-2} = \frac{1}{8}$ **j** $3^{x+1} = \frac{1}{9}$ **k** $2^{x+1} = 32$ **l** $2^{1-2x} = \frac{1}{4}$

Example 8

  ◀》 **Self Tutor**

Solve for x: **a** $4^x = 8$ **b** $9^{x-2} = \frac{1}{3}$

> Remember to use the index laws correctly!

a
$$4^x = 8$$
$$\therefore \quad (2^2)^x = 2^3$$
$$\therefore \quad 2^{2x} = 2^3$$
$$\therefore \quad 2x = 3$$
$$\therefore \quad x = \frac{3}{2}$$

b
$$9^{x-2} = \tfrac{1}{3}$$
$$\therefore \quad (3^2)^{x-2} = 3^{-1}$$
$$\therefore \quad 3^{2(x-2)} = 3^{-1}$$
$$\therefore \quad 2x - 4 = -1$$
$$\therefore \quad 2x = 3$$
$$\therefore \quad x = \frac{3}{2}$$

5 Solve for x:

a $9^x = 27$ **b** $4^x = \frac{1}{2}$ **c** $9^x = \frac{1}{27}$ **d** $36^x = \frac{1}{6}$

e $4^x = \frac{1}{16}$ **f** $25^x = \frac{1}{5}$ **g** $8^{x+1} = 16$ **h** $8^{2-x} = \frac{1}{64}$

i $4^{2x+1} = \frac{1}{2}$ **j** $9^{x+3} = 3$ **k** $(\frac{1}{2})^{x-1} = 4$ **l** $(\frac{1}{3})^{x-2} = 9$

m $8^x = 4^{-x}$ **n** $(\frac{1}{4})^{1-x} = 32$ **o** $(\frac{1}{7})^x = 49$ **p** $(\frac{1}{2})^{x+1} = 64$

D SOLVING HARDER EQUATIONS WITH TECHNOLOGY

Consider the equation $x^2 = 2x + 3$.

Solving algebraically, if $x^2 = 2x + 3$
then $x^2 - 2x - 3 = 0$
$$\therefore \quad (x+1)(x-3) = 0$$
$$\therefore \quad x = -1 \text{ or } 3$$

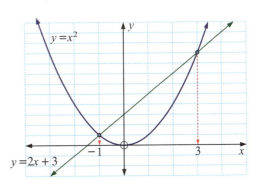

To solve this equation graphically, we graph $y = x^2$ and $y = 2x + 3$ on the same set of axes. Notice that the graphs meet at points which have x-coordinates -1 and 3.

So,   to solve $f(x) = g(x)$ we graph $y = f(x)$ and $y = g(x)$ and write down the x-coordinates where the two graphs meet.

In particular, to solve $f(x) = 0$ we could graph $y = f(x)$ and observe where it meets the x-axis $y = 0$.

Instructions for graphing functions, finding their x-intercepts, and finding where two functions intersect can be found starting on page **21**.

Example 9   ◀) **Self Tutor**

Solve for x: $x^3 - 3x^2 + x + 1 = 0$

From a graphics calculator the graph
of $y = x^3 - 3x^2 + x + 1$ is as shown.

The solutions are where the graph
meets the x-axis.

These are: $x \approx -0.414$,
             $x = 1$
        and $x \approx 2.41$

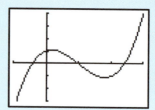

EXERCISE 22D

1 Use a graphics calculator to find all solutions of the equation:

a $x^2 - 4x - 1 = 0$ **b** $x^2 - 14x + 34 = 0$

c $2^x - 4x + 1 = 0$ **d** $3^{-x} + \frac{1}{20}x - \frac{1}{2} = 0$

e $2x^3 + x^2 - 14x - 7 = 0$ **f** $3x^3 - 8x^2 - 8x + 8 = 0$

g $3^x - x^3 = 0$ **h** $x^2 + 3x - 1 - \dfrac{2}{x} = 0$

i $\dfrac{2x + 1}{1 - x} - \dfrac{5}{x} = 0$ **j** $\dfrac{x^2}{x - 2} - 3x - 1 = 0$

k $2^x - 3^{-x} + 5 = 0$ **l** $\dfrac{x}{x + 3} - 2^{-x} = 0$

Example 10   ◀) **Self Tutor**

Solve for x: $x^4 - 3x^3 = (0.5)^x$

The graphs of $y = x^4 - 3x^3$ and
$y = (0.5)^x$ alongside were obtained
using a graphics calculator.

The solutions are the x-coordinates
where the two graphs meet.

So, $x \approx -0.767$ or $x \approx 3.00$

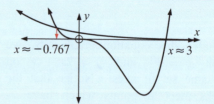

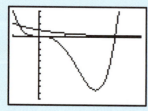
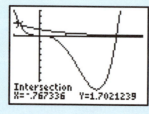
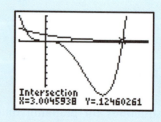

Note: In **Example 10**, we could have written the equation as $x^4 - 3x^3 - (0.5)^x = 0$ and found the x-intercepts as before.

2 Use a graphics calculator to solve these equations.
Include a sketch graph in your answer.

a $x^2 = 2x + 1$

b $\dfrac{x^3}{3} = 2x - 1$

c $\dfrac{x^4}{3} - x^3 = 5 - x$

d $2^x = x^2$

e $3^x = 5x + 2$

f $x + \dfrac{1}{x} = 3$

g $x^2 = 3^{-x}$

h $x^2 - \dfrac{1}{x} = 2^x$

i $\dfrac{x^4}{3} - x^3 = 2^x$

3 Solve simultaneously:

a $y = x^2 - 3x + 7$ and $y = x + 5$ **b** $y = x^2 - 5x + 2$ and $y = x - 7$

c $y = -x^2 - 2x + 4$ and $y = x + 8$ **d** $y = -x^2 + 4x - 2$ and $y = 5x - 6$

4 Find the coordinates of the point(s) of intersection of these functions:

a $y = x^2 - 2x + 8$ and $y = x + 6$ **b** $y = -x^2 + 3x + 9$ and $y = 2x - 3$

c $y = -x^2 + 4x + 7$ and $y = 5x - 4$ **d** $y = x^2 - 5x + 9$ and $y = 3x - 7$

REVIEW SET 22A

1 Solve for x:

  a $3x(x - 2) = 0$ **b** $(x - 3)(x + 4) = 0$ **c** $-(x - 3)^2 = 0$

2 Solve for x:

  a $2x - x^2 = 0$ **b** $5x^2 + 10x = 0$ **c** $4x^2 = 12x$

3 Solve for x:

  a $x^2 - 25 = 0$ **b** $(2x - 1)^2 = 0$

4 Solve for x:

  a $x^2 + 5x - 6 = 0$ **b** $x^2 + 6x + 9 = 0$ **c** $x^2 - 2x = 15$

5 **a** Two numbers have a sum of 11. If one of them is x, what is the other number?

  b If the sum of the squares of the numbers in **a** is 61, find the numbers.

6 A rectangle has length 5 cm greater than its width. If its area is 104 cm², find the dimensions of the rectangle.

7 A bicycle manufacturer finds that its profit, P per day, is given by the formula $P = 80x - 4x^2$ where x is the number of bicycles made per day. How many bicycles does the manufacturer make for:

  a \$300 profit per day   **b** no profit per day?

8 Solve for x:

    a $5^x = 25$ **b** $5^{x+1} = \frac{1}{25}$ **c** $5^x = 1$

9 Solve for x:

    a $3^x = \frac{1}{9}$ **b** $9^{2-x} = \frac{1}{27}$

10 Use a graphics calculator to solve the equation $2^x = 3 - x$.   Include a sketch graph in your answer.

REVIEW SET 22B

1 Solve for x:

    a $x(1 - 5x) = 0$ **b** $(x - 2)(x - 7) = 0$ **c** $(3 + 2x)^2 = 0$

2 Solve for x:

    a $x^2 - 6x = 0$ **b** $8x^2 - 6x = 0$ **c** $25x^2 = 5x$

3 Solve for x:

    a $9 - x^2 = 0$ **b** $(4x + 3)^2 = 0$

4 Solve for x:

    a $x^2 - 7x + 12 = 0$ **b** $4x^2 + 4x + 1 = 0$ **c** $x^2 + 3x = 18$

5 If a number is subtracted from its square, the result is 20. What is the number?

6 The base of a triangle is 3 cm longer than its height. The area of the triangle is 20 cm^2. Find the height.

7 When a ball is hit directly upwards, its height h above the ground is given by $h = 1 + 21t - 3t^2$ metres, where t is the time in seconds after the ball is hit.

    When is the ball at a height of:

    a   31 metres   **b**   1 metre above the ground?

8 Solve for x:

    a $3^x = 81$ **b** $3^{2x-1} = \frac{1}{3}$ **c** $3^x = \frac{1}{27}$

9 Solve for x:

    a $4^x = \frac{1}{8}$ **b** $125 = \frac{1}{5^x}$

10 Use a graphics calculator to solve the equation $x^3 = \frac{1}{x}$.

    Include a sketch graph in your answer.

Chapter **23**

Finance

Contents:

A Profit and loss
B Percentage profit and loss
C Discount
D Using a multiplier
E Chain percentage problems
F Simple interest
G Compound interest
H Foreign exchange

OPENING PROBLEM

Liam makes timber furniture. He calculates the cost of the timber and other hardware items such as glue, screws and doorknobs that he uses. He also adds the cost of wages for making the furniture. He is then able to list the 'cost per item' as shown.

Item	Cost
dining table	$670
chair	$105
small table	$150
dresser	$860
cupboard	$126

Liam adds a mark up for profit on each item. He marks up the tables by 50%, chairs by 40%, and dressers and cupboards by 60%. He then adds on a Goods and Services Tax (GST) of 10% to determine the final selling price of the item.

Consider the following:

1 Find:

   a his profit on each item

   b the GST exclusive price of each item

   c the GST inclusive price of each item

2 Find Liam's profit if he sells:

   a two small tables and a cupboard

   b a dining table, 6 chairs and a dresser.

3 Find Liam's profit as a percentage of his cost if he sells a dining table, 6 chairs and a dresser.

4 Liam offers a 15% discount for orders over $3000. How much would a customer pay if he ordered the items in **2b**?

A   PROFIT AND LOSS

We use money nearly every day, so we need to understand profit, loss and discount.

Profit is an example of an **increase**.

Loss and discount are examples of a **decrease**.

> A **profit** occurs if the selling price is *higher* than the cost price.
>
> **Profit = selling price − cost price**
>
> A **loss** occurs if the selling price is *lower* than the cost price.
>
> **Loss = cost price − selling price**

EXERCISE 23A.1

1 Giovanna makes cakes for her 'Home-made Cakes' shop. If a cake costs €2.10 to make and she sells it for €3.70, find her profit or loss on the sale.

2 Alain knitted a jumper which he sold for $135. He calculated that the cost of the jumper, including his time spent, was $160. Find his profit or loss on the sale.

3 Brad bought an old car for £600. He spent £1038 restoring it and sold it for £3500. Find his profit or loss on the sale.

4 Julie bought a house for €170 000. She spent €6000 having the house repainted, €7800 on new carpets, and €2040 on curtains. A year later she sold the house for €189 000. Find her profit or loss on the sale.

5 At the start of summer, Joe bought 200 beach umbrellas at $25 each to sell from his beach-side café. Unfortunately for Joe it was not a very hot summer. He only sold 128 umbrellas at $39 each. Find his profit or loss on the sale of umbrellas for that summer.

MARK UP AND MARK DOWN

If a purchase price is **marked up** then it is increased, and a *profit* will be made.

If a purchase price is **marked down** then it is decreased, and a *loss* will be made.

Example 1   ◀)) Self Tutor

A camera is purchased for €650 and is marked up by 20%.
Find: **a**   the profit   **b**   the selling price.

a   Profit = 20% of cost price

= 20% of €650

$= \frac{20}{100} \times €650$

= €130

b   Selling price
= cost price + profit
= €650 + €130
= €780

Calculator: 20 ÷ 100 × 650 =

> Marked up by 20% means *increased* by 20%.

Example 2   ◀)) Self Tutor

A pair of board shorts was bought for $35. They were marked down by 20% and sold in an end-of-summer clearance. Find:

a   the loss   **b**   the selling price.

a   Loss
= 20% of cost price
= 20% of $35
$= \frac{20}{100} \times 35
= $7

b   Selling price
= cost price − loss
= $35 − $7
= $28

> Marked down 20% means *decreased* by 20%.

Calculator: 20 ÷ 100 × 35 =

EXERCISE 23A.2

1 Find   **i**   the profit   **ii**   the selling price for the following items:

    a   a shirt is purchased for $20 and marked up 10%

    b   a DVD player is purchased for $250 and marked up 80%

    c   a rugby ball is purchased for £50 and sold at a 15% profit

    d   a house is purchased for $255 000 and sold at a 21% profit.

2

Find   **i**   the loss   **ii**   the selling price   for the following items:

    a   a cap is purchased for €25 and marked down 20% as it is shop-soiled

    b   a necklace is purchased for £325 and marked down 35% as the shop is closing down

    c   a skateboard is purchased for $90 and is sold at a 20% loss in a stock-clearance

    d   a car is purchased for €12 600 and sold at a 16% loss as the car dealer has too many used cars.

3   A contractor buys his materials from a wholesaler and sells them at a 12% mark up. For one particular job the materials cost him $920. What profit does he make on the materials?

4   Phuong bought a cupboard for $140. She marked it down by 15% as the paintwork was scratched. What was:

    a   her loss   **b**   her selling price?

B   PERCENTAGE PROFIT AND LOSS

Sometimes it is important for a retailer to express profit or loss as a **percentage of the cost price**.

Profit and loss correspond to a percentage increase or decrease in the price respectively.

Example 3	◀) Self Tutor

A bicycle was bought for $240 and sold for $290.
Find the profit as a percentage of cost price.

$$\begin{aligned} \text{Profit} &= \text{selling price} - \text{cost price} \\ &= \$290 - \$240 \\ &= \$50 \end{aligned}$$

∴   profit as a *percentage* of cost price

$$= \frac{\text{profit}}{\text{cost price}} \times 100\%$$

$$= \frac{50}{240} \times 100\%$$

$$\approx 20.8\%$$ *Calculator:*   50 ÷ 240 × 100 =

> We are really calculating the *percentage increase* in the price!

EXERCISE 23B

1   A handbag bought for €125 was then sold for €160. Find the profit as a percentage of the cost price.

2   A 25 m roll of carpet was bought wholesale for $435. If the whole roll is sold at $32.50 per metre, find:
    a   the selling price   **b**   the profit
    c   the profit as a percentage of the wholesale (cost) price.

3   Rosa bought a box of tomatoes for $19.60. There were 14 kg of tomatoes in the box. She sold the tomatoes in her shop in 1 kilogram bags for $2.45 each.
    a   How much did 1 kg of tomatoes cost Rosa?
    b   What was her profit per kilogram?
    c   Find her profit as a percentage of her cost price.

Example 4   ◀ᴗ) Self Tutor

Monika bought shares in Woolworths at €21.00 per share but was forced to sell them at €18.60 each. Find:
    a   her loss per share   **b**   the loss per share as a percentage of the cost price.

a   Loss
    = cost price − selling price
    = €21.00 − €18.60
    = €2.40
    ∴   the loss made was €2.40 per share.

b   Loss as a percentage of the cost price

$$= \frac{\text{loss}}{\text{cost price}} \times 100\%$$

$$= \frac{€2.40}{€21.00} \times 100\%$$

$$\approx 11.4\%$$

Calculator: 2.4 ÷ 21 × 100 =

---

4   At the end of winter JK's Ski Centre has a clearance sale. If a pair of skis costing €800 is marked down to €720, find:
    a   the loss made on the sale
    b   the loss as a percentage of the cost price.

> We are really calculating the *percentage decrease* in the price!

5 An amateur flying club pays $38 200 for a second hand plane, but because of financial difficulties they are soon forced to sell it for $27 500.

  a Find the loss on this sale.
  b Express this loss as a percentage of the cost price.

6 Sue bought a concert ticket for $55 but was unable to go to the concert. She sold the ticket to a friend for $40, as that was the best price she could get. Find:

  a her loss   **b** her loss as a percentage of her cost price.

7 A newly married couple purchased a two-bedroom unit for £126 000. They spent another £14 300 putting in a new kitchen and bathroom. Two years later they had twins and were forced to sell the unit so they could buy a bigger house. Unfortunately, due to a down-turn in the market they received only £107 500 for the sale. What was:

  a the total cost of the unit   **b** the loss on the sale
  c the loss as a percentage of their total costs?

C   DISCOUNT

> A **discount** is a **reduction** in the marked price of an item.

When retail stores advertise a **sale**, they take a **percentage off** the **marked price** of most goods. This price reduction is a discount.

Discounts are often given to tradespeople as encouragement to buy goods at a particular store.

Example 5   ◀》 **Self Tutor**

A street merchant offers a tourist the special discount of 25% for a brass tray originally selling for 250 dirham.
Find the: **a** discount   **b** sale price.

  a   Discount $= 25\%$ of 250 dirham   **b**   Sale price
                 $= 0.25 \times 250$ dirham $=$ original price $-$ discount
                 $= 62\frac{1}{2}$ dirham $= 250 - 62\frac{1}{2}$
                                                                      $= 187\frac{1}{2}$ dirham

  Calculator: 25 $\boxed{\div}$ 100 $\boxed{\times}$ 250 $\boxed{=}$

EXERCISE 23C

1 Find the discount given on the following items, and hence find the sale price:

  a a vacuum cleaner marked at €130 and discounted 20%
  b a glass vase marked at $68 and discounted 35%
  c an electric fan marked at £28 and discounted $22\frac{1}{2}\%$.

2 An electrician buys supplies worth $186 but is given a 14% discount. How much does he save with the discount?

3 A discount sports warehouse offers 8% discount to anyone paying in cash. Joachim pays for a €96 pair of shoes in cash. How much does he actually pay?

4 A candlemaker buys 22 kg of beeswax priced at $15 per kg. Due to the size of her order she is given a $12\frac{1}{2}\%$ discount. What does she actually pay for the wax?

Example 6 ◀) Self Tutor

Fereshta buys a hijab marked at €85 but only pays €69.70. What percentage discount was she given?

$$\text{Discount} = €85 - €69.70$$
$$= €15.30$$

$$\therefore \quad \% \text{ discount} = \frac{\text{discount}}{\text{marked price}} \times 100\%$$

$$= \frac{€15.30}{€85} \times 100\%$$

$$= 18\%$$

So, Fereshta was given 18% discount.

Calculator: 15.3 ÷ 85 × 100 =

We are really calculating the *percentage decrease* in the price.

---

5 Kathryn purchased a DVD marked at $24.80 but actually paid $20.46. What percentage discount was she given?

6 Andre saw a piano advertised for sale at €13 875 after being discounted from €19 990. Calculate the percentage discount.

7 An employee at a shoe store buys a pair of sandals worth €48 but is only charged €39.36. What employee discount did she receive?

8 Helga buys a dress marked down from $180 to $126. What percentage discount was given?

Example 7   ◀) Self Tutor

'Everything Electrical' chain stores offer a trade discount of 25% to electricians.
They also offer an extra 5% discount if they pay their accounts within 7 days.
Bert is an electrician. He orders €825 worth of goods from 'Everything Electrical'.

a How much does Bert pay for the goods if he pays in 14 days?

b How much does he save by paying within 7 days?

a   Trade discount $= 25\%$ of €825
        $= 0.25 \times$ €825
        $=$ €206.25   *Calculator:*   25 ÷ 100 × 825 =

Bert pays   €825 − €206.25 = €618.75

b   If Bert pays within 7 days he receives 5% discount off the €618.75.

∴   extra discount $= 5\%$ of €618.75
                     $= 0.05 \times$ €618.75
                     $=$ €30.94

∴   Bert saves an extra €30.94.   *Calculator:*   5 ÷ 100 × 618.75 =

9 Ingrid is a painter. She purchased $1020 of paint
and brushes and was given a trade discount of
25%. She was given an extra 3% discount for
paying within 7 days.

   a Find Ingrid's trade discount.

   b Find how much she paid for the paint and
brushes for paying within 7 days.

10 Carlo is a plumber. He ordered €3270 of plumbing supplies and received 30% trade
discount. He received an extra 5% discount for paying cash.

   a Find Carlo's trade discount.

   b Find how much Carlo saved by paying cash.

11 Louise works in a store that sells fine china. As an employee, she is allowed 10%
discount off items that she purchases from the store. During a '20% off' sale, Louise
purchases a dinner set marked at €870.

   a Find the sale price of the dinner set.

   b Find: **i** Louise's employee's discount

           ii the price that Louise pays.

   c What percentage discount off the marked
price of €870 did Louise actually receive?

D USING A MULTIPLIER

In Susan's Casualwear business she buys items at a certain price and has to increase this price by 40% to make a profit and pay tax.

Suppose she buys a pair of slacks for $80. At what price should she mark them for sale?

One method is to find 40% of $80 and add this on to $80,

40% of $80 = $\frac{40}{100} \times \$80 = \$32$

So, the marked price would be $80 + $32 = $112.

This method needs **two steps**.

A **one-step** method is to use a **multiplier**.

Increasing by 40% is the same as multiplying by $100\% + 40\%$ or   140%.

So, $\$80 \times 140\% = \$80 \times 1.4$
$= \$112$

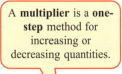

A **multiplier** is a one-step method for increasing or decreasing quantities.

Example 8   ◀) Self Tutor

What multiplier corresponds to:
a a 25% increase   **b** a 15% decrease?

a $100\% + 25\% = 125\%$ $\therefore$ multiplier is 1.25
b $100\% - 15\% = 85\%$ $\therefore$ multiplier is 0.85

EXERCISE 23D

1 What multiplier corresponds to a:

a   10% increase   **b**   10% decrease   **c**   33% increase
d   21% decrease   **e**   7.2% increase   **f**   8.9% decrease?

Example 9   ◀) Self Tutor

State the percentage increase or decrease corresponding to the following multipliers:
a   1.2   **b**   0.85

a $1.2 = 1.2 \times 100\%$ **b** $0.85 = 0.85 \times 100\%$
$= 120\%$ $= 85\%$
which is an increase over 100%   which is a decrease below 100%
by 20%   of 15%

2 For the following multipliers, state the corresponding percentage increase or decrease:

a   1.3   **b**   1.25   **c**   0.94   **d**   0.86
e   1.47   **f**   0.68   **g**   2.5   **h**   0.4

Example 10   ◀)) **Self Tutor**

> **a** Increase $860 by 7%.   **b** Decrease £1200 by 22%.

a   New amount

$= 107\%$ of $\$860$ {to increase by 7%, multiply by 107%}

$= 1.07 \times \$860$

$= \$920.20$

b   New amount

$= 78\%$ of £1200   {to decrease by 22%, multiply by 78%}

$= 0.78 \times £1200$

$= £936$

3   Calculate the following:

     a   increase $80 by 6%   **b**   increase £68 by 20%   **c**   increase 50 kg by 14%

     d   decrease €27 by 15%   **e**   decrease £780 by 16%   **f**   decrease 35 m by 10%

4   **a**   Jason was being paid a wage of €25 per hour. His employer agreed to increase his wage by 4%. What is Jason's new wage per hour?

     b   At the school athletics day Sadi increased her previous best javelin throw of 29.5 m by 8%. How far did she throw the javelin?

     c   Giuseppe thinks that the 2.5 m high hedge around his garden needs to be trimmed. If he reduces the height by 30%, how high will it be?

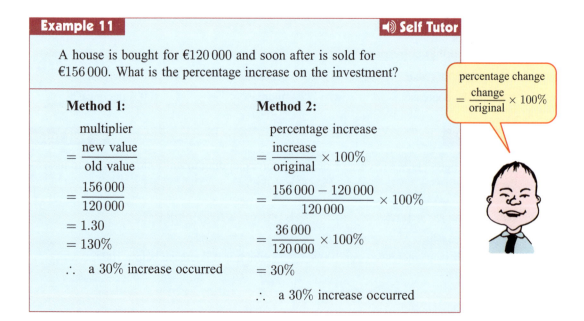

Example 11   ◀)) **Self Tutor**

> A house is bought for €120 000 and soon after is sold for €156 000. What is the percentage increase on the investment?

percentage change

$= \dfrac{\text{change}}{\text{original}} \times 100\%$

Method 1:

multiplier

$= \dfrac{\text{new value}}{\text{old value}}$

$= \dfrac{156\,000}{120\,000}$

$= 1.30$

$= 130\%$

∴   a 30% increase occurred

Method 2:

percentage increase

$= \dfrac{\text{increase}}{\text{original}} \times 100\%$

$= \dfrac{156\,000 - 120\,000}{120\,000} \times 100\%$

$= \dfrac{36\,000}{120\,000} \times 100\%$

$= 30\%$

∴   a 30% increase occurred

5 Find the percentage change that occurs when:

    a $80 increases to $120   **b** £9000 decreases to £7200

    c €95 reduces to €80   **d** €90 increases to €118

    e 16 kg increases to 20 kg   **f** 8 m reduces to 6.5 m

6 A block of land is bought for €75 000 and sold later for €110 000.   Calculate the percentage increase in the investment.

7 A share trader buys a parcel of shares for $4250 and sells them for $3800. Calculate the percentage decrease in the investment.

8 Claude found that after the Christmas season his weight had increased from 85 kg to 91 kg. What percentage increase in weight was this?

9 Frederik left a wet piece of timber, originally 3.80 m long, outside to dry.   In the sun it shrank to a length of 3.72 m. What percentage reduction was this?

10 Shelley was originally farming 250 ha of land.   However, she now farms 270 ha.   What percentage increase is this?

E   CHAIN PERCENTAGE PROBLEMS

We can use the multiplier more than once within a problem to change the value of a quantity.

Example 12   🔊 **Self Tutor**

Increase $3500 by 10% and then decrease the result by 14%.

Increasing by 10% has a multiplier of $110\% = 1.1$

Decreasing by 14% has a multiplier of $86\% = 0.86$

So, the final amount $= \$3500 \times 1.1 \times 0.86$
$ = \$3311$

EXERCISE 23E

1 **a** Increase $2000 by 20% and then by 20%.

    b Increase €3000 by 10% and then decrease by 15%.

    c Decrease €4000 by 9% and then decrease by 11%.

    d Decrease €5000 by 6% and then increase by 10%.

2 True or false?

"If we increase an amount by a certain percentage and then decrease by the same percentage, we get back to the original value."

Example 13
🔊 Self Tutor

A 1.25 L soft drink is bought by a deli for $0.80. The deli owner adds 60% mark up then 15% goods tax. What price does the customer pay (to the nearest 5 cents)?

A 60% mark up means we multiply by $160\% = 1.6$

A 15% goods tax indicates we multiply by a further $115\% = 1.15$

$$\begin{aligned} \therefore \quad \text{cost to customer} &= \$0.80 \times 1.6 \times 1.15 \\ &= \$1.472 \\ &\approx \$1.45 \quad \{\text{to the nearest 5 cents}\} \end{aligned}$$

3 Hamji buys a wallet for $35 to be sold in his shop. He adds 60% for profit and also adds $12\frac{1}{2}\%$ goods tax. What price will he write on the sales tag?

4 Super Sneakers are bought by a sports shop owner for £175. They are marked up by 45% in order for profit to be made. When these items prove very popular a further 20% mark up is made. A goods tax of 8% is applied at the point of sale. What does the customer pay?

5 An electric coffee maker costs a retail shop €85. In order to make a profit, a 65% mark up is made. As the item does not sell, two months later the price is reduced by 20%. When it is sold a value added tax (VAT) of 17.5% is added. What is the price paid by the customer to the nearest euro?

APPRECIATION

When the value of an item such as a house or investment increases, we say it **appreciates** in value. You may have noticed that the prices of everyday goods and services also appreciate over time due to **inflation**.

Example 14
🔊 Self Tutor

An investment of ¥600 000 attracts interest rates of 6.8%, 7.1% and 6.9% over 3 successive years. What is it worth at the end of this period?

A 6.8% increase uses a multiplier of $106.8\% = 1.068$

A 7.1% increase uses a multiplier of $107.1\% = 1.071$

A 6.9% increase uses a multiplier of $106.9\% = 1.069$

$$\begin{aligned} \therefore \quad \text{final value} &= ¥600\,000 \times 1.068 \times 1.071 \times 1.069 \\ &= ¥733\,651 \end{aligned}$$

6 A motorcycle today costs £3750. The inflation rates over the next four years are predicted to be 3%, 4%, 5% and 5%. If this occurs, what is the expected cost of the motorcycle at the end of this period?

7 If the rate of inflation is expected to remain constant at 3% per year for the next 5 years, what would you expect a €35 000 car to cost in 5 years' time?

8 An investment of $30 000 is left to accumulate interest over a 4-year period. During the first year the interest paid was 8.7%. In successive years the rates paid were 8.4%, 7.6% and 5.9%. Find the value of the investment after 4 years.

9 Jian invests $34 000 in a fund which accumulates interest at 8.4% per annum. If the money is left in the fund for a 6-year period, what will be its maturing value?

Example 15 ◀) **Self Tutor**

Over a three year period the value of housing increases by 6%, decreases by 5%, and then increases by 8%. What is the overall effect of these changes?

Let x be the original value of a house.

$\therefore$ value after one year $= \$x \times 1.06$ {6% increase}

value after two years $= \$x \times 1.06 \times 0.95$ {5% decrease}

value after three years $= \$x \times 1.06 \times 0.95 \times 1.08$ {8% increase}

$= \$x \times 1.087\,56$

$\approx \$x \times 108.76\%$

So, an 8.76% increase has occurred.

---

10 What is the overall effect of:

a increases of 8%, 9% and 12% over three consecutive years

b decreases of 3%, 8% and 6% over three consecutive years

c an increase of 5% over four consecutive years?

11 Joshua's wages increase by 3.2%, 4.8% and 7.5% over three consecutive years. What is his overall percentage increase over this period?

12 Jasmin's income increases by 11%, decreases by 7%, increases by 2%, and then increases by 14% over four consecutive years. What is her overall percentage increase for this four year period?

F # SIMPLE INTEREST

Whenever money is lent, the person lending the money is known as the **lender** and the person receiving the money is known as the **borrower**. The amount borrowed from the lender is called the **principal**.

The lender usually charges a fee called **interest** to the borrower. This fee represents the cost of using the other person's money. The borrower has to repay the principal borrowed plus the interest charged for using that money.

The amount of interest charged on a loan depends on the **principal**, the **time** the amount is borrowed for, and the **interest rate**.

There are two common ways of calculating interest. These are:
- **simple interest**
- **compound interest**.

SIMPLE INTEREST

Under this method, interest is calculated on the initial amount borrowed for the entire period of the loan.

Suppose $4000 is borrowed at 7% per annum for 3 years.

$$\text{The interest payable for 1 year} = 7\% \text{ of } \$4000$$
$$= \tfrac{7}{100} \times \$4000$$

$\therefore$ the interest payable for 3 years $= \tfrac{7}{100} \times \$4000 \times 3$

$$\text{i.e.,} \quad I = \$4000 \times 0.07 \times 3$$

From examples like this one we construct the **simple interest formula**:

> $I = Crn$ where I is the **simple interest**
> C is the **principal** or amount borrowed
> r is the **flat rate of interest per annum**
> n is the **time** or **duration** of the loan in **years**.

Example 16   ◄⑩ Self Tutor

Calculate the simple interest on a $6000 loan at a rate of 8% p.a. over 4 years. Hence find the total amount to be repaid.

$C = 6000$	Now $I = Crn$
$r = 8 \div 100 = 0.08$	$\therefore \quad I = 6000 \times 0.08 \times 4$
$n = 4$	$\therefore \quad I = \$1920$

The total amount to be repaid is $6000 + 1920$
$$= \$7920$$

p.a. reads *per annum* or *per year*.

EXERCISE 23F

1   Calculate the simple interest on a loan of:
   a $2000 at a rate of 6% p.a. over 4 years
   b   £9600 at a rate of 7.3% p.a. over a 17 month period
   c $30 000 at a rate of 6.8% p.a. over a 5 year 4 month period
   d   €7500 at a rate of 7.6% p.a. over a 278 day period.

2   Which loan charges less simple interest?
   •   ¥2 500 000 at a rate of 7% p.a. for 4 years,   *or*
   •   ¥2 500 000 at a rate of 6.75% p.a. for $4\tfrac{1}{2}$ years

We can use the same simple interest formula to find the other three variables C, r, and n.

FINDING THE ORIGINAL VALUE (C)

Example 17

Self Tutor

How much is borrowed if a flat rate of 8.5% p.a. results in an interest charge of $5100 after 5 years?

A **flat rate** is a simple interest rate.

$r = 8.5 \div 100 = 0.085$
$I = 5100$
$n = 5$

$\quad$ Now $\quad I = Crn$
$\quad \therefore \quad 5100 = C \times 0.085 \times 5$
$\therefore \quad C \times 0.425 = 5100$

$\quad \therefore \quad C = \dfrac{5100}{0.425} \quad$ {dividing both sides by 0.425}

$\quad \therefore \quad C = 12\,000$

$\therefore \quad$ \$12\,000 is borrowed

3 How much is borrowed if a flat rate of 6% p.a. results in an interest charge of £900 after 4 years?

4 How much is borrowed if a flat rate of 9% p.a. results in an interest charge of €6561 after 3 years?

5 An investor wants to earn $3500 in 8 months. How much would he need to invest given that the current interest rates are $7\frac{3}{4}\%$ for a flat rate?

FINDING THE RATE (r)

Example 18

Self Tutor

If you wanted to earn $5000 in interest on a 4 year loan of $17\,000$, what flat rate of interest would you need to charge?

$I = 5000$ $\qquad$ Now $\quad I = Crn$
$n = 4$ $\qquad \quad \therefore \quad 5000 = 17\,000 \times r \times 4$
$C = 17\,000$ $\qquad \therefore \quad 68\,000r = 5000$

$\qquad \qquad \therefore \quad r = \dfrac{5000}{68\,000} \quad$ {dividing both sides by 68\,000}

$\qquad \qquad \therefore \quad r \approx 0.0735$

$\therefore \quad$ you would need to charge a flat rate of 7.35% p.a.

6 What flat rate of interest must be charged if you want to earn:
$\quad$ **a** $800 after 5 years on $6000 $\qquad$ **b** €1000 after 20 months on €8800?

7 What rate of simple interest would need to be charged on a loan of £20\,000 if you wanted to earn £3000 in interest over 2 years?

8 A student wants to buy a car costing \$3500 in 18 months' time. She has already saved \$3000 and deposits this in an account that pays a flat rate of interest.

What flat rate of interest must the account pay to enable the student to reach her target?

FINDING THE DURATION OF A LOAN (n)

Example 19   ◀)) **Self Tutor**

How long would it take to earn interest of \$4000 on a loan of \$15 000 if a flat rate of 7.5% p.a. is charged?

$I = 4000$

$C = 15\,000$

$r = 7.5 \div 100 = 0.075$

Now $I = Crn$

$\therefore \quad 4000 = 15\,000 \times 0.075 \times n$

$\therefore \quad 4000 = 1125n$

$\therefore \quad n \approx 3.56$

So, it would take 3 years 7 months to earn the interest.

---

9 How long would it take to earn interest of:

   a   \$3000 on a loan of \$10 000 at a flat rate of 8% p.a.

   b   ¥82 440 on a loan of ¥229 000 at a flat rate of 6% p.a.?

10 If you deposited \$8000 in an investment account that paid a flat rate of 7.25% p.a., how long would it take to earn \$1600 in interest?

ACTIVITY   **SIMPLE INTEREST CALCULATOR**

Click on the icon to obtain a simple interest calculator.

What to do:

Check the answers to **Examples 16** to **19**.

SIMPLE INTEREST

CALCULATING REPAYMENTS FOR SIMPLE INTEREST LOANS

Whenever money is borrowed, it has to eventually be repaid along with the interest charges.

The repayment of the amount owed (principal plus interest) is normally done by making regular (usually equal) payments over the length of the loan. These may be weekly, fortnightly, monthly, or at other time intervals.

The regular payment made is calculated by dividing the total amount to be repaid by the number of repayment periods:

$$\text{regular payment} = \frac{\text{total to be repaid}}{\text{number of repayments}}$$

Example 20   ◀)) **Self Tutor**

Calculate the monthly repayments on a loan of $15 000 at 7% p.a. flat rate over 4 years.

Step 1:   Calculate the interest on the loan.

$C = 15\,000$ Now $I = Crn$

$r = 7 \div 100 = 0.07$ $\therefore$ $I = 15\,000 \times 0.07 \times 4$

$n = 4$ $\therefore$ interest = $4200

Step 2:   Calculate the total amount to be repaid.

total repayment   = $15\,000 + $4200

principal   interest

= $19\,200

Step 3:   Repayments are made each month.
So, in 4 years we have $4 \times 12 = 48$ months.

Step 4:   Monthly repayment $= \dfrac{\$19\,200}{48} = \$400$

11   Calculate the monthly repayments on a loan of €9500 at 7.5% p.a. flat rate over 4 years.

12   A loan of $24 000 at a flat rate of 6.5% p.a. is repaid quarterly (4 times a year) over 6 years. Calculate the amount of each repayment.

13   Sam obtains a loan of £6000 for 4 years at a flat rate of 8.5% p.a. If payments on the loan are made every 6 months, calculate the size of each repayment.

14   Thierry pays $330.65 per month for $3\frac{1}{2}$ years for a loan of $11 000. How much interest will he pay for this loan?

G   COMPOUND INTEREST

If you bank $1000, then you are actually lending the money to the bank. The bank in turn uses your money to lend to other people. While banks pay you interest to encourage your custom, they charge interest to borrowers at a higher rate. That way the banks make a profit.

If you leave the money in the bank for a period of time, the interest is automatically added to your account and so the principal is increased. The next lot of interest will then be calculated on the higher principal. This creates a **compounding** effect on the interest as you are getting **interest on interest**.

Consider an investment of $1000 with interest of 6% p.a. paid each year and compounded.

After year	Interest paid	Value
0		$1000.00
1	6% of $1000.00 = $60.00	$1000.00 + $60.00 = $1060.00
2	6% of $1060.00 = $63.60	$1060.00 + $63.60 = $1123.60
3	6% of $1123.60 = $67.42	$1123.60 + $67.42 = $1191.02

We can use **chain percentage increases** to calculate the account balance after 3 years.

Each year, the account balance is 106% of its previous value.

$$\therefore \quad \text{future value after 3 years} \quad = \$1000 \times 1.06 \times 1.06 \times 1.06$$
$$= \$1000 \times (1.06)^3$$
$$= \$1191.02$$

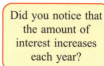

Did you notice that the amount of interest increases each year?

In this section we are only interested in **one interest payment per year**.

Example 21   ◆) Self Tutor

$5000 is invested at 8% p.a. compound interest with interest calculated annually.
a   What will it amount to after 3 years?
b   Find the interest earned.

a   The multiplier is   108% = 1.08
$$\therefore \quad \text{value after 3 years} \quad = \$5000 \times (1.08)^3$$
$$= \$6298.56$$

b   Interest earned   = $6298.56 − $5000
$$= \$1298.56$$

EXERCISE 23G

1   Find the final value of a compound interest investment of:

    a $2500 after 3 years at 6% p.a. with interest calculated annually

    b   £4000 after 4 years at 7% p.a. with interest calculated annually

    c   €8250 after 4 years at 8.5% p.a. with interest calculated annually.

2   Find the total interest earned for the following compound interest investments:

    a   €750 after 2 years at 6.8% p.a. with interest calculated annually

    b $3350 after 3 years at 7.25% p.a. with interest calculated annually

    c   £12 500 after 4 years at 8.1% p.a. with interest calculated annually.

3 Xiao Ming invests 12 000 Yuan into an account which pays 7% p.a. compounded annually. Find:

  a the value of her account after 2 years

  b the total interest earned after 2 years.

4 Kiri places $5000 in a fixed term investment account which pays 5.6% p.a. compounded annually.

  a How much will she have in her account after 3 years?

  b What interest has she earned over this period?

5 Nindi invests 30 000 rupee in an account which pays 5.2% p.a. interest compounded annually.

  a How much will he have in his account after 7 years assuming no withdrawals?

  b How much interest will he earn?

6 Which investment would earn you more interest on an 8000 peso investment for 5 years:

  • one which pays 8% p.a. simple interest   *or*

  • one which pays 7.5% p.a. compound interest?

COMPOUND INTEREST CALCULATOR

COMPOUND INTEREST CALCULATOR

Click on the icon to load a **compound interest calculator** which can be used to check your answers to **Exercise 23G**.

ACTIVITY	A SPREADSHEET FOR COMPOUND INTEREST

The purpose of this activity is to construct a spreadsheet for finding the annual growth of an amount of money which is earning interest at a given rate each year. The spreadsheet must show the final amount at the end of each year and the amount of interest earned each year.

Consider the original example in this section where $1000 is invested at a rate of 6% p.a. over several years.

SPREADSHEET

What to do:

1 Click on the icon to open a new spreadsheet. Type in cell A1 *After year*, in cell B1 *Interest paid* and in cell C1 *Account balance*. In cell D1 type *Interest rate (%)*.

2 In A2 type 0. In A3 type the formula   =A2+1.   Highlight A3 and fill down to A12.

3 In cell C2 type 1000 and in D2 type 6.

4 In B3 type   =D2/100*C2.   In C3 type   =C2+B3.

5 Highlight cells C3 and B3 and fill both down to row 12.

6 Set the number of decimal places in columns 2 and 3 to reflect your currency. For example, if you use dollars, euros or pounds, set these cells to 2 decimal places so that you round to the nearest cent or penny.

Your spreadsheet should now look like:

	A	B	C	D
1	After year	Interest paid	Account balance	Interest rate (%)
2	0		1000.00	6
3	1	60.00	1060.00	
4	2	63.60	1123.60	
5	3	67.42	1191.02	
6	4	71.46	1262.48	
7	5	75.75	1338.23	
8	6	80.29	1418.52	
9	7	85.11	1503.63	
10	8	90.22	1593.85	
11	9	95.63	1689.48	
12	10	101.37	1790.85	

7 Replace the 6 in D2 by 7 and explain what data the spreadsheet calculates.

8 Replace the 1000 in C2 by 22 500 and the 7 in D2 by 5.5 and explain what the data in the spreadsheet calculates.

9 Use only your spreadsheet to calculate the final value and the total interest earned on a $12 750 investment at 6.8% p.a. for 5 years.   **Hint:**   In D7 type =C7−C2.

H FOREIGN EXCHANGE

When you are in another country you need to use the **currency** or money system of that country. This means that you must exchange your money for the equivalent amount of the local currency. The equivalent amount is found using **exchange rates**.

Exchange rates show the relationship between the values of currencies. They are published daily in newspapers, in bank windows, and on the internet at various bank and travel agency sites.

Suppose you are a citizen of the European Union (EU) and you want to know how much each currency is worth compared with **one euro**.

The following is a table of exchange rates. Note that it is an example only since exchange rates change constantly.

Country	Currency Name	Symbol	Value of EU euros (€)	
			Buying	Selling
Singapore	Dollar	$SG	2.0675	1.9848
Japan	Yen	¥	158.317	151.984
China	Yuan	元	10.0372	9.6357
United Kingdom	Pound	£	0.682 95	0.655 63
Australia	Dollar	$AUD	1.5927	1.5291
USA	Dollar	$US	1.3462	1.2923

You can see that there are different rates for **buying and selling** euros. This ensures that the bank or money exchange makes a profit on the transaction. In addition, some exchange places will also charge commission.

BUYING AND SELLING EUROS

SELLING

- How much foreign currency will you receive by selling euros?
  Use the **selling exchange rate** and the formula:

$$\textbf{Foreign currency bought} = \textbf{euros sold} \times \textbf{selling exchange rate}$$

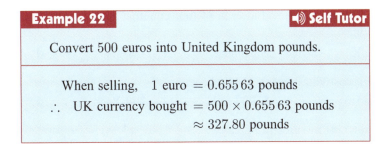

Example 22   ◀) **Self Tutor**

Convert 500 euros into United Kingdom pounds.

When selling,   1 euro $= 0.655\,63$ pounds
$\therefore$ UK currency bought $= 500 \times 0.655\,63$ pounds
≈ 327.80 pounds

- How many euros do you need to purchase foreign currency?
  Use the **selling exchange rate** and the formula:

$$\textbf{Cost in euros} = \frac{\textbf{foreign currency bought}}{\textbf{selling exchange rate}}$$

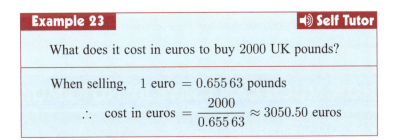

Example 23   ◀) **Self Tutor**

What does it cost in euros to buy 2000 UK pounds?

When selling,   1 euro $= 0.655\,63$ pounds
$\therefore$ cost in euros $= \dfrac{2000}{0.655\,63} \approx 3050.50$ euros

BUYING

- You have **currency from another country** and want to change it to **euros**.
  You are **buying** euros, so we use the **buying exchange rate** and the formula:

$$\textbf{Euros bought} = \frac{\textbf{foreign currency sold}}{\textbf{buying exchange rate}}$$

> ### Example 24   ◄)) Self Tutor
>
> If you have $365AUD and exchange it for euros, how many euros will you receive?
>
> When buying,   1 euro = 1.5927 AUD
>
> $$\therefore \quad \text{euros bought} = \frac{365}{1.5927} \approx 229.15 \quad \text{(to the nearest 0.05)}$$

EXERCISE 23H

In questions **1** to **4**, suppose you are a citizen of the EU and use the currency table on page **470**.

1 You have 400 euros to spend in each of four countries. How much local money can be purchased in:

    a the UK   **b** Singapore   **c** USA   **d** Japan?

2 What will it cost you in euros to purchase:

    a $950 US   **b** $5000 SG   **c** 380 Yuan   **d** 7000 Yen?

3 Calculate the cost in euros to purchase:

    a a plate of noodles for 9 Singapore dollars

    b a suit marked at $265 US   **c** a camera for 21 000 Yen

4 How much in euros would you expect in exchange for:

    a 20 000 Yen   **b** $300 SG   **c** $150 AUD   **d** $417 US?

5 Obtain current exchange rates using the daily newspaper or the internet over a 5-day period. What do you notice?

6 Construct a table of exchange rates for your country's currency, and use it to redo questions **1** to **4** wherever possible.

HOW MUCH CAN I SAVE BY NOT SMOKING?

LINKS
click here

Areas of interaction:
Environments/Health and social education

REVIEW SET 23A

1 a What multiplier corresponds to:

     i a 13% decrease   **ii** a 10.9% increase?

   b For the following multipliers, state the percentage increase or decrease occurring:

     i 3.5   **ii** 0.73

2 a Increase $2500 by 16%.   **b** Decrease 65 kg by 10%.

3 Sam buys a bicycle for €225 and sells it for €385 after repainting it. What is Sam's:

  a profit   **b** percentage profit?

4 Yuka purchases a shirt for ¥3400 and marks it up 35% for sale. What is:

  a the selling price   **b** the profit?

5 Moira bought a car for £4500 but had to sell it for £4000 a few weeks later. What was her:

  a loss   **b** percentage loss?

6 A store has an item for $80 and discounts it by 15%. Find:

  a the discount   **b** the sale price.

7 Barbara purchased a coin collection for $1200. Two years later it was valued at $2150. Calculate the percentage increase in the value of the investment.

8 A publisher sells a book for $20 per copy to a retailer. The retailer marks up the price by 75% and then adds 10% for a goods tax.

What price does the customer pay?

9 The annual rate of inflation is predicted to be 3% next year, then 3.5% in the year after that. What will be the cost in two years' time of an item that currently costs $50 if the cost rises in line with inflation?

10 How much is borrowed if a flat rate of 8% p.a. results in an interest charge of $3600 after 3 years?

11 A person wants to earn $3000 interest on an investment of $17 000 over 3 years. What is the minimum flat rate that will achieve this target?

12 How long would it take to earn $5000 interest on an investment of $22 500 at a flat rate of 9.5% p.a.?

13 **a** Calculate the simple interest on a $6000 loan at a rate of 8.5% p.a. over 3 years.
  b Calculate the monthly repayments.

14 Find the final value of a compound interest investment of $20 000 after 3 years at 7.5% p.a. with interest calculated annually.

15 Which of the following would earn more interest on a $7500 investment for 4 years:
  • 9% p.a. simple interest calculated annually   *or*
  • 8% p.a. compounded interest calculated annually?

REVIEW SET 23B

1 a What multiplier corresponds to: **i** a 10% increase   **ii** an 11.7% decrease?

  b For these multipliers, state the percentage increase or decrease occurring:

    i 1.037   **ii** 2   **iii** 0.938

2 a Increase £3625 by 8%.   **b** Decrease 387 km by 1.8%.

3 Jason bought a tennis racquet for $185 and sold it soon after for $140. What was Jason's: **a** loss   **b** percentage loss?

4 Pancho bought a car for 2000 pesos, improved it mechanically then sold it for a 30% profit. What was his:

  a selling price   **b** profit?

5 A furniture store bought a chair for €380, marked it up by 35% and then discounted it by 15%. What was:

  a the marked-up price   **b** the discounted price?

6 A company cut its advertising budget by 12%. If the company previously spent $80 000 on advertising, what was the new advertising budget?

7 A superannuation fund reports a decrease in value of 4% in year 1, an increase of 8% in year 2, and a 4% decrease in year 3. What was the overall percentage increase or decrease of the fund over the period?

8 A toaster is sold to a retailer for €38. The retailer marks it up by 40%, discounts it by 15%, and then sells it to a customer after adding on 16% VAT. What did the customer pay?

9 For the next three years the annual inflation rate is predicted to be 3.2%, 4.1% and 4.8%. If this occurs, what should be the value of a house currently at $325 000?

10 What simple interest is earned on an investment of $6500 for 4 years at 6.8% p.a.?

11 How much is borrowed if a flat rate of 7.2% p.a. results in an interest charge of $216 after $2\frac{1}{2}$ years?

12 How long would it take for a loan of €45 000 to earn €15 120 interest at a rate of 8% p.a. simple interest?

13 An investment of $25 000 is made for 4 years at 8.2% p.a. compounded yearly. Find:

  a the final value of the investment   **b** the interest earned.

14 Hector has a £15 000 loan for 4 years at 7.5% p.a. simple interest. Calculate:

  a the amount of simple interest   **b** the monthly repayments.

15 €8000 is invested for 10 years at 8% p.a. compounded interest. Find:

  a the final value of the investment   **b** the amount of interest earned

  c the simple interest rate needed to be paid for the same return on the investment.

Chapter 24

Quadratic functions

Contents:

A   Graphs of quadratic functions

B   Axes intercepts

C   The axis of symmetry

D   Quadratic modelling

OPENING PROBLEM

A cannonball fired vertically upwards from ground level has height H metres given by the relationship $H = 36t - 3t^2$, where t is the time in seconds after firing.

Consider the following:

1 If we sketch a graph of the height H against the time t after firing, what shape would result?

2 How long would it take for the cannonball to reach its maximum height?

3 What would be the maximum height reached?

4 How long would the person who fired the cannonball have to clear the area?

A   GRAPHS OF QUADRATIC FUNCTIONS

The graphs of all quadratic functions are **parabolas**. The parabola is one of the *conic sections*.

Conic sections are curves which can be obtained by cutting a cone with a plane. The Ancient Greek mathematicians were fascinated by conic sections.

You may like to find the conic sections for yourself by cutting an icecream cone.

Cutting parallel to the side produces a parabola, as shown in the diagram.

There are many examples of parabolas in everyday life:

The name parabola comes from the Greek word for **thrown** because when an object is thrown, its path makes a parabolic shape.

Parabolic mirrors are used in car headlights, heaters, radar discs and radio telescopes because of their special geometric properties.

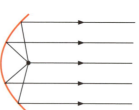

Below is a single span parabolic bridge. Other suspension bridges, such as the Golden Gate bridge in San Francisco, also form parabolic curves.

THE SIMPLEST QUADRATIC FUNCTION

The simplest quadratic function is $y = x^2$. Its graph can be drawn from a table of values.

x	-3	-2	-1	0	1	2	3
y	9	4	1	0	1	4	9

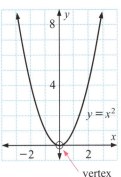

Notice that:

- The curve is a **parabola** and it opens upwards.

- There are no negative y values, i.e., the curve does not go below the x-axis.

- The curve is **symmetrical** about the y-axis because, for example, when $x = -3$, $y = (-3)^2 = 9$ and when $x = 3$, $y = 3^2 = 9$.

- The curve has a **turning point** or **vertex** at $(0, 0)$.

The **vertex** is the point where the graph is at its maximum or minimum.

Example 1   ◉ **Self Tutor**

Draw the graph of $y = x^2 + 2x - 3$ from a table of values from $x = -3$ to $x = 3$.

Consider $f(x) = x^2 + 2x - 3$

Now, $f(-3) = (-3)^2 + 2(-3) - 3$
$\qquad\qquad = 9 - 6 - 3$
$\qquad\qquad = 0$

We can do the same for the other values of x.

Tabled values are:

x	-3	-2	-1	0	1	2	3
y	0	-3	-4	-3	0	5	12

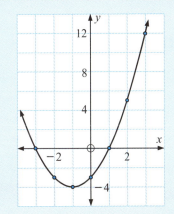

EXERCISE 24A

1 From a table of values for $x = -3, -2, -1, 0, 1, 2, 3$ draw the graph of:

    a $y = x^2 - 2x + 1$ **b** $y = -2x^2 + 4$ **c** $y = x^2 + x + 4$

    d $y = -x^2 - 4x - 4$ **e** $y = 2x^2 + 3x$ **f** $y = -x^2 + 4x - 9$

2 What is the effect on the graph of the sign in front of the x^2 term in the equations in **1**?

From the graphs drawn in this exercise you can see that a parabola may:

- cut the x-axis in two places   (two x-intercepts)
- touch the x-axis   (one x-intercept)   or
- lie entirely above or entirely below the x-axis   (no x-intercepts).

B AXES INTERCEPTS

Given the equation of any curve:

An **x-intercept** is a value of x where the graph meets the x-axis.

A **y-intercept** is a value of y where the graph meets the y-axis.

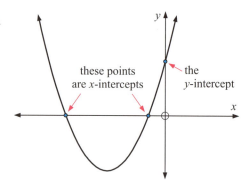

these points are x-intercepts

the y-intercept

x-intercepts are found by letting y be 0 in the equation of the curve.

y-intercepts are found by letting x be 0 in the equation of the curve.

THE y-INTERCEPT OF A QUADRATIC FUNCTION

You will have noticed that for a quadratic function of the form $y = ax^2 + bx + c$, the y-intercept is the constant term c. This is because any curve cuts the y-axis when $x = 0$.

For example,   if $y = x^2 - 2x - 3$ and we let $x = 0$

then $y = 0^2 - 2(0) - 3$

$\therefore \quad y = -3$ (the constant term)

EXERCISE 24B

1   For the following functions state the y-intercept:

    a $y = x^2 + 3x + 3$
    b $y = x^2 - 5x + 2$
    c $y = 2x^2 + 7x - 8$

    d $y = 3x^2 - x + 1$
    e $y = -x^2 + 3x + 6$
    f $y = -2x^2 + 5 - x$

    g $y = 6 - x - x^2$
    h $y = 8 + 2x - 3x^2$
    i $y = 5x - x^2 - 2$

INVESTIGATION x-INTERCEPTS OF A QUADRATIC

What to do:

GRAPHING PACKAGE

1   For the following quadratic functions, use your graphing package or graphics calculator to:

    i draw the graph   **ii** find the x-intercepts (if any exist)

    a $y = x^2 - 3x - 4$
    b $y = -x^2 + 2x + 8$
    c $y = 2x^2 - 3x$

    d $y = -2x^2 + 2x - 3$
    e $y = (x - 1)(x - 3)$
    f $y = -(x + 2)(x - 3)$

    g $y = 3(x + 1)(x + 4)$
    h $y = 2(x - 2)^2$
    i $y = -3(x + 1)^2$

2   From your observations in question **1**:

    a   State the x-intercepts of a quadratic function of the form $y = a(x - \alpha)(x - \beta)$.

    b   What do you notice about the x-intercepts of quadratic functions in the form $y = a(x - \alpha)^2$?   What else do you notice?

THE x-INTERCEPTS OF A QUADRATIC FUNCTION

You should have noticed that for a quadratic function of the form $y = a(x - \alpha)(x - \beta)$, the x-intercepts are α and β. This is because any curve cuts the x-axis when $y = 0$.

So, if we substitute $y = 0$ into the function we get $a(x - \alpha)(x - \beta) = 0$

$$\therefore \quad x = \alpha \text{ or } \beta \qquad \{\text{by the Null Factor law, since } a \neq 0\}$$

This suggests that x-intercepts are easy to find when the quadratic is in **factorised** form.

Example 2   ◀ঠ **Self Tutor**

Find the x-intercepts of:

a $y = 2(x - 3)(x + 2)$ **b** $y = -(x - 4)^2$

a We let $y = 0$

$\therefore \quad 2(x - 3)(x + 2) = 0$

$\therefore \quad x = 3 \quad \text{or} \quad x = -2$

$\therefore$ the x-intercepts are 3 and -2.

b We let $y = 0$

$\therefore \quad -(x - 4)^2 = 0$

$\therefore \quad x = 4$

$\therefore$ the x-intercept is 4.

> If a quadratic function has only one x-intercept then its graph must **touch** the x-axis.

---

2 For the following functions, find the x-intercepts:

a $y = (x - 3)(x + 1)$ **b** $y = -(x - 2)(x - 4)$

c $y = 2(x + 3)(x + 2)$ **d** $y = -3(x - 4)(x - 5)$

e $y = 2(x + 3)^2$ **f** $y = -5(x - 1)^2$

FACTORISING TO FIND x-INTERCEPTS

> For any quadratic function of the form $y = ax^2 + bx + c$, the x-intercepts can be found by solving the equation $ax^2 + bx + c = 0$.

You will recall from **Chapter 22** that quadratic equations may have *two solutions, one solution* or *no solutions*.

These solutions correspond to *two x-intercepts, one x-intercept* or *no x-intercepts* found when the graphs of the quadratic functions are drawn.

Example 3   ◀ঠ **Self Tutor**

Find the x-intercept(s) of the quadratic functions:

a $y = x^2 - 6x + 9$ **b** $y = -x^2 - x + 6$

a When $y = 0$,

$x^2 - 6x + 9 = 0$

$\therefore \quad (x - 3)^2 = 0$

$\therefore \quad x = 3$

$\therefore$ x-intercept is 3.

b When $y = 0$,

$-x^2 - x + 6 = 0$

$\therefore \quad x^2 + x - 6 = 0$

$\therefore \quad (x + 3)(x - 2) = 0$

$\therefore \quad x = -3 \text{ or } 2$

$\therefore$ x-intercepts are -3 and 2.

3 For the following functions find the x-intercepts:

a $y = x^2 - 9$
b $y = 2x^2 - 6$
c $y = x^2 + 7x + 10$
d $y = x^2 + x - 12$
e $y = 4x - x^2$
f $y = -x^2 - 6x - 8$
g $y = -2x^2 - 4x - 2$
h $y = 4x^2 - 24x + 36$
i $y = x^2 - 4x + 1$
j $y = x^2 + 4x - 3$
k $y = x^2 - 6x - 2$
l $y = x^2 + 8x + 11$

4 Check your answers to **3** using technology.

Example 4   ◀ **Self Tutor**

Sketch the graph of $y = x^2 - 3x + 2$ using axes intercepts only.

When $x = 0$, $y = 2$.
So, the y-intercept is 2.
When $y = 0$,
$$x^2 - 3x + 2 = 0$$
$$\therefore \ (x - 1)(x - 2) = 0$$
$$\therefore \ x = 1 \text{ or } 2$$
So, the x-intercepts are 1 and 2.

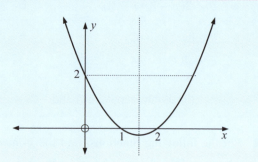

---

5 Sketch the quadratic functions using axes intercepts:

a $y = (x + 1)(x - 3)$
b $y = -(x - 1)(x - 3)$
c $y = x^2 - 2x$
d $y = x^2 + 3x$
e $y = -x^2 + 6x - 5$
f $y = x^2 + 6x + 5$
g $y = x^2 - 6x + 8$
h $y = x^2 + 6x + 8$
i $y = 4x^2 - 1$
j $y = -9x^2 + 4$
k $y = -2x^2 + 7x + 4$
l $y = 3x^2 - x - 2$

C   THE AXIS OF SYMMETRY

The axis of symmetry of a quadratic function is a vertical line.

If the quadratic function cuts the x-axis twice, the axis of symmetry cuts the x-axis midway between the x-intercepts.

How do we quickly find the equation of the axis of symmetry if the quadratic function is given in the form $y = ax^2 + bx + c$?

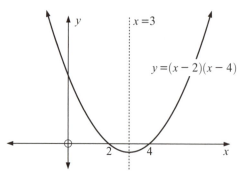

The following argument is one of several that can be used to find the equation.

Suppose the quadratic cuts the x-axis at α and β and has an axis of symmetry $x = h$.

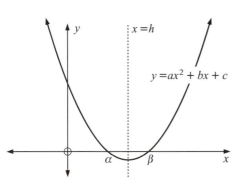

Firstly, we notice that $h = \dfrac{\alpha + \beta}{2}$. Why?

Also the quadratic has factored form
$$y = a(x - \alpha)(x - \beta).$$

Expanding gives
$$y = a(x^2 - \beta x - \alpha x + \alpha\beta)$$
$$\therefore \quad y = a(x^2 - [\alpha + \beta]x + \alpha\beta)$$
$$\therefore \quad y = ax^2 \underbrace{-a[\alpha + \beta]}_{b}\, x + a\alpha\beta$$

But $b = -a[\alpha + \beta]$ is the coefficient of x

$$\therefore \quad \alpha + \beta = -\frac{b}{a}$$

and so $h = \dfrac{\alpha + \beta}{2} = \dfrac{-b}{2a}$

Summary:

If a quadratic function is $y = ax^2 + bx + c$, then

its axis of symmetry has equation $x = \dfrac{-b}{2a}$.

It can be shown that this equation is correct regardless of whether the quadratic function has x-intercepts or not.

Example 5 ◆) Self Tutor

Find the equation of the axis of symmetry of $y = 2x^2 + 3x + 1$.

$y = 2x^2 + 3x + 1$ has $a = 2$, $b = 3$, $c = 1$

$\therefore$ axis of symmetry has equation $x = \dfrac{-b}{2a} = \dfrac{-3}{2 \times 2}$ i.e., $x = -\dfrac{3}{4}$

EXERCISE 24C

1 Determine the equation of the axis of symmetry of:

   a $y = x^2 + 4x + 1$ **b** $y = 2x^2 - 6x + 3$ **c** $y = 3x^2 + 4x - 1$

   d $y = -x^2 - 4x + 5$ **e** $y = -2x^2 + 5x + 1$ **f** $y = \frac{1}{2}x^2 - 10x + 2$

   g $y = \frac{1}{3}x^2 + 4x$ **h** $y = 100x - 4x^2$ **i** $y = -\frac{1}{10}x^2 + 30x$

TURNING POINT OR VERTEX

The **turning point** (or **vertex**) of any parabola is the point at which the function has a

maximum value (for $a < 0$) or, a minimum value (for $a > 0$) .

As the turning point lies on the axis of symmetry, its x-coordinate will be $x = \dfrac{-b}{2a}$.

The y-coordinate can be found by substituting for x into the function.

Example 6   Self Tutor

Determine the coordinates of the vertex of $f(x) = 2x^2 - 8x + 1$.

> The vertex is either a *maximum* turning point or a *minimum* turning point, depending on whether the graph opens downwards or upwards.

$f(x) = 2x^2 - 8x + 1$ has $a = 2, \quad b = -8, \quad c = 1$

and so $\dfrac{-b}{2a} = \dfrac{-(-8)}{2 \times 2} = 2$

$\therefore$ equation of axis of symmetry is $x = 2$

When $x = 2, \quad f(2) = 2(2)^2 - 8(2) + 1 = 8 - 16 + 1 = -7$

$\therefore$ the vertex has coordinates $(2, -7)$.

2   Find the turning point (vertex) for the following quadratic functions:

   a $y = x^2 - 4x + 2$ **b** $y = x^2 + 2x - 3$ **c** $y = 2x^2 + 4$

   d $y = -3x^2 + 1$ **e** $y = 2x^2 + 8x - 7$ **f** $y = -x^2 - 4x - 9$

   g $y = 2x^2 + 6x - 1$ **h** $y = 2x^2 - 10x + 3$ **i** $y = -\frac{1}{2}x^2 + x - 5$

Example 7   Self Tutor

For the quadratic function $y = -x^2 + 2x + 3$:

a   find its axes intercepts

b   find the equation of the axis of symmetry

c   find the coordinates of the vertex

d   sketch the function showing all important features.

a   When $x = 0, \ y = 3$

    $\therefore$ y-intercept is 3.

    When $y = 0, \qquad -x^2 + 2x + 3 = 0$

    $\therefore \quad x^2 - 2x - 3 = 0$

    $\therefore \quad (x - 3)(x + 1) = 0$

    $\therefore \quad x = 3 \text{ or } -1$

  so, x-intercepts are 3 and -1.

b $a = -1, \quad b = 2, \quad c = 3$

    $\therefore \quad \dfrac{-b}{2a} = \dfrac{-2}{-2} = 1$

    $\therefore$ axis of symmetry is $x = 1$.

c   Using **b**, when $x = 1$

    $y = -(1)^2 + 2(1) + 3$

    $= -1 + 2 + 3$

    $= 4$

  $\therefore$ the vertex is $(1, 4)$.

d

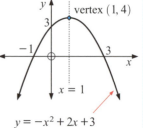

To check the answers to **Example 7**, consult the graphics calculator section **Working with Functions** on page 21.

3 For each of the following quadratic functions find :

      i   the axes intercepts   **ii**   the equation of the axis of symmetry

     iii   the coordinates of the vertex   **iv**   and hence sketch the graph.

  a $y = x^2 - 2x - 8$ **b** $y = x^2 + 3x$ **c** $y = 4x - x^2$

  d $y = x^2 + 4x + 4$ **e** $y = x^2 + 3x - 4$ **f** $y = -x^2 + 2x - 1$

  g $y = -x^2 - 6x - 8$ **h** $y = -x^2 + 3x - 2$ **i** $y = 2x^2 + 5x - 3$

  j $y = 2x^2 - 5x - 12$ **k** $y = -3x^2 - 4x + 4$ **l** $y = -\frac{1}{4}x^2 + 5x$

4 Check your answers to **3** using a graphics calculator.

D   QUADRATIC MODELLING

If the relationship between two variables is a quadratic function, then its graph will be either

⋃   or   ⋂   and the function will have a minimum or maximum value.

The process of finding the maximum or minimum value of a function is called **optimisation**. Optimisation is a very useful tool when looking at such issues as:

- maximising profits   •   minimising costs   •   maximising heights reached etc.

Example 8   ◀) **Self Tutor**

The height H metres, of a rocket t seconds after it is fired, is given by $H(t) = -5t^2 + 80t, \quad t \geqslant 0$.

  a   How long does it take for the rocket to reach its maximum height?

  b   What is the maximum height reached by the rocket?

  c   How long does it take for the rocket to fall back to Earth?

---

  a   For $H(t) = -5t^2 + 80t, \quad a = -5 \quad \therefore \quad$ shape is   ⋂

      The maximum height is reached when $t = \dfrac{-b}{2a} = \dfrac{-80}{2(-5)} = 8$

      $\therefore$ the maximum height is reached after 8 seconds.

  b $\begin{aligned} H(8) &= -5(8)^2 + 80(8) \\ &= -320 + 640 \\ &= 320 \end{aligned}$

      $\therefore$ the maximum height reached is 320 m.

  c   The rocket falls back to Earth when $H(t) = 0$

         $\therefore \quad -5t^2 + 80t = 0$

         $\therefore \quad 5t^2 - 80t = 0$

         $\therefore \quad 5t(t - 16) = 0$ {factorising}

            $\therefore \quad t = 0$ or $t = 16$

      $\therefore$ the rocket falls back to Earth after 16 seconds.

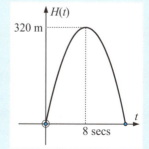

EXERCISE 24D

Use the equation of the axis of symmetry to help answer questions **1**, **2** and **3**.

1 The height H metres, of a ball hit vertically upwards, is given by
$H(t) = -2t^2 + 24t$,   where t is the time in seconds after it is hit.
   a How long does it take for the ball to reach its maximum height?
   b What is the maximum height reached by the ball?
   c How long does it take for the ball to hit the ground?

2 A skateboard manufacturer finds that the cost per skateboard $\$C$ of making x skateboards per day is given by $C(x) = x^2 - 24x + 244$.
   a How many skateboards should be made per day to minimise the cost of production per skateboard?
   b What is the minimum cost?
   c What is the cost to the company if no skateboards are made in a day?

3 The driver of a car travelling downhill on a road applies the brakes. The speed s of the car in $km\,h^{-1}$, t seconds after the brakes were applied, is given by $s(t) = -4t^2 + 12t + 80$.
   a How fast was the car travelling when the driver applied the brakes?
   b After how many seconds was the speed of the car $88\ km\,h^{-1}$? Can you explain your answer?
   c After how many seconds did the car reach its maximum speed?
   d What was the maximum speed reached?

Use technology to answer questions **4**, **5** and **6**.

4 The hourly profit (€P) obtained from operating a fleet of n taxis is given by $P(n) = -2n^2 + 84n - 45$.
   a What number of taxis gives the maximum hourly profit?
   b What is the maximum hourly profit?
   c How much money is lost per hour if no taxis are on the road?

5 The temperature $T°C$ in a greenhouse t hours after dusk (7.00 pm) is given by $T(t) = \frac{1}{4}t^2 - 5t + 30$,   where $t \leqslant 20$.
   a What was the temperature in the greenhouse at dusk?
   b At what time was the temperature at a minimum?
   c What was the minimum temperature?

6 A vegetable gardener has 40 m of fencing to enclose a rectangular garden plot where one side is an existing brick wall. If the width is x m as shown:
   a Show that the area enclosed is given by
         $A = -2x^2 + 40x$ m^2.
   b Find x such that the vegetable garden has maximum area.
   c What is the maximum area?

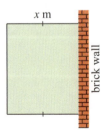

Extension:

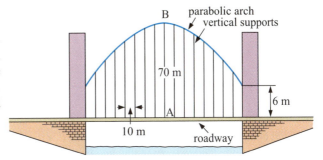

7 AB is the longest vertical support of a bridge which contains a parabolic arch. The vertical supports are 10 m apart. The arch meets the vertical end supports 6 m above the road.

a If axes are drawn on the diagram of the bridge above, with the x-axis being the road and the y-axis being AB, find the equation of the parabolic arch in the form $y = ax^2 + c$.

b Hence, determine the lengths of all other vertical supports.

8 Two towers OP and RQ of a suspension bridge are 50 m high and 60 m apart.   A cable is suspended between P and Q and approximates the shape of a parabola under its own weight.

The maximum sag in the middle of the cable is 20 m.

a Find the coordinates of the vertex of the parabola.

b Hence, find the equation of the parabola.

c How high is the cable directly above X, given that XR $= 10$ m?

LINKS
click here

WHAT IS THE STRONGEST ARCH?

Areas of interaction:
Approaches to learning/Environments/Human ingenuity

REVIEW SET 24A

1 Draw the graph of $y = x^2 - 3x + 2$ using a table of values from $x = -2$ to $x = 5$.

2 State the y-intercepts of the following quadratics:

  a $y = x^2 - 4x + 1$ **b** $y = -x^2 + 9$ **c** $y = 2x^2 + 5x + 2$

3 State the x-intercepts of the following quadratics:

  a $y = (x + 5)(x - 1)$ **b** $y = -2(x + 1)(x - 7)$ **c** $y = (2x - 3)^2$

4 Find the x-intercepts of the following quadratics:

  a $y = 2x - x^2$ **b** $y = x^2 - x - 12$ **c** $y = 3x^2 + 9x - 54$

5 Sketch these quadratic functions using axes intercepts:

  a $y = (x + 2)(x - 1)$ **b** $y = -2x^2 - x + 1$

6 Use the formula $x = \dfrac{-b}{2a}$ to determine the equation of the axis of symmetry of $y = -x^2 - 2x + 5$.

7 Determine the coordinates of the vertex of $f(x) = x^2 - 4x - 8$.

8 **a** For the quadratic function $y = x^2 - 5x + 4$ find:
> **i** the axes intercepts   **ii** the equation of the axis of symmetry
> **iii** the coordinates of the vertex.

b Hence sketch the graph.

9 The height h metres, of a jet of water is given by $h = -3t^2 + 24t + 1$, where t is the time in seconds after the jet started.

> **a** How long does the jet take to reach its maximum height?
> **b** What is the maximum height of the water?
> **c** How long does it take for the water to reach the ground?

REVIEW SET 24B

1 Draw the graph of $y = x^2 + 3x + 1$ using a table of values from $x = -4$ to $x = 1$.

2 For the following functions, state the y-intercepts:
> **a** $y = x^2 + 6x + 9$ **b** $y = 3 - x^2$ **c** $y = 3x^2 + 11x - 4$

3 For the following functions, state the x-intercepts:
> **a** $y = (x + 1)(x - 4)$ **b** $y = -3(x - 1)^2$ **c** $y = (2x - 1)(x + 7)$

4 For the following functions, find the x-intercepts:
> **a** $y = x^2 + 7x$ **b** $y = x^2 - 6x + 9$ **c** $y = 2x^2 - x - 1$

5 Sketch these quadratic functions using axes intercepts:
> **a** $y = (x - 1)(x - 6)$ **b** $y = -x^2 + 4x - 4$

6 Use the formula $x = \dfrac{-b}{2a}$ to determine the equation of the axis of symmetry of $y = 3x^2 + 6x + 1$.

7 Determine the coordinates of the vertex of $f(x) = x^2 - 3x - 10$.

8 **a** For the quadratic function $y = -x^2 - 2x + 8$ find:
> **i** the axes intercepts   **ii** the equation of the axis of symmetry
> **iii** the coordinates of the vertex.

b Hence sketch the graph.

9 Use technology to answer this question:

The height H metres of a cannonball t seconds after it is fired into the air is given by $H(t) = -4t^2 + 16t + 9$.

> **a** Find the time taken for the cannonball to reach its maximum height.
> **b** What is the maximum height reached by the cannonball?
> **c** How long does it take for the cannonball to fall back to Earth?

Chapter 25

Click on the icon to access this printable chapter

Transformation geometry

Contents:

A   Reflection
B   Rotation
C   Translation
D   Enlargement

Chapter 26

 PRINTABLE CHAPTER Click on the icon to access this printable chapter

Sine and cosine rules

Contents:

- **A** Obtuse angles
- **B** Area of a triangle using sine
- **C** The sine rule
- **D** The cosine rule
- **E** Problem solving with the sine and cosine rules

ANSWERS

EXERCISE 1A

1 a 16 238 kWh **b** 35 624 kWh
2 a 4772 kWh **b** 6308 kWh
3 a 94 **b** 121.5 **c** 37.5 **d** 46.5 **e** 23.5 **f** 56
4 a $\frac{1}{5}$ **b** $\frac{3}{5}$ **c** $\frac{9}{10}$
5 a 70 km h^{-1} **b** 25 km h^{-1} **c** 75 km h^{-1}
6 a 4500 rpm **b** 2750 rpm **c** 2500 rpm **d** 4200 rpm
7 a 38.5°C **b** 36.8°C **c** 40.2°C **d** 39.7°C

EXERCISE 1B

1 a cm **b** mm **c** km **d** m **e** mm **f** cm
3 a 52 000 m **b** 1150 mm **c** 165 cm **d** 6300 mm
  e 62 500 cm **f** 8 100 000 mm
4 a 4.8 m **b** 5.4 cm **c** 5.28 km **d** 2 m **e** 5.8 km
  f 7 km
5 a 42 100 m **b** 2.1 m **c** 7.5 cm **d** 1.5 km **e** 185 cm
  f 425 mm **g** 280 000 cm **h** 16.5 m **i** 250 000 mm
6 a 7000 mg **b** 0.007 kg **c** 0.58 kg **d** 580 000 g
  e 0.023 cg **f** 56 000 mg **g** 450 mg **h** 4.5 g
  i 0.02 g **j** 24 cg **k** 3 000 000 mg **l** 0.0065 kg
7 a 2000 mL **b** 0.45 L **c** 1200 W **d** 20 mL **e** 0.2 cL
  f 350 L **g** 0.45 dL **h** 0.04 sec **i** 2 kW
8 5.3 km **9** 12.375 km **10** 6 km **11** 256 666 lengths
12 4 **13** 80 light bulbs **14** 50 000 stamps **15** 5 g
16 100 spoonfuls **17** 1.56 tonnes **18** 3000 strides

EXERCISE 1C

1 a cm^2 **b** m^2 **c** ha **d** m^2 **e** km^2 **f** mm^2
2 a 0.23 cm^2 **b** 36 000 m^2 **c** 0.0726 m^2
  d 7 600 000 mm^2 **e** 0.853 ha **f** 35 400 000 cm^2
  g 1354 mm^2 **h** 4 320 000 cm^2 **i** 4820 mm^2
  j 3 000 000 m^2 **k** 70 ha **l** 6 600 000 m^2 **m** 6.6 km^2
  n 500 cm^2 **o** 0.0025 m^2 **p** 0.052 cm^2
  q 720 000 000 000 m^2
3 a 1000 cm^2 **b** 240 cm^2 **c** 1.2 cm^2 **d** 80 000 m^2
4 a 2100 chickens **b** 100 rectangles

EXERCISE 1D

1 a 8650 mm^3 **b** 86 cm^3 **c** 0.3 m^3 **d** 124 000 mm^3
  e 0.3 cm^3 **f** 3 700 000 cm^3
2 a 7.5 m^3 **b** 47 400 sinkers

EXERCISE 1E

1 a ML **b** mL **c** kL **d** L
2 a 3760 mL **b** 47.32 kL **c** 3500 L **d** 423 mL
  e 54 000 mL **f** 0.058 34 kL
3 a 13 750 bottles **b** 9 tanks **4** 8 full glasses **5** 1.8 L **6** 200 g
7 a 110.5 L **b** 0.036 mL **c** 1296 L **d** 24 kL **e** 0.015 L
  f 0.936 kL
8 a 25 mL **b** 3200 m^3 **c** 7320 L

EXERCISE 1F

1 a 3.2 kg **b** 1870 kg **c** 0.047 835 kg **d** 4.653 g
  e 2 830 000 g **f** 63 200 g **g** 0.074 682 t
  h 1 700 000 000 mg **i** 91.275 kg
2 a 150 000 sweets **b i** 5.136 t **ii** $2311.20
3 a 9000 cm^3 **b** 72 000 cm^3 = 72 L **c** 72 kg **d** 33.3 kg
  e 120.9 kg

EXERCISE 1G

1 a 300 minutes **b** 4320 minutes **c** 3780 minutes
  d 37 minutes
2 a 52 days **b** 16 days **c** 1095.75 days **d** 0.25 days
3 a 2100 seconds **b** 11940 seconds **c** 432 000 seconds
  d 777 600 seconds
4 a 5 h 8 min **b** 7 h 11 min 10 sec **c** 4 h 5 min **d** 2 h 35 min
5 54 hours
6 a 2 h 25 min **b** 7 h 44 min **c** 5 h 48 min **d** 6 h 35 min

7 1 h 14 min **8 a** 42 hours **b** €378
9 a 11.16 am **b** 8.45 am **c** 3.45 pm **d** 9.48 am
10 3.15 pm **11** 129.6 km

EXERCISE 1H

1 a 0957 **b** 1106 **c** 1600 **d** 1425 **e** 0800 **f** 0106
  g 2058 **h** 1200 **i** 0002
2 a 11.40 am **b** 3.46 am **c** 4.34 pm **d** 7.00 pm
  e 8.00 am **f** 11.30 pm **g** 12.23 pm **h** 8.40 pm
3

	Departure	Travelling Time	Arrival
a	0520	6 h 20 min	1140
b	0710	6 h 55 min	1405
c	0931	56 min	1027
d	1229	4 h 23 min	1652
e	2012	8 h 35 min	0447 (next day)

REVIEW SET 1A

1 a 3410 kWh **b** $\frac{3}{5}$ full **c** 45 km h^{-1}
2 a i 3280 m **ii** 75.5 cm **iii** 0.32 m **b** 40 000 staples
3 a 5000 mg **b** 0.023 kg **c** 0.5126 kg **d** 2500 mL
  e 4 000 000 L **f** 250 dL
4 a 5.6 kW **b** 4500 J **5** 7.5 km
6 a 19.5 cm^2 **b** 64 000 cm^2 **c** 2.5 km^2
7 a 0.7 m **b** 225 cm^2
8 a 2.6 cm^3 **b** 8 m^3 **c** 1 200 000 cm^3 **d** 5600 mL
  e 0.25 kL **f** 56 mL
9 4 cans **10 a** 0.056 g **b** 0.45 kg **c** 250 kg **11** 3 trips
12 4.33 pm **13** 10 h 24 min **14 a** 1731 **b** 12.14 am

REVIEW SET 1B

1 a 2750 rpm **b** 39.2°C
2 a i 1.56 km **ii** 265 mm **iii** 180 cm **b** 80 m
3 a 0.35 g **b** 0.25 t **c** 16 800 g **d** 0.15 L
  e 0.000 26 ML **f** 800 mL
4 a 2500 W **b** 0.55 kJ **5** 50 mL **6** Carl ran faster
7 a 540 mm^2 **b** 5.6 m^2 **c** 800 000 m^2 **d** 600 mm^3
  e 18 000 cm^3 **f** 0.025 m^3
8 6 ha **9** 9000 cartons **10** 1.2 m^3 **11** 7.5 t
12 a 10 days 16 hours **b** 8340 seconds
13 a 2.45 pm **b** 7.59 am **14 a** 1630 **b** 7.45 am

PUZZLE

YOU ARE GOOD AT CONVERTING FROM ONE UNIT TO ANOTHER

EXERCISE 2A

1 a 8 **b** 8 **c** 26 **d** −8 **e** −26 **f** −8 **g** −8
  h 26 **i** 40 **j** −14 **k** −14 **l** 40 **m** 14 **n** −40
  o 14 **p** 14
2 a 48 **b** −48 **c** −48 **d** 48 **e** 63 **f** −63
  g −63 **h** 63
3 a −36 **b** 36 **c** −27 **d** −27 **e** −72 **f** 48
  g −72 **h** 32 **i** −48 **j** −81 **k** 81 **l** 225
4 a 6 **b** −6 **c** −6 **d** 6 **e** 5 **f** −5 **g** −5
  h 5 **i** $\frac{1}{3}$ **j** −$\frac{1}{3}$ **k** −$\frac{1}{3}$ **l** $\frac{1}{3}$
5 a 10 **b** 2 **c** −8 **d** 6 **e** 6 **f** 24
6 a 37 **b** 43 **c** 3 **d** 24 **e** 6 **f** 19 **g** 12
  h 10 **i** 6 **j** 16 **k** 20 **l** 2
7 a 17 **b** 13 **c** 1 **d** 9 **e** 69 **f** 9 **g** 43 **h** 7
  i 21 **j** 3 **k** 16 **l** −2
8 a 4 **b** 21 **c** 13 **d** 92 **e** 10 **f** 15
9 a 5 **b** 3 **c** $\frac{1}{2}$ **d** 5 **e** 7 **f** 7 **g** 18 **h** 1
10 a 438 **b** 874 **c** 33 **d** 8 **e** −1053 **f** 4
  g −6 **h** −83 **i** −8

EXERCISE 2B

1 a $\frac{12}{13}$ **b** $\frac{11}{16}$ **c** $\frac{5}{8}$ **d** $\frac{17}{30}$ **e** $4\frac{3}{7}$ **f** $2\frac{1}{6}$ **g** $3\frac{1}{2}$ **h** $6\frac{1}{6}$

2 a $\frac{4}{11}$ **b** $\frac{1}{6}$ **c** $\frac{1}{9}$ **d** $\frac{5}{8}$ **e** $1\frac{3}{4}$ **f** $1\frac{1}{10}$ **g** $1\frac{5}{6}$ **h** $2\frac{2}{21}$

3 a $\frac{1}{9}$ **b** $\frac{2}{7}$ **c** $1\frac{1}{2}$ **d** $4\frac{2}{3}$ **e** $1\frac{1}{7}$ **f** $\frac{1}{2}$ **g** $6\frac{1}{4}$ **h** $2\frac{10}{27}$

4 a $\frac{6}{7}$ **b** $\frac{11}{16}$ **c** $\frac{2}{3}$ **d** $\frac{1}{10}$ **e** $1\frac{2}{3}$ **f** $3\frac{5}{9}$ **g** $\frac{4}{9}$ **h** $1\frac{7}{20}$

5 a $5\frac{8}{35}$ **b** $\frac{81}{256}$ **c** $2\frac{1}{2}$ **d** $\frac{2}{5}$ **e** 12 **f** $1\frac{1}{11}$ **g** $4\frac{2}{3}$
h $\frac{1}{2}$ **i** $1\frac{1}{6}$ **j** $\frac{3}{5}$ **k** $2\frac{3}{5}$ **l** $\frac{1}{10}$ **m** 11 **n** $1\frac{1}{4}$ **o** $4\frac{2}{5}$

6 a $\frac{4}{15}$ **b** $45 **c** $272.00 **d** $\frac{2}{9}$ **e** $\frac{1}{4}$ **7** 100 sweets

8 a $\frac{8}{15}$ **b** $\frac{13}{21}$ **c** $\frac{19}{56}$ **d** $\frac{5}{12}$ **e** $\frac{3}{5}$ **f** $\frac{8}{21}$ **g** $\frac{12}{35}$
h $2\frac{7}{10}$ **i** $4\frac{1}{8}$ **j** $4\frac{5}{28}$ **k** $1\frac{6}{11}$

EXERCISE 2C

1 a 8 **b** 27 **c** 32 **d** 125 **e** 540 **f** 1176 **g** 2925
h 4400

2 a $50 = 2 \times 5^2$ **b** $98 = 2 \times 7^2$ **c** $108 = 2^2 \times 3^3$
d $360 = 2^3 \times 3^2 \times 5$ **e** $1128 = 2^3 \times 3 \times 47$ **f** $784 = 2^4 \times 7^2$
g $952 = 2^3 \times 7 \times 17$ **h** $6500 = 2^2 \times 5^3 \times 13$

3 a $2^1 = 2$, $2^2 = 4$, $2^3 = 8$, $2^4 = 16$, $2^5 = 32$, $2^6 = 64$
b $3^1 = 3$, $3^2 = 9$, $3^3 = 27$, $3^4 = 81$
c $5^1 = 5$, $5^2 = 25$, $5^3 = 125$, $5^4 = 625$
d $7^1 = 7$, $7^2 = 49$, $7^3 = 343$

4 a $n = 5$ **b** $n = 8$ **c** $n = 12$

5 a $n = 3$ **b** $n = 6$ **c** $n = 10$ **6** 3 **7** 7

8 a 1 **b** -1 **c** 1 **d** -1 **e** 1 **f** -1 **g** -1
h -27 **i** -27 **j** 27 **k** -36 **l** 64

9 a 256 **b** 625 **c** -243 **d** 2401 **e** 512 **f** 117 649
g $-117\,649$ **h** 1.795 856 326 **i** $-0.005\,487\,423\,935$
j $-325\,687.9871$

10 a $0.\overline{1}$ **b** $0.\overline{1}$ **c** 0.0625 **d** 0.0625
e 0.012 345 679 **f** 0.012 345 679 **g** 1 **h** 1
So, $a^{-b} = \dfrac{1}{a^b}$ and $a^0 = 1$, $a \neq 0$.

11 a $\frac{1}{4}$ **b** $\frac{1}{2}$ **c** $\frac{1}{6}$ **d** $\frac{1}{8}$ **e** $\frac{1}{4}$ **f** $\frac{1}{9}$ **g** $\frac{1}{49}$
h $\frac{1}{81}$ **i** $\frac{1}{27}$ **j** $\frac{1}{100\,000}$

12 a 3 **b** $\frac{5}{2}$ **c** $\frac{3}{4}$ **d** 12 **e** $\frac{7}{2}$ **f** $\frac{4}{5}$ **g** $\frac{16}{9}$
h $\frac{16}{81}$ **i** $\frac{8}{27}$ **j** $3\frac{1}{2}$

13 a 10^3 **b** 10^6 **c** 10^{-3} **d** 10^{-8}

14 a 2^3 **b** 2^{-3} **c** 3^2 **d** 3^{-2} **e** 5^3 **f** 5^{-3} **g** 2^5
h 2^{-5} **i** 3^4 **j** 3^{-4} **k** 5^{-2} **l** 2^0 or 3^0 or 5^0

15 a $p = 2, q = 1, r = 1$ **b** $p = 2, q = 1, r = 2$
c $p = 2, q = -2, r = 2$ **d** $p = 1, q = 0, r = 3$
e $p = -6, q = 1, r = -3$ **f** $p = 2, q = 1, r = -1$
g $p = -3, q = -2, r = 2$ **h** $p = 0, q = 0, r = 0$
i $p = -3, q = 1, r = 2$ **j** $p = 0, q = -1, r = -1$
k $p = 2, q = 2, r = -2$ **l** $p = -2, q = 3, r = -3$

EXERCISE 2D

1 a 16 **b** 16 **c** 19 683 **d** 3125 **e** x^6 **f** a^4 **g** n^{10} **h** b^8

2 a 2 **b** 27 **c** 625 **d** 256 **e** x^3 **f** y^3 **g** a **h** b^4

3 a 64 **b** 531 441 **c** 262 144 **d** 10 000 000 000 **e** x^6
f x^{15} **g** a^{20} **h** b^{24}

4 a a^7 **b** n^8 **c** a^4 **d** a^6 **e** b^5 **f** a^{18} **g** a^{n+5}
h b^8 **i** b^3 **j** m^{14} **k** a^{10} **l** g^{11}

5 a 2 **b** 5 **c** 8 **d** 10 **e** 15 **f** 3 **g** 4 **h** 10
i 3 **j** 2 **k** 2 **l** $\frac{1}{2}$ **m** $\frac{1}{4}$ **n** $\frac{1}{2}$ **o** $\frac{1}{2}$

6 a 8 **b** 9 **c** 8 **d** $\frac{1}{9}$ **e** $\frac{1}{16}$

7 a $2\frac{1}{4}$ **b** $\frac{4}{9}$ **c** $\frac{25}{36}$ **d** $1\frac{11}{25}$ **e** $1\frac{1}{2}$ **f** $\frac{2}{3}$ **g** 64 **h** $\frac{4}{9}$

REVIEW SET 2A

1 a 9 **b** -23 **c** -21 **d** -9 **e** -1 **f** 7

2 a 3 **b** 27 **c** 2 **3 a** 4 **b** 64 **c** 1

4 a $2\frac{1}{10}$ **b** $1\frac{9}{20}$ **c** $3\frac{7}{8}$ **5** 2.56 kg **6 a** 81 **b** 40

7 a $36 = 2^2 \times 3^2$ **b** $242 = 2 \times 11^2$ **8 a** $\frac{1}{27}$ **b** $\frac{9}{16}$ **c** -2

9 2^{-4} **10 a** 78 125 **b** b^5 **c** x^{12} **11 a** 4 **b** $\frac{1}{3}$

REVIEW SET 2B

1 a 8 **b** 19 **c** 15 **d** -27 **e** -36 **f** -8

2 a 6 **b** -5 **c** 20 **3 a** 8 **b** 0 **c** 9

4 a $6\frac{1}{12}$ **b** $3\frac{1}{3}$ **c** $2\frac{3}{4}$ **5 a** $\frac{1}{5}$ **b** 208 km

6 a 343 **b** 225 **7 a** $42 = 2 \times 3 \times 7$ **b** $144 = 2^4 \times 3^2$

8 a $\frac{1}{36}$ **b** $\frac{2}{3}$ **c** $2\frac{7}{9}$ **9** $n = 3$

10 a 6561 **b** 1 **c** y^{15} **11 a** 5 **b** $\frac{1}{2}$

EXERCISE 3A

1 a i $7 \in A$ **ii** $17 \notin A$ **b** $n(A) = 9$

2 $M_3 = \{3, 6, 9, 12, 15, 18, 21, 24, ...\}$

3 $F_8 = \{1, 2, 4, 8\}$, $n(F_8) = 4$ **4 a** Fahran $\notin B$ **b** $n(B) = 3$

5 a $\{6, 12, 18, 24, ...\}$ **b** $\{11, 22, 33, 44, ...\}$ **c** $\{1, 3\}$
d $\{1, 3, 9\}$ **e** $\{1, 2, 3, 4, 6, 8, 12, 24\}$
f $\{1, 2, 4, 8, 16, 32\}$ **g** $\{1, 3\}$

6 a i $\{2, 3, 5, 7, 11, 13, 17, 19\}$ **ii** $n(P_{20}) = 8$
b i $\{31, 37, 41, 43, 47\}$ **ii** $n(Y) = 5$
c i 3 **ii** 2 **iii** 7, 11 **iv** 2, 3, 5

7 a 6 has factors 1, 2, 3 and 6, i.e., it has more than two factors so it is a composite number.
b $\{2, 3, 5, 7, 11\}$ **c** $\{4, 6, 8, 9, 10, 12\}$
d $\{2, 3, 4, 5, 6, 7, 8, 9, 10, 11, 12\}$

EXERCISE 3B

1 a true **b** true **c** true **d** true **e** false **f** false
g true **h** true

2 a, b, c, d, f, g, h are rational; **e** is irrational

3 a $0.\overline{7} = \frac{7}{9}$ **b** $0.\overline{41} = \frac{41}{99}$ **c** $0.\overline{324} = \frac{12}{37}$

4 0.527 can be written as $\frac{527}{1000}$, and 527, 1000 are integers

5 Let $x = 0.\overline{9} = 0.999\,99 ......$
$\therefore 10x = 9.999\,99 ...... = 9 + x$
i.e., $9x = 9$ so $x = 1$ which is an integer that can be written as $\frac{1}{1}$ which is rational.

6 a e.g., $\sqrt{2} + (-\sqrt{2}) = 0$ which is rational
b e.g., $\sqrt{2} \times \sqrt{50} = \sqrt{100} = 10$ which is rational

7 a $S = \{1, 2, 3, 4, 6, 12\}$ **b** $S' = \{5, 7, 8, 9, 10, 11\}$
c Every element of S is also in U $\therefore$ $S \subseteq U$.
d $P = \{2, 3, 5, 7, 11\}$ **e** $P' = \{1, 4, 6, 8, 9, 10, 12\}$
f Every element of P' is also in U $\therefore$ $P' \subseteq U$.

8 $E' = \{$odd integers$\}$ **9** $E' = \{0, \mathbb{Z}^-\}$

10 $P' = \{1, \text{composites}\}$

11 a The empty set $\varnothing$ has no elements, so every element of $\varnothing$ is also in every other set, so $\varnothing \subseteq$ any other set.
b i $\varnothing, \{a\}$ **ii** $\varnothing, \{a\}, \{b\}, \{a, b\}$
iii $\varnothing, \{a\}, \{b\}, \{c\}, \{a, b\}, \{a, c\}, \{b, c\}, \{a, b, c\}$

EXERCISE 3C

1 a The set of all values of real x such that x is greater than 4.
b The set of all values of real x such that x is less than or equal to 5.
c The set of all values of real y such that y lies between 0 and 8.
d The set of all values of real x such that x lies between 1 and 4 or is equal to 1 or 4.
e The set of all values of real t such that t lies between 2 and 7.
f The set of all values of real n such that n is less than or equal to 3 or n is greater than 6.

2 a $\{x \mid x > 3\}$ **b** $\{x \mid 2 < x \leqslant 5\}$
c $\{x \mid x \leqslant -1 \text{ or } x \geqslant 2\}$ **d** $\{x \mid -1 \leqslant x < 5, \ x \in \mathbb{Z}\}$
e $\{x \mid 0 \leqslant x \leqslant 6, \ x \in \mathbb{N}\}$ **f** $\{x \mid x < 0\}$

3 a

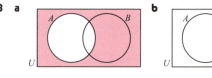

b

c

d

e

f

EXERCISE 3D

1 a

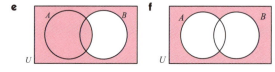

$A = \{2, 3, 5, 7\}$
b $A' = \{1, 4, 6, 8\}$

2 a

b $V' = \{b, c, d, f, g, h, j, k, l, m, n, p, q, r, s, t, v, w, x, y, z\}$

3 a i $U = \{1, 2, 3, 4, 5, 6, 7, 8, 9, 10\}$ **ii** $N = \{3, 8\}$
iii $M = \{1, 3, 4, 7, 8\}$
b $n(N) = 2, n(M) = 5$ **c** No, $N \subseteq M, \ M \not\subseteq N$

4 a

b ".... the circle representing S lies inside T."

5 a

b

c

6 a/b

c i true
ii true
iii true
d (shaded section of diagram above)

EXERCISE 3E

1 a i $C = \{1, 3, 7, 9\}$ **ii** $D = \{1, 2, 5\}$
iii $U = \{1, 2, 3, 4, 5, 6, 7, 8, 9\}$ **iv** $C \cap D = \{1\}$
v $C \cup D = \{1, 2, 3, 5, 7, 9\}$
b i $n(C) = 4$ **ii** $n(D) = 3$ **iii** $n(U) = 9$
iv $n(C \cap D) = 1$ **v** $n(C \cup D) = 6$
2 a i $A = \{2, 7\}$ **ii** $B = \{1, 2, 4, 6, 7\}$
iii $U = \{1, 2, 3, 4, 5, 6, 7, 8\}$ **iv** $A \cap B = \{2, 7\}$
v $A \cup B = \{1, 2, 4, 6, 7\}$

b i $n(A) = 2$ **ii** $n(B) = 5$ **iii** $n(U) = 8$
iv $n(A \cap B) = 2$ **v** $n(A \cup B) = 5$

3 a

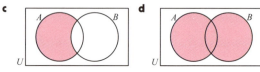

b i $A \cap B = \{2, 9, 11\}$
ii $A \cup B = \{1, 2, 7, 9, 10, 11, 12\}$
iii $B' = \{3, 4, 5, 6, 7, 8, 10\}$
c i $n(A) = 5$ **ii** $n(B') = 7$ **iii** $n(A \cap B) = 3$
iv $n(A \cup B) = 7$
4 a $A \cap B = \{1, 3, 9\}$
b $A \cup B = \{1, 2, 3, 4, 6, 7, 9, 12, 18, 21, 36, 63\}$
5 a $X \cap Y = \{B, M, T, Z\}$
b $X \cup Y = \{A, B, C, D, M, N, P, R, T, W, Z\}$
6 a i $n(A) = 8$ **ii** $n(B) = 10$ **iii** $n(A \cap B) = 3$
iv $n(A \cup B) = 15$
b $n(A) + n(B) - n(A \cap B) = 8 + 10 - 3 = 15 = n(A \cup B)$
7 $n(A) + n(B) - n(A \cap B) = (a + b) + (b + c) - b$
$= a + b + c$
$= n(A \cup B)$

8 a **b**

c **d**

e **f**

g **h**

9 a i $X \cup Y = \{1, 2, 3, 4, 5, 6, 7, 8\}$ **ii** $X \cap Y = \{\}$ or $\varnothing$
b i $A \cup A' = U$ **ii** $A \cap A' = \{\}$ (an empty set)

10

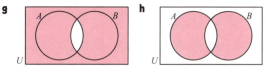

represents $A \cap B$
represents $(A \cap B)'$

represents A'
represents B'

whole shaded region represents $A' \cup B'$

EXERCISE 3F

1 a 18 **b** 2 **c** 17 **d** 12
2 a 75 **b** 9 **c** 24 **d** 42

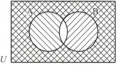

3

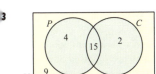

a 21 **b** 4
c 6 **d** 9

4 a 19 **b** 20 **c** 32 **d** 25 **e** 13
5 10 play both **6 a** 18 **b** 38 **7 a** 22 **b** 18
8 a 15 **b** 14 **c** 8 **9** 200 families had both

EXERCISE 3G

1 a The next two terms are 7, 8. The rule is *start with 2 and add 1 each time.*

b The next two terms are 19, 17. The rule is *start with 29 and subtract 2 each time.*

c The next two terms are 32, 64. The rule is *start with 1 and multiply by 2 each time.*

d The next two terms are 3, $1\frac{1}{2}$. The rule is *start with 48 and divide by 2 each time.*

e The next two terms are 17, 20. The rule is *start with 2 and add 3 each time.*

f The next two terms are 65, 58. The rule is *start with 100 and subtract 7 each time.*

g The next two terms are 125, 216. The rule is *start with 1 and find the cube of each positive integer in consecutive order.*

h The next two terms are 13, 21. The rule is *start with 1 and 1 and add the previous two terms to get the next one.*

2 a 1, 3, 5, 7, 9, 11 **b** 3, 6, 12, 24, 48, 96
c 24, 16, 8, 0, -8, -16 **d** 32, 16, 8, 4, 2, 1
e 5, 10, 20, 40, 80, 160 **f** 1, 2, 3, 5, 8, 13

3 a 2, 4, 6, 8, 10 **b** 3, 5, 7, 9, 11 **c** 1, 3, 5, 7, 9
d 7, 9, 11, 13, 15 **e** 3, 6, 9, 12, 15 **f** 5, 8, 11, 14, 17
g 6, 11, 16, 21, 26 **h** 9, 16, 23, 30, 37
i -1, -2, -3, -4, -5 **j** 2, 1, 0, -1, -2
k 3, 1, -1, -3, -5 **l** 1, -2, -5, -8, -11

4 The difference between consecutive terms is the value of a in $u_n = an + b$.

5 a $u_n = 3n + 1$ **b** $u_n = 5n - 7$ **c** $u_n = 6n - 5$
d $u_n = 7n - 4$ **e** $u_n = -3n + 43$ **f** $u_n = -4n + 80$
g $u_n = -5n + 13$ **h** $u_n = -6n + 133$ **i** $u_n = \dfrac{n}{2n+1}$
j $u_n = \dfrac{2n-1}{3n+1}$

6 a i 1, 3, 9, 27, 81 **ii** 2, 6, 18, 54, 162 **iii** 5, 15, 45, 135, 405
b i Multiply the previous term by 3.
ii Multiply the previous term by 3.
iii Multiply the previous term by 3. **c** 3^{n-1}

7 a $u_1 = 2$ **b** $u_9 = 82$ **c** $u_{57} = 3250$
8 a $D_3 = 0$, $D_4 = 2$, $D_6 = 9$, $D_7 = 14$, $D_8 = 20$
b Using Jian's reasoning, each diagonal is counted twice.
c i $D_{20} = 170$ **ii** $D_n = \dfrac{n(n-3)}{2}$

9 a This board contains 9 small squares, 4 medium squares, 1 large square.
i.e., $1^2 + 2^2 + 3^2 = 1 + 4 + 9$ is the total number of squares.
b $1^2 + 2^2 + 3^2 + 4^2 = 30$ squares
c $1^2 + 2^2 + 3^2 + 4^2 + 5^2 + 6^2 + 7^2 + 8^2 = 204$ squares

EXERCISE 3H

1 b, **d**, **f**, **g** and **h** are all propositions.
2 a I will not go skiing today. **b** Today is not Saturday.
c I do not enjoy Art lessons. **d** The train will be on time.
e It will not be sunny today. **f** This exercise is easy.
3 a Wendy dislikes Mathematics. **b** He owns at most 2 cats.
c No student in my class snores.

d My brother is shorter than me.
4 a The train will be late today and I will miss the first lesson.
b There is hot weather forecast and we will go to the beach.
c I will go to the cafe and I will go to the cinema.
5 a We will have eggs for breakfast or we will have porridge for breakfast.
b We will play tennis or we will ride horses.
c x is a factor of 8 or x is a factor of 12.

6 a

q	$\neg q$	$\neg(\neg q)$
T	F	T
F	T	F

b

p	q	$p \wedge q$	$\neg(p \wedge q)$
T	T	T	F
T	F	F	T
F	T	F	T
F	F	F	T

c

p	q	$\neg p$	$\neg q$	$\neg q \vee \neg p$
T	T	F	F	F
T	F	F	T	T
F	T	T	F	T
F	F	T	T	T

d

p	q	$\neg q$	$p \wedge \neg q$
T	T	F	F
T	F	T	T
F	T	F	F
F	F	T	F

7 a q: I will go to the beach
b q: He is the best mathematician in the class.

8 a

p	q	$\neg p$	$\neg q$	$\neg p \wedge \neg q$	$p \vee q$	$\neg(p \vee q)$
T	T	F	F	F	T	F
T	F	F	T	F	T	F
F	T	T	F	F	T	F
F	F	T	T	T	F	T

these two columns are identical

$\therefore$ $\neg p \wedge \neg q$ is logically equivalent to $\neg(p \vee q)$.

b

p	q	$\neg p$	$\neg q$	$\neg p \vee \neg q$	$p \wedge q$	$\neg(p \wedge q)$
T	T	F	F	F	T	F
T	F	F	T	T	F	T
F	T	T	F	T	F	T
F	F	T	T	T	F	T

these two columns are identical

$\therefore$ $\neg p \vee \neg q$ is logically equivalent to $\neg(p \wedge q)$.

9 a It will not be sunny today or I will not go to the beach.
b I will not go shopping and I will not go to the cinema.
c I dislike football or I dislike basketball.
d I dislike skiing or I like swimming.
e I will not walk to school and I will not cycle to school.
f It will rain today and it will snow today.

REVIEW SET 3A

1 a $F_{12} = \{1, 2, 3, 4, 6, 12\}$ **b i** $4 \in F_{12}$ **ii** $9 \notin F_{12}$
c $n(F_{12}) = 6$
2 a $P = \{23, 29\}$ **b** $n(P) = 2$
3 a i true **ii** false **iii** true **iv** true
b **ii**, **iii** and **iv** are all rational.
4 a $F = \{1, 2, 5, 10\}$
b Every element of F is also in U. $\therefore$ $F \subseteq U$
c $E = \{2, 4, 6, 8, 10\}$ **d** $E' = \{1, 3, 5, 7, 9\}$
e $O = \{1, 3, 5, 7, 9\}$ **f** $E' = O$
5 a $\{x \mid x < 3, \ x \in \mathbb{R}\}$ **b** $\{x \mid x \geqslant -1, \ x \in \mathbb{R}\}$
c $\{x \mid -2 \leqslant x < 5, \ x \in \mathbb{R}\}$
6 a **b** $A' = \{1, 4\}$

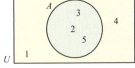

7 a i $U = \{1, 2, 3, 4, 5, 6, 7, 8\}$ **ii** $A = \{1, 2, 3, 4\}$
iii $B = \{1, 5, 6\}$

b i $n(U) = 8$ **ii** $n(A) = 4$ **iii** $n(A \cap B) = 1$
  iv $n(A \cup B) = 6$
c $A \cup B = \{1, 2, 3, 4, 5, 6\}$

8 a 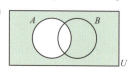 **b**

c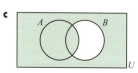

9 a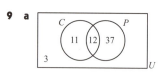

C: car
P: public transport

b 37 workers
10 a Start with 3 and add 6 each time. **b** 17, 14, 11, 8, 5, 2
  c 3, 1, −1, −3, −5 **d** $U_n = \dfrac{n}{n+1}$
11 a My room is untidy.
  b Sally has brown hair and Sally wears glasses.
  c I will go to a football match or I will go to the movies.

REVIEW SET 3B

1 a $M = \{3, 6, 9, 12, 15, 18\}$ **b** $n(M) = 6$ **c** $N = \{9, 18\}$
  d Every element of N is also in M $\therefore$ $N \subseteq M$.
2 a i true **ii** false
  b Let $x = 0.\overline{1} = 0.111\,111\,.....$
    $\therefore$ $10x = 1.\overline{1} = 1.111\,11\,...... = 1 + x$
    $\therefore$ $9x = 1$ so $x = \frac{1}{9}$ which is rational.
3 $O' = \{\text{even integers}\}$
4 a The set of all values of real x such that x is less than or equal
  to -5 or x is more than 2.
  b i $\{x \mid 0 \leqslant x \leqslant 3,\ x \in \mathbb{Z}\}$ **ii** $\{x \mid x \leqslant -3 \text{ or } x > 4\}$
  c
5 a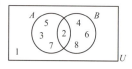

b i $A' = \{1, 4, 6, 8\}$ **ii** $A \cup B = \{2, 3, 4, 5, 6, 7, 8\}$
  iii $A \cap B = \{2\}$
  c $n(B') = 4$
6 a i $n(A) = 6$ **ii** $n(B) = 5$ **iii** $n(A \cap B) = 2$
  iv $n(A \cup B) = 9$
  b $n(A) + n(B) - n(A \cap B) = 6 + 5 - 2$
    $= 9$
    $= n(A \cup B)$
7

L: left handed
G: wear glasses

a 4 **b** 6 **c** 12

---

8 a $u_n = 2^{n-1}$ **b i** −3, 2, 7, 12, 17 **ii** 12, 24, 48, 96, 192
  c i $u_1 = 99$ **ii** $u_5 = 75$ **iii** $u_{10} = 0$
9 a i It is raining. **ii** Sarah is not playing her flute.
  b Raphael plays tennis and Raphael plays best on clay courts.
  c I will ride my bike to school or I will go to school by bus.
10

p	q	$p \wedge q$	$\neg(p \wedge q)$
T	T	T	F
T	F	F	T
F	T	F	T
F	F	F	T

p	q	$\neg p$	$\neg q$	$\neg p \vee \neg q$
T	T	F	F	F
T	F	F	T	T
F	T	T	F	T
F	F	T	T	T

$\neg(p \wedge q)$ is logically equivalent to $\neg p \vee \neg q$.

EXERCISE 4A

1 a 20 **b** 70 **c** 70 **d** 100 **e** 350 **f** 560 **g** 410
  h 600 **i** 3020 **j** 2860 **k** 3090 **l** 8890 **m** 2900
  n 10 000 **o** 30 910 **p** 49 900
2 a 100 **b** 700 **c** 600 **d** 900 **e** 300 **f** 1000
  g 2100 **h** 3900 **i** 1000 **j** 13 500 **k** 99 200 **l** 10 100
3 a €190 **b** £19 000 **c** 380 km **d** 800 Ft **e** 29 000 people
  f 10 m **g** 9 kL **h** $270 000 **i** 500 000 sheep

EXERCISE 4B

1 a $1.00 **b** $2.75 **c** $1.85 **d** $1.85 **e** $34.00
  f $25.05 **g** $16.75 **h** $5.00 **i** $13.00 **j** $102.25
  k $430.85 **l** $93.90
2 a $84.70 **b** $31.65 **c** $10.00
3 a £4.00 **b** €9.00 **c** 4.00 rubles **d** ¥511.00 **e** $8.00
  f Fr 19.00 **g** $20.00 **h** €39.00 **i** £40.00 **j** Rs 61.00
4 a $6 **b** $19 **c** $14 **d** $37 **e** $60 **f** $140 **g** $84
  h $848 **i** $1027
5 a £195 **b** ¥594 **c** $54 **d** $36 **e** RM 48 **f** €26 950

EXERCISE 4C

1 a 320 **b** 400 **c** 420 **d** 540 **e** 180 **f** 200
2 a 900 **b** 4200 **c** 3600 **d** 3000 **e** 6400 **f** 14 000
3 a 2400 **b** 4200 **c** 9000 **d** 15 000 **e** 28 000
  f 150 000 **g** 90 000 **h** 360 000 **i** 720 000
4 a 100 **b** 1000 **c** 10 000 **d** 300 **e** 2000 **f** 200
  g 75 **h** 250 **i** 2000
5 a 9291 **b** 62 382 **c** 347 723 **d** 36
6 a 400 books **b** 12 000 words **c** 16 000 bricks **d** 80 min
  e 10 000 vines **f** 5 000 000 bottles **g** 50 km h^{-1} **h** 400 m

EXERCISE 4D

1 a 1 **b** 7 **c** 8 **d** 12 **e** 128
2 a 2.4 **b** 3.6 **c** 4.9 **d** 6.4 **e** 4.3
3 a 4.24 **b** 2.73 **c** 5.63 **d** 4.38 **e** 6.52
4 a 0.5 **b** 0.49 **5 a** 3.8 **b** 3.79
6 a 0.2 **b** 0.18 **c** 0.184 **d** 0.1838
7 a 3.9 **b** 4 **c** 6.1 **d** 0.462 **e** 2.95 **f** 0.1756
8 a 4.3 **b** 9.13 **c** 11.2 **d** 0.05 **e** 0.73 **f** 0.025
  g 0.5 **h** 6.17 **i** 2.429
9 7.45 cm $\approx$ 7.5 cm is correct however Julie should have used the
  original value of 7.45 cm to round to the nearest integer,
  i.e., 7.45 cm $\approx$ 7 cm.

EXERCISE 4E

1 a $\dfrac{20}{2 \times 5} = 2$, $\dfrac{36}{12 - 3} = 4$ **b** Frank **c** Melanie

  d Brackets are needed to separate parts of the equation so
    operations are done in the correct order.

2 a 8.704 $+$ 6.93 $\div$ 0.74 $=$

  b $($ 8.704 $+$ 6.93 $)$ $\div$ 0.74 $=$

  c 0.74 $\div$ $($ 8.704 $+$ 6.93 $)$ $=$

3 a 2.6 **b** 6.5 **c** 101.0
4 a 396.89 **b** 1.19 **c** 2767.70 **d** 202.33 **e** 50.15 **f** 1.99
5 a $78.53 **b** $399.23 **c** ≈ 19 min 43 sec **d** CHF 31.39

EXERCISE 4F

1 a 42 **b** 6.24 **c** 0.046 **d** 0.25 **e** 440 **f** 2100
g 31 000 **h** 10.3 **i** 1 **j** 1.0 **k** 264 000 **l** 0.037 64
m 3699 **n** 0.0076 **o** 30 000 **p** 70
2 a i 30 000 people **ii** 26 000 people **b** 26 000 people
3 2549 people **4** probably 133 000 **5** $1850 **6** $190
7 $40 625

EXERCISE 4G

1 a 3 min 34 sec **b** 6 h 55 min 21 sec **c** 4 h 50 min 6 sec
d 5.383 min **e** 1.30 h **f** 8 h 21 sec
g 4 weeks 5 days 20 hours **h** 2.75 days
2 1038 **3** 184.6 km h^{-1}

REVIEW SET 4A

1 a 3580 **b** 3600 **c** 4000
2 a 390 km **b** 4 kL **c** 70 000 sheep
3 a $13.70 **b** £14 **4 a** €160 **b** RM 70
5 a 600 **b** 24 000 **c** 50
6 a 2800 tiles **b** 3024 tiles
c 224 tiles less than the actual number
7 83 metres per minute **8 a** 29 **b** 28.9 **c** 28.91
9 a 3.1 **b** 3.14 **10 a** 42.54 **b** 2.02 **c** 0.07
11 $3000 **12 a** 40 000 people **b** 44 000 people
13 2.7242 hours

REVIEW SET 4B

1 a 4610 **b** 4600 **c** 5000
2 a 700 km **b** 20 000 tonnes **c** 160 000 people
3 a $69.75 **b** €173 **4 a** ¥156 **b** $96
5 a 540 **b** 800 **c** 50 **6** 2000 minutes (≈ 33 h 20 min)
7 a 55 **b** 55.0 **c** 55.04 **8 a** 0.727 **b** 0.17
9 a 4.60 **b** 2286.76 **10** 11 hours 37 minutes
11 a Rs 6 000 000 **b** Rs 5 700 000 **12 a** 2040 **b** 12.4
13 8 hours 28 minutes 4 seconds

EXERCISE 5A

1 a 5 cm **b** 8.6 cm **c** 9.4 cm **d** 8.1 cm **e** 13.6 cm
f 11.2 cm **g** 8.4 cm **h** 16.4 cm **i** 21.5 cm
2 44.0 cm **3 a** 10.28 m **b i** 61.7 m **ii** 64 m **4** 145.1 cm
5 a 5.7 cm **b** 8.7 cm **c** 9.6 cm **d** 8.3 cm **e** 13.2 cm
f 5.4 cm
6 a 5.86 m **7 a** 0.86 m **b** 1.81 m
8 a 48.2 cm **b** 100.3 cm **c** $2.31

EXERCISE 5B

1 a 9.43 m **b** 7.52 m **2 a** 5.88 m **b** 2.72 m
3 1.4 m **4** 3.61 m **5** 37.8 m
6 a 600.3 m **b** 1420.3 m **c** 5681.3 m **d** $1676
7 a 1103.1 m **b** 4274.3 m
8 a 31.6 cm **b** 189.8 cm **c** 4.55 kg
9 a 7.07 cm **b** 148.3 cm
10 a 2.68 m **b** 14.05 m **c** 42.15 m
11 a 10.4 cm **b** 62.4 cm^2 **12 a** 7.42 cm **b** 22.25 cm^2
13 a 173.21 m **b** 17 321 m^2 **c** $73 612.16

EXERCISE 5C

1 a no **b** yes **c** yes **d** yes **e** no **f** no
2 yes (to 2 d.p.) **3** yes (to 2 d.p.)

EXERCISE 5D

1 11.4 km **2** 12.8 km

3 a 10.8 km **b** 1.08 hours (1 hour 5 minutes)
4 a X: 45 km, Y: 60 km **b** 75 km
5 Yes, since $240^2 + 100^2 = 260^2$ **6** 21.1 km
7 a 1 h 53$\frac{1}{3}$ min **b** 1 h 46 min
c train from A to C via B is faster
8 B: 13.4 km h^{-1} and C: 26.8 km h^{-1}
9 a Max: 36 km, Kyle: 45 km **b** 57.6 km **c** 2 h 8 min 4 sec

REVIEW SET 5A

1 1.6 m **2** 7.54 m **3** 27.5 cm **4** 803.0 m
5 AP = 9.8 km, BP = 17.5 km **6** 75 cm **7** 65.2 m
8 a Mia: 7.5 km, Yvette: 6 km
b $7.5^2 + 6^2 \approx 9.6^2$, i.e., Mia and Yvette travelled at right angles to each other.
c either north or south

REVIEW SET 5B

1 35.4 m **2** 3.44 m **3** 0.87 m **4** 17 km
5 a 5.31 m **b** 7.50 m
6 a i 81 km **ii** 54 min **b i** 58.2 km **ii** 58.2 min
c P to X to Q at 90 km h^{-1} is quicker
7 a 5.20 m **b** 15.6 m^2
8 $59^2 + 41^2 \approx 71.85^2$ $\therefore$ the frame is rectangular

EXERCISE 6A

1 a $9 + 2$ **b** $5 + a$ **c** $m + 3n$ **d** $d + e + f$
2 a 8×6 **b** $6p$ **c** $4mn$ **d** bde
3 a $\frac{6}{5}$ **b** $\frac{d}{3}$ **c** $\frac{m}{5n}$ **d** $\frac{p+q}{x}$
4 a $\frac{6+10}{2}$ **b** $\frac{9+d}{2}$ **c** $\frac{k+4v}{2}$ **d** $\frac{d+e+f}{3}$
5 a $8 - 5$ **b** $s - 6$ **c** $8 - p$
6 a $m - 7a$ **b** xy^2 **c** $d + 3e$ **d** $a - 5$ **e** $2 + b$ **f** $16c$
g $(ab)^2$ **h** $p^2 + q^2$

EXERCISE 6B

1 a 200 cents **b** $50x$ cents **c** cx cents
2 a £1.20 **b** £0.20y **c** £$\left(\frac{cd}{100}\right)$
3 a CHF 40 **b** CHF $(100 - 10n)$ **c** CHF $(100 - np)$
4 a €22 **b** €$(30 - m)$ **c** €$(30 + t)$
5 $(14 + k + n)$ km **6** $(16 + b)$ years **7** $12h$ km
8 $(9 - 4x)$ m **9** $(60p + 95b)$ cents **10 a** 96 km **b** kh km

EXERCISE 6C

1 a $p + 8$ **b** $g - 3$ **c** $n + 2$ **d** $c + 4$ **e** $x - 3$ **f** $4f$
g $\frac{h}{3}$ **h** $2a + 4$ **i** $2p + 14$
2 a $x + 3$ **b** $x - 5$ **c** $\frac{x}{2}$ **d** $3x$ **e** $\frac{x}{4}$ **f** $12 - x$
g $2x + 1$ **h** $5x - 6$
3 a ...... $4 - s$ **b** ...... $2a$ **c** ...... $3c$ **d** ...... $27 - b$ girls
e ...... $y + 1$ **f** ...... $x, x + 1, x + 2$ **g** ...... $d + 2$
h ...... $a, a - 1, a - 2$ **i** ...... $m - 1$ and $m + 1$ **j** ...... $s + 3$
4 a $13 - x$ **b** $k - 1$ **c** $n + 1, n + 2$ **d** $v - 2$
e $m - 2, m + 2$ **f** $s - g$
5 a $x + (x + 1)$ **b** $x + (x + 2)$ **c** ¥$(50x + 20(x + 4))$
d €$(5x + 20(8 - x))$

EXERCISE 6D

1 a $A = 300 \times 15$ **b** $A = 300m$ **c** $A = dm$
2 a $A = 3000 + 200 \times 6$ **b** $A = 3000 + 200w$
c $A = 3000 + mw$ **d** $A = P + mw$
3 a $C = 60 + 50 \times 5$ **b** $C = 60 + 50t$ **c** $C = 60 + dt$
d $C = F + dt$

4 a $A = 300 - 10 \times 6$ **b** $A = 300 - 6x$ **c** $A = 300 - bx$
   d $A = P - bx$
5 a $C = 6000 - 20 \times 100$ **b** $C = 6000 - 100d$
   c $C = 6000 - dm$ **d** $C = L - dm$

EXERCISE 6E

1 a

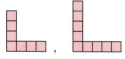

b

Diagram number (n)	1	2	3	4	5	6
Number of squares (S)	1	3	5	7	9	11

   c iii $S = 2n - 1$ **d i** $S = 21$ **ii** $S = 133$

2 a i 8 people   **ii** 10 people

b

Number of tables (n)	1	2	3	4	5	6
Number of people (P)	4	6	8	10	12	14

   c $P = 2n + 2$

3 a

b

Diagram number (n)	1	2	3	4	5	6
Number of crosses (C)	1	5	9	13	17	21

   c $C = 4n - 3$ **d i** $C = 37$ **ii** $n = 25$

4 a

b

Number of squares (n)	1	2	3	4
Number of triangles (C)	0	4	8	12

   c $t = 4n - 4$ **d i** 36 triangles   **ii** 15 squares

5 a

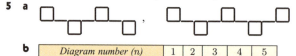

b

Diagram number (n)	1	2	3	4	5
Number of matchsticks (M)	4	9	14	19	24

   c $M = 5n - 1$ **d i** 149 matchsticks   **ii** 63

EXERCISE 6F

1 a 7   **b** 8   **c** 10   **d** 21   **e** 3   **f** 12   **g** 54   **h** 72
   i 14   **j** 9   **k** 64   **l** 256
2 a 18   **b** 19   **c** 7   **d** 27   **e** 81   **f** 128   **g** 512
   h 0   **i** 10   **j** 10   **k** 24   **l** 24
3 a 4   **b** -8 **c** -18 **d** 4   **e** -1 **f** 8   **g** -8
   h 7   **i** 8   **j** 8   **k** 7   **l** 1
4 a -2 **b** -5 **c** -1 **d** 2   **e** 5   **f** 10   **g** -2
   h -1 **i** 1   **j** 3   **k** 1   **l** 9
5 a -1 **b** 1   **c** -2 **d** -3 **e** 5   **f** 2   **g** -1
   h 0   **i** -3 **j** 6   **k** -1 **l** 3
6 a $G = 17$ **b** $M = 55$ **c** $A = 11$ **d** $T = 11$
   e $S = 5$ **f** $P = 44$ **g** $M = 5$
7 a $3.3°C$ **b** $18.3°C$ **c** $37.8°C$
8 a 63.5 m   **b** 254.0 m   **9 a** 7.96 km   **b** 15.92 km
10 a 132 cm²   **b** 40 cm²

11 a 6 cm²   **b** 6 cm²   **c** 14.7 cm²   **d** 28 520.8 m²

REVIEW SET 6A

1 a $a + b$ **b** cd **c** $\dfrac{x+y}{2}$ **d** $n - m$

2 a $b - 5$ **b** $a + 5$ **3 a** $40x$ cents   **b** €bn
4 a £$(50 - 5n)$ **b** $5h$ km
5 a ...... $11 - a$ **b** ...... $x + 2$ **6** $(y + 2(7 - y))$
7 a $C = 4 + 1 \times 5$ **b** $C = 4 + k$ **c** $C = F + k$
   d $C = F + dk$

8 a

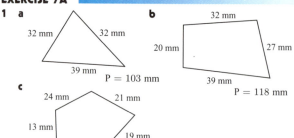

b

Diagram number (n)	1	2	3	4	5
Matches needed (M)	5	8	11	14	17

   c $M = 3n + 2$ **d** 38 matches
9 a 3   **b** 48   **c** -3 **10 a** $C = 1550$ **b** $A = 3$
11 a $x = 5$ **b** $s = 2.7$

REVIEW SET 6B

1 a $t - 8$ **b** $2pq$ **c** $x^2 + 6$ **d** $(x + 6)^2$
2 a $a, a + 1, a + 2$ **b** $b - 4$
3 a x^2 **b** $\dfrac{x}{2} + 1$ **c** $2x - 3$ **d** $2(x + 5)$
4 a i $14   **ii** $(20 - x)$ **b i** $30   **ii** $(20 + y)$
5 a $(x + 2)$ years   **b i** $(x + 3)$ years   **ii** $(x + 1)$ years
6 $8x$ kg   **7 a** $C = 50 + 60 \times 1\frac{1}{2}$ **b** $C = D + xt$

8 a

Diagram number (n)	1	2	3	4	5
Matches needed (M)	2	5	8	11	14

   c $M = 3n - 1$ **d i** 59 matches   **ii** 41
9 a -5 **b** -54 **c** -3 **10 a** 11 cm   **b** $c = 10$ cm

EXERCISE 7A

1 a P = 103 mm   **b** P = 118 mm   **c** P = 103 mm

2 a 38.8 cm   **b** 17.8 cm   **c** 11.9 km   **d** 29 m
   e 11.6 cm   **f** 30 m   **g** 17.6 m   **h** 99.6 km   **i** 19.1 m
3 a 1350 m   **b** 4050 m   **c** $1134   **4** 164 m   **5** 30 km
6 a 69.38 m   **b** 146.08 m
7 a 41.47 cm   **b** 54.04 m   **c** 361.28 m
8 a 5.341 km   **b** 22.619 m   **c** 1476.549 cm
9 a 22.0 cm   **b** 25.1 m   **c** 25.7 cm   **d** 10.7 m   **e** 441.3 m
   f 14.3 cm   **g** 85.7 cm   **h** 22.8 cm   **i** 75.4 cm
10 a ≈ 25.7 m   **b** ≈ 23.4 m   **c** ≈ 101 m   **11** $2100
12 a 420 m   **b** 350 panels   **c** $4287.50
13 a 4.5 km   **b** 113.4 tonnes   **c** 8 truckloads
14 a 15.8 km   **b** 13.5 km h⁻¹   **15** Yes, Al has 31.9 m of wire.
16 a 39 m   **b** 14 posts   **c** $936.15   **17** £855.26
18 155 cm   **19** $610.65   **20** same length

EXERCISE 7B

1 a 40 cm²   **b** 625 m²   **c** 42 m²   **d** 39 cm²   **e** 15 cm²

f 45 cm² **g** 180 m² **h** 24 cm² **i** 25 cm²
2 a 28.3 m² **b** 38.5 cm² **c** 56.5 m² **d** 12.6 cm²
   e 26.2 m² **f** 51.8 cm² **g** 30.2 cm² **h** 15.7 m²
3 a 112 m² **b** 39 m² **c** 74 m² **d** 84 cm² **e** 31.5 cm²
   f 189 cm²
4 a 6.85 cm² **b** 39.63 cm² **c** 30.90 cm² **d** 6427.43 m²
   e 113.10 cm² **f** 36.86 cm²
5 2475 kg **6** 160 tiles **7** 375 tiles **8** 9.42 m²
9 1.85 m² **10** The width must be reduced by 1.5 cm.

EXERCISE 7C
1 a 54 cm² **b** 121.5 cm² **c** 576.24 mm²
2 a 276 cm² **b** 6880 mm² **c** 8802 m²
3 a ≈ 198 m² **b** ≈ 496 cm² **c** ≈ 148 cm²
4 a 576 cm² **b** 384 m² **c** ≈ 823 m²
5 €173.70 **6** $2537 **7** 1011.3 m²
8 a 207.3 cm² **b** 339.3 cm² **c** 196.3 cm² **d** 56.7 m²
   e 124.4 m² **f** 79.5 cm²
9 a 5026.5 cm² **b** 145.3 km² **c** 84.8 cm²
10 a $A = 18x^2$ **b** $A = 6x^2 + 12x$
   c $A = 5x^2 + 6x + x\sqrt{5}(x+2)$ **d** $A = 10\pi x^2$
   e $A = 7\pi x^2 + 2\pi x$ **f** $A = (39 + 5\sqrt{10})x^2$

EXERCISE 7D
1 $\approx 21.5\%$ **2** 57 m²
3 The square has the larger area, by 6.25 cm².
4 a 4 m **b** $73.60 **c** ≈ 5.85 m² **d** ≈ 0.549 m² **5** 376 balls
6 a ≈ 20.9 L (assuming base is also painted) **b** $413.50
7 Sphere has greater surface area (2123.7 cm² compared to 1470.3 cm² for the cylinder).
8 a $\approx 5.15 \times 10^8$ km² **b** $\approx 3.65 \times 10^8$ km²

REVIEW SET 7A
1 a 9.2 m **b** 42 m **2 a** 9.1 m **b** $305 **3** 9.42 cm
4 41.7 cm **5 a** 20 cm² **b** 19.6 m² **c** 22.5 m²
6 a ≈ 314 m² **b** $\approx \$8796$ **c** ≈ 85.8 m²
7 a 34 cm² **b** 36 cm² **c** ≈ 51.8 m² **8** 113 cm²

REVIEW SET 7B
1 a 105 m **b** $3150 **2** 21.9 km h^{-1} **3** 5.0 km
4 a 40 cm² **b** 24.6 cm² **c** 18.8 cm² **5** 1.21 m²
6 a i 120 m² **ii** 32 m² **iii** 40 m² **b** 24 L
7 ≈ 151 cm² **8 a** $A = 16x^2$ **b** $A = 6\pi x^2$

EXERCISE 8A
1 a $3 + \frac{4}{10}$ **b** $3 + \frac{4}{100}$ **c** $3 + \frac{4}{100} + \frac{7}{10\,000}$
   d $5 + \frac{1}{1000} + \frac{8}{10\,000}$ **e** $\frac{7}{100} + \frac{6}{10\,000}$
2 a 2.4 **b** 0.62 **c** 0.305 **d** 0.081 **e** 3.0002 **f** 2.0107
3 a 11.43 **b** 23.63 **c** 6.24 **d** 2.7 **e** 6.842 **f** 3.299
   g 0.3168 **h** −1.1 **i** 0.138 **j** −0.352 **k** 1.287 **l** −8.11
4 a 2540 **b** 0.006 **c** 34 **d** 3.6 **e** 0.036 **f** 1400
   g 1.68 **h** 25 **i** 0.064 **j** 27 **k** 0.004 **l** 0.203 **m** 0.3
   n 0.54 **o** 7.9 **p** 2.84 **q** 1.5 **r** 7 **s** 6 **t** −4.2
5 a $38.07 **b** €2.24 **c** $23.70
   d i $215.20 **ii** ≈ 25.8 cents **e** 40 000 bottles
   f ≈ 196 items **g** 11 666 bottles **h** 35 555 bearings
6 a 153.75 **b** 98.38 **c** 4.33 **d** 31 **e** 0.69 **f** 2.05
   g 23.16 **h** 0.25

EXERCISE 8B
1 a $6\% = \frac{6}{100}$ **b** $51\% = \frac{51}{100}$ **c** $27\% = \frac{27}{100}$ **d** $86\% = \frac{86}{100}$
2 a $\frac{1}{4}$ **b** $1\frac{3}{10}$ **c** $\frac{13}{20}$ **d** $\frac{2}{5}$ **e** $2\frac{1}{10}$ **f** 1 **g** $\frac{3}{25}$
   h $\frac{1}{50}$ **i** $\frac{9}{40}$ **j** $\frac{1}{40}$ **k** $\frac{31}{40}$ **l** $\frac{249}{400}$

3 a 0.66 **b** 0.29 **c** 0.5 **d** 0.75 **e** 1.8 **f** 2.05
   g 3 **h** 1.28 **i** 0.0001 **j** 0.003 **k** 0.105 **l** 0.5625
4 a 17% **b** 55% **c** 9% **d** 80% **e** 4% **f** 200%
   g 40% **h** 350% **i** 205% **j** 364% **k** 8.8% **l** 140.9%
5 a 25% **b** 30% **c** 35% **d** 44% **e** 100% **f** 160%
   g 54% **h** 47.5% **i** 4% **j** 37.5% **k** 240% **l** 376%

EXERCISE 8C
1 a 50% **b** 56% **c** 90% **d** 70% **2** 65% **3** 94.3%
4 86.4% **5** 122.9% **6 a** 24% **b** 8.67% **c** 21.3% **d** 30%
7 17% **8** 11.9% **9** 16.7%
10 a €4.80 **b** $16 **c** 4.8 L **d** 52.5 kg **e** 0.21 tonnes
   f 100 m **g** ≈ 137 minutes
11 24 **12** 84 marks **13** ≈ 654 miles **14** £2902.50
15 $5208 **16 a** €4.05 **b** €58.05

EXERCISE 8D
1 a CHF 160 **b** 16 L **c** 1300 mL **d** 3200 kg **e** £1300
   f 420 km **g** 350 L **h** 700 kg **i** €2100
2 a $520 **b** 1152 kg **c** €78.75 **d** 104 mL **e** 210 kg
   f $24.80
3 1700 cars **4** $75 500 **5** 300 students

EXERCISE 8E
1 $4.20/kg **2** 80 people **3** 57 **4** $64 800 **5** 44 minutes
6 $9724 **7** 772.8 m **8** 60.8 minutes

EXERCISE 8F
1 a 10^2 **b** 10^3 **c** 10^1 **d** 10^5 **e** 10^{-1} **f** 10^{-2}
   g 10^{-4} **h** 10^8
2 a 3.87×10^2 **b** 3.87×10^4 **c** 3.87×10^0 **d** 3.87×10^{-2}
   e 3.87×10^{-3} **f** 2.05×10^1 **g** 2.05×10^2 **h** 2.05×10^{-1}
   i 2.05×10^4 **j** 2.05×10^7 **k** 2.05×10^{-4}
3 a 4.0075×10^4 km **b** 1.495×10^{11} m **c** 4×10^{-4} mm
   d 4×10^7 bacteria **e** 1.4162×10^{-7} **f** 1×10^{-2} mm
4 a 300 **b** 2000 **c** 36 000 **d** 920 000 **e** 5 600 000
   f 34 **g** 7 850 000 **h** 900 000 000
5 a 0.03 **b** 0.002 **c** 0.000 47 **d** 0.000 063 **e** 1.7
   f 0.000 95 **g** 0.349 **h** 0.000 007
6 a 0.000 000 9 m **b** 6 606 000 000 **c** 100 000 light years
   d 0.000 01 mm **e** $\underset{26 \text{ zeros}}{0.\,000\ldots\ldots001\,66}$ kg
7 a 1.6×10^8 **b** 3.2×10^9 **c** 1.5×10^{10} **d** 8×10^9
   e 3.6×10^7 **f** 4.9×10^{-3} **g** 3×10^1 **h** 2×10^{-1}
8 a $\boxed{4.65^{06}}$ **b** $\boxed{5.12^{-05}}$ **c** $\boxed{5.99^{-04}}$ **d** $\boxed{3.761^{10}}$
   e $\boxed{4.95^{07}}$ **f** $\boxed{8.44^{-06}}$
9 a 3×10^{-8} **b** 1.36×10^{10} **c** 4.64×10^{10} **d** 9.87×10^9
   e 3.57×10^{-8} **f** 8.74×10^{-6}
10 a 2.55×10^8 **b** 7.56×10^{-6} **c** 2.75×10^{-10}
   d 3×10^1 **e** 2.44×10^{-5} **f** 1.02×10^7
11 a 4.80×10^8 mm **b** 3.16×10^7 seconds
   c 3.16×10^{10} seconds **d** 5×10^{-7} kg
12 a 8.64×10^4 km **b** 6.05×10^5 km **c** 6.31×10^7 km
13 a 1.8×10^{10} m **b** 2.59×10^{13} m **c** 9.47×10^{15} m

REVIEW SET 8A
1 a $4 + \frac{2}{10}$ **b** $4 + \frac{2}{100} + \frac{5}{1000}$ **c** $4 + \frac{2}{10} + \frac{5}{10\,000}$
   d $\frac{1}{100} + \frac{5}{10\,000}$
2 a 5.107 **b** 0.049
3 a 82.425 **b** 34 700 **c** 6.3 **d** 0.8 **e** 180 **f** 0.16
4 $127.75 **5** $154.50 **6 a** 32.68 **b** 5.12
7 a i $\frac{3}{4}$ **ii** $\frac{1}{16}$ **iii** $1\frac{1}{5}$ **b i** 0.25 **ii** 0.0625 **iii** 1.2

8 a 70% **b** 137.5% **c** 53% **d** 403%
9 36.7% **10** 90 marks **11** 570 lunches **12** 293.4 kL
13 a 9×10^0 **b** 3.49×10^4 **c** 7.5×10^{-3}
14 a 2 810 000 **b** 2.81 **c** 0.002 81
15 a 4.26×10^8 **b** 6×10^3

REVIEW SET 8B

1 a $6 + \frac{8}{10} + \frac{1}{100}$ **b** $6 + \frac{8}{100} + \frac{1}{1000}$ **c** $6 + \frac{8}{100} + \frac{1}{10\,000}$
d $6 + \frac{8}{1000} + \frac{1}{10\,000}$

2 a 1.4506 **b** 9.012
3 a 66.852 **b** 0.0258 **c** 0.021 **d** 0.72 **e** 0.0001 **f** 9
4 a 91 whole packets **b** 0.8 kg **5** $11.40
6 a 2.0 **b** 135.6
7 a i $\frac{4}{5}$ **ii** $\frac{1}{500}$ **iii** $2\frac{11}{20}$ **b i** 0.46 **ii** 0.125 **iii** 1.05
8 a 40% **b** 105% **c** 97% **d** 2.1% **9** 55%
10 ¥2975 **11** £18 540 **12** 41 562 megalitres
13 a 2.6357×10^2 **b** 5.11×10^{-4} **c** 8.634×10^8
14 a 2.78 **b** 39 900 000 **c** 0.002 081
15 a 6.4×10^7 **b** 6×10^6

EXERCISE 9A

1 a $8 + x$ **b** $11 + a$ **c** $t - 3$ **d** $2b + 5$ **e** $2d + 6$
f $3q$ **g** $4x$ **h** $2c + 3$ **i** $6a$ **j** $2y$ **k** $2z$ **l** $2c^2$
m $3a + 8$ does not simplify **n** $5x^2$
o $12a - 9$ does not simplify **p** $11a$ **q** $3v^2$ **r** $6bc$
s z **t** $b - 4$

2 a 0 **b** $4x$ **c** $5x - 5$ does not simplify **d** $3xy$ **e** $4ab$
f $2p^2$ **g** $7a - 3$ **h** $6x$ **i** $6b - 3$ **j** $5bc$ **k** $3b + 2a$
l $n^2 + 7n$ **m** $7x$ **n** 0 **o** $3b^2 + ab$ **p** $15x - 9$ **q** 0
r $10y$

3 a $10a$ **b** $-2a$ **c** $2a$ **d** $-10a$ **e** $8x$ **f** $6x$ **g** $-6x$
h $-8x$ **i** $3n + n^2$ does not simplify **j** $-13d$ **k** $-3d$
l $3d$ **m** $2 - 2b$ **n** $-2t$ **o** $-5g$ **p** $-m - 7$
q $4 - 3a$ **r** $2c$ **s** $3b$ **t** $5b$

4 a $a - 5$ **b** $5c + b$ **c** $3xy - 2ab + 2$ **d** $-4ab$ **e** $-5x$
f $3m^2 - 9$ **g** $n - 1$ **h** $-a - b$ **i** $2uv + 2$ **j** $-2i^2 - i$
k $-3a^2$ **l** $5x + y$ **m** $-2xy - y$ **n** $-6x - 10$

EXERCISE 9B

1 a $a + 3b$ **b** $a^2 + 2a$ **c** $2b + b^2$ **d** $8a$ **e** $3a - a^2$
f $6a$ **g** $4x^2 - x$ **h** $b^3 - b$ **i** $3a^2 - 2a$
2 a $2x^2 - 3$ **b** b^4 **c** $a^3 - a^2$ **d** $6t^2$ **e** $4m^4$ **f** $12y^3$
g $5b^2 - 2b$ **h** 0 **i** $3ab + 2a^2$
3 a a^3 **b** b^3 **c** c^4 **d** n^4 **e** $18ab$ **f** $20ac$ **g** m^5
h k^5 **i** p^6
4 a a^4 **b** m^6 **c** r^6 **d** a^2b^2 **e** s^8 **f** $9x^6$ **g** $4m^2n^2$
h $27y^6$ **i** $25a^2b^4$ **j** $16x^6$ **k** $8m^9$ **l** $2a^2c^5$
5 a $6y$ **b** $12x^2$ **c** $12a^2c$ **d** $9d^2$ **e** $6s^2t^2$ **f** $2a^4$
g $16y^3$ **h** $12g^2$ **i** $12a^3$ **j** $36b^5$ **k** $-3x^2$ **l** $-2x^3$
m $2x^2$ **n** $-12x^3$ **o** $-5x^4$ **p** $-8x^3$ **q** $-8x^4$
r $-3x^5$ **s** $2d^4$ **t** $27x^3$

EXERCISE 9C

1 a $3x + 6$ **b** $4x - 4$ **c** $5a + 20$ **d** $6a + 6b$ **e** $2b - 8$
f $9m + 27$ **g** $3n - 3m$ **h** $2s - 2t$ **i** $20 + 5x$ **j** $2x - 2y$
k $3t - 21$ **l** $21 + 7p$ **m** $9b + 9c$ **n** $4x - 20$ **o** $12 + 2j$
p $8q - 8p$ **q** $10 - 2k$ **r** $6y - 6z$ **s** $4k - 20$ **t** $50 - 5x$

2 a $12x + 4$ **b** $6a + 21$ **c** $2 - 4x$ **d** $12 - 18n$
e $10m + 5n$ **f** $14x - 7y$ **g** $3b + 9c$ **h** $8a - 4b$
i $2a - 12b$ **j** $15 + 9d$ **k** $28 - 14k$ **l** $2b + 16a$
m $44x + 11y$ **n** $2m - 14n$ **o** $18g - 12h$ **p** $12 + 9x$
q $6x + 2z$ **r** $6c - 18d$ **s** $5p + 30q$ **t** $12a - 4bc$

3 a $a^2 + 4a$ **b** $3b - b^2$ **c** $3c^2 + c$ **d** $5d - 4d^2$
e $2ab + ac$ **f** $g^3 - g$ **g** $7a^2 - 2a^3$ **h** $6x^2 - 9x$
i $10x - 2x^2$ **j** $15x - 3x^2$ **k** $4a^3 - 12a^2$ **l** $28n + 14n^2$

m $3x^2 - 2x$ **n** $4x + 2x^2$ **o** $pq^2 - p^2q$ **p** $ab^3 - ab^2$
q $3m^2n + m^2n^2$ **r** $2ab^2 - a^2b$ **s** $5p - 20p^2q$
t $7k^2l + 2l^2$ **u** $3a^2b^2 - 5b^2$ **v** $2x^2y + 12xy^2$
w $3xy - 4x^3y$ **x** $4st^2 - 3s^2$

4 a $-3x - 3$ **b** $-2x - 6$ **c** $-5x + 10$ **d** $-18 + 6x$
e $-a - 4$ **f** $-x + 2$ **g** $-6 + x$ **h** $-3x - 2$
i $-15 + 5x$ **j** $-27x + 36$ **k** $-10 + 4c$ **l** $-x + 9$

5 a $-2a - a^2$ **b** $-b^2 + 4b$ **c** $-2c - c^2$ **d** $x^2 - 7x$
e $-6n + 3n^2$ **f** $-4y^2 - 12y$ **g** $-18a + 6a^2$ **h** $-4b + 10b^2$

6 a $6x + 8$ **b** $8x + 16$ **c** $7x - 11$ **d** x **e** $m + 18$
f $-3m - 12$ **g** $-2x - 4$ **h** $3x + 13$ **i** $-3x + 3$
j $-51x + 14$ **k** $-17n + 27$ **l** $11y - 23$ **m** -1 **n** $9t - 5$

7 a $2x - 1$ **b** $1 - 8x$ **c** $33 - 12x$ **d** $11x - 6$
e $15x - 1$ **f** $9 - 4x$ **g** $-7 - 18x$ **h** $-7x - 1$
i $16x - 1$ **j** $2x + 3$ **k** $9x + 1$ **l** $12x - 17$

8 a $4x^2 - x + 6$ **b** $-6a$ **c** $5p - q$ **d** $7x^3 - 3x^2 + x$
e $-2x^3 - 8x^2 - 6x$ **f** $4a + 14$

9 a $3a^2 + 9a + 3$ **b** $3b^2 - 9b + 6$ **c** $8c^2 - 12c - 28$
d $-d^3 - 2d^2 + d$ **e** $2e^3 + 6e^2 - 10e$ **f** $6a^3 - 9a^2 + 3a$
g $-12x^3 - 6x^2 + 15x$ **h** $-4b^3 - 10b^2 + 2b$
i $-35y^3 + 7y^2 - 21y$

EXERCISE 9D

1 a $x^2 + 5x + 4$ **b** $a^2 + 5a + 6$ **c** $c^2 - 3c - 4$ **d** $a^2 - 7a + 10$
e $wy + wz + xy + xz$ **f** $ap + bp + aq + bq$ **g** $3x^2 - x - 2$
h $-2x^2 - x + 3$ **i** $2x^2 - x - 15$ **j** $3x^2 + 10x - 8$
k $12x^2 - 29x + 15$ **l** $x^3 - x^2 + 5x - 5$

2 a $x^2 + 4x + 4$ **b** $x^2 - 4x + 4$ **c** $x^2 + 10x + 25$
d $x^2 - 10x + 25$ **e** $4x^2 + 12x + 9$ **f** $4x^2 - 12x + 9$
g $a^2 + 2ab + b^2$ **h** $a^2 - 2ab + b^2$ **i** $x^2 - 12x + 36$
j $z^2 + 22z + 121$ **k** $25x^2 - 30x + 9$ **l** $49x^2 + 28x + 4$

3 a $x^3 + 4x^2 + 8x + 8$ **b** $2x^3 + x^2 + 2x + 3$ **c** $x^3 - 5x^2 + 7x - 3$
d $x^3 + 4x^2 - 2x + 15$ **e** $3x^3 - 11x^2 - 2x + 20$
f $6x^3 - 17x^2 - 12x - 7$ **g** $-2x^3 + 7x^2 + x - 15$
h $x^3 + 5x^2 - 23x + 8$

EXERCISE 9E

1 a $px + py + qx + qy$ **b** $qs + qt + rs + rt$ **c** $x^2 + 9x + 18$
d $x^2 + 6x + 8$ **e** $a^2 + 6a + 5$ **f** $y^2 + 11y + 30$ **g** $b^2 - 9$
h $x^2 - 2x - 15$ **i** $x^2 + 4x - 32$ **j** $x^2 + 3x - 4$
k $k^2 + k - 12$ **l** $x^2 - 4x - 12$ **m** $x^2 + 3x - 10$
n $x^2 - 9x + 18$ **o** $2z^2 - 21z + 27$ **p** $3n^2 + 5n - 2$
q $2x^2 - 9x - 35$ **r** $12x^2 + 11x - 15$

2 a $x^2 + 2x + 1$ **b** $x^2 + 6x + 9$ **c** $x^2 - 6x + 9$
d $x^2 - 16x + 64$ **e** $y^2 + 8y + 16$ **f** $y^2 - 8y + 16$
g $9x^2 + 6x + 1$ **h** $9x^2 - 6x + 1$ **i** $4a^2 + 4a + 1$
j $4a^2 - 4a + 1$ **k** $a^2 + 2ab + b^2$ **l** $a^2 - 2ab + b^2$
m $16x^2 + 8x + 1$ **n** $9x^2 - 24x + 16$ **o** $64x^2 - 48x + 9$
p $36x^2 + 36x + 9$

3 a $c^2 + 2cd + d^2$ **b** $x^2 + 2xy + y^2$ **c** $p^2 + 2pq + q^2$
d $a^2 + 4a + 4$ **e** $x^2 + 14x + 49$ **f** $x^2 + 18x + 81$
g $9a^2 + 6a + 1$ **h** $4b^2 + 4b + 1$ **i** $4x^2 + 20x + 25$
j $25x^2 + 60x + 36$ **k** $x^4 + 4x^2 + 4$ **l** $x^4 + 2x^3 + x^2$

4 a $m^2 - 2mn + n^2$ **b** $p^2 - 2pq + q^2$ **c** $c^2 - 2cd + d^2$
d $h^2 - 4h + 4$ **e** $n^2 - 6n + 9$ **f** $x^2 - 12x + 36$
g $4x^2 - 20x + 25$ **h** $4z^2 - 28z + 49$ **i** $9x^2 - 12x + 4$
j $9a^2 - 24a + 16$ **k** $4x^2 - 12xy + 9y^2$ **l** $x^4 - 6x^2 + 9$

5 a $x^2 - 1$ **b** $a^2 - 4$ **c** $b^2 - 25$ **d** $c^2 - 9$ **e** $16 - x^2$
f $49 - x^2$ **g** $1 - y^2$ **h** $64 - b^2$ **i** $4x^2 - 9$ **j** $16a^2 - 25$
k $4 - 9x^2$ **l** $1 - 36y^2$

6 a $y^2 - 1$ **b** $b^2 - 4$ **c** $a^2 - 49$ **d** $x^2 - 16$ **e** $36 - b^2$
f $25 - x^2$ **g** $64 - a^2$ **h** $4 - 9y^2$ **i** $49 - 4a^2$ **j** $9x^2 - 1$
k $25 - 9y^2$ **l** $x^2 - 4$

7 a $x^2 + 4x - 21$ **b** $x^2 + 8x + 15$ **c** $x^2 + 8x + 16$
d $x^2 - 8x + 15$ **e** $-x^2 + 4x - 3$ **f** $x^2 - 22x + 121$
g $a^2 - 64$ **h** $h^2 + 18h + 81$ **i** $4x^2 - 169$ **j** $2x^2 + x - 15$

k $9x^2 + 30x + 25$ **l** $m^2 - n^2$ **m** $3x^2 + 13x - 10$
n $25x^2 - 20x + 4$ **o** $49x^2 - 1$ **p** $-4x^2 + 19x + 5$
q $4r^2 - 12r + 9$ **r** $12x^2 - 17x + 6$

EXERCISE 9F

1 a $P = (6x + 7)$ cm   **b** $P = (12x - 3)$ cm
c $P = (4x + 24)$ cm   **d** $P = (6x + 8)$ cm
e $P = (9x + 10)$ cm   **f** $P = (8x + 20)$ cm
g $P = (\pi r + 2r)$ cm   **h** $P = (\pi x + 2x)$ cm
i $P = (\pi x + 4x)$ cm

2 a $A = 28x^2$ m^2 **b** $A = \left(\frac{3}{2}b^2 + 12b\right)$ m^2
c $A = (9x + 84)$ m^2 **d** $A = \left(\frac{9}{2}a^2 + 27a\right)$ m^2
e $A = (x^2 + 45x + 30)$ m^2 **f** $A = (3z^2 + 3z - 6)$ m^2

REVIEW SET 9A

1 a $7x$ **b** $7 - 7y$ does not simplify   **c** $-x + y$
d $4a + ab$ does not simplify   **e** $10xy$ **f** x^2 **g** $3a$
h $7y^2$ **i** $3x^2$
2 a $c + 3d$ **b** cd^3 **c** $3d + cd$
3 a x^4 **b** $8x^4$ **c** x^6 **d** $3xy^2$ **e** $6x^2$ **f** $10a^3b^2$
4 a $4y + 8$ **b** $16a - 6b$ **c** $-4 + x$ **d** $-2x - 2$
e $4x + 10$ **f** $-5y - 3$
5 $2x^3 - 10x^2 + 12x$
6 a $x^2 - 3x - 18$ **b** $4y^2 - 4y + 1$ **c** $12a^2 - 23a + 10$
d $4x^2 - 121$ **e** $9x^2 + 12xy + 4y^2$ **f** $a^3 + 6a^2 + 3a - 10$
7 a $P = (3x + 7)$ cm   **b** $P = (8x + 14)$ cm
c $P = (2\pi x + 4x)$ cm
8 a $A = (12a^2 + 11a - 15)$ cm^2 **b** $A = (4\pi x^2)$ cm^2

REVIEW SET 9B

1 a 0 **b** $2a$ **c** $4q - p$ **d** $8ab$ **e** y^2 **f** $9a^2$
2 a $2a + 2b$ **b** b^3c **c** $cd - 5c$
3 a y^3 **b** $2y^3$ **c** y^6 **d** $2xy^2$ **e** $15y^2$ **f** $15x^3y^3$
4 a $15 - 6x$ **b** $-3x + 15$ **c** $-3x - 3x^2$ **d** $-5x^2 + 5x + 7$
e $5y + 7$ **f** $2a^2 - 15$
5 $3x^3 + 12x^2 + 21x$
6 a $x^2 + 17x + 60$ **b** $9a^2 + 6a + 1$ **c** $2a^2 - 11a + 5$
d $x^2 - 49$ **e** $16x^2 - 24xy + 9y^2$ **f** $a^3 - 3a^2 + a - 3$
7 a $P = 12x$ cm   **b** $P = (2x + 8 + \sqrt{68})$ cm
c $P = \left(\frac{\pi r}{4} + 2r\right)$ cm
8 a $A = (10x + 25)$ m^2 **b** $A = (4x^2 + 2\pi x^2 + 4x)$ m^2

EXERCISE 10A

1 a numerical   **b** numerical   **c** categorical   **d** numerical
e numerical   **f** categorical   **g** categorical   **h** numerical
2 a male, female
b soccer, gridiron, AFL, rugby league, rugby union, Gaelic
c black, blond, brown, grey, red
d unleaded, premium unleaded, diesel, LPG, LRP
3 a quantitative discrete   **b** quantitative continuous
c categorical   **d** quantitative discrete   **e** quantitative discrete
f categorical   **g** quantitative discrete
h quantitative continuous   **i** quantitative discrete
j quantitative continuous   **k** categorical   **l** categorical
m quantitative continuous   **n** quantitative discrete
o quantitative discrete
4 a sample   **b** census   **c** sample   **d** census   **e** census
f sample
6 a type of fruit, frequency   **b** frequency   **c** 80
d no, as only one school is sampled   **e** yes   **f** banana

g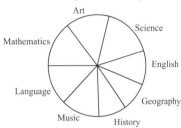

7 a favourite subject, frequency
b dependent: frequency;   independent: subject
c Science   **d** randomly selected   **e** yes
f

Art
Science
Mathematics
English
Language
Geography
Music
History

8 a i $\geqslant 1690$ **ii** $\geqslant 3759$ **iii** $\geqslant 2019$
b

% of households of corresponding size			
Number of persons	Year		
	1935	1960	1985
1	2.1%	0.8%	9.8%
2	15.6%	17.6%	26.2%
3	16.7%	16.1%	35.4%
4	24.9%	37.3%	23.1%
5+	40.7%	28.2%	5.4%
Totals	1	1	1

EXERCISE 10B

1 a continuous   **b** continuous   **c** continuous
d continuous   **e** discrete   **f** discrete   **g** continuous
2 a number of TV sets
b Discrete since you can't have part of a TV set.
c

Household televisions

d positively skewed, no outliers   **e** 30%   **f** 15%
3 a 45 shoppers   **b** 18 shoppers   **c** 15.6%
d positively skewed, no outliers
4 a the number of business appointments out of the office each day
b You can only have whole appointments.   **c** 22.2%   **d** 4.44%
e 2 appointments   **f** positively skewed with an outlier
g Data value 10 is an outlier.
5 a number of toothpicks in a box   **b** discrete
c

No. of toothpicks	Tally	Freq.
47			1
48							5
49												10
50																									23
51												10
52											9
53				2

d

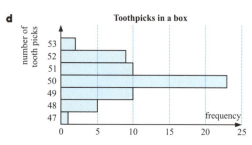

Toothpicks in a box

e approximately symmetrical **f** 38.3%

6 a

No. of pumpkins	Tally	Frequency
2	|	1
3		0
4	||	2
5	|||	3
6	ⅢⅠ	5
7	ⅢⅠ |||	8
8	ⅢⅠ ||	7
9	ⅢⅠ	5
10	ⅢⅠ ||	7
11	|	1
12		0
13		0
14		0
15	|	1
	Total	40

b

Pumpkins with fertiliser

c Yes, data value 15 is an outlier. **d** data is negatively skewed
e On average the number of pumpkins is higher in the "with fertiliser" group.
f Yes, assuming the fertiliser is not too expensive and the pumpkins are as big as they were previously.

EXERCISE 10C

1 a

Test Score	Tally	Freq.
0 - 9		0
10 - 19		0
20 - 29	|	1
30 - 39	||	2
40 - 49	|||	3
50 - 59	ⅢⅠ ||||	9
60 - 69	ⅢⅠ ⅢⅠ |||	13
70 - 79	ⅢⅠ |||	8
80 - 89	ⅢⅠ ⅢⅠ	10
90 - 100	||||	4
	Total	50

b 28%
c 12%

d More students had a test score in the interval 60 - 69 than in any other interval.

2 a

Stem	Leaf		Stem	Leaf
2	9 7 4 1 7 5		2	1 4 5 7 7 9
3	3 0 5 4 6 4		3	0 3 4 4 5 6
4	6 0 2 8		4	0 2 6 8
5	8 7 1 0		5	0 1 7 8

5 | 8   represents   58

3 a 1 **b** 43 **c** 10 **d** 1 **e** 21.4%

4 a

Stem	Leaf
0	
1	8
2	9 9 7
3	4 7 9 3 7 5 9 1 4 7 4
4	4 0 2 3 3 7 1 3 8 4 4 4 5 9 1 2 2 3 3 5
5	1 3 8 0 5 2 4 9 7 1

b

Stem	Leaf
0	
1	8
2	7 9 9
3	1 3 4 4 4 5 7 7 7 9 9
4	0 1 1 2 2 2 3 3 3 3 3 4 4 4 4 5 5 7 8 9
5	0 1 1 2 3 4 5 7 8 9

c The stem-and-leaf plot shows all the actual data values.
d i 59 **ii** 18 **e** 22.2% **f** 8.9%
g The data is slightly negatively skewed with no outliers.

EXERCISE 10D

1 a Weights can take any value from 75 kg to 105 kg.
b

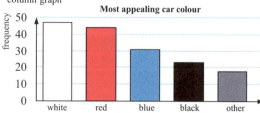

Weights of a volleyball squad

c The modal class is (85 - < 90) kg as this occurred the most frequently.
d approximately symmetrical with no outliers
2 a continuous numerical
b

Stem	Leaf
0	3 6 8 8 8
1	0 0 0 0 2 2 4 4 4 5 5 5 6 6 6 6 7 8 8 8 8 9
2	0 0 0 1 4 5 5 5 6 7 7
3	2 2 3 4 7
4	0 2 5 5 6

c positively skewed
d The modal travelling time was between 10 and 20 minutes.
3 a column graph

Most appealing car colour

b column graph

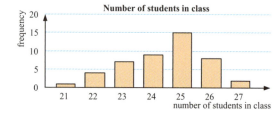

Number of students in class

c histogram

Time taken to make pizzas

d histogram

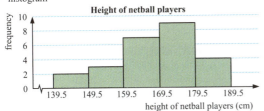

Height of netball players

e histogram

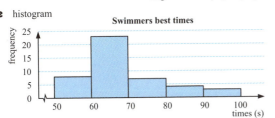

Swimmers best times

4 a

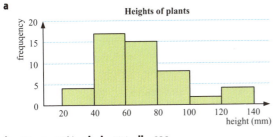

Heights of plants

b 46 **c** 30% **d i** 754 **ii** 686

EXERCISE 10E

1 a i 24 **ii** 24 **iii** no mode **b i** 13.3 **ii** 11.5 **iii** 8
 c i 10.3 **ii** 10.0 **iii** 11.2
 d i 428.6 **ii** 428 **iii** 415 and 427
2 a A: 7.73 B: 8.45 **b** A: 7 B: 7
 c The data sets are the same except for the last value, and the last value of A is less than the last value of B (12 < 20), so the mean of A is less than the mean of B.
 d The middle value of the data sets is the same, so the median is the same.
3 a mean: $582 000, median: $420 000, mode: $290 000
 b The mode is the second lowest value, so does not take the higher values into account.
 c No, since the data is unevenly distributed, the median is not in the centre.
4 a mean: 3.11, median: 0, mode: 0
 b The data is very positively skewed so the median is not in the centre.
 c The mode is the lowest value so does not take the higher values into account.
 d yes, 15 and 27 **e** No, they should be included.
5 a 44 **b** 44 **c** 40.6 **d** increase mean to 40.75
6 105.6 **7** 2275 km **8** $2 592 000 **9** 27
10 a 1696 km **b** 1632 km **c** 475.4 km
11 a 1 **b** 1 **c** 1.4

12 a i 5.74
 ii 7
 iii 8
 c bimodal

b

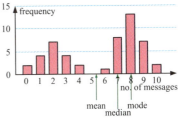

d The values below the median are generally much less than the median, so the mean value is less than the median.
 e median
13 a

Donation ($)	Frequency
1	7
2	9
3	2
4	4
5	8

 b 30
 c i $2.90 **ii** $2
 iii $2
 d mode
14 a i 2.61 **ii** 2 **iii** 2
 b This school has more children per family than the average Canadian family.
 c positively skewed
 d The positive skewness makes the value of the mean larger than the mode or the median.

EXERCISE 10F

1 a

Salmon lengths (cm)	Freq.	Cum. Freq.
$24 \leqslant x < 27$	2	2
$27 \leqslant x < 30$	5	7
$30 \leqslant x < 33$	7	14
$33 \leqslant x < 36$	11	25
$36 \leqslant x < 39$	12	37
$39 \leqslant x < 42$	2	39
$42 \leqslant x < 45$	1	40

b

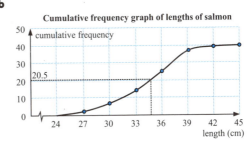

Cumulative frequency graph of lengths of salmon

c median ≈ 35 cm
d Median is 34. The graph indicates a steady increase from one interval point to the next, however this is not necessarily the case.
2 a 71 **b** 77 **c** 61 students **d** 26 students **e** 84
3 a $7\frac{1}{2}$ **b i** 43 people **ii** 43 people
4 a 32.5 mins **b** 77 runners **c** 27.5 mins

EXERCISE 10G

1 a i 9 **ii** $Q_1 = 7, Q_3 = 10$ **iii** 7 **iv** 3
 b i 18.5 **ii** $Q_1 = 16, Q_3 = 20$ **iii** 14 **iv** 4
 c i 26.9 **ii** $Q_1 = 25.5, Q_3 = 28.1$ **iii** 7.7 **iv** 2.6
2 a median = 2.35, $Q_1 = 1.4, Q_3 = 3.7$
 b range = 5.1, IQR = 2.3
 c i ..... greater than 2.35 minutes **ii** ..... less than 3.7 minutes
 iii The minimum waiting time was 0.1 minutes and the maximum waiting time was 5.2 minutes. The waiting times were spread over 5.1 minutes.
3 a 20 **b** 58 **c** 40 **d** 30 **e** 49 **f** 38 **g** 19

EXERCISE 10H

1 a i 31 **ii** 54 **iii** 16 **iv** 40 **v** 26 **b i** 38 **ii** 14

2 a ...... 89 points **b** ...... 25 points **c** ...... 62 points
d ...... at least 73 points
e ...... between 45 and 73 points **f** 64 **g** 28

3 a i min = 2, Q_1 = 5, median = 6, Q_3 = 9, max = 11
ii

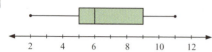

iii range = 9 **iv** IQR = 4
b i min = 0, Q_1 = 4, median = 7, Q_3 = 8, max = 9
ii

iii range = 9 **iv** IQR = 4

4 a median = 20.2 kg, Q_1 = 19.8 kg, Q_3 = 21.1 kg
max. weight = 22.3 kg, min. weight = 18.8 kg
b

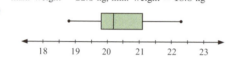

c i IQR = 1.3 kg **ii** range = 3.5 kg
d i ...... 20.2 kg **ii** 31.8% of the bags ......
iii ...... 1.3 kg **iv** ...... 19.8 kg or less
e approximately symmetrical

5 a

Statistic	A	C
min value	2	8
Q_1	7	10
median	10	14
Q_3	12	16
max value	16	17

b i A: 14, C: 9
ii A: 5, C: 6

6 a i class B **ii** class B **iii** class B **b i** 49 **ii** 13
c 75% **d i** almost symmetrical **ii** almost symmetrical
e The students in class A generally scored higher marks.
The marks in class B were more varied.

7 a

Statistic	Boys	Girls
min value	160	152
Q_1	167	162.5
median	170.5	166
Q_3	174	170
max value	188	177

b The distributions show that in general, the boys are taller than the girls and are more varied in their heights.

EXERCISE 10I

1 $\overline{x} \approx 4.87$, min = 1, Q_1 = 3, median = 5, Q_3 = 7, max = 9

2

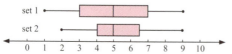

3

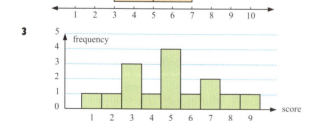

4 $\overline{x} \approx 5.24$, min = 2, Q_1 = 4, median = 5, Q_3 = 6.5, max = 9

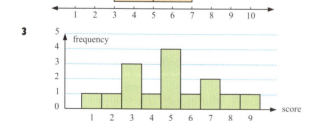

5 Set 1
mean = 6.625, mode = 7, min = 3, Q_1 = 6, median = 7,
Q_3 = 8, max = 9, range = 6, IQR = 2
Set 2
mean = 7.7, mode = 7, min = 2, Q_1 = 6, median = 8,
Q_3 = 9, max = 15, range = 13, IQR = 3

6 Set 1
mean = 11.936, mode = 11.9, min = 11.6, Q_1 = 11.8,
median = 11.9, Q_3 = 12, max = 12.2, range = 0.6, IQR = 0.2
Set 2
mean = 11.84, mode = 11.8, min = 11.5, Q_1 = 11.7,
median = 11.8, Q_3 = 11.9, max = 12.2, range = 0.7,
IQR = 0.2

REVIEW SET 10A

1 a 49 **b** 15 **c** 26.5% **d** positively skewed
2 a the number of children in the household
b Discrete, since you cannot have part of a child.
c

Children in a household

d positively skewed, one outlier at 8

3 a

Stem	Leaf
0	9
1	88
2	58492650387
3	52493491656352
4	00 4 | 0 represents 40

b

Stem	Leaf
0	9
1	88
2	02345567889
3	12233445556699
4	00 4 | 0 represents 40

c The stem-and-leaf plot displays all the actual data values.
d i 40 **ii** 9 **e** 20%

4 a Mass can be any decimal of a gram.
b

Histogram of masses of eggs

c Modal class is 50 g - < 51 g. This class has the most eggs.
d approximately symmetrical

5 a $\overline{x} \approx 29.6$ **b** 16 and 28 **c** 29 **d** 45
e Q_1 = 22, Q_3 = 41.5 **f** 19.5

6 a i 48 **ii** 98 **iii** 15 **iv** 66 **v** 42 **b i** 83 **ii** 24

REVIEW SET 10B

1 a 14.55 **b** 14.5 **c** 14 and 15
2 a

Stem	Leaf
3	1
4	95
5	887835
6	9085964164163
7	012567840
8	023922
9	14024117 .9 | 1 represents 91

b

Stem	Leaf
3	1
4	5 9
5	3 5 7 8 8 8
6	0 1 1 3 4 4 5 6 6 6 8 9 9
7	0 0 1 2 4 5 6 7 8
8	0 2 2 2 3 9
9	0 1 1 1 2 4 4 7

9 | 1 represents 91

c The stem-and-leaf plot displays all the actual data values.

d **i** 97 **ii** 31 **e** 20% **f** **iii** neither symmetric nor skewed

3 a i 8.47 **ii** 9 **iii** 9 **iv** 4 **b** well above average
c negative

4 a

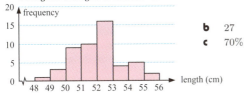

Histogram of lengths of newborn babies

b 27
c 70%

d

Length (cm)	Frequency	Cum. Freq.
$48 \leqslant l < 49$	1	1
$49 \leqslant l < 50$	3	4
$50 \leqslant l < 51$	9	13
$51 \leqslant l < 52$	10	23
$52 \leqslant l < 53$	16	39
$53 \leqslant l < 54$	4	43
$54 \leqslant l < 55$	5	48
$55 \leqslant l < 56$	2	50

e

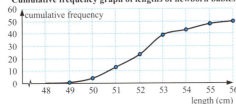

Cumulative frequency graph of lengths of newborn babies

f i 52.1 cm **ii** 18 babies

5 a Comparing the median swim times for girls and boys shows that, in general, boys swim 2.5 seconds faster than the girls.

b The range of the girls' swim times is 10 seconds compared to the range of 7 seconds for the boys.

c The fastest 25% of the boys swim faster than 100% of the girls.

d 100% of the boys swim faster than 60 seconds whereas 75% of the girls swim faster than 60 seconds.

EXERCISE 11A

1 a $n = 9$ **b** $x = -8$ **c** $t = -2$ **d** $x = 4$ **e** $x = -5$
f $y = 13$ **g** $a = 6$ **h** $b = 9$ **i** $x = 3$ **j** $a = 1$
k $x = 8$ **l** $x = -15$ **m** $y = 18$ **n** $a = 5$ **o** $b = -6$
p $a = 9$ **q** $y = -3$ **r** $x = 5$ **s** $b = -3$ **t** $a = -6$

2 a $y = 2$ **b** $b = 3$ **c** $x = -2$ **d** $a = -4$

3 a A **b** C **c** A **d** B **e** C **f** D **g** A **h** D
i A **j** C **k** B **l** E

EXERCISE 11B

1 a $x = 7$ **b** $x = 8$ **c** $2x = 10$ **d** $3x = 9$
2 a $x = 3$ **b** $x = -10$ **c** $2x = -4$ **d** $3x = -9$
3 a $4x = -8$ **b** $18x = -6$ **c** $x = 12$ **d** $x = -9$
e $x = 16$ **f** $x = -20$
4 a $x = 2$ **b** $x = -10$ **c** $x + 1 = 0$ **d** $x - 2 = 4$
e $x + 2 = -4$ **f** $x - 1 = 5$

EXERCISE 11C

1 a $x = -11$ **b** $x = -3$ **c** $x = -7$ **d** $x = -3$

e $x = 5$ **f** $x = 9$ **g** $x = 1$ **h** $x = -5$ **i** $x = -2$
j $x = 3$ **k** $x = -1\frac{1}{2}$ **l** $x = -6$

2 a $x = 11$ **b** $x = -5\frac{1}{2}$ **c** $x = -4$ **d** $x = 3\frac{1}{2}$
e $x = 1$ **f** $x = 11$ **g** $x = -6$ **h** $x = 11$
i $x = -\frac{1}{2}$ **j** $x = -2$ **k** $x = 4$ **l** $x = -9$

3 a $x = 28$ **b** $x = -15$ **c** $x = -16$ **d** $x = -12$
e $x = 19$ **f** $x = -11$ **g** $x = 10$ **h** $x = 24$

4 a $x = -5\frac{1}{2}$ **b** $x = -3$ **c** $x = 17$ **d** $x = -7$
e $x = 3$ **f** $x = 8\frac{1}{2}$

EXERCISE 11D

1 a $x = 9$ **b** $x = -12$ **c** $x = 1$ **d** $x = -2$ **e** $x = 2\frac{2}{3}$
f $x = -3$

2 a $x = -3$ **b** $x = 6$ **c** $x = 2$ **d** $x = 3$ **e** $x = 2$
f $x = 1$

3 a $x = 6$ **b** $x = -3$ **c** $x = 1\frac{1}{5}$ **d** $x = -3$
e $x = -3\frac{1}{2}$ **f** $x = -4$

4 a $x = 3$ **b** $x = 2$ **c** $x = 2$ **d** $x = 6\frac{1}{2}$ **e** $x = 1$
f $x = 6$

5 a $x = 0$ **b** $x = 2$ **c** $x = 3$ **d** $x = 3$ **e** $x = -1$
f $x = -\frac{7}{9}$ **g** $x = -5$ **h** $x = 6$ **i** $x = 3\frac{1}{2}$ **j** $x = \frac{2}{3}$
k no solution **l** infinite number of solutions (true for all x)

EXERCISE 11E

1 a $x = \frac{4}{5}$ **b** $x = 14$ **c** $x = \frac{4}{15}$ **d** $x = 1\frac{3}{4}$ **e** $x = \frac{2}{45}$
f $x = \frac{3}{14}$ **g** $x = 3\frac{3}{4}$ **h** $x = 5\frac{1}{4}$

2 a $x = -\frac{1}{4}$ **b** $x = -18$ **c** $x = -5$ **d** $x = 18$ **e** $x = -1$
f $x = -\frac{1}{5}$ **g** $x = -1$ **h** $x = -5$ **i** no solution

EXERCISE 11F

1 a $x = 15$ **b** $x = 4\frac{1}{2}$ **c** $x = 17\frac{1}{2}$ **d** $x = 2\frac{1}{4}$ **e** $x = \frac{3}{8}$
f $x = -\frac{7}{12}$ **g** $x = \frac{4}{15}$ **h** $x = -\frac{2}{15}$

2 a $x = 1$ **b** $x = -1$ **c** $x = 8\frac{1}{2}$ **d** $x = -12$ **e** $x = \frac{1}{5}$
f $x = -1$

3 a $x = \pm\sqrt{12}$ **b** $x = \pm 6$ **c** $x = \pm\sqrt{3}$ **d** $x = \pm 7$
e $x = \pm\sqrt{10}$ **f** $x = \pm\sqrt{35}$ **g** $x = \pm 4$ **h** no solution

EXERCISE 11G

1 a $x + 6 = 13$ **b** $x - 5 = -4$ **c** $2x + 7 = 1$
d $\frac{x-1}{2} = 45$ **e** $3x = 17 - x$ **f** $5x = x + 2$

2 a $x + (x + 1) = 33$ **b** $x + (x + 1) + (x + 2) = 102$
c $x + (x + 2) = 52$, where x is odd
d $x + (x + 2) + (x + 4) = 69$, where x is odd

3 a $30a + 25(a + 5) = 455$ **b** $35s + 49(9 - s) = 357$
c $2(f - 7) + 5f = 224$

EXERCISE 11H

1 The number is 8. **2** The numbers are 86 and 87.
3 The smallest is 35. **4** The number is 12. **5** The number is 4.
6 The number is 84. **7** Eight 5-cent coins **8** 9 bananas
9 five 500 g containers

EXERCISE 11I

1 a 14 cm **b** 1 m **2 a** 7 cm **b** 7 cm
3 a 92 km **b** 2 h 48 min **4 a** 12.5 m s^{-1} **b** 127.6 m
5 3 hours **6 a** 3.58 cm **b** 2.39 cm **7** $8 **8** 28 people
9 a $x = 8.5$ **b** $x = 11$ **c** $x = 5.1$ **d** $x = 9$ **e** $x \approx 5.2$
f $x \approx 11.9$

10 $x \approx 31.83$

EXERCISE 11J

1 **a** $y = \frac{9}{5} - \frac{3}{5}x$ **b** $y = 6 - \frac{4}{3}x$ **c** $y = 4x - 8$
d $y = 21 - \frac{7}{2}x$ **e** $y = 4 - \frac{2}{3}x$ **f** $y = \frac{5}{3}x + 20$

2 **a** $x = b - a$ **b** $x = \frac{z}{y}$ **c** $x = \frac{q - p}{2}$ **d** $x = \frac{r - 2y}{3}$
e $x = \frac{c - by}{a}$ **f** $x = \frac{y - c}{m}$ **g** $x = \frac{q - 7}{p}$ **h** $x = \frac{c - a}{b}$
i $x = \frac{7 - p}{q}$

3 **a** $y = mx - c$ **b** $y = \frac{a - b}{3}$ **c** $y = \frac{p - q}{5}$ **d** $y = \frac{5 - b}{a}$
e $y = \frac{p - r}{q}$ **f** $y = \frac{q - p}{r}$

4 **a** $z = \frac{4}{xy}$ **b** $z = \frac{y}{x}$ **c** $z = \frac{4}{5}w$ **d** $z = \pm\sqrt{3y}$
e $z = \pm\sqrt{xy}$ **f** $z = \pm\sqrt{wp - wq}$

5 **a** $m = \frac{F}{a}$ **b** $r = \frac{C}{2\pi}$ **c** $l = \frac{V}{dh}$ **d** $M = DV$
e $b = \frac{2A}{h}$ **f** $R = \frac{100I}{PT}$

6 **a** $xy = 800$ **b** $y = \frac{800}{x}$ **c** $P = 2\left(x + \frac{800}{x}\right)$

7 **a** $2x + 2y = 100$ **b** $y = 50 - x$ **c** $A = x(50 - x)$
8 28.6 cm **9** **a** 88.0 cm **b** 227 revs
10 **a** 45 239 km **b** 26 400 km h^{-1} **11** 37.0 m
12 8.46 cm **13** 3.00 m

REVIEW SET 11A

1 $x = 7$ **2** $3x = 12$ **3** **a** $x = -10$ **b** $x = 19$
4 **a** $x = 2\frac{6}{7}$ **b** $x = -2$ **5** **a** $x = \frac{1}{15}$ **b** $x = 9$
6 **a** $2(x + 11) = 48$ **b** $x + (x + 1) + (x + 2) = 63$
7 The number is 7. **8** twelve 5-cent coins
9 **a** 22.1 m s^{-1} **b** 81.6 m **10** $x = 18$
11 **a** $y = \frac{5}{3}x - 5$ **b** $d = \frac{C}{\pi}$

REVIEW SET 11B

1 B **2** $x + 2 = 3$ **3** **a** $x = -19\frac{1}{2}$ **b** $x = 2$
4 **a** $x = \frac{3}{4}$ **b** $x = 1$ **5** **a** $x = 1\frac{1}{9}$ **b** $x = -2$
6 **a** $4x = x + 15$ **b** $x + (x + 2) = 36$, x is odd
7 The number is 7. **8** **a** 204 800 units **b** 7.75 cm
9 $V = \frac{M}{D}$ **10** **a** $y = 4 - \frac{6}{5}x$ **b** $r = \frac{C}{2\pi}$ **11** $r \approx 4.46$ cm

EXERCISE 12A

1 **a** 7 : 11 **b** 14 : 9 **c i** 13 : 9 **ii** 9 : 13 **iii** 5 : 9 **iv** 9 : 5
2 **a** 8 : 3 **b** 3 : 7 **c** 35 : 45 **d** 300 : 50 **e** 500 : 3000
f 400 : 2500 **g** 9000 : 150 **h** 12 : 8000 **i** 240 : 40

EXERCISE 12B

1 **a** 3 : 4 **b** 2 : 1 **c** 1 : 3 **d** 3 : 5 **e** 1 : 2 **f** 7 : 4
g 1 : 2 **h** 3 : 4 **i** 5 : 4 **j** 1 : 2 : 3 **k** 20 : 1 **l** 1 : 2 : 4
2 **a** 5 : 2 **b** 3 : 7 **c** 3 : 2 **d** 2 : 1 **e** 7 : 12 **f** 1 : 4
g 4 : 1 **h** 1 : 20
3 **a** 1 : 2 **b** 3 : 1 **c** 3 : 1 **d** 3 : 5 **e** 2 : 1 **f** 1 : 2
g 4 : 1 **h** 6 : 4 : 3
4 **a** 2 : 3 **b** 8 : 15 **c** 8 : 39 **d** 39 : 50
5 **a** 2 : 1 **b** 1 : 3 **c** 1 : 4 **d** 7 : 10 **e** 3 : 7 **f** 40 : 1
g 1 : 50
6 **a** 1 : 2 **b** 1 : 2 **c** 1 : 4 **d** 4 : 1

7 **a** 2 : 3 **b** 2 : 1 **c** 2 : 3 **d** 4 hours mowing, 6 hours weeding, 4 hours edging, 2 hours sweeping u

EXERCISE 12C

1 **a** $x = 12$ **b** $x = 3$ **c** $x = 10$ **d** $x = 28$ **e** $x = 35$
f $x = 42$ **g** $x = 96$ **h** $x = 56$ **i** $x = 36$
2 **a** $\square = 15$ **b** $\square = 6$ **c** $\square = 15$ **d** $\square = 9$ **e** $\square = 3$
f $\square = 16$
3 6 kg of onions **4** 300 apple trees **5** $30 **6** 90 kg
7 **a** 28 kg **b** 76 kg **8** 34 kg **9** Yes, volume 210 000 cm^3

EXERCISE 12D

1 97.65 kg **2** $18 938 **3** 9.38 cm **4** 88.3 mL **5** 12.0 g
6 477 m^2

EXERCISE 12E

1 **a** 5 **b** 5 **c** 16 **d** 17 **e** 13 **f** 19 **g** 11 **h** 19
2 **a** 25 cm : 25 cm **b** 40 cm : 10 cm **c** 30 cm : 20 cm
d 17.5 cm : 32.5 cm
3 **a** $10 : $40 **b** €15 : €20 **c** 40 kg : 50 kg
4 $250 000 **5** 510 girls **6** 800 m^2 **7** 40 succeed, 16 fail
8 **a** 58 years **b** €103 333 **c** €96 667
9 £6000 : £10 000 : £20 000
10 **a** 7.5 kg **b** 2.5 kg **11** **a** 16 **b** 20 **c** 12

EXERCISE 12F

1 **a** 6.2 m **b** 6.9 m **c** 9.75 m
2 **a** 9.2 cm **b** 2.88 cm **c** 11.2 cm
3 **a**

6 cm / 4 cm

b
7.19 cm / 5.44 cm

4 **a** 27.5 km **b** 3.6 cm **5** 1 : 2 000 000 **6** 300 km^2

EXERCISE 12G

1 **a** $2 per metre **b** $15 per hour **c** $1.80 per litre
d 200 L per minute
2 **a** cost and mass **b** capacity and time **c** capacity and time
d capacity and capacity **e** cost and length
3 **a** $180 **b** $540 **4** **a** 34 L **b** £31.93 **c** £23.94
5 **a i** 980 **ii** 612 **iii** 1960 **b** 10 h 21 min

6 a i 29 runs **ii** 72 runs **iii** 22 runs **b** 20.8 overs

7 a 13 h 20 min **b** 17.1 L **c** $425 (5 cans)

8 a $21 **b** $8 **c** $37
d Yes, because it costs less than having 5 DVDs for 3 nights (**c**). She will save $7.

9 a 27.8 m s^{-1} **b** 72 km h^{-1}

10 a 15 km h^{-1} **b** 2.1 metres per hour

11 a 15 km **b** 140 km **c** 40 km **d** 50 km
e 12 000 km h^{-1} **f** 410 km **g** 19 km h^{-1} **h** 5 h 12 min

EXERCISE 12H

1 a

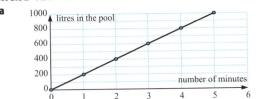

b 200 litres per minute

2

Number of minutes	0	1	2	3	4	5
Number of litres	0	40	80	120	160	200

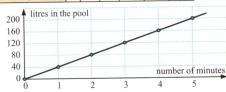

3 a i Sarah **ii** Cleo
b The dotted line is drawn at 1 hour. The point where the dotted line cuts each person's graph shows how much they earned in 1 hour.

4 a Lawrence. Lawrence reservoir started with more water than Cannon, but was empty sooner. The slope of its graph is steeper.
b Lawrence. Its volume was greater than Cannon's at time 0 days (at the start of summer).

5 a Nindi **b** Syd
c Nindi. The water level went down at a constant rate (there were no flat sections in the graph).
d Syd. He had the longest time when the water level did not change (the longest flat section in the graph).

6 a 3°C per hour **b** the temperature was constant
c from 8 am to 9 am **d** 36°C **e** 7 hours
f 3 pm and 4 pm

EXERCISE 12I

1 a 1.8 km **b** 28 minutes **c i** 1 km **ii** 1.6 km
d i 6 minutes **ii** 16 minutes **e** 3.86 km h^{-1}

2 a 12 minutes **b** 80 km each **c** 20 km each
d A: 1 h 48 min, B: 2 h 12 min **e** 24 minutes faster
f A: 44.4 km h^{-1}, B: 36.4 km h^{-1}

3 a Bourke family **b** Adams family **c** Adams family
d 1 h 45 min **e** 1 h 15 min **f** ≈ 92 km

4 a after 2 minutes (1 km from home) **b** 2 minutes
c 4 minutes **d** $2\frac{1}{3}$ km
e between the 4th and 6th minutes (after she left the traffic light until she reached the supermarket)

REVIEW SET 12A

1 a 13 : 25 **b** 3 : 8 **2 a** 4 : 3 **b** 4 : 9 **c** 6 : 5

3 a 5 : 12 **b** 5 : 7 **4** □ = 15 **5** 25 boys **6** 35 kg, 40 kg

7 €1200 **8 a** 26 m **b** 11.5 cm **9 a** $148.80 **b** $46.50

10 a 95 km h^{-1} **b** 11.7 km L^{-1} **11** 12.6 km h^{-1}

12 a 500 kL **b i** 400 kL, 100 kL, 50 kL per day
ii 250 kL, 250 kL, 50 kL per day
c Yes, the tank loses the same amount of water each day.

---

d after 10 days

REVIEW SET 12B

1 a 5 : 12 **b** 1 : 2 **2 a** 2 : 3 : 5 **b** 2 : 5 **c** 3 : 2

3 a 5 : 3 **b** 9 : 25 **c** 27 : 125 **4** 9 **5** 37.5 mL

6 1600 apricot trees, 2000 peach trees **7** 12 000 Yen

8 a 50 km **b** 6.9 cm **9** 1 minute

10

No. of minutes	0	1	2	3	4	5	6
No. of litres	800	775	750	725	700	675	650

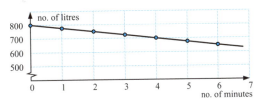

11 35.3 km h^{-1}

12 a 325 km **b** 30 minutes
c Mahler: 100 km h^{-1}, Schumann: 90 km h^{-1} **d** 88.6 km h^{-1}

EXERCISE 13A

1 a 9 **b** 5 **c** 12 **d** 40 **e** 7 **f** 9

2 a 2a **b** 5b **c** 4xy **d** 4x **e** x **f** −2x **g** −b
h 4a **i** −3xy

3 a 2 **b** c **c** 1 **d** k **e** 3a **f** 5x **g** 5x **h** 8y **i** 18

4 a ab **b** abc **c** 12a **d** a **e** r **f** q **g** 3b **h** dp
i 4r **j** 3pq **k** 2ab **l** 6xy **m** 5 **n** 12wz **o** 12pqr

5 a (x + 2) **b** 2(x + 5) **c** x **d** 2(x + 1) **e** 2(x + 3)
f 2x(x − 3)

EXERCISE 13B

1 a 2(x + 2) **b** 3(a − 4) **c** 5(3 − p) **d** 6(3x + 2)
e 4x(x − 2) **f** 2m(1 + 4m)

2 a 4(x + 4) **b** 5(2 + d) **c** 5(c − 1) **d** d(c + e)
e 2a(3 + 4b) **f** 2x(3 − x) **g** 7a(b − 1) **h** 2b(2a − 3c)

3 a 3(a + b) **b** 8(x − 2) **c** 3(p + 6) **d** 14(2 − x)
e 7(x − 2) **f** 6(2 + x) **g** c(a + b) **h** 6(2y − a)
i a(5 + b) **j** c(b − 6d) **k** x(7 − y) **l** y(x + 1)
m a(1 + b) **n** y(x − z) **o** p(3q + r) **p** c(d − 1)

4 a x(x + 2) **b** x(5 − 2x) **c** 4x(x + 2) **d** 7x(2 − x)
e 6x(x + 2) **f** x²(x + 9) **g** xy(x + y) **h** 2x²(2x − 3)
i 9x(x² − 2y) **j** a(a² + a + 1) **k** 2(a² + 2a + 4)
l 3a(a² − 2a + 3)

5 a 9(b − a) **b** 3(2b − 1) **c** 4(b − 2a) **d** c(d − 7)
e a(b − 1) **f** 6x(2 − x) **g** 5x(3x − 1) **h** 2b(2a − b)
i a(a − 1)

6 a −6(a + b) **b** −4(1 + 2x) **c** −3(y + 2z) **d** −c(9 + d)
e −x(1 + y) **f** −5(x + 4) **g** −3y(4 + y) **h** −9a(2a + b)
i −8x(2x + 3)

7 a (x − 7)(2 + x) **b** (x + 3)(a + b) **c** (x + 2)(4 − x)
d (x + 9)(x + 1) **e** (b + 4)(a − 1) **f** (b + c)(a + d)
g (m + n)(a − b) **h** (x + 3)(x − 1)

8 a (x + 3)(x − 1) **b** (x − 7)(x + 7) **c** (x + 6)(x − 4)
d (x − 2)(x − 8) **e** x + 2 **f** (a + b)(4 − a)
g 3(a − 2)(a − 4) **h** (x + 4)(4x + 1) **i** 5(x − 1)(6 − x)
j −(x + 5)(4x + 17)

EXERCISE 13C

1 a (a + 1)(3 + b) **b** (c + d)(6 + a) **c** (b + 3)(a + 2)
d (n + 3)(m + p) **e** (x + 3)(x + 6) **f** (x + 3)(x + 8)
g (x + 1)(3x + 1) **h** (x + 2)(3x + 4) **i** (2x + 1)(5x + 3)

2 a (x + 4)(x − 5) **b** (x − 7)(x + 3) **c** (x − 3)(x + 2)

d $(x-6)(x-3)$ **e** $(x+7)(x-9)$ **f** $(2x+1)(x-3)$
g $(3x+2)(x-4)$ **h** $(4x-3)(x-2)$ **i** $(x-1)(9x+4)$

EXERCISE 13D

1 **a** $2, 5$ **b** $2, 6$ **c** $2, 8$ **d** $5, 6$ **e** $-2, 7$ **f** $3, -7$
g $3, -6$ **h** $-3, 10$

2 **a** $(x+1)(x+4)$ **b** $(x+2)(x+5)$ **c** $(x+3)(x+7)$
d $(x+6)(x+9)$ **e** $(x+2)(x+10)$ **f** $(x+3)(x+6)$
g $(x+2)(x+12)$ **h** $(x+3)(x+12)$ **i** $(x+3)(x+16)$

3 **a** $(x-1)(x-4)$ **b** $(x-1)(x-3)$ **c** $(x-2)(x-3)$
d $(x-2)(x-11)$ **e** $(x-7)(x-8)$ **f** $(x-4)(x-12)$
g $(x-2)(x-14)$ **h** $(x-1)(x-24)$ **i** $(x-3)(x-12)$

4 **a** $(x+1)(x-9)$ **b** $(x+7)(x-3)$ **c** $(x+2)(x-3)$
d $(x-6)(x+3)$ **e** $(x+8)(x-3)$ **f** $(x-12)(x+1)$
g $(x+9)(x-6)$ **h** $(x+8)(x-7)$ **i** $(x-7)(x+4)$
j $(x-5)(x+4)$ **k** $(x-9)(x+7)$ **l** $(x+12)(x-5)$

5 **a** $(a-3)(a-4)$ **b** $(b-3)(b+2)$ **c** $(c-1)(c-6)$
d $(d+2)^2$ **e** $(e-5)(e+4)$ **f** $(f+4)(f+9)$
g $(g-3)^2$ **h** $(h-1)(h-9)$ **i** $(i+3)(i-3)$
j $(j+5)(j-5)$ **k** $(k+10)(k-10)$ **l** $(l+25)(l-25)$
m $2(x+2)(x-2)$ **n** $3(x+3)(x-3)$ **o** $(2x+1)(2x-1)$

EXERCISE 13E

1 **a** $(2x+1)(x+3)$ **b** $(2x+1)(x+5)$ **c** $(7x+2)(x+1)$
d $(3x+2)(x+2)$ **e** $(3x+2)(x+3)$ **f** $(3x+4)(x+1)$
g $(2x+1)(4x+3)$ **h** $(3x+2)(7x+1)$ **i** $(6x+1)(x+1)$
j $(6x+1)(x+3)$ **k** $(5x+3)(2x+1)$ **l** $(7x+5)(2x+1)$

2 **a** $(2x-5)(x+1)$ **b** $(3x-2)(x+1)$ **c** $(3x+1)(x-2)$
d $(2x-1)(x+2)$ **e** $(2x-1)(x+7)$ **f** $(5x+1)(x-2)$
g $(5x-1)(x-3)$ **h** $(11x+3)(x-1)$ **i** $(3x+2)(x-3)$
j $(2x-3)(x-3)$ **k** $(3x-5)(x-2)$ **l** $(5x-2)(x+3)$
m $(3x-2)(x+4)$ **n** $(2x-1)(x+9)$ **o** $(2x-3)(x+6)$
p $(2x+7)(x-3)$ **q** $(3x-1)(5x+2)$ **r** $(15x+1)(x-3)$
s $(3x-1)(3x-4)$ **t** $(3x+10)(4x-3)$ **u** $(8x-5)(x+3)$

EXERCISE 13F

1 **a** $(a+b)(a-b)$ **b** $(p+q)(p-q)$ **c** $(q+p)(q-p)$
d $(m+x)(m-x)$ **e** $(x+5)(x-5)$ **f** $(x+9)(x-9)$
g $(a+3)(a-3)$ **h** $(2x+1)(2x-1)$ **i** $(2x+3)(2x-3)$
j $(3y+4)(3y-4)$ **k** $(8+x)(8-x)$ **l** $(4+3a)(4-3a)$
m $(x+10)(x-10)$ **n** $(x+13)(x-13)$
o $(3x+2y)(3x-2y)$ **p** $(1+t)(1-t)$ **q** $(3+y)(3-y)$
r $(11u+2v)(11u-2v)$ **s** $(x+1)(x-1)$
t $(7a+20)(7a-20)$

REVIEW SET 13A

1 **a** 3 **b** $5a$ **c** cd **2** **a** $(x+1)$ **b** $(x-2)$
3 **a** $b(a+1)$ **b** $3x(x-2)$ **c** $-4c(1+3c)$
4 **a** $(x-y)(3-2x)$ **b** $(x+2)^2$
5 **a** $(x-4)(x-7)$ **b** $(2x+3)(3x-2)$
6 **a** $(x+2)(x+8)$ **b** $(x-3)(x+2)$ **c** $(x+4)(x-4)$
7 **a** $(2x+7)(x+1)$ **b** $(3x-5)(2x-3)$ **c** $(5x+1)(5x-1)$

REVIEW SET 13B

1 **a** $4y$ **b** d **c** ab **2** **a** $x(5-x)$ **b** $(x+2)$
3 **a** $7(2-b)$ **b** $2a(4a-3)$ **c** $xy(y-1)$
4 **a** $(2-x)(a-3)$ **b** $(x+y)(x-y-3)$
5 **a** $(x+6)(x-7)$ **b** $(2x-1)(x-4)$
6 **a** $(x-6)(x+4)$ **b** $(x-3)(x-8)$ **c** $(x+7)(x-7)$
7 **a** $(2x+1)(x+1)$ **b** $(3x+2)(x-3)$ **c** $(3x+2)(3x-2)$

PUZZLE
CONGRATULATIONS YOU CAN FACTORISE EXPRESSIONS NOW

EXERCISE 14A

1 **a** and **d**; **b** and **e** **2** **A** and **O**; **E**, **I** and **M**; **F** and **H**

3 **a** **i** FG **ii** $F\hat{G}H$ **b** **i** ON **ii** $O\hat{N}M$
c **i** QR **ii** $Q\hat{R}P$ **d** **i** TS **ii** $T\hat{S}R$
e **i** ON **ii** $O\hat{N}M$ **f** **i** FE **ii** $F\hat{E}D$

EXERCISE 14B

1 **a** A and C {SSS} **b** A and B {RHS} **c** B and C {AAcorS}
d A and C {SAS} **e** A and C {SAS} **f** B and C {RHS}
g A and C {SSS} **h** B and C {AAcorS}

2 **a** $\triangle PRQ \cong \triangle ZXY$ {SAS} **b** $\triangle ABC \cong \triangle LKM$ {SSS}
c $\triangle ABC \cong \triangle FED$ {AAcorS} **d** $\triangle ABC \cong \triangle EDF$ {AAcorS}
e $\triangle ABC \cong \triangle FED$ {AAcorS}
f Only one pair of sides and one angle are the same $\therefore$ $\triangle$s may or may not be congruent (not enough information).
g $\triangle ABC \cong \triangle PQR$ {SSS}
h $\triangle$s are similar {all angles equal} but may or may not be congruent (not enough information).
i α and β are common to both however sides EF and CB are equal but not corresponding $\therefore$ $\triangle$s are not congruent.
j $\triangle DEF \cong \triangle ZYX$ {RHS}

EXERCISE 14C

1 **a** $x = 0.8$ **b** $x \approx 1.13$ **c** $x \approx 0.71$
2 **a** $x = 8$ **b** $x = 8.75$ **c** $x = 4.8$ **d** $x \approx 3.18$

EXERCISE 14D

2 **a** $x = 2.4$ **b** $x = 2.8$ **c** $x \approx 3.27$ **d** $x = 9.6$
e $x = 11.2$ **f** $x = 5$ **g** $x \approx 6.67$ **h** $x = 7$ **i** $x = 7.2$

EXERCISE 14E

1 **a** 7 m **b** 7.5 m **2** 1.8 m **3** 7 m **4** 2.67 m
5 **a** **b** 176 cm

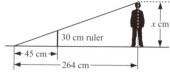

6 **a** $T\hat{E}M = K\hat{S}M = 90^o$; $T\hat{M}E = \angle K\hat{M}S$ {vert. opposite}
$\therefore$ $\triangle$s TEM and KSM are equiangular, i.e., similar
b 40 m

7 1.35 m **8** 116.7 m **9** 1013.3 m **10** 61.8 m

REVIEW SET 14A

1 **A**, **D** and **E**; **B** and **C**
2 **a** **A** and **B** {AAcorS} **b** **A** and **C** {AAcorS}
3 $x = 2.8$ **5** 66.7 m

REVIEW SET 14B

1 **a** FE **b** $F\hat{E}D$ **2** **a** yes {RHS} **b** no **c** no
3 **a** $x = 2\frac{1}{3}$ **h** $x = 3\frac{17}{20}$
4 **a** $x = 3$ **b** $x = 4$ **c** $x = 12$
5 **a** $\angle BAC = \angle NMC = 90^o$ {given}
$\angle C$ is common to both $\therefore$ $\triangle$s ABC and MNC are equiangular, i.e., similar
b $\dfrac{x}{8} = \dfrac{6}{15}$ $\therefore$ $x = \dfrac{48}{15} = 3.2$ **c** 6.4 cm

EXERCISE 15A

1 **a** 385 m^3 **b** 339 cm^3 **c** 320 cm^3 **d** 45 cm^3 **e** 704 cm^3
f 432 cm^3 **g** 254 cm^3 **h** 288 cm^3 **i** 2321 cm^3
2 **a** 670 cm^3 **b** 32 cm^3 **c** 288 cm^3 **d** 58.3 cm^3
e 85.3 cm^3 **f** 24 cm^3
3 **a** 125 m^3 **b** 1437 cm^3 **c** 262 cm^3
4 **a** $V = \frac{2}{3}\pi r^3$ **b** $V = \frac{2}{3}\pi r^3$ **c** $V = 3\pi r^3$

5 a

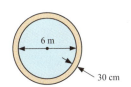

b 5.94 m^2

c 3.56 m^3

6 a 32.5 m^2 **b** 195 m^3 **7** 4500 m^3
8 a 30.8 m^3 **b** 34.7 m^3 **c** 65.5 m^3 **d** $9493.26
9 30 people **10** 1145 sinkers **11** 888 cm^3 **12** 116 029 cm^3
13 397 kg **14** 3.85 cm^3 **15** 1.79 m

EXERCISE 15B

1 a 22.1 kL **b** 23.6 kL **c** 186 kL
2 a 24.4 mL **b** $3.27 per mL
3 **A** costs $1.44 per litre, **B** costs $1.50 per litre ∴ **A** is better value
4 a 1.32 m^3 **b** 1.32 kL **c** 10.5 cm **5** 618 km
6 a 18.1 m^3 **b** 0.08 m^3 min^{-1} **c** 3 h 46 min
7 1.53 L **8** 0.101 L **9** 368 bottles **10** 22.6 kL
11 a 0.0209 kL **b** 6.98 minutes **c** 53 min 20 sec
12 8.33 cm **13** 72.6 cm

EXERCISE 15C

1 a 13.5 m^3 **b** 10 358 kg **c** €8804.39 **2** 3927 bottles
3 a 100 m^2 **b** $1650
4 a 2.54 cm^2 **b** 6362 cm^3 **c** 0.891 kg **5** 4.37 cm
6 8.00 cm **7** 1.42 m **8 a** 2149 kL **b** 18.1 m **c** 11.1 m

REVIEW SET 15A

1 a 729.17 cm^3 **b** 302.58 cm^3 **2** 65.4 cm^3
3 $V = \left(\frac{20}{3}\pi x^3\right)$ cm^3 **4** 50.75 m^3
5 a 19.8 m^3 **b** 19 800 L **c** 5 h 30 min **6** 27.5 kL
7 a 300 kL **b** 285 kL
8 a ≈ 2 590 000 m^3 **b** 6.9 × 10^6 tonnes **c** 188 kL

REVIEW SET 15B

1 a 339.29 cm^3 **b** 1272.35 cm^3 **c** 14 137.17 cm^3
2 256 cm^3 **3** $V = 10x^3$ cm^3 **4** 2.04 m^3
5 a 212 m^2 **b** $5 089 380
6 a 5.65 m^3 **b** 14.6 m^3 **c** 20.2 m^3 **d** 98.5 kL
7 a 210 900 kL **b** 39 m **c** 44 230 kL **d** 8579 kL **e** 263 709 kL

EXERCISE 16A

1 a i BC **ii** AC **iii** AB **b i** KM **ii** KL **iii** LM
c i PR **ii** QR **iii** PQ **d i** XZ **ii** XY **iii** YZ
e i CE **ii** DE **iii** CD **f i** ST **ii** RT **iii** RS
2 a i PR **ii** QR **iii** PQ **iv** PQ **v** QR
b i AC **ii** AB **iii** BC **iv** BC **v** AB

EXERCISE 16B

1 a i $\frac{3}{5}$ **ii** $\frac{4}{5}$ **iii** $\frac{3}{4}$ **b i** $\frac{5}{13}$ **ii** $\frac{12}{13}$ **iii** $\frac{5}{12}$
c i $\frac{12}{13}$ **ii** $\frac{5}{13}$ **iii** $\frac{12}{5}$ **d i** $\frac{3}{5}$ **ii** $\frac{4}{5}$ **iii** $\frac{3}{4}$
e i $\frac{4}{5}$ **ii** $\frac{3}{5}$ **iii** $\frac{4}{3}$ **f i** $\frac{7}{25}$ **ii** $\frac{24}{25}$ **iii** $\frac{7}{24}$
g i $\frac{15}{17}$ **ii** $\frac{8}{17}$ **iii** $\frac{15}{8}$ **h i** $\frac{5}{13}$ **ii** $\frac{12}{13}$ **iii** $\frac{5}{12}$
i i $\frac{24}{25}$ **ii** $\frac{7}{25}$ **iii** $\frac{24}{7}$

EXERCISE 16C

1 a $x = 5.74$ **b** $x = 1.53$ **c** $x = 47.55$
2 a $x = 8.6$ **b** $x = 200$ **c** $x = 117$
3 a $\theta = 38.7$ **b** $\theta = 39.8$ **c** $\theta = 28.1$

EXERCISE 16D

1 a $x = 5.14$ **b** $x = 10.1$ **c** $x = 74.9$
2 a $x = 56.1$ **b** $x = 15.5$ **c** $x = 17.3$
3 a $\theta = 66.4$ **b** $a = 41.4$ **c** $b = 48.2$

EXERCISE 16E

1 a $x = 2.70$ **b** $x = 10.07$ **c** $x = 8.90$
2 a $x = 15.0$ **b** $x = 44.4$ **c** $x = 16.9$
3 a $\phi = 63.43$ **b** $\phi = 29.74$ **c** $\phi = 56.31$

EXERCISE 16F

1 39.4° **2** 63.6 m **3** 65.5 m **4** 5.82 m **5** 4.76 m **6** 57.3°
7 5.64 m **8** 3.30° **9** 311.9 m **10** 12.2 m **11** 50.4 m
12 46 m **13** 33.6 m **14** 187 m **15** 32.7° **16** 53.7 m

EXERCISE 16G

1 a 040° **b** 235° **c** 297° **d** 132° **e** 225° **f** 337°
2 a 055° **b** 235° **c** 095° **d** 275° **e** 145° **f** 325°
3 a 220° **b** 055° **c** 117° **d** 312° **e** 045° **f** 157°

4 a

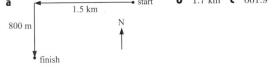

b 35 km **c** 31.5 km

5 a

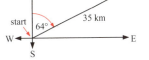

b 107.7 km **c** 111.8°

6 a

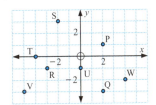

b 1.7 km **c** 061.9°

REVIEW SET 16A

1 a $x = 3.18$ **b** $x = 7.20$ **c** $x = 9.40$
2 a $\theta = 42$ **b** $\theta = 44$ **c** $\theta = 46$
3 a 97.5 cm **b** 3.15 m **4** 55.2 m **5** 2.10 m **6** 2.67 m
7 a 84 km **b** 48.2 km **c** 24.1 km h^{-1}
8 Yes, by about 11.5 cm. **9 a** 230° **b** 165° **c** 140°

REVIEW SET 16B

1 a $x = 9.95$ **b** $x = 22.45$ **c** $x = 3.02$
2 a $\theta = 46$ **b** $\theta = 23$ **3** 58.5 cm **4** 187 m
5 338.5 m **6** 37.8 m **7 a** 45.0 km h^{-1} **b** 302°
8 a

b 18.8 km

c 080.0°

EXERCISE 17A

1 J(4, 3), K(−2, −3), L(−4, 2), M(3, −1), N(0, 3)
2

3 a 1st **b** 4th **c** 3rd **d** 2nd
e None, it is on the negative x-axis.
f None, it is on the negative y-axis. **g** 3rd **h** 4th

4 a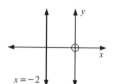

b

c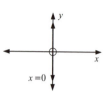

d

e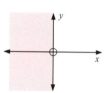

f

g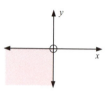

h

5 a 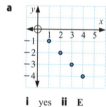   **b** 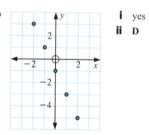   **i** yes   **ii** D

i yes   **ii** E

EXERCISE 17B

1 a 3 units **b** 3 units **c** 7 units **d** $\sqrt{34}$ units
  e $\sqrt{13}$ units **f** $2\sqrt{10}$ units **g** $2\sqrt{5}$ units **h** $\sqrt{37}$ units
2 a $2\sqrt{2}$ units **b** $\sqrt{13}$ units **c** $\sqrt{106}$ units
3 a $\sqrt{13}$ units **b** 8 units **c** $2\sqrt{5}$ units **d** 6 units
  e 8 units **f** $\sqrt{10}$ units **g** $2\sqrt{13}$ units **h** $\sqrt{5}$ units

EXERCISE 17C

1 a $(3, 2)$ **b** $(-1, 3)$ **c** $(1\frac{1}{2}, \frac{1}{2})$ **d** $(2\frac{1}{2}, -\frac{1}{2})$
  e $(-\frac{1}{2}, -2\frac{1}{2})$ **f** $(-2\frac{1}{2}, 2\frac{1}{2})$ **g** $(-2, 1)$ **h** $(2\frac{1}{2}, -\frac{1}{2})$
2 a $(5, 2)$ **b** $(2, 0)$ **c** $(-1, 2)$ **d** $(-3, 1\frac{1}{2})$ **e** $(2, 2\frac{1}{2})$
  f $(2, \frac{1}{2})$ **g** $(-\frac{1}{2}, -1\frac{1}{2})$ **h** $(-3, \frac{1}{2})$
3 a $(-4, -1)$ **b** $(3, -2)$ **c** $(2, 4)$ **d** $(0, -2)$ **e** $(-1, 3)$
  f $(-1, -5)$

EXERCISE 17D

1 a $\frac{1}{2}$ **b** 0 **c** 3 **d** $\frac{1}{2}$ **e** -1 **f** undefined **g** -3 **h** $-\frac{2}{3}$
2 a   **b**

c

d

e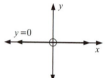

f

3 a $\frac{1}{3}$ **b** $\frac{1}{3}$ **c** $\frac{3}{2}$ **d** 0 **e** undefined **f** $\frac{1}{4}$ **g** $-\frac{4}{9}$ **h** -1

4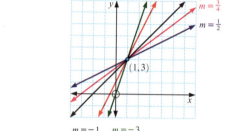

5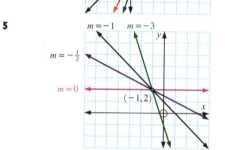

EXERCISE 17E

1 a Independent variable is the number of passengers.
Dependent variable is the total charge.

b

P	0	1	2	3	4	5
$C	200	225	250	275	300	325

P	6	7	8	9	10
$C	350	375	400	425	450

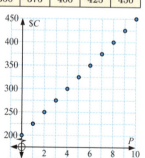

c Yes, it is linear.
d No, as we cannot have part of a passenger.
e $25 **f** **i** $200 **ii** $25 per passenger

2 a

n	0	1	2	3	4	5	6	7	8
€C	0	2.30	4.60	6.90	9.20	11.50	13.80	16.10	18.40

b

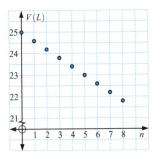

c Independent variable is the number of blocks of chocolate. Dependent variable is the total cost.

d Yes, it is linear.

e No, as only whole blocks of chocolate can be bought.

f €2.30 increase **g** €11.50 **h** 9 blocks

3 a

n	0	1	2	3	4	5	6	7	8
$V(L)$	25	24.6	24.2	23.8	23.4	23	22.6	22.2	21.8

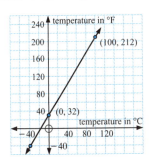

b Independent variable is the number of bowls of soup served. Dependent variable is the volume of soup remaining.

c Yes, it is linear.

d No, as only whole serves of soup are sold.

e 0.4 L decrease **f** 22.2 L **g** 9 customers

4 a, c

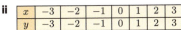

b Independent variable is the temperature in degrees Celsius. Dependent variable is the temperature in degrees Fahrenheit.

d −40°C **e i** 1.7°C **ii** −3.9°C

f

°F	50	68	86	104	20	10	0
°C	10	20	30	40	−6.7	−12.2	−17.8

EXERCISE 17F

1 a i Independent variable is x, dependent variable is y.

ii

x	−3	−2	−1	0	1	2	3
y	−3	−2	−1	0	1	2	3

iii

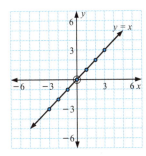

b i Independent variable is x, dependent variable is y.

ii

x	−3	−2	−1	0	1	2	3
y	−9	−6	−3	0	3	6	9

iii

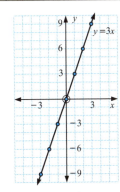

c i Independent variable is x, dependent variable is y.

ii

x	−3	−2	−1	0	1	2	3
y	−1	$-\frac{2}{3}$	$-\frac{1}{3}$	0	$\frac{1}{3}$	$\frac{2}{3}$	1

iii

d i Independent variable is x, dependent variable is y.

ii

x	−3	−2	−1	0	1	2	3
y	9	6	3	0	−3	−6	−9

iii

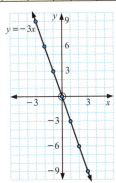

e i Independent variable is x, dependent variable is y.

ii

x	−3	−2	−1	0	1	2	3
y	−5	−3	−1	1	3	5	7

iii

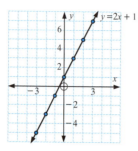

f i Independent variable is x, dependent variable is y.

ii

x	-3	-2	-1	0	1	2	3
y	7	5	3	1	-1	-3	-5

iii

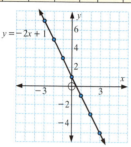

g i Independent variable is x, dependent variable is y.

ii

x	-3	-2	-1	0	1	2	3
y	$1\frac{1}{2}$	2	$2\frac{1}{2}$	3	$3\frac{1}{2}$	4	$4\frac{1}{2}$

iii

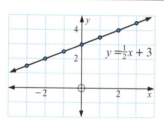

h i Independent variable is x, dependent variable is y.

ii

x	-3	-2	-1	0	1	2	3
y	$4\frac{1}{2}$	4	$3\frac{1}{2}$	3	$2\frac{1}{2}$	2	$1\frac{1}{2}$

iii

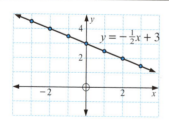

2 b, a, c; coefficient of x **3** the sign of the coefficient of x
4 the constant term

EXERCISE 17G

1 a $y = 4x - 1$ **b** $y = 2x + 3$ **c** $y = -3x$ **d** $y = -5x + \frac{1}{2}$
2 a gradient 2, y-intercept -3 **b** gradient -1, y-intercept 0
c gradient -1, y-intercept 6 **d** gradient $\frac{1}{2}$, y-intercept 1
e gradient $\frac{3}{2}$, y-intercept 0 **f** gradient $\frac{1}{2}$, y-intercept $-\frac{1}{2}$
g gradient $\frac{2}{3}$, y-intercept -3 **h** gradient $-\frac{3}{4}$, y-intercept 3

3 a $y = 3x - 5$ **b** $y = -2x - 9$ **c** $y = -3x + 13$
d $y = \frac{1}{3}x - \frac{1}{3}$ **e** $y = -\frac{1}{4}x + \frac{15}{2}$ **f** $y = -3$
g $y = \frac{2}{3}x + \frac{16}{3}$ **h** $y = \frac{3}{5}x + 7$ **i** $y = -\frac{1}{4}x + 2$
j $y = -\frac{3}{4}x + 4$ **k** $y = 3x + 2$ **l** $y = -5x + 24$

4 a $y = x + 4$ **b** $y = \frac{1}{2}x + 4$ **c** $y = -2$ **d** $y = -\frac{1}{3}x +$
e $y = \frac{1}{5}x - \frac{9}{5}$ **f** $y = x - 1$

5 a $y = \frac{1}{2}x + 3$ **b** $y = 2x + 6$ **c** $y = \frac{2}{5}x - 2$
d $y = -2x - 2$

6 a 4 **b** -3 **c** 0 **d** undefined **e** $\frac{4}{3}$ **f** -6 **g** $\frac{4}{5}$
h $-\frac{4}{5}$ **i** 3 **j** $-\frac{3}{4}$ **k** $\frac{A}{B}$ **l** $-\frac{A}{B}$

7 a $y = \frac{2}{3}x + 2$ **b** $y = \frac{5}{4}x - 2$ **c** $y = -\frac{3}{5}x + 3$
d $y = x + 5$ **e** $y = -\frac{5}{3}x - \frac{10}{3}$ **f** $y = -\frac{5}{7}x - \frac{15}{7}$

8 a $Y = \frac{1}{3}X + 4$ **b** $N = \frac{2}{3}x - 2$ **c** $G = -\frac{3}{4}s + 3$
d $H = -g + 2$ **e** $V = \frac{3}{10}t + 5$ **f** $P = -\frac{1}{3}t - 2$

EXERCISE 17H

1 a

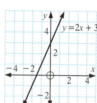

b

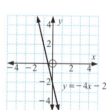

c

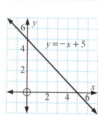

d

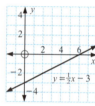

e

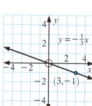

f

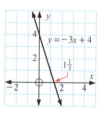

g

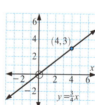

h

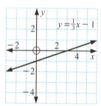

i

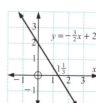

2 a

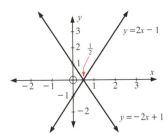

b

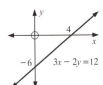

b

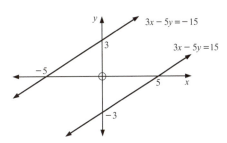

EXERCISE 17I

1 a yes **b** no **c** yes **2 a** $k = -4$ **b** $k = 1$
3 a $a = 7$ **b** $a = 9$ **c** $a = 5$ **d** $a = 8$

EXERCISE 17J

1 a horizontal line   **b** vertical line

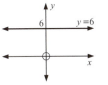

c vertical line   **d** horizontal line

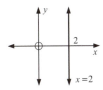

2 a horizontal line **b** vertical line
3 a $y = 0$ **b** $x = 0$ **c** $y = -3$ **d** $x = 4$
4 a $y = 3$ **b** $x = 4$

EXERCISE 17K

1 a -2 **b** $-\frac{5}{2}$ **c** $-\frac{1}{3}$ **d** $-\frac{1}{7}$ **e** $\frac{5}{2}$ **f** $\frac{3}{7}$ **g** $\frac{1}{5}$ **h** 1
2 c, d, f and **h** are perpendicular
3 a $a = 13$ **b** $a = -4$ **c** $a = 1\frac{2}{7}$
4 a $t = 0$ **b** $t = 5$ **c** $t = \frac{2}{5}$
5 a $t = 4$ **b** $t = 4$ **c** $t = 14$ **d** $t = 3\frac{1}{7}$

EXERCISE 17L

1 a $2\frac{1}{2}$ **b** Inge swims $2\frac{1}{2}$ metres per second.
   c Inge's speed is constant as the gradient is constant.
2 a 105 km h^{-1} **b i** 115 km h^{-1} **ii** 126.7 km h^{-1}
   c From time 2 hours until time 5 hours.
3 a The y-intercept $(0, 40)$ indicates that taxi drivers earn a base
     rate of \$40 before doing any work.
   b The gradient of 18 means that a taxi driver earns \$18 per
     hour of work.
   c i \$148 **ii** \$310 **d** \$23 per hour
4 a A has gradient $\frac{350}{29} = 12\frac{2}{29}$; B has gradient $\frac{320}{33} = 9\frac{23}{33}$
   b A travels $12\frac{2}{29}$ km per litre of fuel; B travels $9\frac{23}{33}$ km per
     litre of fuel.
   c \$25.13 more
5 a \$3 base charge
   b AB has gradient $1\frac{1}{2}$; BC has gradient 1. These gradients
     indicate the charge per kilometre travelled.
   c AC has gradient $1\frac{1}{5}$ which means that the average charge is
     \$1.20 per kilometre travelled.

3 a 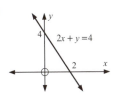 **b**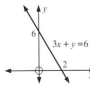

c **d**

e **f**

g 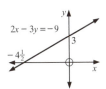 **h**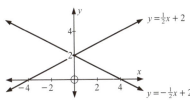

i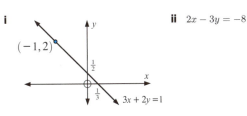

4 a i   **ii** $2x - 3y = -8$

REVIEW SET 17A

1

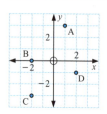

2 a 5 units **b** $\sqrt{13}$ units **3** $(5, -1)$ **4 a** $\frac{2}{5}$ **b** $-3\frac{3}{4}$

5 a Independent variable is the number of saws.
Dependent variable is the total cost.

b

x	0	100	200	300	400
$C	2000	2400	2800	3200	3600

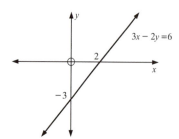

c Yes, it is linear.

d $2000 is the set-up cost, i.e., the cost before any saws are produced.

e $4600

6 a

x	0	1	2	3	4
y	2	5	8	11	14

b

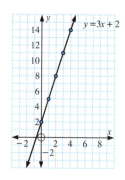

7 $y = -2x + 3$ **8** gradient $-\frac{1}{3}$, y-intercept $\frac{1}{3}$ **9** $y = \frac{2}{3}x + 6$

10

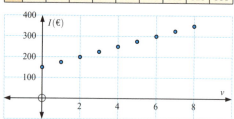

11 $k = -11$ **12** $y = -4$ **13** $t = 2\frac{4}{5}$

14 a i 40 km h^{-1} **ii** 90 km h^{-1} **iii** 20 km h^{-1}
b i 40 **ii** 90 **iii** 20
The gradients are the same as the average speeds in **a**.
c 60 km h^{-1}

REVIEW SET 17B

1 a

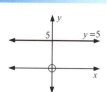

b

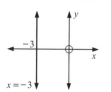

c

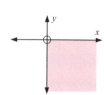

2 $3\sqrt{10}$ units **3** B is $(5, -4)$ **4 a** -1 **b** undefined

5 a Independent variable is the number of vacuum cleaners sold.
Dependent variable is the income earned.

b

v	0	1	2	3	4	5	6	7	8
€I	150	175	200	225	250	275	300	325	350

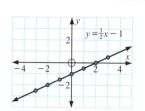

c Yes, it is linear.

d No, as Jacques can only sell whole vacuum cleaners. **e** €25

f i €150 **ii** €25 per vacuum cleaner sold **g** €275

6

x	-3	-2	-1	0	1	2	3
y	$-2\frac{1}{2}$	-2	$-1\frac{1}{2}$	-1	$-\frac{1}{2}$	0	$\frac{1}{2}$

7 a $y = 3$ **b** $x = -1$ **c** $y = \frac{8}{5}x + 20$ **8** $y = 4x - 2$

9 a gradient 5, y-intercept -7 **b** gradient $-\frac{3}{2}$, y-intercept 6
c gradient 10, y-intercept 0

10 $-\frac{4}{3}$ **11** $y = \frac{1}{3}x - \frac{16}{3}$ **12 a** 2 **b** $y = -\frac{1}{2}x + 3$

13 a The value of 60 at A indicates that the plumber charges a call-out fee of $60.

b AB has gradient 50; BC has gradient 40
These gradients indicate the average hourly charge for a job lasting 3 hours (AB) or 5 hours (AB + BC).

c AC has gradient 46 which means that the plumber charges an average of $46 per hour for a job lasting 5 hours.

EXERCISE 18A

1 a $(2, 2)$ **b** $(1, -3)$ **c** $(0, 3)$ **d** $(1, -2)$ **e** $(2, 1)$
f $(-2, 7)$

2 a $x = -4$, $y = -6$ **b** $x = 3$, $y = 4$ **c** $x = \frac{1}{2}$, $y = 4\frac{1}{2}$
d $x = 1$, $y = -3$ **e** $x = 1$, $y = 5$ **f** $x = -2$, $y = -9$

EXERCISE 18B

1 a $x = -4, y = -6$ **b** $x = 5, y = 7$ **c** $x = 2, y = 6$
d $x = -4, y = -7$ **e** $x = -2, y = -8$ **f** no solution
g $x = 1, y = 5$ **h** no solution **i** $x = \frac{2}{5}, y = 0$
2 a $(\frac{1}{2}, 4\frac{1}{2})$ **b** $(3, 4)$ **c** $(2, -1)$ **d** $(0, -4)$ **e** $(-1, -1)$
f $(0, 6)$

EXERCISE 18C

1 a $x = 2, y = 5$ **b** $x = 3, y = 1$ **c** $x = 0, y = 5$
d $x = 5, y = 9$ **e** $x = 0, y = 4$ **f** $x = 2, y = 1$
2 a $x = 5, y = 3$ **b** $x = 1, y = \frac{2}{5}$ **c** $x = 2, y = 1\frac{1}{3}$
d $x = 5, y = -2$ **e** $x = -3, y = -\frac{1}{2}$ **f** $x = -4\frac{1}{2}, y = -3\frac{1}{2}$
3 a reduces to $5 = 7$ which is never true
b no solution - the two lines are parallel (same gradient)
∴ they never intersect
4 a reduces to $8x + 6 = 8x + 6$ which is always true
b infinite number of solutions - the lines are coincident
5 a $11x = 11$ **b** $4y = 12$ **c** $9x = 9$ **d** $9x = 6$
e $-y = 11$ **f** $-11y = -11$
6 a $x = 2, y = 6$ **b** $x = 1, y = -2$ **c** $x = -1, y = -3$
d $x = 1, y = -5$ **e** $x = 2, y = -2$ **f** $x = -3, y = 1$
7 a $10x + 25y = 5$ **b** $-3x + y = -4$ **c** $3x - 21y = 24$
d $-10x - 8y = -18$ **e** $-18x - 12y = 12$
f $-16x + 8y = -12$
8 a $x = 5, y = -2$ **b** $x = 1, y = 2$ **c** $x = 1, y = -6$
d $x = 5, y = 1$ **e** $x = 1, y = 1$ **f** $x = -3, y = 4$
g $x = 2, y = -3$ **h** $x = 1, y = -1$ **i** $x = -5, y = -4$
9 a infinite number of solutions, lines are coincident
b no solution, lines are parallel

EXERCISE 18D

1 56 and 16 **2** 22 and 8 **3** 17 and 51
4 fish costs £2.20 each, chips cost £0.75 per serve
5 coffee costs €2.90 per cup, muffins cost €1.25 each
6 30, 50-cent coins; 26, 10-cent coins
7 André has €26.10, Michelle has €39.15
8 33, 600 mL cartons; 60, 1 L cartons **9** $a = 3, b = 5$
10 length 18 cm, width 10 cm

EXERCISE 18E

1 a $y = 10 - 5x$ **b** $y = 8 - 4x$ **c** $y = 12 - 2x$
d $y = \dfrac{6 - 2x}{3}$ **e** $y = \dfrac{12 - 4x}{3}$ **f** $y = \dfrac{10 - 7x}{3}$
g $y = \dfrac{-7 - 2x}{9}$ **h** $y = \dfrac{88 - 11x}{8}$ **i** $y = \dfrac{40 - 16x}{5}$
2 a $y = 5x - 5$ **b** $y = 2x - 3$ **c** $y = 9x - 18$
d $y = \dfrac{2x - 7}{3}$ **e** $y = \dfrac{4x - 5}{3}$ **f** $y = \dfrac{6x - 20}{5}$
g $y = \dfrac{3x - 14}{7}$ **h** $y = \dfrac{8x - 3}{11}$ **i** $y = \dfrac{11x - 33}{9}$
3 a $(16, -2)$ **b** $(-14, 5)$ **c** $(21, 9)$ **d** $(-5, 15)$
e $(15, -7)$ **f** $(22, -13)$
4 a 18 giraffes, 21 ostriches **b** 17 chairs, 6 stools
c one apple costs 65 cents, one orange costs 85 cents
d eleven 1.5 m lengths, twelve 4 m lengths
e CDs cost RM12.50 each, DVDs cost RM19.95 each
f small bags weigh 2 kg each, large bags weigh 5 kg each

REVIEW SET 18A

1 a $(-2, -4)$ **b** $(1, -2)$ **2** $x = 2, y = 7$ **3** $x = -1, y = 3$
4 infinite number of solutions (the two lines are coincident)
5 $x = 2, y = -1$
6 adult tickets cost $18 each, student tickets cost $12 each
7 14, 50 pence coins; 7, 20 pence coins

REVIEW SET 18B

1 a $(1, 4)$ **b** $(1\frac{1}{2}, -2)$ **2** $x = -2, y = -2$
3 $x = -4, y = -16$
4 no solution - the two lines are parallel (same gradient) ∴ they never intersect
5 $x = 1, y = 0$ **6** 5 and 17
7 sausages cost $0.80 each, chops cost $2.50 each

EXERCISE 19A

1 0.55 **2** 0.84 **3** 0.0894 **4** 0.256 **5** 0.331
6 a 0.243 **b** 0.486

EXERCISE 19B

1 a $\frac{1}{6}$ **b** $\frac{1}{2}$ **c** 1 **d** $\frac{1}{6}$ **e** $\frac{5}{6}$ **f** 0
2 a $\frac{1}{3}$ **b** $\frac{5}{6}$ **c** $\frac{2}{3}$ **d** $\frac{2}{3}$ **e** $\frac{1}{6}$ **f** $\frac{5}{6}$
3 a $\frac{2}{5}$ **b** $\frac{1}{5}$ **c** $\frac{4}{5}$ **d** $\frac{4}{5}$ **4 a** $\frac{1}{2}$ **b** $\frac{1}{10}$ **c** $\frac{9}{10}$
5 a i $\frac{1}{3}$ **ii** 0 **b** $\frac{3}{5}$
6 a $\frac{1}{5}$ **b** $\frac{7}{30}$ **c** $\frac{2}{5}$ **d** $\frac{1}{30}$ **e** $\frac{2}{15}$ **f** $\frac{1}{6}$
7 a $\frac{1}{7}$ **b** $\frac{2}{7}$ **c** $\frac{1}{12}$ or $\frac{31}{365}$ or $\frac{124}{1461}$ **d** $\frac{1}{6}$ or $\frac{59}{365}$ or $\frac{237}{1461}$
8 a one red, one any colour other than red or black
b both squares any colour other than red or yellow

EXERCISE 19C

1 65 days **2 a** $\frac{1}{4}$ **b** 75 times **3 a** 0.36 **b** 26 backs
4 125 **5 a** 100 **b** 200 **c** 400 **d** 500
6 a i $\frac{1}{6}$ **ii** $\frac{1}{3}$ **iii** $\frac{1}{2}$ **b i** $1.33 **ii** $0.50 **iii** $3.50
c lose 50 cents **d** lose $50

EXERCISE 19D

1 a 407 people **b**
c i 0.229
ii 0.201
iii 0.307

Brand	Freq	Rel Freq
Silktouch	125	0.307
Super	107	0.263
Just Soap	93	0.229
Indulgence	82	0.201
Total	407	1

2 a

Outcome	Freq	Rel Freq
0 heads	121	0.247
1 head	259	0.530
2 heads	109	0.223
Total	489	1

b i 0.247
ii 0.530
iii 0.223

3 a 1083 people **b**
c i 0.25
ii 0.75

Colour	Freq	Rel Freq
Green	361	0.25
Red	1083	0.75
Total	1444	1

4 a 5235 tickets **b**
c 0.207

Ticket Type	Freq	Rel Freq
Adult	3762	0.719
Concession	1084	0.207
Child	389	0.074
Total	5235	1

5 a

Councillor	Freq	Rel Freq
Mr Tony Trimboli	2167	0.361
Mrs Andrea Sims	724	0.121
Mrs Sara Chong	2389	0.398
Mr John Henry	720	0.12
Total	6000	1

b 0.519

EXERCISE 19E

1 a {A, B, C, D}　**b** {BB, BG, GB, GG}

　c {ABCD, ABDC, ACBD, ACDB, ADBC, ADCB,
　　　BACD, BADC, BCAD, BCDA, BDAC, BDCA,
　　　CABD, CADB, CBAD, CBDA, CDAB, CDBA,
　　　DABC, DACB, DBAC, DBCA, DCAB, DCBA}

　d {GGG, GGB, GBG, BGG, GBB, BGB, BBG, BBB}

　e i {HH, HT, TH, TT}

　　ii {HHH, HHT, HTH, THH, HTT, THT, TTH, TTT}

　　iii {HHHH, HHHT, HHTH, HTHH, THHH, HHTT,
　　　　HTHT, HTTH, THHT, THTH, TTHH, HTTT,
　　　　THTT, TTHT, TTTH, TTTT}

2 a
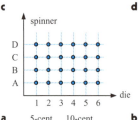

　b
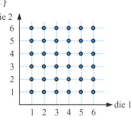

　c
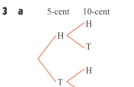

　d
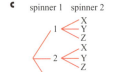

3 a
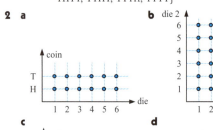

　b

　c

　d

　e
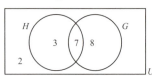

4

EXERCISE 19F

1 a {ODG, OGD, DOG, DGO, GOD, GDO}

　b i $\frac{1}{6}$　**ii** $\frac{1}{3}$　**iii** $\frac{2}{3}$　**iv** $\frac{1}{3}$

2 a $\frac{17}{43}$　**b** $\frac{5}{43}$　**c** $\frac{24}{43}$　**d** $\frac{19}{43}$　**e** $\frac{19}{43}$　**f** $\frac{17}{24}$　**g** $\frac{5}{17}$

3
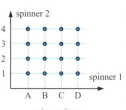
　a $\frac{1}{4}$　**b** $\frac{1}{4}$
　c $\frac{1}{2}$　**d** $\frac{3}{4}$

4 a

　b 10 outcomes　**c i** $\frac{1}{10}$　**ii** $\frac{3}{10}$　**iii** $\frac{2}{5}$　**iv** $\frac{3}{5}$

5 {ABK, AKB, BAK, BKA, KAB, KBA}

　a $\frac{1}{3}$　**b** $\frac{1}{3}$　**c** $\frac{1}{3}$　**d** $\frac{2}{3}$

6 a {GGG, GGB, GBG, BGG, GBB, BGB, BBG, BBB}

　b i $\frac{1}{8}$　**ii** $\frac{1}{8}$　**iii** $\frac{1}{8}$　**iv** $\frac{3}{8}$　**v** $\frac{1}{2}$　**vi** $\frac{7}{8}$

7 a $\frac{3}{8}$　**b** $\frac{19}{24}$

8 a {PQRS, PQSR, PRQS, PRSQ, PSQR, PSRQ, QPRS, QPSR,
　　QRPS, QRSP, QSPR, QSRP, RPQS, RPSQ, RQPS, RQSP,
　　RSPQ, RSQP, SPQR, SPRQ, SQPR, SQRP, SRPQ, SRQP}

　b i $\frac{1}{2}$　**ii** $\frac{1}{2}$　**iii** $\frac{1}{2}$　**iv** $\frac{1}{2}$

9 a
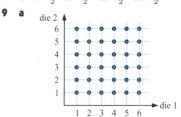

　b i $\frac{1}{18}$　**ii** $\frac{1}{6}$　**iii** $\frac{11}{36}$　**iv** $\frac{5}{9}$　**v** $\frac{1}{4}$　**vi** $\frac{1}{6}$

10 a $\frac{4}{15}$　**b** $\frac{3}{10}$　**c** $\frac{7}{10}$

11 {HHHH, HHHT, HHTH, HTHH, THHH, HHTT, HTHT, HTTH,
　　THTH, TTHH, THHT, TTTH, TTHT, THTT, HTTT, TTTT}

　a $\frac{1}{16}$　**b** $\frac{3}{8}$　**c** $\frac{5}{16}$　**d** $\frac{15}{16}$　**e** $\frac{1}{4}$

12 a
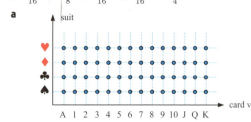

　b i $\frac{1}{13}$　**ii** $\frac{1}{52}$　**iii** $\frac{1}{4}$　**iv** $\frac{3}{13}$　**v** $\frac{1}{26}$　**vi** $\frac{1}{2}$　**vii** $\frac{4}{13}$
　　viii 0

13 a $\frac{11}{14}$　**b** $\frac{9}{28}$　**c** $\frac{1}{28}$

EXERCISE 19G

1 a $\frac{8}{21}$　**b** $\frac{1}{7}$　**c** $\frac{2}{7}$　**2 a** 0.0441　**b** 0.6241

3 a $\frac{2}{15}$　**b** $\frac{2}{5}$　**c** $\frac{1}{5}$　**d** $\frac{4}{15}$

4 a i 0.405　**ii** 0.595　**b** 0.164　**c** 0.354

EXERCISE 19H

1 a

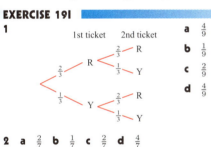

1st spin   2nd spin

b $\frac{1}{4}$

c $\frac{1}{16}$

d $\frac{5}{8}$

e $\frac{3}{4}$

2 a i $\frac{5}{9}$ **ii** $\frac{4}{9}$

b

tile 1   tile 2

c i $\frac{25}{81}$

ii $\frac{16}{81}$

iii $\frac{20}{81}$

iv $\frac{40}{81}$

3 a

$\frac{1}{4}$ rain $\begin{cases} \frac{2}{5} \text{ win} \\ \frac{3}{5} \text{ lose} \end{cases}$

$\frac{3}{4}$ no rain $\begin{cases} \frac{1}{20} \text{ win} \\ \frac{19}{20} \text{ lose} \end{cases}$

b $\frac{11}{80}$

4 0.034 **5** $\frac{23}{60}$ **6 a** $\frac{11}{30}$ **b** $\frac{19}{30}$

EXERCISE 19I

1

1st ticket   2nd ticket

$\frac{2}{3}$ R $\begin{cases} \frac{2}{3} \text{ R} \\ \frac{1}{3} \text{ Y} \end{cases}$

$\frac{1}{3}$ Y $\begin{cases} \frac{2}{3} \text{ R} \\ \frac{1}{3} \text{ Y} \end{cases}$

a $\frac{4}{9}$

b $\frac{1}{9}$

c $\frac{2}{9}$

d $\frac{4}{9}$

2 a $\frac{2}{7}$ **b** $\frac{1}{7}$ **c** $\frac{2}{7}$ **d** $\frac{4}{7}$

3 a $\frac{3}{28}$ **b** $\frac{5}{14}$ **c** $\frac{15}{56}$ **d** $\frac{15}{56}$

These cases cover all possibilities, so their probabilities must add up to 1.

4 a

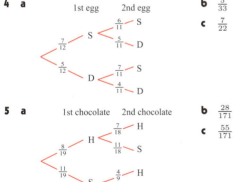

1st egg   2nd egg

b $\frac{5}{33}$

c $\frac{7}{22}$

5 a

1st chocolate   2nd chocolate

$\frac{8}{19}$ H $\begin{cases} \frac{7}{18} \text{ H} \\ \frac{11}{18} \text{ S} \end{cases}$

$\frac{11}{19}$ S $\begin{cases} \frac{4}{9} \text{ H} \\ \frac{5}{9} \text{ S} \end{cases}$

b $\frac{28}{171}$

c $\frac{55}{171}$

6 a $\frac{1}{25}$ **b** $\frac{24}{25}$ **c** $\frac{8}{199}$

EXERCISE 19J

1 a A and B, A and D, A and E, A and F, B and D, B and F, C and D

b i $\frac{2}{3}$ **ii** $\frac{5}{6}$ **iii** $\frac{2}{3}$ **iv** $\frac{1}{2}$ **v** 1 **vi** $\frac{5}{6}$

2 a

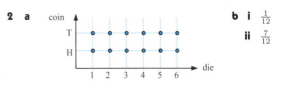

coin

b i $\frac{1}{12}$

ii $\frac{7}{12}$

c $P(H) + P(5) - P(H \text{ and } 5) = \frac{6}{12} + \frac{2}{12} - \frac{1}{12} = \frac{7}{12} = P(H \text{ or } 5)$

3 a

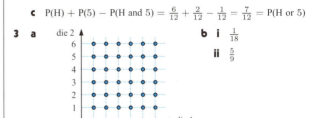

die 2

b i $\frac{1}{18}$

ii $\frac{5}{9}$

c $P(3) + P(4) - P(3 \text{ and } 4) = \frac{11}{36} + \frac{11}{36} - \frac{2}{36} = \frac{5}{9} = P(3 \text{ or } 4)$

EXERCISE 19K

1 a $\frac{1}{12}$ **b** $\frac{1}{4}$ **c** $\frac{5}{12}$ **2 a** $\frac{1}{36}$ **b** $\frac{1}{9}$ **c** $\frac{4}{9}$ **d** $\frac{1}{18}$

3 a 0.0103 **b** 0.00104 **4 a** $\frac{1}{16}$ **b** $\frac{1}{16}$ **c** $\frac{1}{16}$

5 a 0.7353 **b** 0.0007 **c** 0.9993

6 a 0.72 **b** 0.02 **c** 0.26

REVIEW SET 19A

1 a $\frac{47}{384}$ **b** $\frac{337}{384}$

2 a $\frac{1}{3}$ **3 a**

die 2

b i $\frac{1}{9}$

b 0

ii $\frac{7}{18}$

c $\frac{2}{3}$

iii $\frac{1}{9}$

d $\frac{1}{2}$

iv $\frac{1}{3}$

e $\frac{1}{2}$

v $\frac{3}{4}$

die 1

4 10 times

5 a

Student	Freq	Rel Freq
Chen	179	0.216
Hendry	213	0.258
Shustrai	168	0.203
McKay	267	0.323
Total	827	1

b i $\frac{4}{827} \approx 0.00484$

ii 0.323

6 a {GGG, GGB, GBG, BGG, GBB, BGB, BBG, BBB}

b i $\frac{1}{8}$ **ii** $\frac{7}{8}$ **iii** $\frac{3}{8}$

7 a $\frac{21}{43}$ **b** $\frac{15}{43}$ **c** $\frac{8}{43}$ **d** $\frac{13}{43}$ **e** $\frac{28}{43}$

8 a

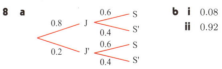

b i 0.08

ii 0.92

REVIEW SET 19B

1 a $\frac{1}{4}$ **b** 22 times **2 a** $\frac{1}{6}$ **b** $\frac{5}{12}$

3 a

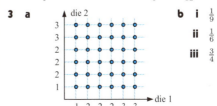

die 2

b i $\frac{1}{9}$

ii $\frac{1}{6}$

iii $\frac{3}{4}$

4 a Two events are said to be independent if one event does not affect the outcome of the other event.

b i For example, rolling a die and tossing a coin.

ii For example, selecting two tickets from a bag where the first ticket is not replaced.

5 a 0.216 **b** 0.064 **c** 0.096

6 a

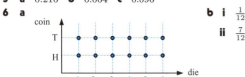

b i $\frac{1}{12}$

ii $\frac{7}{12}$

c $P(T) + P(2) - P(T \text{ and } 2) = \frac{6}{12} + \frac{2}{12} - \frac{1}{12} = \frac{7}{12} = P(T \text{ or } 2)$

7 a

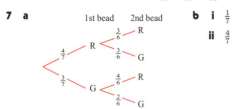

b i $\frac{1}{7}$

ii $\frac{4}{7}$

8 a

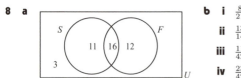

b i $\frac{8}{21}$

ii $\frac{13}{14}$

iii $\frac{11}{42}$

iv $\frac{23}{42}$

EXERCISE 20A

1 a E **b** E **c** yes: B and C

d The more training an employee has, the more productive they are.

2 a A **b** A **c** yes: B and C

d The less sleep an employee has, the more likely they are to have an accident.

3 a Josie is travelling with constant speed {shown by AB}. Realising she is running late, she quickens her speed a little {shown by BC}. Now back on time, she slows to her usual speed {shown by CD}. She slows to a stop {shown by DE}. She delivers her parcel, and awaits further instruction {shown by E ....}.

b Josie is at her delivery base awaiting instructions {shown by AB}. She is given parcels to deliver, so she begins to move {shown by BC}. She travels with a constant speed {shown by CD}. She slows to a stop {shown by DE}. She delivers a parcel {shown by EF}. She increases her speed to her usual rate {shown by FG}. She travels with a constant speed toward her next destination {shown by G ....}.

5 a The bath is filling for one minute, at which time someone gets in. The person immediately turns off the taps and soaks for two minutes. The person then turns the tap on for one minute, then soaks for a further three minutes. The person gets out of the bath and lets the water out, taking 1 minute.

b A person gets in the bath then fills it, taking two minutes. The taps are turned off and the person soaks for three minutes. The person gets out of the bath and leaves the water for two minutes. The water is then let out of the bath, taking 1 minute.

6 a

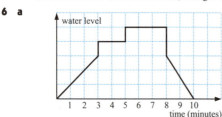

b

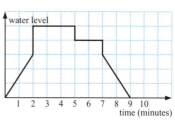

EXERCISE 20B

1 a 11 am **b** 8 pm

c The number of shoppers in the store increased by 25.

d 28 people

e The graph shows the exact number of shoppers in the store at each hour, but only estimates the number in between.

2 a 39°C **b** 16 minutes **c** 25°C **d i** 18°C **ii** 8°C

3 a i 50 km **ii** 5 km **b** 1 min 40 sec **c** 6 laps

d 2 minutes **e** 161 km h^{-1}

EXERCISE 20C

1 a i 211 USD **ii** 170 USD **b i** 73 euros **ii** 183 euros

2 a i 28 miles **ii** 17.5 miles **b i** 77 km **ii** 48 km

3 a 100°C **b i** 104°F **ii** 167°F **iii** 32°F

EXERCISE 20D

1 a The number of kg of tomatoes produced is increasing with time.

b 2001 and 2005 are outliers
A low yield might be due to a very cold year or pests; a high yield might be due to excellent fertiliser and warmer conditions.

c 23 kg, should be fairly accurate as it follows the overall trend of the previous data values.

2 a Participation in sport is decreasing each year.

b 2004 is an outlier. A large sporting event such as the Olympic Games that year may have inspired more students to participate in sport.

c Less exercise at school may lead to an increase in obesity, and heart disease in later life.

3 a

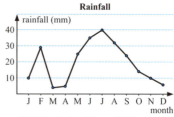

b Highest rainfall is during June and July with July having the maximum. Rainfall declines over the other months except in February when it increases dramatically. A study of one year is not enough to establish a pattern.

c February was an outlier with a lot of rain. This could have been the result of a large tropical storm.

4 a

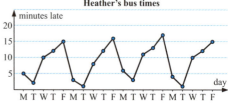

b The bus is latest on Fridays and earliest on Mondays and Tuesdays. There could be a different driver on Mondays and Tuesdays from the rest of the week.

c She should be able to sleep in 10 minutes on Thursdays and Fridays.

EXERCISE 20E

1 a i $2 **ii** $8 **iii** $12 **b i** 4 hours **ii** 10 hours
 c 5 hours < time ≤ 6 hours

2 a i CHF5 **ii** CHF10 **c**

Weight (kg)	Cost (CHF)
$0 < w \leqslant 0.5$	5
$0.5 < w \leqslant 1$	8
$1 < w \leqslant 2$	10
$2 < w \leqslant 3$	11

 b 2 kg

3 a i $470 **ii** $610 **b** $123\,000 \leqslant$ value $< 141\,000$

EXERCISE 20F

1 a

one-one

b

many-many

c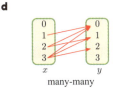

one-many

d

many-many

e

one-one

2 a {real numbers} **b** {multiples of 2 which are not multiples of 4}
 c {positive real numbers} **d** {real numbers $\geqslant 10$}
 e {all integers} **f** {real numbers between 0 and 1 (inclusive)}

EXERCISE 20G

1 a $\{2, 3, 5, 10, 12\}$ **b** $\{0, \frac{1}{2}, 2\}$ **c** $\{y \mid -3 < y < 5\}$
 d $\{y \mid -27 \leqslant y \leqslant 64\}$

2 a Domain is $\{x \mid -2 \leqslant x \leqslant 4\}$. Range is $\{y \mid 0 \leqslant y \leqslant 3\}$.
 b Domain is $\{x \mid -3 < x \leqslant 4\}$. Range is $\{y \mid -1 < y \leqslant 2\}$.
 c Domain is $\{x \mid x \in \mathbb{R}\}$. Range is $\{y \mid y \leqslant 4\}$.
 d Domain is $\{x \mid -3 \leqslant x \leqslant 5\}$. Range is $\{y \mid -7 \leqslant y \leqslant 4\}$.
 e Domain is $\{x \mid -3 \leqslant x < 4\}$. Range is $\{y \mid 0.2 \leqslant y < 6\}$.
 f Domain is $\{x \mid -5 \leqslant x < 7\}$. Range is $\{y \mid -4 \leqslant y < 5\}$.
 g Domain is $\{x \mid x \in \mathbb{R}\}$. Range is $\{y \mid 0 \leqslant y \leqslant 1\}$.
 h Domain is $\{x \mid -5 < x \leqslant 6\}$. Range is $\{y \mid -3 \leqslant y \leqslant 4\}$.

3 a i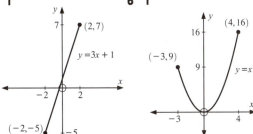

ii Range is $\{y \mid -5 \leqslant y \leqslant 7\}$.

b i

ii Range is $\{y \mid 0 \leqslant y \leqslant 16\}$.

c i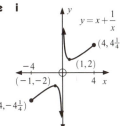

ii Range is $\{y \mid \frac{1}{4} \leqslant y \leqslant 8\}$.

d i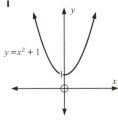

ii Range is $\{y \mid y \leqslant -1 \text{ or } y \geqslant \frac{1}{2}\}$.

e i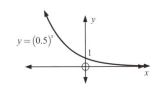

ii Range is $\{y \mid y \leqslant -2 \text{ or } y \geqslant 2\}$.

f i

ii Range is $\{y \mid y \geqslant 1\}$.

g i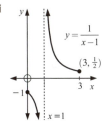

ii Range is $\{y \mid y > 0\}$.

4 a $y = x + 5, x \in D$ **b** $y = x + 7, x \in D$
 c $y = 6 - x, x \in D$ **d** $y = x^2, x \in D$ **e** $y = x^2, x \in D$
 f $y = \sqrt{x}, x \in D$ **g** $y = 2x + 1, x \in D$ **h** $y = \frac{1}{x}, x \in D$
 i $y = 3x - 7, x \in D$ **j** $y = 5 - 2x, x \in D$ **k** $y = 2^x, x \in D$
 l $y = x^2 + 1, x \in D$ **m** $y = 43 - 3x, x \in D$

EXERCISE 20H

1 a $f(5) = 8$ which means that 5 is mapped onto 8 and $(5, 8)$ lies on the graph of the function f.
 b $g(3) = -6$ which means that 3 is mapped onto -6 and $(3, -6)$ lies on the graph of the function g.
 c $H(4) = 4\frac{1}{3}$ which means that 4 is mapped onto $4\frac{1}{3}$ and $(4, 4\frac{1}{3})$ lies on the graph of the function H.

2 a i 5 **ii** -7 **iii** 21 **iv** -395
 b i 1 **ii** 2 **iii** 32 **iv** $\frac{1}{4}$
 c i -2 **ii** $2\frac{1}{2}$ **iii** $1\frac{3}{7}$ **iv** $\frac{7}{10}$

3 a i $f(4) = -11$ **ii** $x = \pm 2$
 b i $g(4) = 81$ **ii** $a = -2$
 c i $x = \pm\sqrt{3}$ **ii** $x = \pm 2$ **d** $x = \frac{3}{2} \pm \frac{\sqrt{29}}{2}$

4 a $V(0) = 35\,000$ euros which is the original purchase price of the car.
 b $V(3) = 26\,000$ euros which is the value of the car 3 years after purchase.
 c $t = 10$, i.e., the value of the car is 5000 euros after 10 years.

5

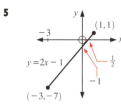

Range is
$\{y \mid -7 \leqslant y \leqslant 1\}$.

6

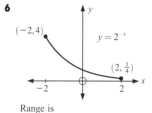

$y = 2^{-x}$

Range is
$\{y \mid \frac{1}{4} \leqslant y \leqslant 4\}$.

7 a $f(2) = -3$ **b** $x \approx -1.4,\ 2$ or 3.4

REVIEW SET 20A

1 a E **b** A
  c The greater the time spent on player fitness, the smaller the chance of player injury.
2 a 2 pm **b i** 9 am **ii** 46 cents **c** 1 pm - 2 pm
3 a 120 km **b i** 2 hours **ii** 3 hours **c** 1 pm
  d i $15\ \text{km}\,\text{h}^{-1}$ **ii** $20\ \text{km}\,\text{h}^{-1}$
4 a \$30 **b** \$55 **c** \$20
5 a Domain is $\{x \mid -4 < x \leqslant 3\}$. Range is $\{y \mid -2 \leqslant y < 4\}$.
  b Domain is $\{x \mid x \geqslant -5\}$. Range is $\{y \mid y \geqslant -145\}$.
  c Domain is $\{x \mid x \in \mathbb{R},\ x \neq 0\}$. Range is $\{y \mid y \in \mathbb{R},\ y \neq 0\}$.
6 a $f(-3) = -13$ which means that -3 is mapped onto -13 and $(-3, -13)$ lies on the graph of the function f.
  b i 0 **ii** -21 **c i** $f(5) = 32$ **ii** $x = -3$

REVIEW SET 20B

1 a i 23 000 people **ii** 36 000 people **b** 1991
  c 1990 - 2000
2 a 42 km **b** 8.30 am
  c Jacob: 135 minutes; Sandy 150 minutes **d** $16\ \text{km}\,\text{h}^{-1}$
3 a 320 USD **b** 125 AUD **c** 150 AUD $\approx$ 120 USD $\therefore$ no
4 i As time goes by, the turnover of the store is increasing, possibly due to an increase in people shopping there, and inflation.
  ii Each year the greatest sales are around Christmas time when people spend more money on buying gifts.

5

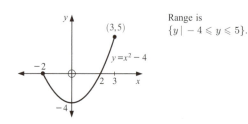

Range is
$\{y \mid -4 \leqslant y \leqslant 5\}$.

6 $y = 4x - 5,\quad x \in \{1, 2, 3, 4, 5\}$
7 $G(2) = \frac{3}{5}$ which means that 2 is mapped onto $\frac{3}{5}$ and $(2, \frac{3}{5})$ lies on the graph of the function G.

EXERCISE 21A

1 a $y = 44$ **b** $x = 122$ **c** $x = 141$ **d** $y = 180$
  e $y = 99$ **f** $x = y = 90$
2 a 65° **b** 27° **c** $(90 - x)^{o}$ **d** y^{o}
3 a 91° **b** 63° **c** $(180 - x)^{o}$ **d** x^{o} **e** $(90 - a)^{o}$
4 a $y = 55$ {angles in right angle}
  b $f = 117$ {co-interior angles}
  c $c = 102$ {co-interior angles} **d** $y = 65$ {alternate angles}
  e $x = 100$ {corresponding angles}
  f $x = 49$ {co-interior angles}
  g $x = 112$ {vertically opposite angles}
  h $x = 45$ {angles at a point} **i** $d = 333$ {angles at a point}

j $a = 116$ {corresponding angles}
k $x = 138$ {angles on a line} **l** $b = 108$ {alternate angles}
m $a = 65$ {angles on a line}, $b = 65$ {corresponding angles}
n $a = 57$ {vert. opp. angles}, $b = 57$ {corresponding angles}
o $a = 102$ {co-interior angles}, $b = 102$ {co-interior angles}
p $c = 90$ {angles on a line}
q $a = 59$ {angles on a line}, $b = 59$ {corresponding angles}
r $i = 218$ {angles at a point}
s $a = 122$ {vert. opp. angles}, $b = 58$ {co-interior angles}
  $c = 58$ {corresponding angles}, $d = 122$ {angles on a line}
t $b = 137$ {angles at a point}
u $r = 81$, $s = 81$ {corresponding angles}
5 a $d = 125$ {angles at a point} **b** $e = 120$ {angles at a point}
  c $f = 45$ {angles at a point} **d** $h = 36$ {angles on a line}
  e $g = 60$ {corresponding angles / angles on a line}
  f $x = 65$ {co-interior angles} **g** $x = 45$ {angles on a line}
  h $x = 15$ {angles in right angle}
  i $x = 42$ {angles at a point}
6 a KL $\parallel$ MN {alternate angles equal}
  b KL $\nparallel$ MN {co-interior angles not supplementary}
  c KL $\parallel$ MN {corresponding angles equal}

EXERCISE 21B

1 a $a = 62$ {angles of a triangle}
  b $b = 91$ {angles of a triangle}
  c $c = 109$ {angles of a triangle}
  d $d = 128$ {exterior angle of a triangle}
  e $e = 136$ {exterior angle of a triangle}
  f $f = 58$ {exterior angle of a triangle}
2 a AB **b** AC **c** BC **d** AC and BC **e** BC **f** BC
  g BC **h** BC **i** AB
3 a true **b** false **c** false **d** false **e** true
4 a $a = 20$ {angles of a triangle}
  b $b = 60$ {angles of a triangle}
  c $c = 56$ {corresponding angles / angles of a triangle},
    $d = 76$ {angles of a triangle}
  d $a = 84$ {vert. opp. angles}, $b = 48$ {angles of a triangle}
  e $a = 60$ {angles on a line}, $b = 100$ {ext. angle of a triangle}
  f $a = 72$, $b = 65$ {vertically opposite angles},
    $c = 137$ {ext. angles of triangle}, $d = 43$ {angles on a line}
5 46.5^{o}, 34.5^{o} and 99°

EXERCISE 21C

1 a $x = 36$ {isosceles triangle theorem / angles of a triangle}
  b $x = 55$ {isosceles triangle theorem / angles of a triangle}
  c $x = 36$ {isosceles triangle theorem / angles of a triangle}
  d $x = 73$ {isosceles triangle theorem}
  e $x = 60$ {angles on a line / isos. $\triangle$ theorem. / angles of a $\triangle$}
  f $x = 32.5$ {isos. $\triangle$ theorem / angles on a line / angles of a $\triangle$}
2 a $x = 16$ {isosceles triangle theorem}
  b $x = 9$ {isosceles triangle theorem}
  c $x = 90$ {isosceles triangle theorem /
    line from apex to midpoint of base}
3 a equilateral **b** isosceles **c** equilateral **d** isosceles
  e equilateral **f** isosceles
4 a $x = 52$ **b** $\triangle$ABC is isosceles (BA = BC)
5 a $\theta = 72$ **b** $\phi = 54$ **c** $\widehat{ABC} = 108^{o}$
6 a $\theta = 36$ **b** $\phi = 72$ **c** $\widehat{ABC} = 144^{o}$

EXERCISE 21D

1 a $x = 77$ {angles of a quadrilateral}
  b $x = 110$ {angles of a quadrilateral}

c $x = 75$ {angles of a quadrilateral}

d $x = 102$ {angles on a line / angles of a quadrilateral}

e $x = 54$ {angles of a quadrilateral}

f $x = 75$ {angles on a line / angles of a quadrilateral}

a $a + b + c = 180$, $d + e + f = 180$

b $b + (c + f) + e + (a + d) = 360$

c The angle sum of a quadrilateral is equal to the angle sums of two triangles, i.e., $2 \times 180^o = 360^o$.

a $x = 60$, $y = 60$ **b** $a = 90$, $b = 35$
c $p = 90$, $q = 25$, $r = 25$ **d** $a = 40$, $b = 50$
e $x = 65$, $y = 125$ **f** $x = 90$, $y = 45$

a trapezium {alternate angles equal ∴ one pair of parallel opposite sides}

b rectangle {all angles 90°}

c rhombus {opposite sides parallel / diagonals bisect at right angles}

d parallelogram {alternate angles equal ∴ two pairs of parallel opposite sides}

e parallelogram {opposite sides equal}

f square {diagonals equal in length and bisect each other at right angles}

EXERCISE 21E

1 a 360° **b** 540° **c** 720° **d** 1080°

2 a $x = 87$ **b** $x = 43$ **c** $x = 52.5$ **d** $a = 108$
e $a = 120$ **f** $a = 65$

3 a $x = 60$ {angles of a pentagon}
b $x = 72$ {angles of a hexagon}
c $x = 120$ {angles of a hexagon}
d $x = 60$ {angles of a hexagon}
e $x = 125$ {angles of a heptagon}
f $x = 135$ {angles of an octagon}

4 135° **5 a** 108° **b** 120° **c** 135° **d** 144°

6 12 angles **7** No such polygon exists.

8

Regular Polygon	No. of sides	No. of angles	Size of each angle
equilateral triangle	3	3	60°
square	4	4	90°
pentagon	5	5	108°
hexagon	6	6	120°
octagon	8	8	135°
decagon	10	10	144°

9 • $180(n - 2)^o$ • $\dfrac{180(n - 2)^o}{n}$

EXERCISE 21F

1 a 108° **b** 135° **c** 144° **d** 162° **e** 176.4^o

f $\left(180 - \dfrac{360}{n}\right)^o$

2 a 8 sides **b** 24 sides **c** 180 sides **d** 720 sides

3 a 6 sides **b** 12 sides **c** 72 sides **d** 360 sides

EXERCISE 21G

1 a

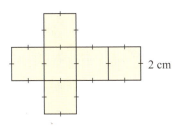

2 cm

b

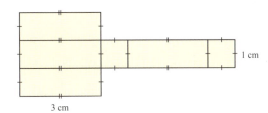

3 cm · 1 cm

c

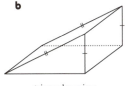

2 cm · 2.5 cm

2 a

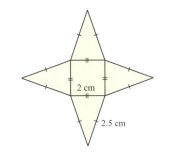

rectangular-based pyramid

b

triangular prism

c

triangular prism

d

rectangular prism

e

triangular-based pyramid (tetrahedron)

f

cone

3 P

4 a

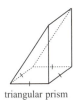

1.2 cm

b 8.64 cm^2

5 a

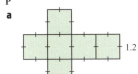

5 cm · 8 cm · 10 cm

b 340 cm^2

6 a

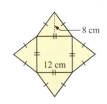
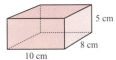

8 cm · 12 cm

b 336 cm^2

7 a 8.06 cm **b**

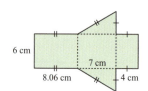

c 142.37 cm²

REVIEW SET 21A

1 a

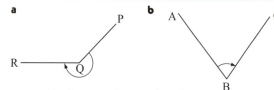

b

2 a $x = 72$ {corresponding angles}
b $x = 20$ {angles on a line}
c $x = 242$ {angles at a point}
d $x = 65$ {angles on a line/alternate angles}

3 yes {angles on a line/alternate angles equal}

4 a $x = 62$ **b** $x = 152$ **c** $x = 68$

5 $\triangle ABC$ is isosceles since $\widehat{ACB} = \widehat{ABC} = 62°$ {angles on a line/angles in a triangle/isosceles triangle theorem}

6 $x = 122$ {angles in a quadrilateral}

7 a $x = 60$ {opposite angles of parallelogram}
$y = 5$ {opposite sides of parallelogram}
b $x = 90$ {diagonals of rhombus}, $y = 28$ {alternate angles}

8 a rectangle {opposite sides equal/diagonals equal and bisect each other}
b parallelogram {co-interior angles supplementary}

9 a $x = 110$ {angles in a pentagon}
b $x = 120$ {angles in a hexagon}

10

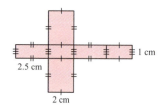

REVIEW SET 21B

1 a i $55°$ **ii** $(90 - x)°$ **b i** $108°$ **ii** $(90 + x)°$

2 a $a = 73$ {angles on a line} **b** $b = 90$ {angles on a line}
c $c = 56$ {vertically opposite angles}
d $a = 110$ {alternate angles}, $b = 110$ {vert. opp. angles}
e $x = 40$ {angles on a line}

3 a $x = 60$ {angles in a triangle}
b $a = 131$ {exterior angle of a triangle}
c $x = 2$ {equal sides of equilateral triangle}

4 $x = 96$ {corr. angles/isosceles $\triangle$ theorem/angles in a $\triangle$}, $y = 96$ {corr. angles}

5 a right angled scalene **b** obtuse angled scalene
c obtuse angled isosceles

6 $x = 56$ {angles on a line/angles in a quadrilateral}

7 a kite {diagonals cut each other at right angles/ figure is symmetrical about one diagonal}
b parallelogram {diagonals bisect each other}
c trapezium {alternate angles equal $\therefore$ one pair of parallel opposite sides}

8 $a = 44$ {angles in a triangle}, $b = 46$ {alternate angles}, $c = 88$ {isosceles triangle theorem/angles in a triangle}

9

Polygon	Number of sides	Sum of angles
pentagon	5	540°
hexagon	6	720°
octagon	8	1080°

10

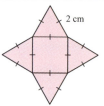

EXERCISE 22A

1 a $x = 0$ **b** $y = 0$ **c** $p = 0$ **d** $q = 0$ **e** $r = 0$
f $p = 0$ or $q = 0$ **g** $x = 0$ or $y = 0$
h $p = 0$ or $q = 0$ or $r = 0$ **i** $x = 0$ **j** $a = 0$
k $w = 0$ or $x = 0$ or $y = 0$ or $z = 0$ **l** $x = 0$ or $y = 0$

2 a $x = 0$ or -2 **b** $x = 0$ or 3 **c** $x = 4$ or 7
d $x = 0$ or 2 **e** $x = 0$ or $-\frac{2}{3}$ **f** $x = -\frac{2}{3}$ or $\frac{5}{2}$
g $x = 2$ or $-\frac{1}{3}$ **h** $x = 3$ **i** $x = \frac{2}{3}$

3 a $x = 0$ or 1 **b** $x = 0$ or 6 **c** $x = 0$ or 4
d $x = 0$ or 2 **e** $x = 0$ or -4 **f** $x = 0$ or $-\frac{2}{9}$
g $x = 0$ or $\frac{9}{4}$ **h** $x = 0$ or $\frac{7}{3}$ **i** $x = 0$ or 2

4 a $x = \pm 1$ **b** $x = \pm 2$ **c** $x = \pm\frac{1}{3}$ **d** $x = \pm\frac{3}{2}$
e $x = 3$ **f** $x = -7$ **g** $x = -\frac{1}{3}$ **h** $x = \frac{5}{4}$ **i** $x = -\frac{3}{7}$

5 a $x = -1$ or -3 **b** $x = 1$ or 3 **c** $x = -1$ or -4
d $x = 1$ or 4 **e** $x = -1$ or -8 **f** $x = -2$ or -5
g $x = -1$ **h** $x = 1$ **i** $x = -3$ **j** $x = 2$ **k** $x = 3$
l $x = -5$ **m** $x = -4$ or -7 **n** $x = -3$ or 5
o $x = -2$ or 6 **p** $x = -2$ or 12 **q** $x = 4$
r $x = -6$ or 5 **s** $x = -4$ or 6 **t** $x = -7$ or 3
u $x = -5$ or 7

EXERCISE 22B

1 The number is 3 or -4. **2** The number is 8 or -9.
3 The number is 8 or -7. **4** The number is 11 or -10.
5 a $9 - x$ **b** The numbers are 3 and 6.
6 a $16 - x$ **b** The numbers are 7 and 9.
7 a $(x + 3)$ cm **b** width 10 cm, length 13 cm
8 width 8 cm, length 14 cm
9 a $(24 - x)$ m **b** width 8 m, length 16 m
10 5 m by 14 m **11 a** 8 cm **b** 12 cm
12 a when 0 or 15 surfboards per hour are made
b when 5 or 10 surfboards per hour are made
13 a when 10 or 14 pairs of skates per hour are made
b when 0 or 24 pairs of skates per hour are made
14 a 0 or 6 seconds after the ball is hit
b 1 or 5 seconds after the ball is hit
15 a 1 or 7 seconds after the ball is hit
b 4 seconds after the ball is hit

EXERCISE 22C

1 a $4 = 2^2$ **b** $8 = 2^3$ **c** $1 = 2^0$ **d** $16 = 2^4$
e $\frac{1}{2} = 2^{-1}$ **f** $32 = 2^5$ **g** $\frac{1}{4} = 2^{-2}$

2 a $3 = 3^1$ **b** $9 = 3^2$ **c** $27 = 3^3$ **d** $1 = 3^0$
e $\frac{1}{3} = 3^{-1}$ **f** $\frac{1}{9} = 3^{-2}$ **g** $\sqrt{3} = 3^{\frac{1}{2}}$

3 a $25 = 5^2$ **b** $5 = 5^1$ **c** $1 = 5^0$ **d** $125 = 5^3$
e $\frac{1}{25} = 5^{-2}$ **f** $0.2 = 5^{-1}$

4 a $x = 1$ **b** $x = 2$ **c** $x = 4$ **d** $x = 0$ **e** $x = -1$
f $x = -1$ **g** $x = -2$ **h** $x = 1$ **i** $x = -1$ **j** $x = -3$
k $x = 4$ **l** $x = \frac{3}{2}$

5 a $x = \frac{3}{2}$ **b** $x = -\frac{1}{2}$ **c** $x = -\frac{3}{2}$ **d** $x = -\frac{1}{2}$

e $x=-2$ **f** $x=-\frac{1}{2}$ **g** $x=\frac{1}{3}$ **h** $x=4$ **i** $x=-\frac{3}{4}$
j $x=-\frac{5}{2}$ **k** $x=-1$ **l** $x=0$ **m** $x=0$ **n** $x=\frac{7}{2}$
o $x=-2$ **p** $x=-7$

EXERCISE 22D

1 a $x\approx-0.236$ or $x\approx4.24$ **b** $x\approx3.13$ or $x\approx10.9$
c $x\approx0.639$ or $x\approx3.85$ **d** $x\approx0.697$ or $x\approx10.0$
e $x\approx-2.65$ or $x=-0.5$ or $x\approx2.65$
f $x\approx-1.24$ or $x\approx0.667$ or $x\approx3.24$
g $x\approx2.48$ or $x=3$
h $x\approx-3.11$ or $x\approx-0.746$ or $x\approx0.861$
i $x\approx-3.68$ or $x\approx0.679$ **j** $x\approx-0.351$ or $x\approx2.85$
k $x\approx-1.53$ **l** $x\approx-3.33$ or $x\approx1.55$

2 a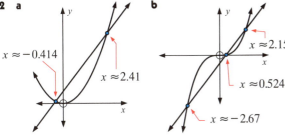

$x\approx-0.414$ or $x\approx2.41$

b $x\approx-2.67$ or $x\approx0.524$ or $x\approx2.15$

c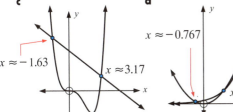

$x\approx-1.63$ or $x\approx3.17$

d $x\approx-0.767$ or $x=2$ or $x=4$

e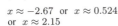

$x\approx-0.248$ or $x\approx2.40$

f $x\approx0.382$ or $x\approx2.62$

g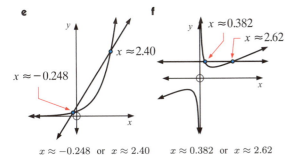

$x\approx0.686$

h $x\approx2.35$ or $x\approx3.91$

i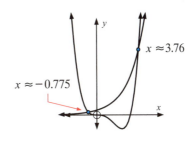

$x\approx-0.775$ or $x\approx3.76$ or $x\approx12.7$

3 a $x\approx0.586,\ y\approx5.59$ or $x\approx3.41,\ y\approx8.41$
b $x=3,\ y=-4$ **c** no solution (do not intersect)
d $x\approx-2.56,\ y\approx-18.8$ or $x\approx1.56,\ y\approx1.81$
4 a $(1,7)$ and $(2,8)$ **b** $(-3,-9)$ and $(4,5)$
c $(-3.85,-23.3)$ and $(2.85,10.3)$ **d** $(4,5)$

REVIEW SET 22A

1 a $x=0$ or 2 **b** $x=3$ or -4 **c** $x=3$
2 a $x=0$ or 2 **b** $x=0$ or -2 **c** $x=0$ or 3
3 a $x=\pm5$ **b** $x=\frac{1}{2}$
4 a $x=-6$ or 1 **b** $x=-3$ **c** $x=-3$ or 5
5 a $11-x$ **b** The numbers are 5 and 6.
6 width 8 cm, length 13 cm
7 a 5 or 15 bicycles per day **b** 0 or 20 bicycles per day
8 a $x=2$ **b** $x=-3$ **c** $x=0$
9 a $x=-2$ **b** $x=\frac{7}{2}$
10 $x=1$

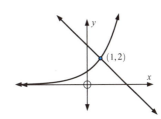

REVIEW SET 22B

1 a $x=0$ or $\frac{1}{5}$ **b** $x=2$ or 7 **c** $x=-\frac{3}{2}$
2 a $x=0$ or 6 **b** $x=0$ or $\frac{3}{4}$ **c** $x=0$ or $\frac{1}{5}$
3 a $x=\pm3$ **b** $x=-\frac{3}{4}$
4 a $x=3$ or 4 **b** $x=-\frac{1}{2}$ **c** $x=-6$ or 3
5 The number is -4 or 5. **6** 5 cm
7 a 2 and 5 seconds after the ball is hit
b 0 and 7 seconds after the ball is hit
8 a $x=4$ **b** $x=0$ **c** $x=-3$
9 a $x=-\frac{3}{2}$ **b** $x=-3$
10 $x=\pm1$

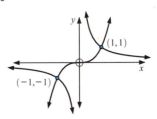

EXERCISE 23A.1

1 €1.60 profit **2** $25 loss **3** £1862 profit **4** €3160 profit
5 $8 loss, but still has 72 to sell next season.

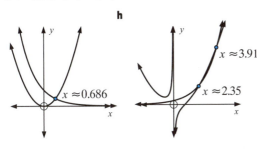

EXERCISE 23A.2

1 **a** **i** $2 **ii** $22 **b** **i** $200 **ii** $450
c **i** £7.50 **ii** £57.50 **d** **i** $53 550 **ii** $308 550
2 **a** **i** €5 **ii** €20 **b** **i** £113.75 **ii** £211.25
c **i** $18 **ii** $72 **d** **i** €2016 **ii** €10 584
3 $110.40 **4** **a** $21 **b** $119

EXERCISE 23B

1 28% **2** **a** $812.50 **b** $377.50 **c** 86.8%
3 **a** $1.40 **b** $1.05 **c** 75% **4** **a** €80 **b** 10%
5 **a** $10 700 **b** 28.0% **6** **a** $15 **b** 27.3%
7 **a** £140 300 **b** £32 800 **c** 23.4%

EXERCISE 23C

1 **a** €26, €104 **b** $23.80, $44.20 **c** £6.30, £21.70 **2** $26.04
3 €88.32 **4** $288.75 **5** 17.5% **6** 30.6% **7** 18%
8 30% **9** **a** $255 **b** $742.05 **10** **a** €981 **b** €114.45
11 **a** €696 **b** **i** €69.60 **ii** €626.40 **c** 28%

EXERCISE 23D

1 **a** 1.1 **b** 0.9 **c** 1.33 **d** 0.79 **e** 1.072 **f** 0.911
2 **a** 30% increase **b** 25% increase **c** 6% decrease
d 14% decrease **e** 47% increase **f** 32% decrease
g 150% increase **h** 60% decrease
3 **a** $84.80 **b** £81.60 **c** 57 kg **d** €22.95 **e** £655.20
f 31.5 m
4 **a** €26 per hour **b** 31.86 m **c** 1.75 m
5 **a** 50% increase **b** 20% decrease **c** 15.8% decrease
d 31.1% increase **e** 25% increase **f** 18.8% decrease
6 46.7% increase **7** 10.6% decrease **8** 7.06% increase
9 2.11% decrease **10** 8% increase

EXERCISE 23E

1 **a** $2880 **b** €2805 **c** €3239.60 **d** €5170
2 False, e.g., $1000 increased by 10% is $1100,
$1100 decreased by 10% is $990, not $1000.
3 $63 **4** £328.86 **5** €132 **6** £4428.74 **7** €40 575
8 $40 279.90 **9** $55 163.86
10 **a** 31.8% increase **b** 16.1% decrease **c** 21.6% increase
11 16.3% **12** 20.0%

EXERCISE 23F

1 **a** $480 **b** £992.80 **c** $10 880 **d** €434.14
2 First ¥700 000, Second ¥759 375 ∴ the first plan
3 £3750 **4** €24 300 **5** $67 742
6 **a** 2.67% p.a. **b** 6.82% p.a. **7** 7.5% p.a. **8** 11.1% p.a.
9 **a** 3 years 9 months **b** 6 years **10** ≈ 2 years 9 months
11 €257.30 **12** $1390 **13** £1005 **14** $2887.30

EXERCISE 23G

1 **a** $2977.54 **b** £5243.18 **c** €11 433.33
2 **a** €105.47 **b** $782.73 **c** £4569.19
3 **a** 13 738.80 Yuan **b** 1738.80 Yuan
4 **a** $5887.92 **b** $887.92 **5** **a** 42 779 rupee **b** 12 779 rupee
6 1st plan earns 3200 pesos, 2nd plan earns 3485 pesos ∴ plan 2

EXERCISE 23H

1 **a** £262.25 **b** $793.90 SG **c** $516.92 US **d** ¥60 794
2 **a** €735.10 **b** €2519.15 **c** €39.45 **d** €46.05
3 **a** €4.55 **b** €205.05 **c** €138.15
4 **a** €126.35 **b** €145.10 **c** €94.20 **d** €309.75
5 They vary each day, some increase, some decrease.

REVIEW SET 23A

1 **a** **i** 0.87 **ii** 1.109 **b** **i** 250% increase **ii** 27% decrease

2 **a** $2900 **b** 58.5 kg **3** **a** €160 **b** 71.1%
4 **a** ¥4590 **b** ¥1190 **5** **a** £500 **b** 11.1%
6 **a** $12 **b** $68 **7** 79.2% increase **8** $38.50 **9** $53.30
10 $15 000 **11** 5.88% p.a. **12** ≈ 2 years 4 months
13 **a** $1530 **b** $209.17 **14** $24 845.94
15 *Plan 1:* $2700, *Plan 2:* $2703.67
∴ *Plan 2* earns more interest.

REVIEW SET 23B

1 **a** **i** 1.1 **ii** 0.883
b **i** 3.7% increase **ii** 100% increase **iii** 6.2% decrease
2 **a** £3915 **b** ≈ 380 km **3** **a** $45 **b** 24.3%
4 **a** 2600 pesos **b** 600 pesos **5** **a** €513 **b** €436.05
6 $70 400 **7** 0.467% decrease **8** €52.45 **9** $365 911
10 $1768 **11** $1200 **12** 4.2 years i.e., 4 years 73 days
13 **a** $34 264.87 **b** $9264.87 **14** **a** £4500 **b** £406.25
15 **a** €17 271.40 **b** €9271.40 **c** 11.6% p.a.

EXERCISE 24A

1 **a**

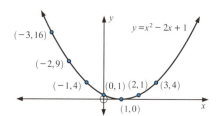

b

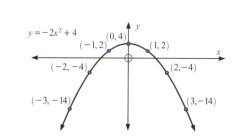

c

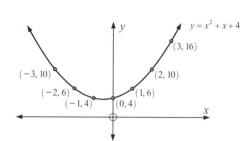

d

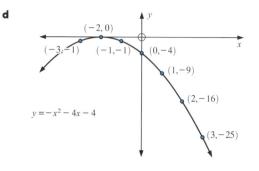

e

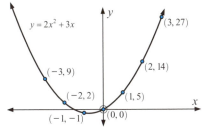

$y = 2x^2 + 3x$
(3, 27)
(−3, 9)
(2, 14)
(−2, 2) (1, 5)
(−1, −1) (0, 0)

f

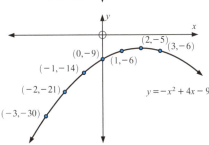

(2, −5)
(0, −9) (3, −6)
(−1, −14) (1, −6)
(−2, −21)
$y = -x^2 + 4x - 9$
(−3, −30)

2 The sign determines whether the graph opens upwards (postive) or downwards (negative).

EXERCISE 24B

1 a 3 **b** 2 **c** −8 **d** 1 **e** 6 **f** 5 **g** 6 **h** 8 **i** −2

2 a 3 and −1 **b** 2 and 4 **c** −3 and −2 **d** 4 and 5
e −3 (touching) **f** 1 (touching)

3 a ±3 **b** $\pm\sqrt{3}$ **c** −5 and −2 **d** 3 and −4 **e** 0 and 4
f −4 and −2 **g** −1 (touching) **h** 3 (touching) **i** $2 \pm \sqrt{3}$
j $-2 \pm \sqrt{7}$ **k** $3 \pm \sqrt{11}$ **l** $-4 \pm \sqrt{5}$

5 a

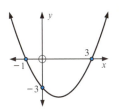

−1 3

−3

b

1 3

−3

c

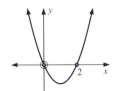

2

d

−3

e

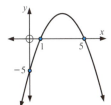

1 5

−5

f

−5 −1
5

g

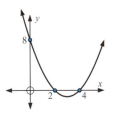

8

2 4

h

8

−4 −2

i

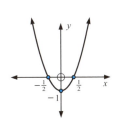

$-\frac{1}{2}$ $\frac{1}{2}$
−1

j

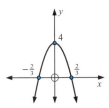

4
$-\frac{2}{3}$ $\frac{2}{3}$

k

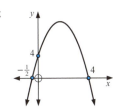

4
$-\frac{1}{2}$ 4

l

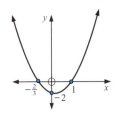

1
$-\frac{2}{3}$
−2

EXERCISE 24C

1 a $x = -2$ **b** $x = \frac{3}{2}$ **c** $x = -\frac{2}{3}$ **d** $x = -2$ **e** $x = \frac{5}{4}$
f $x = 10$ **g** $x = -6$ **h** $x = \frac{25}{2}$ **i** $x = 150$

2 a $(2, -2)$ **b** $(-1, -4)$ **c** $(0, 4)$ **d** $(0, 1)$ **e** $(-2, -15)$
f $(-2, -5)$ **g** $(-\frac{3}{2}, -\frac{11}{2})$ **h** $(\frac{5}{2}, -\frac{19}{2})$ **i** $(1, -\frac{9}{2})$

3 a i x-intercepts −2 and 4, y-intercept −8
ii axis of symmetry $x = 1$ **iii** vertex $(1, -9)$
iv

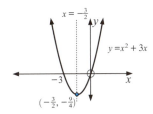

$x = 1$
−2 4
−8 (1, −9)
$y = x^2 - 2x - 8$

b i x-intercepts 0 and −3, y-intercept 0
ii axis of symmetry $x = -\frac{3}{2}$
iii vertex $(-\frac{3}{2}, -\frac{9}{4})$
iv

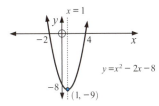

$x = -\frac{3}{2}$
−3
$y = x^2 + 3x$
$(-\frac{3}{2}, -\frac{9}{4})$

c i x-intercepts 0 and 4, y-intercept 0
ii axis of symmetry $x = 2$ **iii** vertex $(2, 4)$
iv

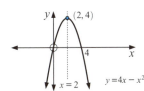

(2, 4)
4
$x = 2$ $y = 4x - x^2$

d　**i** x-intercept -2,　y-intercept 4
　ii axis of symmetry　$x = -2$　**iii** vertex $(-2, 0)$
　iv

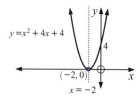

e　**i** x-intercepts -4 and 1,　y-intercept -4
　ii axis of symmetry　$x = -\frac{3}{2}$　**iii** vertex $(-\frac{3}{2}, -\frac{25}{4})$
　iv

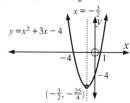

f　**i** x-intercept 1,　y-intercept -1
　ii axis of symmetry　$x = 1$
　iii vertex $(1, 0)$
　iv

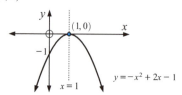

g　**i** x-intercepts -2 and -4,　y-intercept -8
　ii axis of symmetry　$x = -3$
　iii vertex $(-3, 1)$
　iv

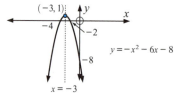

h　**i** x-intercepts 1 and 2,　y-intercept -2
　ii axis of symmetry　$x = \frac{3}{2}$
　iii vertex $(\frac{3}{2}, \frac{1}{4})$
　iv

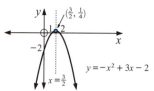

i　**i** x-intercepts -3 and $\frac{1}{2}$,　y-intercept -3
　ii axis of symmetry　$x = -\frac{5}{4}$
　iii vertex $(-\frac{5}{4}, -\frac{49}{8})$
　iv

j　**i** x-intercepts $-\frac{3}{2}$ and 4,　y-intercept -12
　ii axis of symmetry　$x = \frac{5}{4}$
　iii vertex $(\frac{5}{4}, -\frac{121}{8})$
　iv

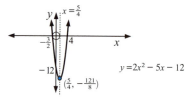

k　**i** x-intercepts -2 and $\frac{2}{3}$,　y-intercept 4
　ii axis of symmetry　$x = -\frac{2}{3}$
　iii vertex $(-\frac{2}{3}, \frac{16}{3})$
　iv

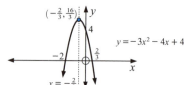

l　**i** x-intercepts 0 and 20,　y-intercept 0
　ii axis of symmetry $x = 10$
　iii vertex $(10, 25)$
　iv

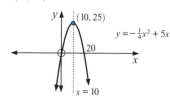

EXERCISE 24D

1　**a** 6 seconds　**b** 72 m　**c** 12 seconds
2　**a** 12 skateboards　**b** \$100 per skateboard　**c** \$244
3　**a** 80 km h^{-1}
　b after 1 second and after 2 seconds;
　　car continues to speed up before slowing down
　c $1\frac{1}{2}$ seconds　**d** 89 km h^{-1}
4　**a** 21 taxis　**b** €837　**c** €45
5　**a** 30°C　**b** 5.00 am　**c** 5°C　**6** **b** $x = 10$　**c** 200 m^2
7　**a** $y = -\frac{1}{100}x^2 + 70$
　b supports are 21 m, 34 m, 45 m, 54 m, 61 m, 66 m, 69 m
8　**a** vertex $(30, 30)$　**b** $y = \frac{1}{45}x^2 - \frac{4}{3}x + 50$
　c 38.9 m

REVIEW SET 24A

1

x	-2	-1	0	1	2	3	4	5
y	12	6	2	0	0	2	6	12

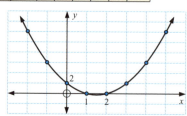

2　**a** 1　**b** 9　**c** 2
3　**a** -5 and 1　**b** -1 and 7　**c** $\frac{3}{2}$ (touching)
4　**a** 0 and 2　**b** -3 and 4　**c** -6 and 3

5 a

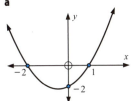

b

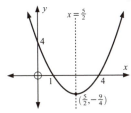

6 a $x = -1$ **7** vertex is $(2, -12)$

8 a i x-intercepts 1 and 4, y-int. 4 **ii** $x = \frac{5}{2}$ **iii** $(\frac{5}{2}, -2\frac{1}{4})$

b

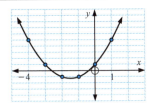

9 a 4 seconds **b** 49 m **c** 8.04 seconds

REVIEW SET 24B

1

x	-4	-3	-2	-1	0	1
y	5	1	-1	-1	1	5

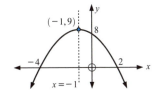

2 a 9 **b** 3 **c** -4

3 a -1 and 4 **b** 1 (touching) **c** -7 and $\frac{1}{2}$

4 a 0 and -7 **b** 3 **c** $-\frac{1}{2}$ and 1

5 a

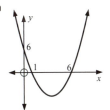

b

6 $x = -1$ **7** vertex is $(\frac{3}{2}, -12\frac{1}{4})$

8 a i x-intercepts -4 and 2, y-int. 8 **ii** $x = -1$ **iii** $(-1, 9)$

b

9 a 2 seconds **b** 25 m **c** 4.5 seconds

INDEX

acute angle   415
adjacent angles   418
adjacent side   312
algebraic equation   222
alternate angles   418
angle of depression   321
angle of elevation   321
apex   424
area   32, 133
average speed   257
axis of symmetry   481
base angles   424
bearing   325
biased sample   190
bimodal   203
box-and-whisker plot   213
capacity   34, 304
categorical variable   189
census   190
circumference   128
co-interior angles   419
coincident lines   358
collinear points   338, 415
common factor   266
complement   65
complementary angles   417
complementary event   375
concurrent lines   415
cone   300
congruent triangles   283
conjunction   76
conversion graph   400
corresponding angles   418
cross-section   298
cube   434
cylinder   142, 299
data   189
decimal number   150
denominator   49
dependent variable   191
disjoint events   390

disjunction   76
distributive law   172
domain   405
dot plot   195
element   62
ellipse   134
empty set   65
enlargement factor   287
equal ratios   249
equation of line   342
equilateral triangle   415
equivalent fractions   49
expansion   268
expectation   376
experimental probability   373
exponential equation   446
factorisation   268
finite set   62
five-number summary   213
formula   237
frequency   373
frequency histogram   200
function   406
general form   344
gradient   335
gradient-intercept form   342
Heron's formula   124
highest common factor   266
horizontal bar chart   192
horizontal line   350
hypotenuse   99, 312
improper fraction   49
independent events   392
independent variable   191
index   170
infinite set   62
integer   44, 63
interquartile range   211
irrational number   64
isosceles triangle   415, 424
kite   429
like terms   168
line graph   398